MW00846143

A–Z of Quantitative PCR

IUL Biotechnology Series

Igor F. Tsigelny, Series Editor

1. **Protein Crystallization: Techniques, Strategies, and Tips.**
   A Laboratory Manual.
   Terese M. Bergfors, ed.

2. **Pharmacophore Perception, Development, and Use in Drug Design.**
   Osman Güner, ed.

3. **Protein Structure Prediction: Bioinformatic Approach.**
   Igor F. Tsigelny, ed.

4. **Methods and Results in Crystallization Membrane Proteins.**
   So Iwata, ed.

5. **A–Z of Quantitative PCR.**
   Stephen A. Bustin, ed.

6. **Comparative Enzymology of Cholinesterases.**
   Serge N. Moralev, Eugene V. Rosengart.

7. **Crystallization Strategies for Structural Genomics.**
   Naomi E. Chayen, ed.

8. **Protein Crystallization, 2nd edition.**
   Terese M. Bergfors, ed.

A–Z of Quantitative PCR

edited by

Stephen A. Bustin

INTERNATIONAL UNIVERSITY LINE
La Jolla, California

Library of Congress Cataloging-in-Publication Data

A–Z of Quantitative PCR / edited by Stephen A. Bustin
    p. ; cm. -- (IUL biotechnology series; 5)
    Includes bibliographical references and index.
    ISBN 978-0-9636817-8-2 (hardcover)
    1. Polymerase chain reaction. 2. Nucleic acids--Analysis. 3. Quantitative genetics.
    I. Bustin, Stephen A. II. Series.

QP606.D46.A9 2004
572.8'6—dc22

                     2004054845
                     CIP

© International University Line, 2004–2009
Post Office Box 2525,
La Jolla, CA 92038-2525, USA

Library of Congress Catalog Card Number 2004054845

Printed in the United States of America

10 9 8 7 6 5 4 3

ISBN   978-0-9636817-8-2 $119.95   Hardcover

Contents

Preface

This is not just a cook book for real-time quantitative PCR (qPCR). Admittedly, there are lots of recipes from distinguished contributors and I have attempted to collect, sift through and rationalize the vast amount of information that is available on this subject. And yes, this book was conceived as a comprehensive hands-on manual to allow both the novice researcher and the expert to set up and carry out qPCR assays from scratch. However, this book also sets out to explain as many features of qPCR as possible, provide alternative viewpoints and methods and, perhaps most importantly, aims to stimulate the researcher into generating, interpreting and publishing data that are reproducible, reliable, and biologically meaningful.

The first of the reviews in part I describes the background to quantification using PCR-based assays (S. A. Bustin), the second one provides a fascinating insight into the numerous factors that influence a successful PCR experiment (J. M. Phillips), and the third review discusses in detail the principles underlying real-time quantification (M. Pfaffl). Part II forms the core of this book and presents a detailed dissection of every one of the steps involved in conducting a qPCR experiment. Its emphasis is on providing explanations at each critical step in the PCR assay, starting from sample collection and ending with the interpretation of the quantitative result. Tried and tested sample protocols are included for the main chemistries, together with a "getting started" section for the complete novice and an extensive troubleshooting section which details and explains problems encountered during everyday qPCR assays.

The third part of the book provides an alternative viewpoint and protocol for mRNA quantification (J. C. Willey et al.), specific guidelines for the standardization of qPCR assays (R. Mueller et al.) and protocols designed to optimize the extraction of RNA from formalin-fixed tissue (F. Lewis and N. J. Maughan), perform RT-PCR assays without the need to isolate the RNA in the first place (Q. Hoang and B. Pasloske) and detailed instructions on how to optimize multiplex PCR assays (H. K. Srere et al.). The remaining chapters are concerned with specific applications of real-time PCR assays in breast (P. Pinzani et al.) and colorectal (S. A. Bustin and S. Dorudi) cancer, quantification in single cells (C. Hartshorn et al.; G. Brady and T. Nolan), and SNP analyses (I. A. Afonina et al. and J. Theaker). Each chapter contains an abundance of practical hints and reveals technical information that the authors have acquired as part of their extensive exposure to this technique.

The very nature of the technology means that new chemistries, protocols, and instruments come and go. Any book would struggle to keep up-to-date with such developments. However, by emphasizing and describing the very basic steps that must be right and providing step-by-step guidance on how to achieve reproducible results and interpret them correctly, this book will remain topical. My hope is that this book will contribute to taking quantitative PCR forward to a new stage of use as a standard, reliable, and useful molecular technique.

I am grateful to my numerous friends and contacts at ABI, Ambion, Biorad, Corbett Research, DXS Genotyping, Oswell, Roche, Stratagene, and Quanta Biotech that keep me supplied with a constant stream of useful information, a lot of which has found a home in this book. I would like to acknowledge financial support from Bowel and Cancer Research.

Stephen A. Bustin
London, June 2004

Contributors

Irina A. Afonina
Epoch Biosciences, Inc.,
Bothell, Washington, USA
iafonina@epochbio.com

Yevgeniy S. Belousov
Epoch Biosciences, Inc.,
Bothell, Washington, USA
ebelousov@epochbio.com

Jerry R. Bergman
Departments of Medicine and Pathology,
Medical College of Ohio,
Toledo, Ohio, USA
jdbrg@bright.net

Ged Brady
Epistem Ltd., Manchester,
United Kingdom
g.brady@epistem.co.uk
www.epistem.co.uk

Marni Brisson
University of Pittsburgh
School of Medicine,
Department of Pharmacology,
Pittsburgh, Pennsylvania, USA
marnibris@hotmail.com

Stephen A. Bustin
Barts and The London, Queen Mary's
School of Medicine and Dentistry,
University of London,
London, United Kingdom
s.a.bustin@qmul.ac.uk

Erin L. Crawford
Departments of Medicine and Pathology,
Medical College of Ohio, Toledo, Ohio, USA
ercrawford@mco.edu

Triona Davey
Department of Pathology, Queens
Medical Centre, University Hospital,
Nottingham, United Kingdom
triona.davey@quintiles.com

Sina Dorudi
Barts and the London Queen Mary's
School of Medicine and Dentistry,
University of London,
London United Kingdom
s.dorudi@qmul.ac.uk

Roland C. Grafstrom
Division of Biochemical Toxicology and
Experimental Carcinogenesis,
Institute of Environmental Medicine,
Karolinska Institutet, Stockholm, Sweden
roland.grafstrom@imm.ki.se

Timothy G. Graves
Departments of Medicine and Pathology,
Medical College of Ohio, Toledo, Ohio, USA
tgraves@mco.edu

Li Guo
Department of Pathology, Queens
Medical Centre, University Hospital,
Nottingham, United Kingdom
Li.guo@nottingham.ac.uk

Shannon Hall
Bio-Rad Laboratories,
Hercules, California, USA
shannon_hall@bio-rad.com

Antony Halsall
DxS Ltd, Manchester, United Kingdom
antony.halsall@dxsgenotyping.com

R. Keith Hamby
Bio-Rad Laboratories,
Hercules, California, USA
keith_hamby@bio-rad.com

Cristina Hartshorn
Department of Biology, Brandeis University,
Waltham, Massachusetts, USA
hartcris@brandeis.edu

Quoc Hoang
Ambion, Inc., Austin, Texas, USA
qhoang@ambion.com

David Jenkins
Department of Pathology, Queens
Medical Centre, University Hospital,
Nottingham, United Kingdom
david.jenkins@nottingham.ac.uk

Charles A. Knight
Departments of Medicine and Pathology,
Medical College of Ohio,
Toledo, Ohio, USA
cknight@mco.edu

Fraser Lewis
Molecular Pathology, Histopathology
Department,
The General Infirmary at Leeds,
Leeds, United Kingdom
Fraser.Lewis@leedsth.nhs.uk

Walt Mahoney
Epoch Biosciences, Inc.,
Bothell, Washington, USA
wmahoney@epochbio.com

Nicola J. Maughan
Molecular Pathology, Histopathology
Department,
The General Infirmary at Leeds,
Leeds, United Kingdom
Nicola.Maughan@leedsth.nhs.uk

Mark Metcalf
Epoch Biosciences, Inc.,
Bothell, Washington, USA
mmetcalf@epochbio.com

Alan Mills
Epoch Biosciences, Inc.,
Bothell, Washington, USA
amills@epochbio.com

Cheryl R. Motten
Departments of Medicine and Pathology,
Medical College of Ohio, Toledo, Ohio, USA
cmotten@mco.edu

Reinhold Mueller
Stratagene, La Jolla, California, USA
reinhold.mueller@stratagene.com

Tania Nolan
Stratagene Europe,
Amsterdam, The Netherlands
tania.nolan@stratagene.com

Claudio Orlando
Department of Clinical Physiopathology,
Clinical Biochemistry Unit,
University of Florence, Florence, Italy
c.orlando@dfc.unifi.it

Gothami Padmabandu
Stratagene, La Jolla, California, USA
gothami.padmabandu@stratagene.com

Robert Park
Bio-Rad Laboratories,
Hercules, California, USA
robert_park@bio-rad.com

Brittan L. Pasloske
Ambion, Inc., Austin, Texas, USA
bpasloske@ambion.com

Mario Pazzagli
Department of Clinical Physiopathology,
Clinical Biochemistry Unit,
University of Florence, Florence, Italy
m.pazzagli@dfc.unifi.it

Elizabeth Herness Peters
Gene Express, Inc., Toledo, Ohio, USA
eherness@geneexpressinc.com

Michael W. Pfaffl
Institute of Physiology, Center of Life
and Food Science,
Weihenstephan, Freising, Germany
pfaffl@wzw.tum.de

Jonathan M. Phillips
Mitretek Systems, Inc.,
South Falls Church, Virginia, USA
jonathan.phillips@mitretek.org

Pamela Pinzani
Department of Clinical Physiopathology,
Clinical Biochemistry Unit,
University of Florence, Florence, Italy
p.pinzani@dfc.unifi.it

Paul Ravetto
DxS Ltd, Manchester, United Kingdom
paul.ravetto@dxsgenotyping.com

John E. Rice
Department of Biology,
Brandeis University,
Waltham, Massachusetts, USA
rice@brandeis.edu

John Rippin
Department of Pathology, Queens
Medical Centre, University Hospital,
Nottingham, United Kingdom
john.rippin@nottingham.ac.uk

Silvia Sanders
Epoch Biosciences, Inc.,
Bothell, Washington, USA
ssanders@epochbio.com

Rashmi Seth
Department of Pathology, Queens
Medical Centre, University Hospital,
Nottingham, United Kingdom
rashmi.seth@nottingham.ac.uk

Lisa Simi
Department of Clinical Physiopathology,
Clinical Biochemistry Unit,
University of Florence, Florence, Italy
lisa.simi@dfc.unifi.it

Hilary K. Srere
Bio-Rad Laboratories, Hercules,
California, USA
hilary_srere@bio-rad.com

Roger H. Taylor
Stratagene, La Jolla, California, USA
roger.taylor@stratagene.com

Jane Theaker
AstraZeneca Pharmaceuticals,
Alderley Park, Macclesfield,
United Kingdom
Jane.Theaker@astrazeneca.com

Nicola Thelwell
DxS Ltd, Manchester, United Kingdom
nicola.thelwell@dxsgenotyping.com

Carmela Tricarico
Department of Clinical Physiopathology,
Clinical Biochemistry Unit,
University of Florence, Florence, Italy
spec.biochclin@dfc.unifi.it

Nicolaas M. J. Vermeulen
Epoch Biosciences, Inc.,
Bothell, Washington, USA
nvermeulen@epochbio.com

Martin Vondracek
Division of Biochemical Toxicology and
Experimental Carcinogenesis,
Institute of Environmental Medicine,
Karolinska Institutet, Stockholm, Sweden
martin.vondracek@imm.ki.se

David K. Walburger
Epoch Biosciences, Inc.,
Bothell, Washington, USA
dwalburger@epochbio.com

Lawrence J. Wangh
Department of Biology, Brandeis University,
Waltham, Massachusetts, USA
wangh@brandeis.edu

Kristy A. Warner
Departments of Medicine and Pathology,
Medical College of Ohio, Toledo, Ohio, USA
kwarner@mco.edu

David A. Weaver
Departments of Medicine and Pathology,
Medical College of Ohio,
Toledo, Ohio, USA
dweaver@mco.edu

David M. Whitcombe
DxS Ltd, Manchester, United Kingdom
david.whitcombe@dxsgenotyping.com

James C. Willey
Departments of Medicine and Pathology,
Medical College of Ohio,
Toledo, Ohio, USA
jwilley@mco.edu

Robert J. Zahorchak
Gene Express, Inc., Toledo, Ohio, USA
bzahorchak@knology.net

Acronyms and Abbreviations

ABL   tyrosine kinase Abelson
a.c.   alternate current
AD   allelic discrimination
Agtr1   Angiotensin receptor 1
ALPS   Automated Laboratory Plate Sealer
AMCA   7-amino-4-methylcoumarin-3-acetic acid
AMV   Avian myeloblastosis virus
ANC   absolute neutrophil count
AP   armored RNA
APS   ammonium persulfate
ARMS   amplification refractory mutation system
ASTM   American Society for Testing and Materials
AT1B   Angiotensin type Ib receptor
Bca   Bacillus caldotenax
BCR   B cell receptor
B-DNA   branched DNA
BEC   bronchial epithelial cell
bFGF   basic fibroblast growth factor
BHQ   Black Hole Quencher
BLAST   Basic Local Alignment Search Tool
BNA   bridged nucleic acid
BOGOF   buy one, get one free
BP   binding protein
bp   base pair
BSA   bovine serum albumin
C.therm.   Carboxydothermus hydrogenoformans
CCD   charge-coupled device
CCP   cationic conjugated polymer
cDNA   complementary DNA
CE   capillary electrophoresis
CEA   carcinoembryonic antigen
CF   correction factor
Chy   Carboxydothermus hydrogenoformans
CI   confidence interval
CIN   cervical Intraepithelial Neoplasia
CP   crossing point
C_t threshold cycle
CT   competitive template
Cth   Carboxydothermus hydrogenoformans
            (C.therm.)

CV   coefficient of variation
Cy5   cyanine 5
DABCYL   4-dimethylaminoazobenzene-4'-sulphonyl (4-(4'-dimethylaminophenyla-zo)benzoic acid)
DABSYL   dimethoxytrityloxy-3-[O-(N-4'-sulfonyl-4-(dimethylamino)-azobenzene)-3-aminopropyl]-propyl-2-O-succinoyl-long chain alkylamino-CPG
DASH   dynamic allele-specific hybridization
dATP   2'-deoxyadenosine 5'-triphosphate
dCTP   deoxycytidine 5'-triphosphate
DDDP   DNA directed (or dependent) DNA polymerase
Deep Vent   Pyrococcus species GB-D
DEPC   diethyl pyrocarbonate
dGTP   2'-deoxyguanosine 5'-triphosphate
DIN   Germany Standards Institute (Deutsches Institut für Normung)
DIO2   deiodinase, iodothyronine, type II
dITP   deoxyinosine 5 -triphosphate
DMSO   dimethylsulfoxide
DNA   deoxyribonucleic acid
DNase   deoxyribonuclease
dNTP   deoxyribonucleoside triphosphate
DPI3   dihydrocyclopyrroloindole
ds   double-stranded
dsDNA   double-stranded DNA
DTT   dithiothreitol
dTTP   deoxytimidine triphosphate
dUTP   2'-deoxyuridine 5'-triphosphate
dUTPase   deoxyuridine 5'-triphosphate nucleoti-dohydrolase
ECACC   European Collection of Animal Cell Cultures
ECL   electrochemiluminescent
EDTA   ethylene diaminetetraacetic acid
EGFR   epidermal growth factor receptor
ELISA   Enzyme Linked Immunosorbent Assay
ER   estrogen receptor
EtBr   Ethidium Bromide

FACS	Fluorescence activated cell sorting
FAM	6-carboxy fluorescein
FAS	fatty acid synthase
FCS	fluorescence correlation spectroscopy
FI	fluorophore
FoLT	formamide low temperature
FRET	fluorescence resonance energy transfer
GAPDH	glyceraldehyde-3-phosphate dehydrogenase
GCC	guanylyl cyclase C
gDNA	genomic DNA
GFP	green fluorescent protein
GHR	growth hormone receptor
GMO	genetically modified organism
GSQS	gene-specific quantity standard series
GST	glutathion-S-transferase
GSTM	glutathion-S-transferase μ (mu)
GSTT	glutathion-S-transferase θ (theta)
HBV	Hepatitis B virus
HDPE	high-density polyethylene
HEG	hexaethylene glycol
HeLa	Henrietta Lacks (cells)
HEPES	N-[2-hydroxyethyl]piperazine-N -[2-ethanesulfonic acid]
HEX	hexachloro-6-carboxyfluorescein
HH	hereditary hemochromatosis
HhH	helix-hairpin-helix
HIV	human immunodeficiency virus
HK	housekeeping
HKG	housekeeping gene
HMG	high-mobility group
HPLC	High Performance Liquid Chromatography
HPV	human Papillomavirus
IGEI	interactive gene expression index
IGF	insulin-like growth factor
IGF-1R	insulin-like growth factor type I receptor
IP	ion-pair
IPC	internal positive control
IPTG	Isopropyl b-d-Thiogalactoside
KlenTaq	*Thermus aquaticus*
K_m	Michaelis Menten constant. A low K_m indicates a strong enzyme/substrate affinity
LB	Luria Broth
LC	LightCycler (LC red 640 or 705)
LCM	laser-capture microdissection
LDT	lower detection threshold
LED	light emitting diode
LNA	locked nucleic acid
LUX	Light **u**pon **ex**tension
M.W.	molecular weight
M.Ws.	molecular weights
MB	Molecular Beacon

MBMO	Molecular Beacon plus a single-strand target that produces a probe-target hybrid containing a single mismatched base pair
MBO	Molecular Beacon plus its complementary single-stranded oligonucleatide
MCF-7	breast cancer cell line
McSNP	melting curve single-nucleotide polymorphism
mDNA	mitochondrial DNA
MF	multiplication factor
MGB	minor groove binder
MHC	major histocompatibility
miRNA	microRNA
MMLV	Moloney murine leukemia virus
mRNA	messenger RNA
MRP1-3	multidrug resistance proteins
MSDS	Material Safety Data Sheets
NASBA	nucleic acid sequence-based amplification
NBC	nucleated blood cells
NEP	noise-equivalent power
NF1	neurofibromatosis 1
NIST	National Institute of Standards and Technology
NPC	no probe containing
NT	native template
NTC	no template control (no target control)
OCT	optimum cutting temperature
OD	optical density (unit)
PAGE	polyacrylamide gel electrophoresis
PALM	position ablative laser microbeam
PBGD	porphobilinogen decarboxylase
PBS	phosphate buffered saline
PCO	pseudo-cyclic oligonucleotide
PCR	polymerase chain reaction
PCR-EIA	PCR-enzyme immunoassay
PDAR	Pre-developed TaqMan assay reagents
PDECGF	platelet-derived endothelial cell growth factor
PD-loop	PNA–DNA-loop
PEG300	polyethylene glycol 300
Pfu	*Pyrococcus furiosus*
Pfx	*Thermococcus kodkaraensis* (originally misnamed as a *Pyrococcus*)
PGR	progesterone receptor
PMA	phorbol myristate acetate
PMT	photomultiplier tube
PNA	peptide nucleic acid
PSA	prostate-specific antigen
PVP	polyvinylpyrrolidone
PVP	polyvinyl pyrrolidone
Pwo	*Pyrococcus woesei*
qPCR	quantitative PCR

qRT-PCR	quantitative real-time reverse transcription (transcriptase) mediated/coupled polymerase chain reaction		TAMRA	6-carboxytetra-methylrhodamine
RAR	retinoic acid receptor		*Taq*	*Thermus aquaticus*
RDDP	RNA directed (or dependent) DNA polymerase		TEMED	*N,N,N',N'*-tetramethylethylenediamine
recDNA	recombinant plasmid DNA		TET	6-carboxy-2',4,7,7'-tetrachlorofluorescein
Rn	normalized reporter		*Tfl*	*Thermus flavus*
RNA	ribonucleic acid		*Tfu*	*Thermococcus fumicolans*
RNase	ribonuclease		*Tgo*	*Thermococcus gorgonarius*
ROC	receiver (or relative) operating characteristic		TH	Tissue Homogenizer (OMNI International)
ROX	6-carboxy-X-rhodamine		T_m	melting temperature
RP-HPLC	reversed-phase high-performance liquid chromatography		TMAC	tetramethylammonium chloride
rpm	revolutions per minute		TNF	tumor necrosis factor
rRNA	ribosomal RNA		TNFR	tumor necrosis factor receptor
RT	reverse transcriptase (transcription)		TO	thiazole orange
S	Scorpion		TR	time-resolved
SAGE	Serial Analysis of Gene Expression		TRAP	telomeric repeat amplification protocol
SD	standard deviation		TR-FRET	time-resolved fluorescence resonance energy transfer
SDS	Sequence Detection System (ABI PRISM®)		tRNA	transfer RNA
SDS	sodium dodecyl sulfate		TS	thymidilate synthase
SEM	standard error of the mean		*Tth*	*Thermus thermophilus*
SEM	standardized expression measurement		UMM	universal master mix
SMART	switch mechanism at the 5' end of reverse transcript		UNG	uracil-*N*-glycosylase
			UTR	untranslated region
SMIS	standardized mixture of internal standards		UV	ultraviolet
SNP	single nucleotide polymorphisms		UVB	ultraviolet-B band (280-320 nm)
snRNA	small nuclear RNA		UVC	ultraviolet-C band (200-280 nm)
SOX	sulfite oxidase		VEGF	vascular endothelial growth factor
SPR	surface plasmon resonance		Vent	*Thermococcus litoralis*
Sry	sex-determining region on the Y chromosome		VNTR	variable number of tandem repeat
			Xist	X inactivation-specific transcript
ss	single-stranded		YED	yeast extract D-glucose
ssDNA	single-stranded DNA		ZILOS	*zona* infrared laser optical system
SSP-PCR	sequence specific primers-polymerase chain reaction		$\Delta\Delta C_t$	comparative quantification determination
ssRNA	single stranded RNA		ΔRn	The difference between the Rn of the reaction (including template) and the Rn of the unreacted sample. (Rn is the normalized reporter, or the emission intensity of the reporter dye divided by the emission intensity of a passive reference)
STaRT-PCR	standardized RT-PCR			
TAE	*tris*-acetate			
			µH	Micro Homogenizer (OMNI International)

PART I

OVERVIEWS

- 1 **Quantification of Nucleic Acids by PCR**

- 2 **Real-Time RT-PCR: What Lies Beneath the Surface**

- 3 **Quantification Strategies in Real-Time PCR**

1

Quantification of Nucleic Acids by PCR

Stephen A. Bustin

Abstract

Real-time, fluorescence-based PCR and RT-PCR are currently the methods of choice for quantification of nucleic acids. They are perceived as best fulfilling the four "S" requirements: simplicity, speed, sensitivity, and specificity. However, as with conventional PCR methods, careful experimental design, consistent assay conditions, and reliable reporting of data are the key to obtaining accurate, as well as biologically relevant results.

1

Quantification of Nucleic Acids by PCR

Stephen A. Bustin

*Barts and The London, Queen Mary's School of Medicine and
Dentistry, University of London, London, United Kingdom*

1.1. Introduction

Perhaps the most irritating thing about the polymerase chain reaction
(PCR)[1] is its simplicity: Many of us still cannot understand why we
were not the ones to think of it first. Without a shadow of a doubt, it is
one of a handful of techniques (perhaps *the* technique) that have truly
revolutionized molecular biology.[2] Its specificity, efficiency, and fidelity[3] has turned it into a key technology that has made molecular assays
accessible to every research and diagnostic laboratory.[4] It underpins
most of the spectacular advances that are now common place in every

biological discipline, ranging from microbial detection[5-7] and microbiological quality assurance,[8,9] through the detection of genetically manipulated organism in crops and foods[10] to molecular[11] and veterinary medicine.[12] Together with its offshoot, the reverse transcription (RT) PCR,[13,14] it is unrivalled as a qualitative assay for the rapid, inexpensive, and simple detection of nucleic acids. Both techniques allow the processing of numerous samples at any one time, and the ability to amplify several templates in a single reaction (multiplexing)[15,16] gives them the potential to become truly high-throughput assays,[17] limited mainly by the need for post-PCR processing.

1.1.1. PCR Characteristics

Conventionally, the PCR amplification reaction is described as at first stochastic ("lag phase"), then exponential ("exponential phase") and finally stagnant ("plateau phase")[18] (**Fig. 1.1**). For most targets (present at more than about 1,000 copies), the lag phase is related primarily to the threshold sensitivity and variability of the particular method used to measure the amplified product. As long as enzyme reaction kinetics are driven by the concentration of primer and dNTP substrate, both of which are present in vast excess, the influence of the concentration of the target template on the kinetics of amplification should be insignificant. This is not true for single or very low copy number targets (see **Chapter 11**, Part II). In the exponential phase the accumulation of product is predicted by the formula $y = N(1+E)^n$, where y is the amplification factor, N is the number of input target molecules, E is the amplification efficiency, and n is the number of amplification cycles. In real-life, truly exponential amplification is believed to be limited to only very few cycles of a typical 40 cycle amplification run and this formula may be accurate only for those few cycles. Subsequently the amplification slows down to constant amplification rates and eventually it reaches the plateau phase. Here, its effects are difficult to predict or standardize and amplification is affected by limitations of substrate and inhibition of enzyme. Overall amplification efficiency will also vary with the presence of RT and/or DNA polymerase inhibitors and may be affected by the position of the sample in the thermal cycler.

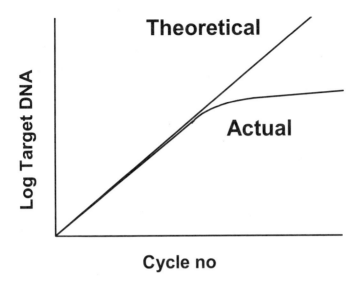

Figure 1.1. Kinetics of PCR amplification. Theoretically, the amount of product doubles during each cycle of the PCR reaction. In practice, the fraction of template replicated during each reaction cycle is less than 100%.

Corbett Rotor-Gene allows the user to calculate the reaction efficiency of each reaction, which is determined using the first few cycles after the take-off point of the reaction. This is useful when comparing the amplification efficiencies of replicates and confirms the highly reproducible nature of real-time PCR assays (**Fig. 1.2A**). It is apparent that the value for *E* is rarely 2, i.e., 100%. Indeed, our data are very similar to the average *E* value of 1.8 reported elsewhere.[19] A detailed statistical analysis of different runs is shown in **Table 1.1**. These are all replicates (either 32 or 72) of various DNA templates and show significantly different *E* values **between** different templates. However, the *E* values **within** the same templates are very similar and highly reproducible. The *E* values from the same reaction over different cycles can be determined by preparing a dilution series of this reaction and comparing the efficiencies of the different reactions. This reveals that the *E* values for each dilution are very similar, but somewhat variable between dilutions.

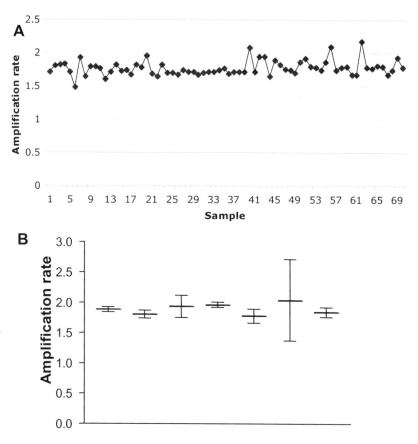

Figure 1.2. Amplification efficiencies. **(A)** 72 replicates 1×10^6 template were amplified and amplification efficiencies determined using the Corbett Rotor-Gene. It is interesting to note that the amplification efficiency is rarely 100%. **(B)** Ten-fold serial dilutions ranging from 10^6 to 10^2 were amplified in quadruplicate and the average amplification efficiency (± 2 standard deviations) is plotted.

1.2. Conventional Quantitative PCR

It is not so very long ago that the words "quantitative" and "PCR" were deemed an oxymoron, with quantitative PCR an aspiration rather than

Table 1.1. Different templates have different amplification efficiencies.

	A	B	C	D
Minimum	1.810	1.490	1.890	1.500
25% Percentile	1.870	1.705	1.930	1.710
Median	1.910	1.750	1.965	1.760
75% Percentile	1.930	1.820	1.990	1.840
Maximum	2.030	2.180	2.010	1.920
Mean	1.904	1.775	1.959	1.764
Std. Deviation	0.0398	0.1123	0.0384	0.0854
Lower 95% CI	1.894	1.749	1.946	1.735
Upper 95% CI	1.913	1.802	1.972	1.793
C.V.	2.09%	6.32%	1.96%	4.84%
Geometric mean	1.903	1.772	1.958	1.762

reality.[20] Conventional PCR is a qualitative assay answering *yes/no* questions and marginal variations in reaction components, thermal cycling conditions, and mispriming events during the early stage of PCR will greatly affect the yield of the amplified product.[21] Therefore, conventional quantitative PCR demands extensive validation and tedious controls. Not least, it requires improved data recording methods that are less subjective than band densitometry. It took several pioneering reports delineating fundamental theoretical and practical considerations[22-25] to promote a more general recognition of the inherent quantitative capacity of the PCR reaction.[26] This development was driven by the obvious demand for quantitative data, e.g., for measuring viral load in HIV patients,[27] monitoring of occult disease in cancer[28] or examining the genetic basis for individual variation in response to therapeutics through pharmacogenomics.[29] This demand was met by the development of numerous different strategies that promised sensitive and specific PCR product detection and quantification.[30]

The basic attribute of the PCR, cyclic priming and enzymatic replication of target sequences, results in its exquisite sensitivity, but also presents substantial problems when used for quantitative purposes. There are numerous experimental variables that become exaggerated by the exponential amplification. Quantitative results are affected by mispriming, differences in the kinetics of amplification, variation in reagent purity and reaction composition, and, perhaps most significantly, protocol and operator variability.[31] Therefore, it is difficult to attain a consistent relationship between the amount of starting template and absolute amount of amplified product.

1.2.1. Concepts

The concepts at the core of today's quantitative assays have been in place virtually from the beginning of the PCR age and, intriguingly, are still the subject of fierce debate today with investigators carrying out real-time qPCR assays.

1. The first concept is that of an internal heterologous control sequence that should be present at a relatively constant level to permit quantification of any target template relative to that internal control.[32-34] Numerous so-called housekeeping (HK), or reference, genes have been proposed as suitable internal references, based on the belief that they were constitutively and universally expressed. However, this is a simplistic definition and is no longer appropriate: instead, a better definition is that HK genes play a key role in the maintenance of every cell because they specify proteins that are critical to the activities that must be carried out for successful completion of the cell cycle.[35] This implies that they are regulated and hence are not constitutively expressed. Consequently, while this concept is easy to understand and, in theory, makes perfect sense, in practice the variability in mRNA levels of HK (or "maintenance") genes makes them unsuitable as internal reference genes. Furthermore, differences in template sequence and abundance between HK gene and target, as well as distinct primer binding characteristics for different templates create problems and make this approach less than ideal.

2. The alternative concept uses one set of primers in a single reaction together with a synthetic standard whose amplification product can be discriminated from and differentially quantified relative to the product from the template.[36-38] Initially, the PCR assay was spiked with a known copy number of the synthetic internal control, which was coamplified with the target. In addition, identical amounts of template were amplified in replicate reactions with

increasing amounts of the internal control. This effectively resulted in the titration of the unknown copy number of target and
extrapolating against a standard curve generated with the internal
standard could quantitate the amount of template..Again, the concept is reasonably simple but is marred in practice by the problem
of having to construct the internal controls.

There are numerous variations on these two themes that have resulted
in the development of competitive PCR protocols that allow the quantitative identification of target and competitor products through measurement and comparison of band intensities.[39-43] It is termed competitive, because reference and target sequences compete for the same
primer sequences. In practice, the reaction and its justification proceed
as follows:

1. The unknown target (quantity unknown) is amplified with a dilution series of competitor DNA whose amplification efficiency
   must be the same.

2. Amplification products are separated by agarose gel electrophoresis and quantified.

3. The ratio of the quantity of target:competitor PCR products
   remains constant throughout amplification, even during the
   plateau phase. Therefore, the ratio at the end of the assay is equal
   to the ratio of their starting copy numbers. Since the concentration
   of competitor at the start of the reaction is known, the initial concentration of target cDNA in the sample can be calculated.

4. Target and competitor PCR products can be distinguished by
   designing the competitor to have a slight size difference or contain
   a restriction enzyme recognition site. However, heteroduplexes
   between target and competitor can form during the later stages of
   the PCR reaction and can interfere with accurate quantification.

5. Alternatively, heterologous competitors can be used. These share
   the same primer binding sequences as the target but contain different intervening sequences. One easy way of obtaining these is
   by low stringency amplification of DNA from an evolutionarily
   distantly related species.[44] Because these artificially created fragments contain the primer specific ends, they can be used for the
   quantification of target DNA amplified by these primers.
   Competitor DNA fragments that differ in size from the target are

selected to distinguish both fragments visually by gel electrophoresis. It is crucial to confirm (1) that both forward and reverse primers are required for amplification of the putative competitor and (2) that target and competitor amplify with equal efficiency.

It is also possible to make use of an RNA competitor during the RT step by mixing fixed amounts of RNA template with increasing amounts of competitor RNA. This will result in competition during the RT and subsequent PCR reactions and the samples are analyzed as for competitive PCR.

The potential for multiplexing was also recognized at a very early stage: the use of a common synthetic internal standard, together with multiple upstream primers for various target genes followed by the complementary sequences to their downstream primers in the same order, allowed the use of the same internal standard, with appropriate primer pairs, to quantitate multiple different targets.[36]

1.2.2. Limitations

None of the conventional protocols are either straightforward or rapid; all are labor-, time-, and cost-intensive[45] and suffer from significant technical limitations.[30] The lack of standardization often produces strikingly inconsistent results,[46-48] the reproducibility can be highly variable,[49,50] false-positive rates can be as high as 28%[51] with error rates ranging between 10% and 60% dependent on the analysis method.[50,52,53] What is more, theoretical considerations expected *a priori* are not necessarily born out by the empirical observations: The assertion that accurate quantification requires a nearly identical competitor template[41] is contradicted by claims that competitors derived from unrelated sequences can be used for successful quantification[40] or that the use of internal standards with similar sequences results in loss of sensitivity and accuracy.[49]

Some of these underlying problems and discrepancies have been addressed by the development of a computer simulation of competitive PCR that describes the role of each element in the competitive reaction in determining the accuracy of the method.[54] It shows that amplification efficiency differences between templates, while real, also are consistent and, ***once identified*** and measured, can be removed as an obstacle to accuracy. The stumbling block is the "once identified," as this sound simple but, in practice, involves detailed and methodical step-by-step analysis. This may be acceptable for one or two templates, but becomes rate-limiting when attempting to verify the results of tens or hundreds of mRNAs from microarray analyses. One interesting conclusion is that quantification of competitive PCR assays does not have to be carried out in the log-linear phase of the PCR reaction. Using appropriate competitors sharing primer binding sites and high internal sequence similarity, identical amplification efficiencies can be preserved throughout the reaction. Of course, this unexpected conclusion underpins and is dramatically proven correct by the successful quantification method (STaRT-PCR) described in **Chapter 14** (Part III) and published elsewhere.[17,55-59] Amplification products, including heteroduplexes formed between native and competitor templates as reactions progress to plateau, can be identified and quantified accurately using denaturing HPLC. Importantly, the model emphasizes the need to test the accuracy of quantification experimentally with known inputs of both target and competitor, because neither slope nor linearity of competitive titrations are reliable indicators of accuracy. However, it is clear that the need for extensive validation during and after each assay is not compatible with its translation into routine high-throughput practice, nor does it inspire confidence with respect to its accuracy or precision for nonstandard or newly developed assays.

Nevertheless, these considerations prove beyond doubt that under appropriate conditions even conventional PCR methods can be quantitative,[60,61] as evidenced by the most promising of these techniques, StaRT PCR.[17] However, it is also clear that major pitfalls remain and need to be addressed urgently.[45] Finally, even if all the technical problems associated with conventional competitive PCR protocols were to be addressed successfully, this would not affect the sheer tedium associated with having to design, test, and optimize competitors for the numerous targets that are not covered by StaRT-PCR primers.

1.2.3. Alternatives

The identification of gel electrophoresis as one of the major bottlenecks for conventional PCR has led to the development of alternatives, such as flow cytometry,[62] that would avoid the need for gel electrophoresis altogether. There are also alternatives that do not depend on competitive PCR.[63-65] If an endpoint assay suffices, e.g., for SNP analysis, chemiluminescence can provide an alternative to fluorescence-based real-time detection.[66] After completion of the PCR assay, the DNA products are attached to the wells of a microwell plate, denatured, and hybridized to specific probes. One chemiluminescent reaction is specific for the test template, and another is specific for the internal control. One advantage of this system is that it does not require expensive probes or equipment. Furthermore, chemiluminescence-based assays are generally accepted as being more sensitive than fluorescence-based ones. However, its reproducibility and dynamic range are not as good as with real-time fluorescence-based systems.

Another intriguing alternative quantitates target mRNAs by a combination of PCR and an electrochemiluminescent (ECL) detection of the amplified products. Total cellular RNA is reverse-transcribed and amplified with a biotinylated forward primer and a *Tris* (2,2'-bipyridine) ruthenium (II)-labeled reverse primer. The amplification product is captured on streptavidin-coated paramagnetic beads, quantified by ECL detection and results are converted to quantitative values using an external standard curve.[67]

Yet another alternative is provided by fluorescence correlation spectroscopy (FCS), which is a time-averaging fluctuation analysis that combines very high sensitivity with high statistical confidence and is a versatile tool for detection and temporal investigation of biomolecules at ultralow concentrations.[68] In FCS, fluorescent particles, such as a short probe, move through a microscopic detection volume of about 10^{-15} l (1 femtoliter) defined by a focused laser beam that is exciting them. Their fluorescence intensity fluctuates due to the variations in the number density in the detection volume, which is altered by the binding of the labeled probe to a complementary target. Interactions between nucleic acids can be determined irrespective of differences in thermal motion by correlating complementary nucleic acid sequences tagged with different fluorophores.[69] The fluorescence emitted at different wavelengths is cross-correlated and only molecular species containing both colors are observed. FCS can be combined with PCR by using two PCR primers tagged at their 5' ends with different fluorescence dyes. FCS can pick out and quantify cross-correlated signals resulting from the two tags, as the Brownian motion of the excess, unbound primers is stochastic and uncorrelated. Hence only the product containing both primers is detected.[70] The main advantages of cross-correlation PCR are that target detection does not depend on special conditions for energy transfer and, as with the 5'-nuclease assay, enzymatic release of the energy acceptor. Furthermore, FCS determines the absolute number of amplified targets without the need for internal standards. FCS has been applied to the detection of PCR products, e.g., that of hepatitis C virus[71] and genotyping[72] and can detect as little as a single copy of a target gene.[73]

1.3. Real-Time Quantitative PCR

Then of course there are the real-time fluorescence-based PCR[74] and RT-PCR[75] assays that convey the impression of generating actual quantitative data. Both methods are based on the contention that there is a quantitative relationship between the amount of target nucleic acid present at the start of a PCR assay and the amount of product amplified during its exponential phase. The crucial conceptual innovation and the key to understanding quantification by real-time PCR is the threshold cycle (C_t) (**Fig. 1.3**). To determine C_ts, the levels of background fluorescence are first established for a particular run. Next, platform-specific algorithms are used to define a fluorescence threshold. Finally, the algorithm searches the data from each sample for a point that exceeds the baseline. The cycle at which this point occurs is defined as the C_t. Hence the C_t represents a detection threshold for that instrument and is dependent on the starting template copy number, the efficiency of PCR amplification, efficiency of cleavage or hybridization of the fluorogenic probe, and the sensitivity of detection. The fewer cycles it takes to reach a detectable level of fluorescence, the greater the initial copy number. However, note that for most instruments the choice of threshold can be made by the operator, which introduces a subjective element into real-time quantification. Furthermore, it is important to bear in mind that real-time methods are not a cure-all. This is clearly demonstrated in a recent report that compares the reliability of real-time RT-PCR assays carried out in different laboratories.[76] The authors report considerable quantitative and qualitative variation between several laboratories, even when using a commercial kit and standardize protocols and stress the need for standardization and extended quality control studies.

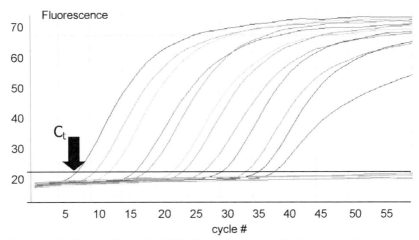

Figure 1.3. Threshold cycle (C_t) is the point where the instrument first detects fluorescence above background noise (arrow).

The development of robust chemistries and the introduction of several combined thermal cycler/fluorimeters has made carrying out a qPCR assay simple; indeed, with appropriate instrumentation qPCR assays can even be carried out in the field.[77] The instruments cost an arm and a leg to buy, service contracts are barely affordable and as for reagent cost, well the less said the better. But, hey, it works, it produces more results than anyone can easily cope with, so why quibble about the dosh?

1.3.1. Uses

Real-time PCR is a technique whose time has come.[78] Over the last five years this technique has been transformed from an experimental tool into a mainstream scientific technology[79] and for those who have converted to real-time quantitative PCR, the old days are but a memory.[80] It may or may not be more sensitive than conventional nested or competitive PCR assays,[81-85] but it sure is hugely more convenient.[86] Real-time assays have a greater detection range,[87] with significantly less inter-assay variation[82] and are highly reproducible and reliable[88-92] (**Fig. 1.4**); they are also easily converted to the nanoscale.[93] Compared to ELISA's, real-time PCR assays are as reliable and as sensitive.[94] Currently their only real drawbacks are the substantial monetary investment in instrumentation and reagents that is required to carry out an assay. Also, note that real-time assays may also be more susceptible to inhibitors, such as those present in manure, feces, and other biological samples.[95,96] In theory, real-time PCR combines the objectivity of fluorescence detection with the simplicity of the original PCR reaction, and results obtained using fluorescence-based PCR chemistries are now accepted as the "Gold Standard"[97] for quantification of viral load in clinical samples,[97-99] quantification of bacterial pathogens such as *Listeria monocytogenes*,[100] *Helicobacter pylori*,[101-105] and many others,[84,106,107] SNP analyses,[108-111] detection of genetic alterations,[112,113] even from single cells,[114,115] sex determination in single human blastomeres,[116] monitoring for minimal residual disease in leukemias,[117,118] solid tumor diagnostics,[119] toxicology,[120] quantification of RNA copy numbers,[121] including the quantification of gene expression levels after gene therapy,[122] pre-implantation screening of RNA in single embryos,[123] and for verifying microarray data.[124-126] For some applications, the technique has evolved from generically detecting the presence of disease cells in individuals to the identification of specific genes that are prognostic for determining therapeutic outcome.[127] Other interesting applications include the quantification of cytomegalovirus DNA in amniotic fluid samples from mothers with primary infection,[128] for the quantification of enterovirus in cerebrospinal fluid,[129-131] and the diagnosis of haploidy and triploidy based on the measurement of gene copy number.[132] It is widely used for biotechnology applications,[133] e.g., for the quantification of genetic modification in food,[134-137] the accurate determination of zygosity in transgenic animals,[138] and, intriguingly, to quantitate nitrifiers in activated sludge as a means of monitoring the performance of activated sludge plants.[139-141] Real-time qPCR shows great promise for monitoring parasitic infections where standard (usually microscope-based) methods for quantification are difficult or are less sensitive for detection of clinically relevant parasite burdens. The ability to quantify low-level parasite burdens allows the monitoring of vaccine efficacy at pre-symptomatic levels, the progression of infections under drug treatment, and diagnosis of low-level infections or carrier states. Correlations of clinical manifestations of disease with parasite burden can be made over a wider range of parasite levels than is currently achievable.[142] Finally, multiplexing (**Fig. 1.5**) has the potential to count parasites with different genotypes in infections of multiple parasite types of the same species. For example, drug-resistant parasites often coexist with drug-sensitive parasites in natural infections of *Plasmodium falciparum*.

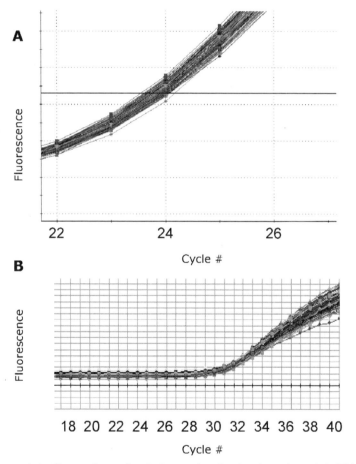

Figure 1.4. Comparison of real-time and end point detection. (**A**) This close-up of the C_ts obtained from 96 identical PCR reactions and analyzed on a Stratagene Mx-4000 shows that their C_ts are very similar. (**B**) A similar result is obtained with the Bio-Rad iCycler. However, it is clear that this correlation is not always as apparent at the end point of the reaction.

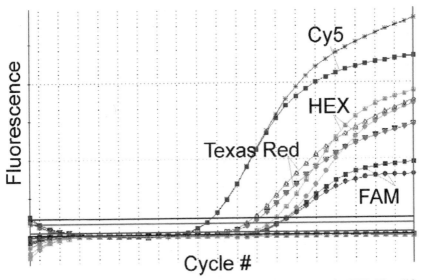

Figure 1.5. Multiplex PCR using Texas Red, Cy5, FAM and HEX. The different background fluorescent levels for the four fluorophores are clearly visible.

1.3.2. Microdissection

The recent emergence of laser-assisted microdissection as a practical proposition[143] is extremely well-timed and serendipitous for quantitative PCR. Frozen tissue microdissection has become one of the key tools in molecular biomedicine and modern pathology as it provides the possibility of cell-type or even cell-specific investigation of DNA, RNA, and proteins. This selective analysis of individual cells or same cell types free from surrounding tissue circumvents the problem of tissue heterogeneity and provides the possibility to assign characteristic gene expression patterns to particular histological phenotypes.[144] DNA and RNA extracted from laser-assisted microdissection in complex tissues is increasingly being used for analyzing genetic alteration[145,146] as well as for the analysis of differential mRNA expression[147-154] and it is clear that expression profiling results obtained from microdissected tissue are significantly different from those obtained from bulk tissue.[155]

An exciting advance is the development of rapid immunostaining procedures for frozen sections, followed by laser capture microdissection and RNA extraction, which allows targeted mRNA analysis of immunophenotypically defined cell populations.[156] Routine immunostaining affects the ability to recover RNA[157] but an improved protocol has been published recently that combines short-term formalin fixation with utmost reduction of antibody incubation times to generate high-quality data from mRNA templates.[158] How useful the ability to extract RNA from LCM archival material will be for reliable quantification remains unclear, but the potential of combining real-time PCR/RT-PCR and LCM to investigate such material is immense.

We have been using PALM laser capture microdissection system to enrich for epithelial cells from colonic crypts and for adjacent stromal cells from 7 µM sections of formalin-fixed, paraffin embedded tissue (**Fig. 1.6**).

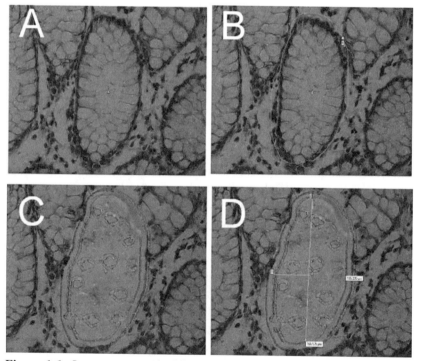

Figure 1.6. Laser-capture microdissection from colonic tissue. The sequence shows (**A**) a colonic crypt, (**B**) its delineation by the electronic drawing tool, (**C**) the remainder of the crypt after laser capture and (**D**) the calculation of the area captured.

RNA was extracted either from 50 individual crypts containing an average of 40 cells or stromal sections and purified using Stratagene's Absolutely RNA™ Microprep kit (*Cat. No. 400805*). The final RNA was eluted into 2×30 μl elution buffer and RNA yield was determined using RiboGreen assays. The yield was between 30 and 85 pg/μl, resulting in a total yield of 1.8–5.1 ng of RNA and corresponding to a yield of between 0.9 and 2.55 pg RNA/cell. When this RNA was used for qRT-PCR analysis, no amplification was observed with GAPDH primers, which amplify a 350 bp amplicon. In contrast, use of c-*myc* primers, which amplify a 71 bp amplicon, respectively, resulted in good amplification, which when extrapolated, gave mRNA copy numbers somewhat lower than those obtained using fresh material (**Fig. 1.7**).

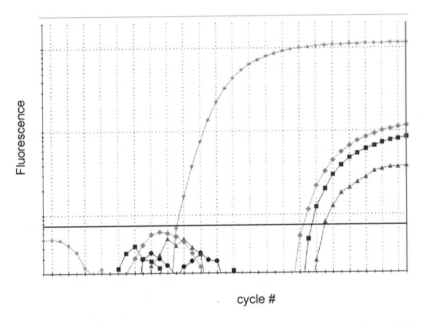

Figure 1.7. Amplification plots of c-*myc* mRNA obtained LCM-dissected tissue. The first amplification plot was obtained from 100 ng of total RNA extracted from a fresh frozen colonic sample and resulted in a C_t of 16.9. The three amplification plots to the right were obtained from 50 pg of RNA obtained from formalin-fixed, paraffin-embedded tissue and gave C_ts of 32.2, 33.2, and 34.9.

1.3.3. Limitations

Inevitably, there is more to qPCR than converting to real-time technology. What is *real-time* anyway? An obvious definition is that it combines amplification and detection to allow the monitoring of a PCR reaction as it progresses. That is simple enough; the problem is how to perform the assay and how to monitor it. There are several routes available, and new ones seem to appear every month: a number of DNA intercalating dyes, numerous probe-based chemistries, various alternative protocols based on different enzymes and reaction conditions, and diverse real-time instruments. This makes it very difficult to compare results obtained using different protocols and detection procedures. A second problem lies with the increased expectation associated with the term qPCR that has resulted in a shifting of goal posts for the molecular biologist during recent years. The copy number obtained at the end of a run gives the impression that this number is in some way relevant. However, this may or may not be so. The interpretation of target copy numbers is not easy as (1) data are inherently logarithmic, (2) are heteroscedastic (variance changes with concentration), (3) and some C_ts are 40 or above, hence have no variance at all. A third problem relates to the way the data are presented. In RT-PCR assays this is very often as a ratio of target RNA over levels of a control RNA species. This data normalization may result in misleading conclusions if the relationship between the target RNA levels and RNA levels of the reference do not regress to a zero intercept[159] (see **Chapter 11**).

1.3.4. PCR

Quantification of DNA copy numbers in genomic[160-162] or viral DNAs,[163-168] transgene copy number,[169] is reasonably straightforward and gives quantitative results that, all things being equal, are comparable and biologically meaningful. What all things being equal means may be, of course, another matter. Similarly, allelic discrimination and SNP assays[108-110,170,171] are reliable, because they provide a *yes/no* answer and only utilize the convenience of using fluorescence detection, but are in effect endpoint assays.

Furthermore, the assay depends only on a single enzyme and the amount of template added to the reaction can be measured reasonably accurately. Normalization to cell number or total DNA is relatively straightforward and the general variability between assays is relatively low (see **Chapter 11**). Therefore, both the assay design and data interpretation can be accurate as well as biologically meaningful and there are good examples where qPCR results have prognostic power.[127]

1.3.5. RT-PCR

The situation is quite different for real-time RT-PCR assays, which involve two enzymes or two activities of the same enzyme. These are expected to provide information about labile and variable mRNA expression profiles to answer questions related to cell behavior, disease state, different environmental effects or tissue-specific expression. This very expectation entails that the starting materials themselves often will be significantly different. Tumor heterogeneity, the diverse genotypes of individuals whose tissue is analyzed, the use of myriads of tissue culture cell lines, different treatment protocols, extraction reagents, handling and storage of samples combine to generate starting materials that are diverse at all times. Combine this with different RT-PCR protocols, and it is clear that any raw data obtained using this technique will be highly diverse, even though they have been generated using highly reproducible standards. They may be precise, they may even be reproducible, but they are not necessarily biologically relevant.[31] The development of nested real-time RT-PCR protocols[172] reopens all the questions associated with conventional nested RT-PCR and the value of such protocols remains a moot point.

The practical aspect of carrying out a qRT-PCR assay is one thing and getting all the technical steps right is an obvious precondition to achieving a meaningful result. Unfortunately, data interpretation makes the acquisition of the raw data child's play.[173] The choice of relative versus absolute quantification, internal or external standard, selection of any one of numerous reference genes, either single or in combinations, and normalization against it (or them), or even against rRNA, total RNA, number of cells or against genomic DNA all combine to produce final data that purport to present a meaningful quantitative mRNA profile for the tissue or treatment under investigation, but really only provide a snapshot of a particular cell or tissue whose nucleic acid has been extracted, handled, and amplified in a particular way.[121] Is this too cynical? The surfeits of contradictory results that litter the quantitative PCR field provide ample evidence of the truth of this statement. Sadly, unless these results are properly validated, excessive reliance on qPCR assays is likely to sow widespread confusion. This is particularly true when considering the routine implementation of this technology in molecular diagnostics.[98]

Therefore, it is essential to bear in mind that a qRT-PCR assay quantitates steady-state mRNA levels and nothing else (**Fig. 1.8**). Accurate quantification of mRNA levels tells the researcher nothing about either transcription levels or mRNA stability. Extrapolating from steady-state mRNA levels to any pronouncement with respect to gene expression requires a key question to be addressed: Can quantitative mRNA data predict protein expression levels? Again, the literature provides conflicting answers. Individual reports suggest that they can for multidrug resistance proteins MRP1-3 in lung cancer,[174] insulin-like growth factor (IGF) binding protein (BP) 3 in breast cancer,[175] IGF type II receptor,[176] VEGF,[177] and the estrogen receptor, but do not for Cathepsin,[178] Cytochrome P450,[179] Metallothionein,[180] Myosin LC3,[181] and dihydropyrimidine dehydrogenase.[182] Numbers are extremely limited and these studies were carried out using different tissues, species, and conditions, hence it would be premature to generalize. Indeed, in at least one case, there appear to be tissue-specific differences: EGFR mRNA levels are predictive for protein levels in the prostate but not in the placenta.[183] The most wide-ranging study on 100-odd proteins in yeast concludes by stating that there is no predictive correlation between steady-state mRNA and protein levels RNA levels.[184] It is likely that there is a correlation between mRNA, protein, and activity levels for most genes under some circumstances but not under others. For some, there will never be any correlation. This makes sense, of course, as for many genes regulation occurs at the post-transcriptional stage; hence RT-PCR data will be uninformative for many genes and biologically relevant analysis of gene expression requires additional information to verify the changes in steady-state mRNA levels, e.g., by using immunohistochemistry or biochemical analyses.

Closely related to this is the question of what is a biologically relevant difference in mRNA expression level? As discussed above, mRNA levels of many proteins are somewhat removed from the ultimate destiny of the gene product, protein activity. This is probably related to pro-

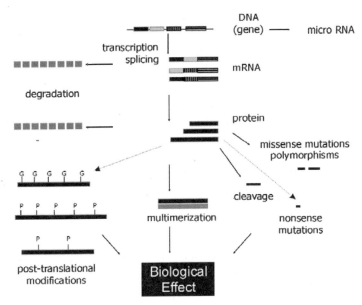

Figure 1.8. Gene expression is more than just the detection of mRNA by qRT-PCR assays. It is a complex network of interlinking steps that start with a stimulus initiating or repressing the transcription of a gene, and ends with a biological affect caused by a protein. qRT-PCR can only detect steady-state mRNA levels and provides no information about any of the other steps.

cessing inefficiencies at every step of the gene expression pathway and a cell's need to compensate by producing an excess of transcript. This certainly appears to be the case for HK genes,[35] which are expressed at moderate levels, 10–50 copies per cell. Therefore, for such genes, differences less than four-fold may not be biologically significant, but there are not sufficient data to conclude that a five- or six-fold difference is more biologically significant than a three- or four-fold difference,[35,185] On the other hand, for genes specifying regulatory proteins, receptor ligands or transcription factors, it is likely that small differences do have biological relevance. We just do not know, and this is one reason why it is so important to get our quantification right: We are exploring new territory and we must tread carefully.

I would like to return to the snapshot metaphor from above. This is particularly pertinent when considering mRNA levels in the context of signal transduction pathways (or networks, as they probably should be described). Their activation transduces signals originating from changes in the environment, converts them into signals within the cell, and ultimately stimulates a response. Therefore, appropriate signaling ensures proper function of the cell in the context of its environment and inappropriate signaling may result in cell death or in a cancer cell. However, cell signaling is not a static process that can be easily captured by a snapshot and any data thus obtained provide little insight into the dynamics of signaling pathways and their interaction with each other. This is time and context dependent and while quantitative data obtained contain such information, they are converted into static presentations of linear pathways.

1.4. Outlook

Where is it all heading? There can be little doubt that there will be two kinds of real-time instrument: the high-throughput, big budget core facility thermal cycler typified by the ABI 7900 that is used to run lots of identical assays on lots of samples using one or two chemistries (probably SYBR® Green I and the 5'-nuclease assay). At the other end of the scale, there will be "personal" real-time thermal cyclers that will be (relatively) inexpensive, but have the flexibility to run all chemistries and allow the researcher to design assays optimized to his/her particular applications. For example, Quanta Biotech Ltd. (www.4quanta.com) have used a completely novel approach to produce a range of instruments for real-time PCR assays based on a new $1/4 \times 384$-well microplate format that is optimized for today's low-volume PCR reactions. These 96-well consumables accommodate reaction volumes of 5–25 µl and are made from plastics with exceptional thermal conductivity. Quanta's instruments range from a portable option attractively priced for individual or field use to a high performance personal unit with in-sample ramp rates of greater than $10°C \cdot s^{-1}$ (!), a uniformity of better than $0.2°C$ and the ability to concurrently detect up to four fluorophores. The low well volume and small overall consumable size allow these instruments to eliminate evaporative losses and achieve near isothermal and homogenous imaging treatment of samples.

In terms of chemistries, intercalating dyes such as SYBR® Green are here to stay, since they offer significant advantages in terms of cost and flexibility and are extremely useful for assay optimization. Whether there is a need for the various other nonspecific chemistries remains to be seen. They do not appear to offer any real advantage over intercalating dyes, yet complicated assay design without increasing its specificity. Among the specific chemistries, the 5'-nuclease (TaqMan) assay was the first and remains the most widely used format. The introduction of MGB attachments as well as nucleotide analogues such as PNA and LNA address most of its weak points and make it the chemistry of choice for most applications. Furthermore, the backing of ABI ensures that it will be further developed and optimized and innovations such as assay-on-demand will fulfill the requirements of most diagnostic, biotechnology or forensic laboratories.

The crucial question is whether any of the other chemistries can offer any real advantage over the now firmly established TaqMan approach. As is apparent from the discussion in **Chapter 6**, lanthanide probes offer advantages in time-resolved multiplex analyses and there are valid reasons for choosing structured probes such as Molecular Beacons or Scorpions™, especially when dealing with allele-specific analyses. However, for some chemistries the feeling must be one of admiration for the ingenuity of the approach coupled with uncertainty about its real-life usefulness or advantage over TaqMan-based assays.

Using the real-time instruments' ability to monitor fluorescence many times during a cycle may also make it possible to associate the kinetics of hybridization with fluorescence detection and quantification. FCS may be an ideal tool for this and indeed it has been used to characterize the binding kinetics in solution of rhodamine-labeled oligodeoxynucleotides to RNA.[186] It allows the monitoring of the binding process by the change in diffusion time of the probe to its target. The average diffusion time of a labeled short, nucleic acid probe through the illuminated focal volume element is inversely related to the diffusion coefficient. Therefore, its binding to a larger target changes its diffusion characteristics by increasing its average diffusion time.

It is also clear that quality control, especially of RNA templates and normalization procedures are issues that will need to be standardized in order to obtain comparability between the vast amounts of real-time results that are being published. The increasing trend towards using

384-well plates and smaller reaction volumes also makes the development of reliable, inexpensive robots an important issue. Corbett Research's CAS-1200 robotic liquid handling system is the first of what is likely to become a wide range of robots designed to allow a reproducible PCR setup. With a bit of luck they will keep their promise and not turn out to be as unreliable as the first generation of robots was.

Finally, there are alternatives to PCR and RT-PCR-based assays, based mainly around the real-time detection of isothermal amplification. The most promising is probably the "Invader" assay, a development of the invasive signal amplification assay[187] that combines two signal amplification reactions in series to generate and amplify a fluorescent signal in the presence of the correct target sequence.[188] It is isothermal and uses a structure-specific thermostable archaebacterial flap endonuclease,[189] which, when used in conjunction with structure-forming probes, cleaves nucleic acids at specific sites based on structure rather than sequence. Because there is no need for special post reaction containment, these assays may be run in standard microtiter plates.[190] The assay is sensitive down to sub-attomole levels and may well become a method of choice in the future.

Another alternative is nucleic acid sequence-based amplification (NASBA).[191] NASBA is based on the simultaneous activity of avian myeloblastosis virus (AMV) RT, RNase H, and T7 RNA polymerase. It is a single-step isothermal RNA-specific amplification process that uses with two oligonucleotide primers to amplify of any RNA more than 10^{12} fold in 90 to 120 minutes. Nucleic acids can act as template for the amplification reaction only if they are single stranded and located in the primer-binding region. Because the reaction is isothermal (41°C), specific amplification of ssRNA is possible if denaturation of dsDNA is prevented in the sample preparation procedure. It is thus possible to detect mRNA in a dsDNA background without getting false-positive results caused by genomic dsDNA, without having to worry about intron-spanning primers.[192] By combining the standard NASBA technology with a molecular beacon that anneals during amplification to the target sequence, a real-time detection system is generated.[193,194] As with real-time PCR, the beacons generate a fluorescent signal during amplification when hybridizing with their target and the time-point at which a reaction rises above a threshold of detection and becomes positive is determined.[195] The real-time assay is capable of multiplexing[196] and has proved successful in the detection of various mRNAs and in the detection of both viral[197] and bacterial[198] RNA in clinical samples.

Yet another novel isothermal method is ramification amplification[199] which makes use of the highly processive bacteriophage phi29 polymerase and a circular probe in which the 3' and 5' ends are brought together in juxtaposition by hybridization to a target. The two ends can then be ligated to produce a closed DNA circle. In the presence of an excess of forward and reverse primers, phi29 extends the bound forward primer along the circular probe and displaces the downstream strand, generating a multimeric ssDNA, analogous to the "rolling circle" replication of bacteriophages *in vivo*. This ssDNA then serves as a template for multiple reverse primers to hybridize, extend, and displace downstream DNA, resulting in an exponential amplification and generating a large branched (ramified) DNA complex.

1.5. Conclusion

It is vital to consider each stage of the experimental protocol, starting with the laboratory setup, proceeding through sample acquisition and template preparation, the RT step if carrying out RT-PCR and the PCR step. Only if every one of these stages is properly validated, is it possible to obtain reliable quantitative data. Of course, choice of chemistries, primers and probes and instruments must be appropriate to whatever is being quantitated. Finally, data must be interpreted, and this remains a real problem. Clearly, real-time qPCR is a valuable, versatile and powerful technique. But, like anything powerful, it needs to be treated with respect.

Recommended Websites

At the end of each chapter there are more sites relevant to its contents. The following ones provide general information and are a useful first stop for exploration.

General Real-Time PCR Information

http://www.wzw.tum.de/gene-quantification/: A super source of comprehensive information on all things quantitative, especially for the expert and the first obligatory stop. The site is maintained by one of the main theoretical innovators of qPCR and its main focus is to describe the technical aspects involved in quantitative gene expression analysis using real-time PCR and RT-PCR. Lots of pdf files to download. Importantly, this website is updated regularly.

http://www.highveld.com/pcr.html: The PCR jump station. Lots of commercial input and diversions, but there is good basic information to be found. The site is of limited value for obtaining more advanced information.

Commercial Sites

www.ambion.com: Ambion's website is a treasure trove of information on all aspects of RNA extraction, handling, and amplification. Obviously, the ultimate aim is to sell their products, but (1) their products are both innovative and excellent and (2) the website is truly first-rate. It is a must for anyone interested in quantitating RNA.

www.qiagen.com: Qiagen's website is more commercial and less informative than Ambion's. Nevertheless, it is comprehensive and easy to navigate. There are no real gold nuggets as with Ambion's, but the general information provided is solid and reliable and there is more information on DNA and PCR than on Ambion's site.

www.promega.com: Promega's website is very comprehensive and informative and deals extensively with DNA as well as with RNA, with PCR as well as with RT-PCR.

User Groups

Do not be alone out there, join user groups such as the qpcrlistserver@yahoo.com. Members have a wealth of experience and are more than willing to offer a helping hand, a range of protocols and a wide range of discussions and opinions, not all sensible, but nevertheless well informed.

References

1. Saiki RK, Scharf S, Faloona F, Mullis KB, Horn GT, Erlich HA, Arnheim N: **Enzymatic amplification of beta-globin genomic sequences and restriction site analysis for diagnosis of sickle cell anemia.** *Science* 1985, **230**:1350–1354.

2. Erlich HA., Gelfand D, Sninsky JJ: **Recent advances in the polymerase chain reaction.** *Science* 1991, **252**:1643–1651.

3. Cha RS, Thilly WG: **Specificity, efficiency, and fidelity of PCR.** *PCR Meth Appl* 1993, **3**:S18–S29.

4. Erlich HA, Arnheim N: **Genetic analysis using the polymerase chain reaction.** *Annu Rev Genet* 1992, **26**:479–506.

5. Olsen E, Aabo S, Hill W, Notermans S, Wernars K, Granum PE, Popovic T, Rasmussen HN, Olsvik O: **Probes and polymerase chain reaction for detection of food-borne bacterial pathogens.** *Intl J Food Microbiol* 1995, **28**:1–78.

6. Sparagano OA, Allsopp MT, Mank RA, Rijpkema SG, Figueroa JV, Jongejan F: **Molecular detection of pathogen DNA in ticks (Acari: Ixodidae): A review.** *Exp Appl Acarol* 1999, **23**:929–960.

7. Lantz PG, Abu Al-Soud W, Knutsson R, Hahn-Hagerdal B, Radstrom P: **Biotechnical use of polymerase chain reaction for microbiological analysis of biological samples.** *Biotechnol Annu Rev* 2000, **5**:87–130.

8. Hofstra H, van der Vossen JM, van der Plas J: **Microbes in food processing technology.** *FEMS Microbiol Rev* 1994, **15**:175–183.

9. van der Vossen JM, Hofstra H: **DNA based typing, identification and detection systems for food spoilage microorganisms: development and implementation.** *Int J Food Microbiol* 1996, **33**:35–49.

10. Ahmed FE: **Detection of genetically modified organisms in foods.** *Trends Biotechnol* 2002, **20**:215–223.

11. Bustin SA, Dorudi S: **Molecular assessment of tumour stage and disease recurrence using PCR- based assays.** *Mol Med Today* 1998, **4**:389–396.

12. Zarlenga DS, Higgins J: **PCR as a diagnostic and quantitative technique in veterinary parasitology.** *Vet Parasitol* 2001, **101**:215–230.

13. Vrieling H, Simons JW, van Zeeland AA: **Nucleotide sequence determination of point mutations at the mouse HPRT locus using in vitro amplification of HPRT mRNA sequences.** *Mutat Res* 1988, **198**:107–113.

14. Simpson D, Crosby RM, Skopek TR: **A method for specific cloning and sequencing of human hprt cDNA for mutation analysis.** *Biochem Biophys Res Commun* 1988, **151**:487–492.

15. Edwards MC, Gibbs RA: **Multiplex PCR: advantages, development, and applications.** *PCR Methods Appl* 1994, **3**:S65–S75.

16. Elnifro EM, Ashshi AM, Cooper RJ, Klapper PE: **Multiplex PCR: Optimization and application in diagnostic virology.** *Clin Microbiol Rev* 2000, **13**:559–570.

17. Willey JC, Crawford EL, Jackson CM, Weaver DA, Hoban JC, Khuder SA, DeMuth JP: **Expression measurement of many genes simultaneously by quantitative RT-PCR using standardized mixtures of competitive templates.** *Am J Respiratory Cell & Molecular Biology* 1998, **19**:6–17.

18. Wittwer CT, Herrmann MG, Moss AA, Rasmussen, RP: **Continuous fluorescence monitoring of rapid cycle DNA amplification.** *Biotechniques* 1997, **22**:130–138.

19. Gentle A, Anastasopoulos F, McBrien NA: **High-resolution semi-quantitative real-time PCR without the use of a standard curve.** *Biotechniques* 2001, **31**:502, 504–506, 508.

20. Ferre F: **Quantitative or semi-quantitative PCR: reality versus myth.** *PCR Methods Appl* 1992, **2**:1–9.

21. Wu DY, Ugozzoli L, Pal BK, Qian J, Wallace RB: **The effect of temperature and oligonucleotide primer length on the specificity and efficiency of amplification by the polymerase chain reaction.** *DNA Cell Biol* 1991, **10**:233–238.

22. Nedelman J, Heagerty P, Lawrence C: **Quantitative PCR with internal controls.** *Comput Appl Biosci* 1992, **8**:65–70.

23. Siebert PD Larrick JW: **Competitive PCR.** *Nature* 1992, **359**:557–558.

24. Raeymaekers L: **Quantitative PCR: theoretical considerations with practical implications.** *Anal Biochem* 1993, **214**:582–585.

25. Kelley MR, Jurgens JK, Tentler J, Emanuele NV, Blutt SE, Emanuele MA: **Coupled reverse transcription-polymerase chain reaction (RT-PCR) technique is comparative, quantitative, and rapid: Uses in alcohol research involving low abundance mRNA species such as hypothalamic LHRH and GRF.** Alcohol *1993,* **10**:185–189.

26. Halford WP, Falco VC, Gebhardt BM, Carr DJ: **The inherent quantitative capacity of the reverse transcription–polymerase chain reaction.** *Anal Biochem* 1999, **266**:181–191.

27. Kappes JC, Saag MS, Shaw GM, Hahn BH, Chopra P, Chen S, Emini EA, McFarland R, Yang LC, Piatak M Jr: **Assessment of antiretroviral therapy by plasma viral load testing: standard and ICD HIV-1 p24 antigen and viral RNA (QC-PCR) assays compared.** *J Acquir Immune Defic Syndr Hum Retrovirol* 1995, **10**:139–149.

28. Tobal K, Liu Yin JA: **Molecular monitoring of minimal residual disease in acute myeloblastic leukemia with t(8;21) by RT-PCR.** *Leukemia & Lymphoma* 1998, **31**:115–120.

29. Jung R, Soondrum K, Neumaier M: **Quantitative PCR.** *Clin Chem Lab Med* 2000, **38**:833–836.

30. Reischl U, Kochanowski B: **Quantitative PCR. A survey of the present technology.** *Mol Biotechnol* 1995, **3**:55–71.

31. Bustin SA: **Quantification of mRNA using real-time reverse transcription PCR (RT-PCR): trends and problems.** *J Mol.Endocrinol* 2002, **29**:23–39.

32. Chelly J, Kaplan JC, Maire P, Gautron S, Kahn A: **Transcription of the dystrophin gene in human muscle and non-muscle tissue.** *Nature* 1988, **333**:858–860.

33. Noonan KE, Beck C, Holzmayer TA, Chin JE, Wunder JS, Andrulis IL, Gazdar AF, Willman, CL, Griffith B, Von Hoff . D et al.: **Quantitative analysis of MDR1 (multidrug resistance) gene expression in human tumors by polymerase chain reaction.** *Proc Natl Acad Sci USA* 1990, **87**:7160–7164.

34. Abe J, Kotzin BL, Jujo K, Melish ME, Glode MP, Kohsaka T, Leung DY: **Selective expansion of T cells expressing T-cell receptor variable regions V beta 2 and V beta 8 in Kawasaki disease.** *Proc Natl Acad Sci USA* 1992, **89**:4066–4070.

35. Warrington JA, Nair A, Mahadevappa M, Tsyganskaya M: **Comparison of human adult and fetal expression and identification of 535 housekeeping/maintenance genes.** *Physiol Genomics* 2000, **2**:143–147.

36. Wang AM, Doyle MV, Mark DF: **Quantitation of mRNA by the polymerase chain reaction.** *Proc Natl Acad Sci USA* 1989, **86**:9717–9721.

37. Becker-Andre M, Hahlbrock K: **Absolute mRNA quantification using the polymerase chain reaction (PCR). A novel approach by a PCR aided transcript titration assay (PATTY).** *Nucleic Acids Res* 1989, **17**:9437–9446.

38. Gilliland G, Perrin S, Blanchard K, Bunn HF: **Analysis of cytokine mRNA and DNA: detection and quantitation by competitive polymerase chain reaction.** *Proc Natl Acad Sci USA* 1990 **87**:2725–2729.

39. Weis JH, Tan SS, Martin BK, Wittwer CT: **Detection of rare mRNAs via quantitative RT-PCR.** *Trends Genet* 1992, **8**:263–264.

40. Siebert PD, Larrick JW: **PCR MIMICS: competitive DNA fragments for use as internal standards in quantitative PCR.** *Biotechniques* 1993, **14**:244–249.

41. Pannetier C, Delassus S, Darche S, Saucier C, Kourilsky P: **Quantitative titration of nucleic acids by enzymatic amplification reactions run to saturation.** *Nucleic Acids Res* 1993, **21**:577–583.

42. Vanden Heuvel JP, Tyson FL, Bell DA: **Construction of recombinant RNA templates for use as internal standards in quantitative RT-PCR.** *Biotechniques* 1993, **14**:395–398.

43. Riedy MC, Timm EA, Jr, Stewart CC: **Quantitative RT-PCR for measuring gene expression.** *Biotechniques* 1995, **18**:70–76.

44. Uberla K, Platzer C, Diamantstein T, Blankenstein T:. **Generation of competitor DNA fragments for quantitative PCR.** *PCR Methods Appl,* 1991, **1**:136–139.

45. Freeman WM, Walker SJ, Vrana KE: **Quantitative RT-PCR: pitfalls and potential.** *Biotechniques* 1999, **26**:112–115.

46. Apfalter P, Blasi F, Boman J, Gaydos CA, Kundi M, Maass M, Makristathis A, Meijer A, Nadrchal R, Persson K, Rotter ML, Tong CY, Stanek G, Hirschl AM: **Multicenter comparison trial of DNA extraction methods and PCR assays for detection of Chlamydia pneumoniae in endarterectomy specimens.** *J Clin Microbiol* 2001, **39**:519–524.

47. Mahony JB, Chong S, Coombes BK, Smieja M, Petrich A: **Analytical sensitivity, reproducibility of results, and clinical performance of five PCR assays for detecting Chlamydia pneumoniae DNA in peripheral blood mononuclear cells.** *J Clin Microbiol* 2000, **38**:2622–2627.

48. Smieja M, Mahony JB, Goldsmith CH, Chong S, Petrich A, Chernesky M: **Replicate PCR testing and probit analysis for detection and quantitation of *Chlamydia pneumoniae* in clinical specimens.** *J Clin Microbiol* 2001, **39**:1796–1801.

49. Henley WN, Schuebel KE, Nielsen DA: **Limitations imposed by heteroduplex formation on quantitative RT-PCR.** *Biochem.Biophys.Res.Commun* 1996, **226**:113–117.

50. Souaze F., Ntodou-Thome A, Tran CY, Rostene W, Forgez P: **Quantitative RT-PCR: limits and accuracy.** *Biotechniques* 1996, **21**:280–285.

51. Johnson PW, Swinbank K, MacLennan S, Colomer D, Debuire B., Diss T., Gabert J, Gupta RK, Haynes A, Kneba M, Lee MS, Macintyre E, Mensink E, Moos M, et al.: **Variability of polymerase chain reaction detection of the bcl-2-IgH translocation in an international multicentre study.** *Ann Oncol* 1999, **10**:1349–1354.

52. Zhang J., Desai M., Ozanne SE, Doherty C, Hales CN, Byrne CD: **Two variants of quantitative reverse transcriptase PCR used to show differential expression of alpha-, beta- and gamma-fibrinogen genes in rat liver lobes.** *Biochem J* 1997, **321**:769–775.

53. Zhang J, Byrne, C. D: **A novel highly reproducible quantitative competitve RT PCR system.** *J Mol Biol* 1997, **274**: 338–352.

54. Hayward AL, Oefner PJ, Sabatini S, Kainer DB, Hinojos CA, Doris PA: **Modeling and analysis of competitive RT-PCR.** *Nucleic Acids Res* 1998, **26**:2511–2518.

55. Crawford EL, Peters GJ, Noordhuis P, Rots MG, Vondracek M, Grafstrom RC, Lieuallen K, Lennon G, Zahorchak RJ, et al.: **Reproducible gene expression measurement among multiple laboratories obtained in a blinded study using standardized RT (StaRT)-PCR.** *Mol Diagn* 2001, 6:217–225.

56. Crawford EL, Warner KA, Khuder SA, Zahorchak RJ, Willey JC: **Multiplex standardized RT-PCR for expression analysis of many genes in small samples.** *Biochem Biophys Res Commun* 2002, **293**:509–516.

57. DeMuth JP, Jackson CM, Weaver DA, Crawford EL, Durzinsky DS, Durham SJ, Zaher A, et al.: **The gene expression index c-*myc* x E2F-1/p21 is highly predictive of malignant phenotype in human bronchial epithelial cells.** *Am J Respir Cell Mol Biol* 1998, **19**:18–24.

58. Rots MG, Willey JC, Jansen G, van Zantwijk CH, Noordhuis P, DeMuth JP, Kuiper E, Veerman AJ, Pieters R, Peters GJ: **mRNA expression levels of methotrexate resistance-related proteins in childhood leukemia as determined by a standardized competitive template-based RT-PCR method.** *Leukemia* 2000, **14**:2166–2175.

59. Vondracek M, Weaver D A, Sarang Z, Hedberg JJ, Willey JC, Warngard L, Grafstrom RC **Transcript profiling of enzymes involved in detoxification of xenobiotics and reactive oxygen in human normal and simian virus 40 T antigen-immortalized oral keratinocytes.** *Int J Cancer* 2002, **99**:776–782.

60. Orlando C, Pinzani P, Pazzagli M: **Developments in quantitative PCR.** *Clin Chem Lab Med* 1998, **36**:255–269.

61. Halford WP: **The essential prerequisites for quantitative RT-PCR.** *Nat Biotechnol* 1999, **17**:835.

62. Wedemeyer N, Potter T, Wetzlich S, Gohde W: **Flow cytometric quantification of competitive reverse transcription-PCR products.** Clin Chem 2002, **48**:1398–1405.

63. Lagoo-Deenadayalan S, Lagoo AS, Barber WH, Hardy KJ: **A standardized approach to PCR-based semiquantitation of multiple cytokine gene transcripts from small cell samples.** *Lymphokine Cytokine Res* 1993, **12**:59–67.

64. Rieckmann P, Albrecht M, Ehrenreich H, Weber T, Michel U: **Semi-quantitative analysis of cytokine gene expression in blood and cerebrospinal fluid cells by reverse transcriptase polymerase chain reaction.** *Res Exp Med (Berl)* 1995, **195**:17–29.

65. Bartlett JM, Hulme MJ, Miller WR: **Analysis of cAMP RI alpha mRNA expression in breast cancer: evaluation of quantitative polymerase chain reaction for routine use.** *Br J Cancer* 1996, **73**:1538–1544.

66. Verhaegen M, Christopoulos TK: **Quantitative polymerase chain reaction based on a dual-analyte chemiluminescence hybridization assay for target DNA and internal standard.** *Anal Chem* 1998, **70**:4120–4125.

67. Vandevyver C, Motmans K, Raus J: **Quantification of cytokine mRNA expression by RT-PCR and electrochemiluminescence.** *Genome Res* 1995, **5**:195–201.

68. Medina MA, Schwille P: **Fluorescence correlation spectroscopy for the detection and study of single molecules in biology.** *Bioessays* 2002, **24**:758–764.

69. Schwille P, Meyer-Almes FJ, Rigler R: **Dual-color fluorescence cross-correlation spectroscopy for multicomponent diffusional analysis in solution.** *Biophys J* 1997, **72**:1878–1886.

70. Rigler R, Foldes-Papp Z, Meyer-Almes FJ, Sammet C, Volcker M, Schnetz A: **Fluorescence cross-correlation: a new concept for polymerase chain reaction.** *J Biotechnol* 1998, **63**:97–109.

71. Weiner OH, Alt M, Durr R, Noegel AA, Caselmann WH: **Rapid and reproducible quantification of hepatitis C virus cDNA by fluorescence correlation spectroscopy.** *Digestion* 2000, **61**:84–89.

72. Weber S, Hummel SA, Weber AA, Zirwes RF, Weiner OH, Reuber BE: **Genotyping of human platelet antigen-1 by gene amplification and labelling in one system and automated fluorescence correlation spectroscopy.** *Br J Haematol* 2002, **116**:839–843.

73. Kinjo M: **Detection of asymmetric PCR products in homogeneous solution by fluorescence correlation spectroscopy.** *Biotechniques* 1998, **25**:706–715.

74. Heid CA, Stevens J, Livak KJ, Williams PM: **Real time quantitative PCR.** *Genome Res* 1996, **6**: 986–994.

75. Gibson UE, Heid CA, Williams PM: **A novel method for real time quantitative RT-PCR.** *Genome Res* 1996, **6**: 995–1001.

76. Vlems FA, Ladanyi A, Gertler R, Rosenberg R, Diepstra JH, Roder C, Nekarda H, Molnar, B, Tulassay Z, van Muijen GN, Vogel, I: **Reliability of quantitative reverse-transcriptase-PCR-based detection of tumour cells in the blood between different laboratories using a standardised protocol.** *Eur J Cancer* 2003, **39**:388–396.

77. Callahan JD, Brown F, Osorio FA, Sur JH, Kramer E, Long GW, Lubroth J, Ellis SJ, Shoulars KS, Gaffney KL, Rock DL, Nelson W: M. **Use of a portable real-time reverse transcriptase-polymerase chain reaction assay for rapid detection of foot-and-mouth disease virus.** *J Am Vet Med Assoc* 2002, **220**:1636–1642.

78. Walker NJ: **A technique whose time has come.** *Science* 2002, **296**:557–559.

79. Ginzinger DG: **Gene quantification using real-time quantitative PCR: An emerging technology hits the mainstream.** *Exp Hematol* 2002, **30**:503–512.

80. Schmittgen TD: **Real-time quantitative PCR.** *Methods* 2001, **25**:383–385.

81. Wattjes MP, Krauter J, Nagel S, Heidenreich O, Ganser A, Heil G: **Comparison of nested competitive RT-PCR and real-time RT-PCR for the detection and quantification of AML1/MTG8 fusion transcripts in t(8;21) positive acute myelogenous leukemia.** *Leukemia* 2000, **14**:329–335.

82. Wall SJ, Edwards DR: **Quantitative reverse transcription-Ppolymerase chain reaction (RT-PCR): A comparison of primer-dropping, competitive, and real-time RT-PCRs.** *Anal Biochem* 2002, **300**:269–273.

83. Chu DC, Chuang CK, Fu JB, Huang HS, Tseng CP, Sun CF: **The use of real-time quantitative polymerase chain reaction to detect hypermethylation of the CpG islands in the promoter region flanking the GSTP1 gene to diagnose prostate carcinoma.** *J Urol* 2002, **167**:1854–1858.

84. Tondella ML, Talkington DF, Holloway BP, Dowell SF, Cowley K, Soriano-Gabarro M, Elkind MS, Fields BS: **Development and evaluation of real-time PCR-based fluorescence assays for detection of *Chlamydia pneumoniae.* *J Clin Microbiol* 2002, **40**:575–583.

85. Guo JQ, Lin H, Kantarjian H, Talpaz M, Champlin R, Andreeff M, Glassman A, Arlinghaus, RB: **Comparison of competitive-nested PCR and real-time PCR in detecting BCR-ABL fusion transcripts in chronic myeloid leukemia patients.** *Leukemia* 2002, **16**:2447–2453.

86. Ke D, Menard C, Picard FJ, Boissinot M, Ouellette M, Roy PH, Bergeron MG: **Development of conventional and real-time PCR assays for the rapid detection of group *B Streptococci.* *Clin Chem* 2000, **46**:324–331.

87. Gerard CJ, Olsson K, Ramanathan R, Reading, C, Hanania EG: **Improved quantitation of minimal residual disease in multiple myeloma using real-time polymerase chain reaction and plasmid-DNA complementarity determining region III standards.** *Cancer Res* 1998, **58**:3957–3964.

88. Puig M, Mihalik K, Yu M, Feinstone S, Major M: **Sensitivity and reproducibility of HCV quantitation in chimpanzee sera using TaqMan real-time PCR assay.** *J Virol Methods* 2002, **105**:253.

89. Schwaiger M, Peter O, Cassinotti P: **Routine diagnosis of *Borrelia burgdorferi* (*sensu lato*) infections using a real-time PCR assay.** *Clin Microbiol Infect* 2001, **7**:461–469.

90. Barragan E, Bolufer P, Moreno I, Martin G, Nomdedeu J, Brunet S, Fernandez P, Rivas C, Sanz MA: **Quantitative detection of AML1-ETO rearrangement by real-time RT-PCR using fluorescently labeled probes.** *Leuk Lymphoma* 2001, **42**:747–756.

91. Max N, Willhauck M, Wolf K, Thilo F, Reinhold U, Pawlita M, Thiel E, Keilholz U: **Reliability of PCR-based detection of occult tumour cells: Lessons from real-time RT-PCR.** *Melanoma Res* 2001, **11**:371–378.

92. Gerard CJ, Olsson K, Ramanathan R, Reading C, Hanania EG: **Improved quantitation of minimal residual disease in multiple myeloma using real-time polymerase chain reaction and plasmid-DNA complementarity determining region III standards.** *Cancer Research* 1998, **58**:3957–3964.

93. Kalinina O, Lebedeva I, Brown J, Silver J: **Nanoliter scale PCR with TaqMan detection.** *Nucleic Acids Res* 1997, **25**:1999–2004.

94. Klein SA, Karsten S, Ruster B, Klebba C, Pape M, Ottmann OG, Hoelzer D, Roth WK: **Comparison of TaqMan real-time PCR and p24 Elisa for quantification of *in vitro* HIV-1 replication.** *J Virol Methods* 2003, **107**:169–175.

95. Higgins JA, Fayer R, Trout JM, Xiao L, Lal AA, Kerby S, Jenkins MC: **Real-time PCR for the detection of Cryptosporidium parvum.** *J Microbiol Methods,* 2001, **47**:323–337.

96. Burkhart C, Norris M, Haber MA: **Simple method for the isolation of genomic DNA from mouse tail free of real-time PCR inhibitors.** *J Biochem Biophys Methods* 2002, **52**:145.

97. Mackay IM, Arden KE, Nitsche A: **Real-time PCR in virology.** *Nucleic Acids Res* 2002, **30**:1292–1305.

98. Niesters HG: **Quantitation of viral load using real-time amplification techniques.** *Methods* 2001, **25**:419–429.

99. Drosten C, Gottig S, Schilling S, Asper M, Panning M, Schmitz H, Gunther S: **Rapid detection and quantification of RNA of Ebola and Marburg viruses, Lassa virus, Crimean-Congo hemorrhagic fever virus, Rift Valley fever virus, dengue virus, and yellow fever virus by real-time reverse transcription-PCR.** *J Clin Microbiol* 2002, **40**:2323–2330.

100. Hough AJ, Harbison SA, Savill MG, Melton LD, Fletcher G: **Rapid enumeration of Listeria monocytogenes in artificially contaminated cabbage using real-time polymerase chain reaction.** *J Food Prot.,* **65**:1329–1332, 2002.

101. Chisholm SA, Owen RJ, Teare EL, Saverymuttu S: **PCR-based diagnosis of** *Helicobacter pylori* **infection and real-time determination of clarithromycin resistance directly from human gastric biopsy samples.** *J Clin Microbiol* 2001, **39**:1217–1220.

102. He Q, Wang JP, Osato M, Lachman LB: **Real-time quantitative PCR for detection of** *Helicobacter pylori. J Clin Microbiol,* 2002, **40**:3720–3728.

103. Kobayashi D, Eishi Y, Ohkusa T, Ishige Suzuki T, Minami J, Yamada T, Takizawa T, Koike M: **Gastric mucosal density of** *Helicobacter pylori* **estimated by real-time PCR compared with results of urea breath test and histological grading.** *J Med Microbiol* 2002, **51**:305–311.

104. Rokbi B, Seguin D, Guy B, Mazarin V, Vidor E, Mion F, Cadoz M., Quentin-Millet MJ: **Assessment of** *Helicobacter pylori* **gene expression within mouse and human gastric mucosae by real-time reverse transcriptase PCR.** *Infect Immun* 2001, **69**:4759–4766.

105. Ruzsovics A, Molnar B, Unger Z, Tulassay Z, Pronai L: **Determination of** *Helicobacter pylori* **cagA, vacA genotypes with real-time PCR melting curve analysis.** *J Physiol (Paris)* 2001, **95**:369–377.

106. Aarts HJ, Joosten RG, Henkens MH, Stegeman H, van Hoek AH: **Rapid duplex PCR assay for the detection of pathogenic** *Yersinia enterocolitica* **strains.** *J Microbiol Methods* 2001, **47**:209–217.

107. McKillip JL, Drake M: **Molecular beacon polymerase chain reaction detection of** *Escherichia coli* **O157:H7 in milk.** *J Food Prot* 2000, **63**:855–859.

108. Walburger DK, Afonina IA, Wydro R: **An improved real time PCR method for simultaneous detection of C282Y and H63D mutations in the HFE gene associated with hereditary hemochromatosis.** *Mutat Res* 2001, **432**:69–78.

109. Oliver DH, Thompson RE, Griffin CA, Eshleman JR: **Use of single nucleotide polymorphisms (SNP) and real-time polymerase chain reaction for bone marrow engraftment analysis.** *J Mol Diagn* 2000, **2**:202–208.

110. Ulvik A, Ueland PM: **Single nucleotide polymorphism (SNP) genotyping in unprocessed whole blood and serum by real-time PCR: Application to SNPs affecting homocysteine and folate metabolism.** *Clin Chem* 2001, **47**:2050–2053.

111. Mhlanga MM, Malmberg L: **Using Molecular B eacons to detect single-nucleotide polymorphisms with real-time PCR.** *Methods* 2001, **25**:463–471.

112. Elenitoba-Johnson KS, Bohling SD, Wittwer CT, King TC: **Multiplex PCR by multicolor fluorimetry and fluorescence melting curve analysis.** *Nat Med* 2001, **7**:249–253.

113. Maes B, Vanhentenrijk V, Wlodarska I, Cools J, Peeters B, Marynen P, Wolf-Peeters C: **The NPM-ALK and the ATIC-ALK fusion genes can be detected in non-neoplastic cells.** *Am J Pathol* 2001, **158**:2185–2193.

114. Hahn S, Zhong XY, Troeger C, Burgemeister R, Gloning K, Holzgreve W: **Current applications of single-cell PCR.** *Cell Mol Life Sci* 2000, **57**:96–105.

115. Liss B: **Improved quantitative real-time RT-PCR for expression profiling of individual cells.** *Nucleic Acids Res* 2002, **30**:E89.

116. Pierce KE, Rice JE, Sanchez JA, Brenner C, Wangh LJ: **Real-time PCR using molecular beacons for accurate detection of the Y chromosome in single human blastomeres.** *Mol.Hum.Reprod* 2000, **6**:1155–1164.

117. Kim YJ, Kim DW, Lee S, Kim HJ, Kim YL, Hwang JY, Oh IH, Park YH., Lee YK, Min C K, Kim TG, Han TH, Min WS, Kim CC: **Comprehensive comparison of FISH, RT-PCR, and RQ-PCR for monitoring the BCR-ABL gene after hematopoietic stem cell transplantation in CML.** *Eur J Haematol* 2002, **68**:272–280.

118. Lee WI, Kantarjian H, Glassman A, Talpaz M, Lee MS: **Quantitative measurement of BCR/abl transcripts using real-time polymerase chain reaction.** *Ann Oncol* 2002, **13**:781–788.

119. Bernard PS, Wittwer CT: **Real-time PCR technology for cancer diagnostics.** *Clin Chem* 2002, **48**:1178–1185.

120. Walker NJ: **Real-time and quantitative PCR: applications to mechanism-based toxicology.** *J Biochem Mol Toxicol* 2001, **15**:121–127.

121. Bustin SA: **Absolute quantification of mRNA using real-time reverse transcription polymerase chain reaction assays.** *J Mol Endocrinol* 2000, **25**:169–193.

122. Rose AC, Goddard CA, Colledge WH, Cheng SH, Gill DR, Hyde SC: **Optimisation of real-time quantitative RT-PCR for the evaluation of non-viral mediated gene transfer to the airways.** *Gene Ther* 2002, **9**:1312–1320.

123. Hartshorn C, Rice JE, Wangh LJ: **Developmentally-regulated changes of Xist RNA levels in single preimplantation mouse embryos, as revealed by quantitative real-time PCR.** *Mol Reprod Dev* 2002, **61**:425–436, .

124. Yuen T, Wurmbach E, Pfeffer RL, Ebersole BJ, Sealfon SC: **Accuracy and calibration of commercial oligonucleotide and custom cDNA microarrays.** *Nucleic Acids Res* 2002, **30**:e48.

125. Rajeevan MS, Vernon SD, Taysavang N, Unger ER: **Validation of array-based gene expression profiles by real-time (kinetic) RT-PCR.** *J Mol Diagn* 2001, **3**:26–31.

126. Rajeevan MS, Ranamukhaarachchi DG, Vernon SD, Unger ER: **Use of real-time quantitative PCR to validate the results of cDNA array and differential display PCR technologies.** *Methods* 2001, **25**:443–451.

127. Snider JV, Wechser MA, Lossos IS: **Human disease characterization: Real-time quantitative PCR analysis of gene expression.** *Drug Discov Today* 2001, **6**:1062–1067.

128. Gouarin S, Gault E, Vabret A, Cointe D, Rozenberg F, Grangeot-Keros L, Barjot P, Garbarg-Chenon A, Lebon P, Freymuth F: **Real-time PCR quantification of human cytomegalovirus DNA in amniotic fluid samples from mothers with primary infection.** *J Clin Microbiol* 2002, **40**:1767–1772.

129. Monpoeho S, Coste-Burel M, Costa-Mattioli M, Besse B, Chomel JJ, Billaudel S, Ferre V: **Application of a real-time polymerase chain reaction with internal positive control for detection and quantification of enterovirus in cerebrospinal fluid.** *Eur J Clin Microbiol Infect Dis* 2002, **21**:532–536.

130. Verstrepen WA, Kuhn S, Kockx MM, Van De Vyvere ME, Mertens AH: **Rapid detection of enterovirus RNA in cerebrospinal fluid specimens with a novel single-tube real-time reverse transcription-PCR assay.** *J Clin Microbiol* 2001, **39**:4093–4096.

131. Verstrepen WA, Bruynseels P, Mertens AH: **Evaluation of a rapid real-time RT-PCR assay for detection of enterovirus RNA in cerebrospinal fluid specimens.** *J Clin Virol* 2002, **25** Suppl:39–43.

132. Wilke K, Duman B, Horst J: **Diagnosis of haploidy and triploidy based on measurement of gene copy number by real-time PCR.** *Hum Mutat* 2000, **16**:431–436.

133. Lovatt A: **Applications of quantitative PCR in the biosafety and genetic stability assessment of biotechnology products.** *J Biotechnol* 2002, **82**:279–300.

134. Brodmann PD, Ilg EC, Berthoud H, Herrmann A: **Real-time quantitative polymerase chain reaction methods for four genetically modified maize varieties and maize DNA content in food.** *J AOAC Int* 2002, **85**:646–653.

135. Shindo Y, Kuribara H, Matsuoka T, Futo S, Sawada C, Shono J, Akiyama H, Goda Y, Toyoda M, Hino A: **Validation of real-time PCR analyses for line-specific quantitation of genetically modified maize and soybean using new reference molecules.** *J AOAC Int* 2002, **85**:1119–1126.

136. Terry CF, Shanahan DJ, Ballam LD, Harris N, McDowell DG, Parkes HC: **Real-time detection of genetically modified soya using LightCycler and ABI 7700 platforms with TaqMan, Scorpion, and SYBR Green I chemistries.** *J AOAC Int* 2002, **85**:938–944.

137. Vaitilingom M, Pijnenburg H, Gendre F, Brignon P: **Real-time quantitative PCR detection of genetically modified Maximizer maize and Roundup Ready soybean in some representative foods.** *J Agric Food Chem* 1999, **47**:5261–5266.

138. Tesson L, Heslan JM, Menoret S, Anegon I: **Rapid and accurate determination of zygosity in transgenic animals by real-time quantitative PCR.** *Transgenic Res* 2002, **11**:43–48.

139. Hall SJ, Hugenholtz P, Siyambalapitiya N, Keller J, Blackall LL: **The development and use of real-time PCR for the quantification of nitrifiers in activated sludge.** *Water Sci Technol* 2002, **46**:267–272.

140. Poiito-Braga CM, von SM, Braga AR, Pena RT: **Real time control of a combined UASB-activated sludge wastewater treatment configuration.** *Water Sci Technol* 2002, **45**:279–287.

141. Suescun J, Ostolaza X, Garcia-Sanz M, Ayesa E: **Real-time control strategies for predenitrification-nitrification activated sludge plants biodegradation control.** *Water Sci Technol* 2001, **43**:209–216.

142. Bell AS, Ranford-Cartwright LC: **Real-time quantitative PCR in parasitology.** *Trends Parasitol* 2002, **18**:337–342.

143. Emmert-Buck MR, Bonner RF, Smith PD, Chuaqui RF, Zhuang Z, Goldstein SR, Weiss RA, Liotta LA: **Laser capture microdissection.** *Science* 1996, **274**:998–1001.

144. Fink L, Seeger W, Ermert L, Hanze J, Stahl U, Grimminger F, Kummer W, Bohle RM: **Real-time quantitative RT-PCR after laser-assisted cell picking.** *Nat Med*, **4**:1329–1333, 1998.

145. Glockner S, Lehmann U, Wilke N, Kleeberger W, Langer F, Kreipe H: **Detection of gene amplification in intraductal and infiltrating breast cancer by laser-assisted microdissection and quantitative real-time PCR.** *Pathobiology* 2000, **68**:173–179.

146. Lehmann U, Glockner S, Kleeberger W, von Wasielewski, H. F, Kreipe H: **Detection of gene amplification in archival breast cancer specimens by laser-assisted microdissection and quantitive real-time polymerase chain reaction.** *Am J Pathol* 2000, **156**:1855–1864.

147. Bohle RM, Hartmann E, Kinfe T, Ermert L, Seeger W, Fink L: **Cell type-specific mRNA quantitation in non-neoplastic tissues after laser-assisted cell picking.** *Pathobiology* 2000, **68**:191–195.

148. Dolter KE, Braman JC: **Small-sample total RNA purification: Laser capture micro-dissection and cultured cell applications.** *Biotechniques* 2001, **30**:1358–1361.

149. Nagasawa Y, Takenaka M, Matsuoka Y, Imai E., Hori M: **Quantitation of mRNA expression in glomeruli using laser-manipulated microdissection and laser pressure catapulting.** *Kidney Int* 2000, **57**:717–723.

150. Specht K, Richter T, Muller U, Walch A, Werner M, Hofler H: **Quantitative gene expression analysis in microdissected archival formalin-fixed and paraffin-embedded tumor tissue.** *Am.J.Pathol* 2001, **158**:419–429.

151. Suzuki K, Matsui H, Hasumi M, Ono Y, Nakazato H, Koike H, Ito K, Fukabori Y, Kurokawa K, Yamanaka H: **Gene expression profiles in human BPH: Utilization of laser-capture microdissection and quantitative real-time PCR.** *Anticancer Res* 2001, **21**:3861–3864.

152. Cohen CD, Grone HJ, Grone EF, Nelson PJ, Schlondorff D, Kretzler M: **Laser microdissection and gene expression analysis on formaldehyde-fixed archival tissue.** *Kidney Int* 2002, **61**:125–132.

153. Zhan G, Shaheen F, Mackiewicz M, Fenik P, Veasey SC: **Single cell laser dissection with molecular beacon polymerase chain reaction identifies 2A as the predominant serotonin receptor subtype in hypoglossal motoneurons.** *Neuroscience,* **113**: 145–154, 2002.

154. Sluka P, O'Donnell L, Stanton PG: **Stage-specific expression of genes associated with rat spermatogenesis: Characterization by laser-capture microdissection and real-time polymerase chain reaction.** *Biol.Reprod* 2002, **67**:820–828.

155. Sugiyama Y, Sugiyama K, Hirai Y, Akiyama F, Hasumi K: **Microdissection is essential for gene expression profiling of clinically resected cancer tissues.** *Am J Clin Pathol* 2002, **117**:109–116.

156. Fend F, Emmert-Buck MR, Chuaqui R, Cole K, Lee J, Liotta LA, Raffeld M: **Immuno-LCM: laser capture microdissection of immunostained frozen sections for mRNA analysis.** *Am J Pathol* 1999 **154**:61–66.

157. Fink L, Kinfe T, Stein MM, Ermert L, Hanze J, Kummer W, Seeger W, Bohle RM: **Immunostaining and laser-assisted cell picking for mRNA analysis.** *Lab Invest* 2000, **80**:327–333.

158. Fink L, Kinfe T, Seeger W, Ermert L, Kummer W, Bohle RM: **Immunostaining for cell picking and real-time mRNA quantitation.** *Am J Pathol* 2000, **157**:1459–1466.

159. Hocquette JF, Brandstetter AM: **Common practice in molecular biology may introduce statistical bias and misleading biological interpretation.** *J Nutr Biochem* 2002, **13**:370–377,.

160. Kariyazono H, Ohno T, Ihara K, Igarashi H, Joh-o K, Ishikawa S, Hara T: **Rapid detection of the 22q11.2 deletion with quantitative real-time PCR.** *Mol Cell Probes* 2001, **15**:71–73.

161. Nigro JM, Takahashi MA, Ginzinger DG, Law M, Passe S, Jenkins RB, Aldape K: **Detection of 1p and 19q loss in oligodendroglioma by quantitative microsatellite analysis, a real-time quantitative polymerase chain reaction assay.** *Am J Pathol 2001*, **158**:1253–1262,.

162. Ginzinger DG, Godfrey TE, Nigro J, Moore DH, Suzuki S, Pallavicini MG, Gray JW, Jensen RH: **Measurement of DNA copy number at microsatellite loci using quantitative PCR analysis.** *Cancer Res* 2000, **60**:5405–5409.

163. Aldea C, Alvarez CP, Folgueira L, Delgado R, Otero JR: **Rapid detection of herpes simplex virus DNA in genital ulcers by real-time PCR using SYBR Green I dye as the detection signal.** *J Clin Microbiol* 2002, **40**:1060–1062.

164. Dhar AK, Roux MM, Klimpel, KR: **Detection and quantification of infectious hypodermal and hematopoietic necrosis virus and white spot virus in shrimp using real-time quantitative PCR and SYBR Green chemistry.** *J Clin Microbiol* 2001, **39**:2835–2845.

165. Nitsche A, Steuer N, Schmidt CA, Landt O, Siegert W: **Different real-time PCR formats compared for the quantitative detection of human cytomegalovirus DNA.** *Clin Chem* 1999, **45**:1932–1937.

166. Rohr U, Wulf M, Stahn S, Steidl U, Haas R, Kronenwett R: **Fast and reliable titration of recombinant adeno-associated virus type-2 using quantitative real-time PCR.** *J Virol Methods* 2002, **106**:81.

167. Cesaire R, Dehee A, Lezin A, Desire N, Bourdonne O, Dantin F, Bera O, Smadja D, Abel S, Cabie A, Sobesky G, Nicolas JC: **Quantification of HTLV type I and HIV type I DNA load in coinfected patients: HIV type 1 infection does not alter HTLV type I proviral amount in the peripheral blood compartment.** *AIDS Res Hum Retroviruses* 2001, **17**:799–805.

168. Desire N, Dehee A, Schneider V, Jacomet C, Goujon C, Girard PM, Rozenbaum W, Nicolas JC: **Quantification of human immunodeficiency virus type 1 proviral load by a TaqMan real-time PCR assay.** *J Clin Microbiol* 2001, **39**:1303–1310.

169. Ingham DJ, Beer S, Money S, Hansen G: **Quantitative real-time PCR assay for determining transgene copy number in transformed plants.** *Biotechniques* 2001, **31**:132–140.

170. Real LM, Gayoso AJ, Olivera M, Caruz A, Ruiz A, Gayoso F: **Detection of nucleotide c985 A-->G mutation of medium-chain acyl-CoA dehydrogenase gene by real-time PCR.** *Clin Chem* 2001, **47**:958–959.

171. Neoh SH, Brisco MJ, Firgaira FA, Trainor KJ, Turner DR, Morley AA: **Rapid detection of the factor V Leiden (1691 G > A) and haemochromatosis (845 G > A) mutation by fluorescence resonance energy transfer (FRET) and real time PCR.** *J Clin Pathol* 1999, **52**:766–769.

172. Max N, Wolf K, Thiel E, Keilholz U: **Quantitative nested real-time RT-PCR specific for tyrosinase transcripts to quantitate minimal residual disease.** *Clin Chim Acta* 2002, **317**:39–46.

173. Klein D: **Quantification using real-time PCR technology: applications and limitations.** *Trends Mol Med* 2002, **8**:257–260.

174. Young LC, Campling BG, Cole SP, Deeley RG, Gerlach JH: **Multidrug resistance proteins MRP3, MRP1, and MRP2 in lung cancer: Correlation of protein levels with drug response and messenger RNA levels.** *Clin Cancer Res* 2001, **7**:1798–1804.

175. Rocha RL, Hilsenbeck SG, Jackson JG, Lee AV, Figueroa JA, Yee D: **Correlation of insulin-like growth factor-binding protein-3 messenger RNA with protein expression in primary breast cancer tissues: Detection of higher levels in tumors with poor prognostic features.** *J Natl Cancer Inst* 1996, **88**:601–606.

176. Melnick M, Chen H, Rich KA, Jaskoll T: **Developmental expression of insulin-like growth factor II receptor (IGF-IIR) in congenic mouse embryonic lungs: Correlation between IGF-IIR mRNA and protein levels and heterochronic lung development.** *Mol Reprod Dev* 1996, **44**:159–170.

177. Yuan A, Yu CJ, Chen WJ, Lin FY, Kuo SH, Luh KT, Yang PC: **Correlation of total VEGF mRNA and protein expression with histologic type, tumor angiogenesis, patient survival and timing of relapse in non-small-cell lung cancer.** *Int J Cancer* 2000, **89**:475–483.

178. Frohlich E, Schlagenhauff B, Mohrle M, Weber E, Klessen C, Rassner G: **Activity, expression, and transcription rate of the cathepsins B, D, H, and L in cutaneous malignant melanoma.** *Cancer* 2001, **91**:972–982.

179. Karenlampi SO, Tuomi K, Korkalainen M, Raunio H: **2-(4'-chlorophenyl)benzothiazole is a potent inducer of cytochrome P450IA1 in a human and a mouse cell line. Anomalous correlation between protein and mRNA induction.** *Eur J Biochem* 1989, **181**:143–148.

180. Misra RR, Crance KA, Bare RM, Waalkes MP: **Lack of correlation between the inducibility of metallothionein mRNA and metallothionein protein in cadmium-exposed rodents.** *Toxicology* 1997, **117**:99–109.

181. Roy RK, Sarkar S: **Correlation between the protein and mRNA levels for myosin light chains and tropomyosin subunits during chick fast muscle development in vivo.** *FEBS Lett* 1982, **149**:22–28.

182. Takenoue T, Kitayama J, Takei Y, Umetani N, Matsuda K, Nita ME, Hatano K, Tsuruo T, Nagawa H: **Characterization of dihydropyrimidine dehydrogenase on immunohistochemistry in colon carcinoma, and correlation between immunohistochemical score and protein level or messenger RNA expression.** *Ann Oncol* 2000, **11**:273–279.

183. Thogersen VB., Bross P, Gregersen N, Nexo E: **Quantitative analysis of the human epidermal growth factor receptor messenger RNA using reverse transcription-PCR: A methodological study of imprecision.** *Clin Chem* 1998, **44**:1344–1346.

184. Gygi SP, Rochon Y, Franza BR, Aebersold R: **Correlation between protein and mRNA abundance in yeast.** *Mol Cell Biol* 1999, **19**:1720–1730.

185. Creanor J, Mitchison JM: **Nucleoside diphosphokinase, an enzyme with step changes in activity during the cell cycle of the fission yeast Schizosaccharomyces pombe. I. Persistence of steps after a block to the DNA-division cycle.** *J Cell Sci* 1986, **86**:207–215.

186. Schwille P, Oehlenschlager F, Walter NG: **Quantitative hybridization kinetics of DNA probes to RNA in solution followed by diffusional fluorescence correlation analysis.** *Biochemistry* 1996, **35**:10182–10193.

187. Lyamichev V, Mast AL, Hall JG, Prudent JR, Kaiser MW, Takova T, Kwiatkowski RW, Sander TJ, de Arruda M, Arco DA, Neri BP, Brow MA: **Polymorphism identification and quantitative detection of genomic DNA by invasive cleavage of oligonucleotide probes.** *Nat Biotechnol* 1999, **17**:292–296.

188. Hall JG, Eis PS, Law SM, Reynaldo LP, Prudent JR, Marshall DJ, Allawi HT, Mast AL, Dahlberg JE, Kwiatkowski RW, de Arruda M, Neri BP, Lyamichev VI: **Sensitive detection of DNA polymorphisms by the serial invasive signal amplification reaction.** *Proc Natl Acad Sci USA* 2000, **97**:8272–8277.

189. Harrington JJ, Lieber MR: **Functional domains within FEN-1 and RAD2 define a family of structure- specific endonucleases: implications for nucleotide excision repair.** *Genes Dev* 1994, **8**:1344–1355.

190. Eis PS, Olson MC, Takova T, Curtis ML, Olson SM, Vener TI, Ip HS, Vedvik KL, Bartholomay CT, Allawi HT, Ma WP, Hall JG, Morin MD, Rushmore TH, Lyamichev VI, Kwiatkowski RW: **An invasive cleavage assay for direct quantitation of specific RNAs.** *Nat Biotechnol* 2001, **19**:673–676.

191. Compton J: **Nucleic acid sequence-based amplification.** *Nature* 1991, **350**:91–92.

192. Heim A, Grumbach IM, Zeuke S, Top B: **Highly sensitive detection of gene expression of an intronless gene: amplification of mRNA, but not genomic DNA by nucleic acid sequence based amplification (NASBA).** *Nucleic Acids Res* 1998, **26**:2250–2251.

193. Leone G, van Schijndel H, van Gemen B, Kramer FR, Schoen CD: **Molecular beacon probes combined with amplification by NASBA enable homogeneous, real-time detection of RNA.** *Nucleic Acids Res* 1998, **26**:2150–2155.

194. Weusten JJ, Carpay WM, Oosterlaken TA, van Zuijlen MC, van de Wiel PA: **Principles of quantitation of viral loads using nucleic acid sequence-based amplification in combination with homogeneous detection using molecular beacons.** *Nucleic Acids Res* 2002, **30**: e26.

195. Deiman B, van Aarle P, Sillekens P: **Characteristics and applications of nucleic acid sequence-based amplification (NASBA).** *Mol Biotechnol* 2002, **20**:163–179.

196. Greijer AE, Adriaanse HM, Dekkers CA, Middeldorp JM: **Multiplex real-time NASBA for monitoring expression dynamics of human cytomegalovirus encoded IE1 and pp67 RNA.** *J Clin Virol* 2002, **24**:57–66.

197. Polstra AM, Goudsmit J, Cornelissen M: **Development of real-time NASBA assays with molecular beacon detection to quantify mRNA coding for HHV-8 lytic and latent genes.** *BMC Infect Dis* 2002, **2**:18.

198. van Beckhoven JR, Stead DE, van der Wolf JM: **Detection of Clavibacter michiganensis subsp. sepedonicus by AmpliDet RNA, a new technology based on real time monitoring of NASBA amplicons with a Molecular Beacon.** *J Appl Microbiol* 2002, **93**:840–849.

199. Zhang DY, Brandwein M, Hsuih T, Li HB: **Ramification amplification: A novel isothermal DNA amplification method.** *Mol Diagn* 2001, **6**:141–150.

2

Real-Time RT-PCR: What Lies Beneath the Surface

Jonathan M. Phillips

Abstract

Quantitative real-time reverse transcription (transcriptase) mediated polymerase chain reaction (qRT-PCR) is an extremely powerful investigational and diagnostic tool that has found wide acceptance in a range of experimental research fields, as well as public health laboratory settings. With respect to pathogens, qRT-PCR is often used in the clinical setting to determine viral load, such as in HIV patients, or in the field during disease outbreaks. With respect to gene expression studies, qRT-PCR is used to examine toxicity of compounds, metabolism of drugs, and alterations in gene expression during the process of carcinogenesis. With the belief that early diagnosis can save lives, cancer researchers continuously seek to identify early markers for cancer detection. There is an abundance of commercially available kits to facilitate the application of qRT-PCR to areas of interest. However, a number of variables can be optimized in order to most ably address the specific needs of the investigator. Variables include (but are not limited to) primer and probe concentration, metal cofactor type and concentration, enzyme type, and finally probe type. The purpose of this document is to provide enlightenment to anyone seeking to maximize the quality of his or her qRT-PCR results.

2

Real-Time RT-PCR: What Lies Beneath the Surface

Jonathan M. Phillips

Illinois Institute of Technology Research Institute, Chicago, Illinois

2.1. Introduction

This chapter is *not* intended to provide a summary of review articles. Instead, it is meant to entice the reader to carefully think about what is trying to be accomplished and the various ways in which this goal can be met. There are many good quantitative reverse transcriptase mediated/coupled polymerase chain reaction (RT-PCR) systems out there; however, some may suit the reader's needs better than others. The goal of this chapter is to reveal some of the inner workings of quantitative real-time reverse transcriptase-mediated PCR. Further purposes of this chapter are to graphically demonstrate how various factors influence the performance of a real-time PCR and to explain which combinations of components are likely to provide good results for a given system.

2.2. What is RT-PCR?

First described by Powell et al. in September of 1987,[1] RT-PCR is a powerful method that when applied properly may be used for the detection of minute quantities of any given RNA species. This method relies upon the successful application of two separate enzymatic activities. In the event that either activity fails or is suboptimal, the entire reaction will fail, or at the very least, perform suboptimally. The first activity results in the generation of a DNA molecule that in terms of nucleotide composition and strand polarity is complementary to the target RNA molecule, hence the term complementary DNA or cDNA for short. An enzyme possessing RNA template-dependent DNA polymerase activity mediates this process. The second enzymatic activity is responsible for either linear or geometric (depending on assay design) amplification of the cDNA through DNA template directed DNA polymerase activity.

There is much confusion over the terminology used to describe the RT-PCR methodology. Most scientists are familiar with the terms "one-step" and "two-step" RT-PCR. These terms are misnomers referring to the handling of PCR tubes. All forms of RT-PCR must be performed in two enzymatic steps: (1) reverse transcription of RNA, and (2) amplification of the cDNA resulting from step 1. RT-PCR is a two-step process that may be completed in two separate reactions in two separate tubes, or as two separate reactions in a single tube. Single-tube reactions may be one of two types. In the first type, the RT reaction is performed in a volume that is usually 1/5 to 1/10 that of the final PCR reaction volume. The buffer used in this step is specifically optimized for reverse transcription activity. After the RT step, the reverse transcription buffer constituents are diluted by increasing the new reaction volume with components optimized to support efficient DNA amplification. Thermal cycling in buffer designed to support DNA polymerase activity is then initiated. This method closely resembles the two-tube system, but may have the advantage of higher sensitivity (the entire cDNA quantity serves as template for the subsequent PCR phase). However it lacks the distinct advantage of using cDNA from one RT reaction in several DNA analysis reactions/experiments. In the second type of single-tube RT-PCR, all reaction components are added at once and the tube is sealed. The reverse transcription and the DNA polymerization steps occur in a single, mutually acceptable buffer. However, since this "all-purpose" buffer is optimized for neither reverse transcription nor DNA amplification, the resulting compromise yields the lowest sensitivity of the three categories of RT-PCR.

There are pros and cons for both single-tube and two-tube RT-PCR systems. The two-tube system is generally believed to be the higher sensitivity and higher specificity system. Sensitivity is gained by running the reverse transcription and the DNA amplification reactions under their own respective optimized conditions that may vary greatly.

The chief advantage of a single-tube RT-PCR system is that only a single reaction needs to be set up. The benefits of setting up only one reaction include less time and effort to run an assay and a reduced risk of contaminating one sample with another sample. There is also less exposure for the scientist should there be a harmful agent in the test sample. Due to the reduced amount of sample handling while setting up single-tube assays, there is a decreased chance of spilling or losing the sample in some way. Finally, with single-tube reactions there is a reduced risk of mixing up samples, i.e., the investigator does not have to be concerned with making sure that product from reverse transcription reaction 'A' gets placed into PCR reaction 'A,' and not accidentally placed in PCR reaction 'B.' Only the single-tube, single-step RT-PCR is amenable to high throughput applications.

Reverse transcription followed by the polymerase chain reaction is today one of the most commonly used molecular biology based techniques (reviewed by Wilkinson, 1998).[2] It is often employed as a method for generating sufficient reagents, including cDNA, for use in cloning and production of cDNA (expression) libraries, as well as to create templates for *in vitro* transcription. RT-PCR is an indirect method for the detection of RNA. RT-PCR was first described in 1987 by Powell et al.[1] and immediately had an impact on several lines of research. None of the other commonly used methods for measuring the steady-state levels of individual RNAs (such as Northern or dot/slot blotting, RNase or S1 nuclease protection assays, or *in situ* hybridization) come close to matching RT-PCR's sensitivity. In its original form, RT-PCR was mainly used for qualitative studies of mRNA expression.[3-6] Today, the two primary uses for RT-PCR are to detect pathogens such as RNA viruses[7,8,9] and for gene expression analysis in any number of biological systems.[10-12] Recently, several modifications of this method have been developed that allow quantitative analyses to be performed.[13-15]

RT-PCR may be performed with as many as four different enzymes in the same reaction or as few as a single enzyme. Even more enzymes can be combined, although it is likely that efficiency would not be improved and could possibly be diminished. Most commercially available kits employ a two-enzyme scheme, although three-enzyme kits have very recently been introduced. In a four-enzyme system, typically two different reverse transcriptases (RNA template dependent DNA polymerases) with different properties (such as K_m, V_m, processivity, RNase H activity, fidelity, thermal stability, nuclease activity, or ability to negotiate certain sequence motifs or secondary structures) are used in the reaction. Likewise, two separate DNA template dependent DNA polymerases are used. Here too, the two enzymes have different properties, such as K_m, V_m, processivity, 5'-to-3' and 3'-to-5' exonuclease activities, fidelity (influenced by, but not entirely explained by 3'-to-5' exonuclease activity), ability to read across certain sequence motifs, and thermal stability. With few exceptions, a universal truism is that a single generalist (same enzyme for both RT and PCR) will be outperformed by two specialists (separate RT and DNA polymerases), let alone a combination of three or four specialized enzymes, each with a unique forte. Four-enzyme systems are unavailable commercially, thus they would have to be "home brews." Three-enzyme RT-PCR kits are commercially available in a two RT + one DNA polymerase (ABgene, Rochester, N.Y.; Qiagen, Valencia, Calif.) or as a one RT + two DNA polymerase configuration (Invitrogen, Carlsbad, Calif.; Roche, Indianapolis, Ind.; Stratagene, La Jolla, Calif.; others).

2.2.1. Reverse Transcription and RT Enzymes

Reverse transcriptases have the ability to utilize both polyribonucleotides and polydeoxyribonucleotides as templates to direct the synthesis of complementary polydeoxyribonucleotides. These enzymatic activities have been termed RNA directed (or dependent) DNA polymerase (RDDP) and DNA directed (or dependent) DNA polymerase (DDDP).[16-18]

In the summer of 1970 Baltimore[19] and Temin and Mizutani,[20] independently reported the presence of a RNA-directed DNA polymerase in the virions of oncogenic RNA viruses. The viral RNA was shown to direct the incorporation of deoxyribonucleoside triphosphates into a growing DNA chain. Since its discovery, RDDP (namely, reverse transcriptase) has been the object of great interest to many investigators, and a formidable amount of data has been accumulated on its properties, function, structure, and applications.[21,22]

Replication of all retroviruses starts with the reverse transcription of the single-stranded viral RNA genome into a double-stranded DNA that is subsequently integrated into the host cell's chromosomal DNA.[23] This stage of proviral DNA synthesis is critical to the retroviral life cycle and is catalyzed by a single enzyme, the viral reverse transcriptase (RT). It is well established that retroviral RTs are highly error-prone.[21,24] Purified reverse transcriptases from avian (AMV) and murine (MMLV) RNA tumor viruses exhibit both a synthetic and a degradative activity. The synthetic activity is characterized by DNA polymerase activity (RNA-dependent as well as DNA-dependent), where the plus-strand RNA genome is copied by the RNA-dependent DNA polymerase activity of the RT, producing a hybrid RNA/DNA duplex. The degradative activity is characterized by ribonuclease H (RNase H) activity.[25-27] Its purpose is to specifically degrade the viral RNA in the RNA/DNA heteroduplex. A double-stranded viral DNA is finally obtained after the synthesis of a second DNA strand facilitated by the DNA-dependent DNA polymerase (DDDP) activity of the RT.[28-30] The activity of reverse transcriptase requires the binding of a preformed primer to the RNA molecule in order to initiate DNA synthesis. Both ribo- and deoxyribo-oligonucleotides can serve as a primer, though deoxyribo-oligomers appear to be more efficient.[31] The efficiency of transcription of a given template differs not only with the source of reverse transcriptase but also with the divalent cation used in the reaction. All reverse transcriptases require divalent cations in order to function and their degree of functionality is influenced by the species of cation. The metals Mg^{2+} and Mn^{2+} are the divalent cations most often determined to be optimum, with reverse transcriptases of avian virus origin preferring Mg^{2+} and those of mammalian virus origin preferring Mn^{2+}.[26] However, the two most important RTs from a molecular biology point of view (AMV and MMLV) function in both Mg^{2+} and Mn^{2+}. AMV RT has a 2.1- to 7.1-fold higher efficiency when Mg^{2+} is the cofactor, irrespective of template and primer combination. The case for MMLV is not nearly as clear. Depending on the specific experimental conditions, MMLV has been shown to have a preference for either Mn^{2+} or Mg^{2+}.[32,33]

After the RNA is reverse transcribed (or more likely during transcription), the ribonuclease H activity that is associated with the reverse transcriptase specifically degrades the RNA moiety of the RNA:DNA hybrid. The degradation of the RNA is not dependent on the concurrent synthesis of complementary DNA, since preformed hybrids have been shown to be susceptible to degradation. Ribonuclease H cleaves at the 3' end of the 3'–5' phosphodiester bond to yield products containing 5'-phosphate and 3'-OH ends. Degradation products usually run from 6 to 20 residues and can serve as primers for second strand synthesis.[32,34] All native reverse transcriptases of retroviral origin have an RNase H activity as do their cloned counterparts (unless specifically mutagenized). This activity appears to be crucial for a virus to make a double-stranded DNA copy of its genome that is suitable for integration into a host cell's genome, thus insuring the viability of the viral infection.

In its original form, RT-PCR used wild-type reverse transcriptases isolated from the Moloney murine leukemia (MMLV/MuLV/M-MuLV/MoMuLV) or the avian myeloblastosis virus (AMV),[35,36] described in great detail by Gerard et al.[37] Subsequently, it was discovered that (in most cases) the application of mutagenized versions of MMLV and AMV selected for attenuated or abolished RNase H activity resulted in higher cDNA yields.[38,39] After a while, certain pitfalls of using RNase H deficient enzymes were noticed. It was observed that the amplification efficiencies of some targets were very low when using RNase H deficient reverse transcriptases and that the efficiency could be dramatically enhanced through the addition of a post cDNA synthesis/pre-PCR application of an RNase H digestion step. These difficult to amplify targets were either relatively G+C rich, long, or both G+C rich and long.[40,41] Since the efficiency of detection of these targets was dramatically improved due to the post reverse transcription application of an RNase H digestion step, this indicates that the "difficult" RNA templates are indeed reverse transcribed but for some reason do not amplify well.

The explanation for the poor amplification is that the regions of the RNA:DNA heteroduplex that are relatively G+C rich have a higher T_m than these same regions when they are comprised entirely of a DNA duplex, thus blocking primer binding sites. This explains the poor amplification efficiency of short G+C-rich amplicons. The reason for the poor amplification efficiency of longer templates is simply the increased probability of patches of G+C-rich sequence, which, just as in the troublesome short sequences, causes the DNA polymerase to pause or dissociate from the template, or again inhibits primer binding. Polumuri et al. have recently shown that to a large extent, a prolonged denaturing step at high temperature can largely substitute for the RNase H digestion step.[41] The likely explanation is that the RNA is being hydrolyzed in the presence of Mg^{2+} and this process is greatly accelerated at elevated temperatures. This is good news for those of us who prefer to use single-step RT-PCR. A 5-minute denaturation (post cDNA synthesis) at 97°C seems to enhance dramatically the sensitivity of detection for at least some difficult to amplify templates.

Nevett and Louwrier recently reported a study investigating the utility of using blends of reverse transcriptases in RT-PCR reactions.[42] They tested the two most commonly used RTs: AMV and MMLV. The enzymes were evaluated individually as well as in combinations. Reverse transcription reactions were performed at three different temperatures (42, 47, and 50°C) for 30 minutes and with two different templates, MS2 viral RNA and human testicular total RNA. Gene-specific primers were used to reverse transcribe and amplify MS2 and beta-actin, respectively, and each template was tested at various concentrations. The conclusion of these studies was that a blend of RT enzymes was better than the individual component enzymes, irrespective of the template source.

Although RT-PCR is a fairly routine tool for investigators, the actual reverse transcription of RNA into cDNA is largely taken for granted. The obsession with scientists has been to focus only on the DNA polymerase. For more than two decades there have been only two choices for commercially prepared reverse transcriptase: from the Moloney murine leukemia virus (MMLV) or from the avian myeloblastosis virus (AMV). Today these two enzymes continue to be workhorses of molecular biology, but now they come in "new" and (reportedly) improved flavors. These modified enzymes may possess reduced or eliminated RNase H activity,[43] and/or enhanced thermal stability.[44] In the case of AMV, RT reactions may be run at temperatures as high as 70°C, thereby eliminating concerns about secondary structures that are often found in RNA molecules.[45] In addition to the "new and improved" forms of MMLV and AMV RTs, today there are reverse transcriptases available that have been isolated from other sources. Some of the sources have been disclosed, such as HIV, *Carboxydothermus hydrogenoformans* (*Chy*) and *Bacillus caldotenax* (*Bca*), while other sources remain proprietary trade secrets.

Enzymes often thought of as being DNA-dependent DNA polymerases such as *Taq* polymerase do have limited reverse transcriptase capabilities, and this is the case with Platinum *Taq* as shown in **Fig. 2.1**. Viral and synthetic RNA, when amplified with Platinum *Taq* alone, result in amplification plots, although they are significantly different from the amplification curves produced when a traditional RT enzyme is included in the reaction.

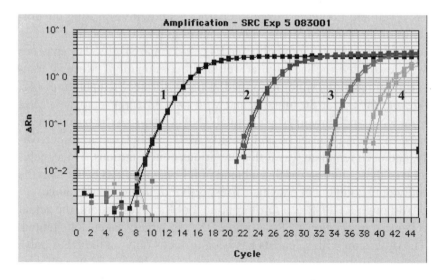

Figure 2.1. RT activity of *Taq* DNA polymerase: 8×10^5 *Pfu* of viral RNA (2 and 4) and 100 pM synthetic RNA (1 and 3) run in an assay using Platinum *Taq* with AMV as the RT enzyme (1 and 2) and Platinum *Taq* with no RT enzyme (3 and 4).

2.2.2. What is Quantitative RT-PCR?

Quantitative RT-PCR can be accomplished in a number of ways such as using radio-labeled primers, photo densitometry, Southern, slot, or dot blot hybridization, incorporation of fluorochromes that specifically bind double-stranded DNA, or detection with fluorogenically labeled probes by fluorescence spectroscopy. Quantitative RT-PCR is an enhancement of the basic "is it there or not?" standard RT-PCR system. With quantitative RT-PCR (qRT-PCR) an estimate is placed on the quantity of a target of interest that is present in a sample.[46,47] Conceptually, there are two fundamentally different means of quantification—absolute and relative. In order to produce a result, there must be some form of comparator or reference to which the amplification signal of the target can be compared. Comparators are simply molecular targets (synthetic or endogenous) that are present in the mixture and are always detected. Usually, the detection sensitivity is predictable. For example, a synthetic internal positive control (IPC) can be placed in the sample mixture. With the IPC present in a known quantity, a standard curve can be constructed and the amount of target can be quantitated relative to the standard curve. Other good comparators are housekeeping genes such as beta actin,[48] beta-tubulin, and glyceraldehyde-3-phosphate dehydrogenase (GAPDH) (among others), or 16S (or 18S) rRNA. These comparators can either be spiked directly into the test sample at known concentrations and both the target and comparator coamplified, or an aliquot of the sample may be spiked with the comparator and the comparator and target separately subjected to amplification. The advantage of the last approach is a potential increase in target detection sensitivity. In each of the examples listed above, the objective is to have some baseline signal to which the signal generated by the target can be compared.

The use of common reverse transcriptase mediated PCR reference target sequences can produce false-positive results by amplification of either contaminating DNA or processed pseudogenes. Furthermore, qualitative (no-reference) RT-PCR alone cannot distinguish between high- and low-quality cDNA preparations and high and low amounts of target. Analysis may be difficult to interpret unless a reference sequence is amplified in parallel. Thus, negative RT-PCR results can only be defined when amplification of the reference target (comparator) reveals a positive result.

2.2.3. Real-Time RT-PCR

The last category is usually referred to as "real-time PCR" or "quantitative real-time PCR," and it has several advantages over the other means of quantification in terms of accuracy, sensitivity, specificity, dynamic range, high-throughput capacity, and absence of post-PCR manipulations. It is this category that will be our primary focus.

Real-time PCR (whether it is standard or RT-PCR) depends upon some form of reporting mechanism whose signal intensity mirrors the accumulation of target amplicon during the thermal cycling program. In the earliest report describing the progenitor of real-time PCR,[49] ethidium bromide was used in a closed tube system. Upon intercalation of the ethidium bromide into double-stranded DNA, a rise in fluorescence could be observed. An increase in fluorescence signal appeared as the thermal cycling program advanced, corresponding to the accumulation of PCR product.[50] A few years later, a better and brighter dye, SYBR Green I was applied in real-time PCR.[51,52] Today, virtually all real-time PCR that depends on dye binding to nucleic acids employs SYBR Green I. DNA-binding dyes are easy to use but since they nonselectively adhere to all nucleic acid sequences (specific or otherwise), they lack the specificity of a probe.

2.2.4. Reaction Internal Positive Controls (IPCs)

To confirm the efficiency and sensitivity of PCR, it is helpful to apply standard molecules as indicators of assay performance. It is also important to detect false-negative results arising from experimental errors or inhibition of amplification that often is observed when PCR is performed on complex samples such as feces, blood, or samples of environmental origin. Ideally, these standard molecules would be included with the actual sample that is to be analyzed; hence the term internal positive control or IPC. In the ideal situation, the IPC would share primer-binding sites with the target but would be distinguishable on the basis of product size or a difference in internal sequence (so it could be probed or differentially cut with a restriction enzyme).

There are two basic types of IPCs—endogenous and exogenous. For endogenous positive controls, a sequence stretch believed to be normally present in the test sample is targeted. In this case only primers and probe are added to the reaction. The endogenous positive control target is usually a "housekeeping" gene such as actin or tubulin. On the other hand, in the case of exogenous IPCs, primers and probes, as well as template, are added to each reaction. This may be necessary in situations where there is no suitable reference sequence in the sample, or it is not known if there is a reference sequence present. This is the case with samples collected from anything other than a plant or animal. Both categories of IPCs may apply to either RT-PCR or conventional PCR, depending on the specific situation.

As a means for assisting in the demonstration/confirmation of an assay's performance, several commercial suppliers offer positive control reagents for sale. However, the bulk of these offerings are not designed for "out-of-the-box" use in real-time probe chemistry based PCR systems. That is to say that these "incomplete" kits come with, at best, primers and control template or, at worst, only primers (the user must supply the template). Commercial IPC kits routinely do not come with probes that are essential for real-time detection chemistry. Most commercially available internal positive control (IPC) reagents that are intended for use in quantitative PCR are designed to function in eukaryotic systems and are usually representatives of "housekeeping" genes. However, at least one company (Applied Biosystems, Foster City, Calif.) produces an IPC that is packaged with primers, probe, and template.

Prior experience indicates that IPC primer concentrations must be limiting in order to prevent preferential amplification of IPC to the extent that target sequence amplification is severely hampered, or may even reach undetectable levels. In principle, IPC primer concentration could be set to a normal range (200 nM or more) and the IPC template titrated to produce the desired extent of amplification. However, it is far more difficult to manage the extent of IPC amplification under these circumstances than if IPC primer concentrations are limiting. This is due to complications associated with depositing consistent yet small quantities of IPC template in the reaction and also the phenomenon that the template that begins amplifying first (IPC or target) will take over the reaction, providing no reaction component is limiting. All too often, amplification of one target will be at the expense of the other target. By limiting the primer concentration of the IPC, a quantity of IPC template can be used that ensures amplification even in the presence of large amounts of the target of interest (or inhibitors). The IPC amplification will be unable to out-compete target sequence amplification because by limiting IPC primer concentration, the IPC amplification reaches plateau phase at a detectable level and long before any of the reaction components are exhausted. Thus, there should be ample opportunity for the target sequence to amplify, even if it was originally found at a much lower concentration.

Typically, and while cycle threshold (C_t—the point at which signal rises above background) remains roughly constant, as primer concentration decreases so does the change in fluorescence (ΔR_n) until a point is reached below which a reliable ΔR_n cannot be achieved. This point cannot always be predicted and extrapolation from one assay to the next is not reliable. This lack of predictability stems from a lack of understanding about the complex interactions between the IPC primers, assay primers, and DNAs present in the reaction. DNAs include IPC amplicons, target amplicons, and other DNAs such as environmental contaminants that may be present in the test sample and amplification artifacts. Far and away, the most common reference genes for qRT-PCR are housekeeping genes (listed above). Housekeeping genes are expressed in all nucleated cells since they are required for basic cell survival. In most cases, the mRNA synthesis of these genes is considered to be stable and secure across tissue types and even under various experimental treatments.[53] However, some studies have shown that the housekeeping genes can be regulated and their expression could vary under certain experimental conditions.[54-56] The use of 18S rRNA is not always the best choice as a comparator, but it does seem to be a good choice as a reference gene in almost all cases. The one drawback of using 18S (or 16S in prokaryotes) is that it's expression level is high and thus may not make the best choice to compare the mRNA levels of low-expressed genes, particularly in a multiplex reaction format. A good alternative for these low-expression cases would be to use a synthetic internal positive control sequence that could be added at a known concentration.

2.2.5. Reporter Technologies

Currently several technologies enabling specific sequence detection in a closed reaction vessel are either commercially available or have been reported in the literature (reviewed by Sinclair and Wolf[57] and

Table 2.1. Probe technologies

Detection / Probe Technology	Reference	Required Enzymatic Activity	
		Minimal	Optimal*
Amplifluor Primer	(59)	NSR	$5'exo^+ + 3'exo^+$
BODIPY FL – guanine quencher	(60)	NSR	Primer $5'exo^+ + 3'exo^+$ Probe $5'exo^- + 3'exo^+$
Cyclicon	(61)	NSR	Primer $5'exo^+ + 3'exo^+$ Probe $5'exo^- + 3'exo^+$
Eclipse	(62)	NSR	$5'exo^+ + 3'exo^+$
Gold nanoprobes	(63)	NSR	$5'exo^- + 3'exo^+$
HyBeacon	(64)	NSR	$5'exo^- + 3'exo^+$
LightCycler – Hybridization	(51,52)	NSR	$5'exo^- + 3'exo^+$
Light-up	(65)	NSR	$5'exo^- + 3'exo^+$
Molecular Beacon	(66)	NSR	$5'exo^- + 3'exo^+$
PNA Molecular Beacon	(67,68)	NSR	$5'exo^+ + 3'exo^+$
Self-reporting PNA/DNA primers	(69)	NSR	$5'exo^+ + 3'exo^+$
Scorpion	(70)	NSR	$5'exo^+ + 3'exo^+$
Duplex Scorpion	(71)	NSR	$5'exo^+ + 3'exo^+$
SYBR Green I	(51,52)	NSR	$5'exo^+ + 3'exo^+$
TaqMan	(72)	$5'exo^+$	$5'exo^+ + 3'exo^+$
Terbium chelate	(73)	$5'exo^+$	$5'exo^+ + 3'exo^+$
Displacement Hybridization	(74)	NSR	$5'exo^- + 3'exo^+$
UniFluor	(75)	NSR	$5'exo^+ + 3'exo^+$

Abbreviations: NSR = no specific requirements; exo− = exonuclease activity is missing; $3'exo^+$ = proofreading activity.

* A blend of two enzymes typically yields superior results.

Didenko).[58] All of them (listed in **Table 2.1**) are based on fluorescence resonance energy transfer (FRET) and some are discussed elsewhere in this book.[51,52,59-75]

2.3. Things That Influence RT-PCR

When developing a successful RT-PCR assay, there are several factors that must be considered. To illustrate this point, and to give you some idea of what you might expect to see, results from several experiments performed in my laboratory are shown. Our experiments have primarily focused on using the ABI Prism® 7700 Sequence Detection System (Applied Biosystems, Foster City, Calif.) for performing quantitative RT-PCR. However, the questions asked in these experiments, and the experimental designs, apply to any platform being used. Most experiments were performed using the *Tth*-based ABI EZ RT-PCR kit. A few additional experiments are shown that compare alternative commercial kits.

A litany of RT-PCR kits from a large number of commercial suppliers is currently available. Furthermore, it appears that no two kits are the same. A survey of the kits reveals that among the kit components (and across manufacturers) a wide range of enzymes may be found. Reverse transcriptases include AMV (cloned wild type and RNase H negative mutant, as well as thermal stable mutant), MMLV (wild type and RNase H negative mutant), *Tth*, *Chy* (from *Carboxydothermus hydrogenoformans*), *Bca*, or *Bst*, (from *Bacillus caldotenax/caldolyticus/stearothermophilus*), and two enzymes of undisclosed proprietary origin (known not to be AMV or MMLV). DNA polymerases available in kit form run the entire gamut of what is available. They include *Tth*, *Taq*, *Pfu*, *Pwo*, Vent, Deep Vent, *Pfx*, *Tgo*, and blends of enzymes. The TaqMan system relies on 5'-exonuclease activity in the reaction. Most multiple enzyme RT-PCR kits use enzymes with 5'-exonuclease activity, with *Taq* polymerase being the most common. With the exception of the *Tgo/Tgo* exo-mixture provided by Roche, all of the DNA polymerase mixtures contain one enzyme with 5'-exonuclease activity and a second enzyme (at a minor concentration) possessing 3'-to-5'-exonuclease (proofreading) activity. Thus, theoretically, almost any commercially available kit could be adapted for use in a TaqMan assay. Most of the other probe technologies do not require 5'-exonuclease activity and could, thus, work with all commercially available RT-PCR kits.

2.3.1. Why Commercial Kits?

Though most laboratories would like to believe otherwise, they simply cannot match the quality control and performance consistency afforded by the commercial kits. On the whole, commercial kits are reliable and once familiar with a particular kit, uniform performance on a day-to-day basis can be expected. Most of us know either first hand, or by word of mouth, that this is usually not the case with homemade reagents. A second benefit of using commercially prepared kits is that they are usually packaged in such a way that a novice can get them to work in the laboratory. Most, if not all reaction components are furnished with a detailed set of instructions. Time and convenience are two other reasons that make commercial kits attractive. Many labs do not have the labor or know-how to produce everything required for RT-PCR from scratch. Finally, in a busy schedule, the convenience of pulling a kit out of a freezer means that more experiments can be conducted in a shorter period of time and with a lower probability of failure.

If you are just starting out, the commercial kit you select to use is probably less important than the effort you put into the design of reaction primers and probes. Each kit is unique in its enzyme and buffering properties. Consequently, there will be selective pressure on primer/probe sets for optimal performance in that particular enzyme/buffering system. Another way to state this is that if the same five primer/probe sets were to be carried through a series of performance optimization experiments using three different commercial RT-PCR kits, three different primer/probe sets could be identified with the best performance. The other side of this coin is that if you already have a specific primer/probe set you are using, but need to change to a different enzyme system for performing the RT-PCR, you may need to try several different kits to find one that provides the same level of performance. However, you may also find one that substantially improves your assay performance.

To demonstrate the differences that can be seen between commercial vendors, dilutions of viral RNA (10,000 pfu to 0.1 pfu) were tested in four commercially available RT-PCR kits: two from Invitrogen, and one each from Qiagen and Applied Biosystems (**Fig. 2.2**). For high concentrations of template (10,000 to 100 pfu), all kits performed adequately, but at low concentrations of template (10 to 0.1 pfu), differences in ΔR_n values and detection were pronounced. Both Invitrogen kits were capable of marginally detecting as low as 0.1 pfu of viral RNA. The Qiagen kit detected template at 1 pfu while the Applied Biosystems kit only marginally detected template at 1 pfu. Thus if assay sensitivity is a priority, it is important to compare amplification efficiency at very low template concentrations. The optimal RT temperature and concentrations of primer, probe, and Mg^{2+}/Mn^{2+} were used for each kit.

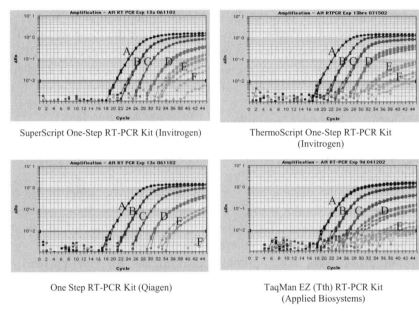

SuperScript One-Step RT-PCR Kit (Invitrogen)   ThermoScript One-Step RT-PCR Kit (Invitrogen)

One Step RT-PCR Kit (Qiagen)   TaqMan EZ (Tth) RT-PCR Kit (Applied Biosystems)

Figure 2.2. Comparison of four RT-PCR Kits: 10-fold serial dilution of viral RNA. 10,000 pfu (A), 1,000 pfu (B), 100 pfu (C), 10 pfu (D), 1 pfu (E), and 0.1 pfu (F).

2.3.2. Divalent Metal Concentration

The concentration of divalent metal ion in the reaction is a critical factor. *Tth* has a preference for Mn^{2+} while other enzymes prefer Mg^{2+}. However, the optimum metal concentrations are similar. Typically for *Tth* the Mn^{2+} optimum is determined by testing 3, 4, 5, and 6 mM Mn^{2+}. **Fig. 2.3** shows that this particular primer/probe set demonstrated a dramatic preference for lower Mn^{2+} concentrations. In the initial testing, at 4 mM Mn^{2+}, sensitivity was very poor and there was a wider C_t difference between 10-fold template dilutions than is typically seen (data not shown). This leads to a limited primer (300, 600, and 900 nM) and Mn^{2+} (3 mM vs. 5 mM) optimization to locate the cause of these atypical results. From the first optimization, it was determined that decreasing the Mn^{2+} to 3 mM greatly increased sensitivity and curve appearance (data not shown). As a result, a more intense Mn^{2+} optimization was performed on this primer/probe set. **Fig. 2.3** demonstrates that a certain amount of Mn^{2+} is required since the 0 mM Mn^{2+} condition did not amplify and the 1 mM condition amplified poorly. It also demonstrates that too much Mn^{2+} can have an adverse effect on amplification (2 mM is optimal and as concentration increases the amplification efficiency decreases). Other primer/probe sets that we have tested showed the opposite pattern; i.e., poor performance at 3 mM Mn^{2+} and optimal performance at 5 mM Mn^{2+}.

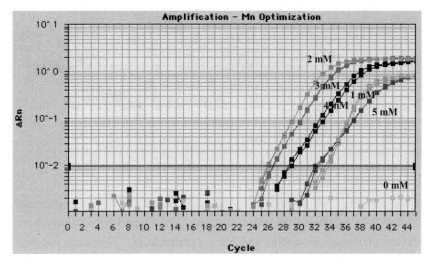

Figure 2.3. Mn^{2+} optimization. Six concentrations of Mn^{2+} ranging from 0 to 5 mM. Optimized primer and probe concentrations of 600 nM primer and 200 nM probe. Template is 100 pfu viral RNA.

2.3.3. Primer Concentration

Another consideration is the amount of primer needed in a reaction. An example of a primer optimization experiment is shown in **Fig. 2.4**. All combinations of forward and reverse primers at 900, 600, 300, and 100 nM were tested against viral RNA at 100 pfu/rxn. For simplicity, only the four equimolar primer concentrations are shown in **Fig. 2.4**. Primer optimization was done prior to probe and Mn^{2+} optimization; therefore customary concentrations of 200 nM probe and 4 mM Mn^{2+} were em-

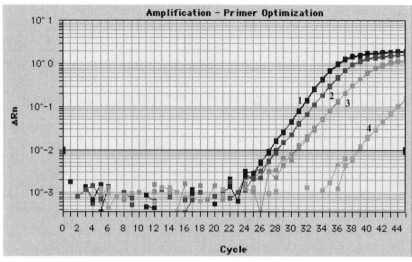

Figure 2.4. Primer optimization: Equal molar forward and reverse primers at 900 nM (1), 600 nM (2), 300 nM (3), and 100 nM (4).

ployed. For analysis, forward and reverse combinations, which resulted in the lowest C_t values or the highest ΔR_n values, were compared and the top two combinations providing the best C_t and ΔR_n values were chosen and used for probe and Mn^{2+} optimization. This decision was somewhat arbitrary as equimolar and lower primer concentrations are normally preferred to minimize the risk of amplification artifacts. In this example very little difference was seen with either 900 or 600 nM of the reverse primer with each concentration of the forward primer (data not shown). Therefore equal molar concentrations were chosen for proceeding into the probe and Mn^{2+} optimization. In addition, although there was a one C_t shift between the 900 and 600 nM concentrations, after complete optimization and analysis of a standard curve, this difference was determined to be inconsequential at low template concentrations. Thus, the 600 nM concentration of primers was ultimately chosen for the assay.

2.3.4. Probe Concentration

Fig. 2.5 demonstrates the typical results from a probe optimization experiment using the Applied Biosystems TaqMan EZ RT-PCR kit. We typically see little difference in C_t values and a slight difference in ΔR_n values between 400 and 200 nM probe, and a slightly more pronounced shift with the 100 nM probe. Although the 400 nM probe appears to be even better, it is not significant enough to warrant the expense of using twice as much probe, and as with the primers, lower concentrations are preferred. Experiments with other RT-PCR kits (such as Invitrogen's SuperScript One-Step RT-PCR kit) have shown a similar pattern between 200 and 100 nM probe (with C_t values being the same and a slight difference in ΔR_n values), thus allowing for even less probe to be used (data not shown). Being able to use lower probe concentrations is a financial consideration, but is also very important in multiplexed experiments, where multiple probes are required. Using a lower probe concentration in these instances will lower the overall background fluorescence and total oligonucleotide concentration.

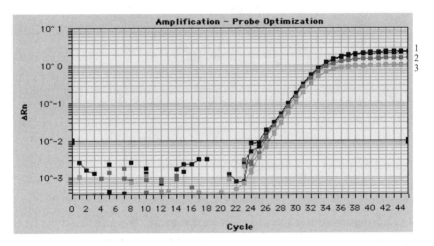

Figure 2.5. Probe optimization. Three concentrations of probe, 400 nM (1), 200 nM (2), and 100 nM (3). Primer concentration at 600 nM and Mn^{2+} at 3 mM (both are near the optimized concentrations).

2.3.5. Reverse Transcription Conditions

One of the most important components for a successful RT-PCR reaction is the reverse transcription phase, including enzyme concentration and temperature. In **Fig. 2.6**, various concentrations of AMV Reverse Transcriptase were used in tandem with Platinum *Taq*. Five units of enzyme were optimal. However, increasing the enzyme from 5 units to 40 units showed decreased amplification efficiency. With 40 units of enzyme, abnormal fluorescence appears early on in the thermocycling. This may be due to the enzyme immediately beginning to degrade the probe, releasing unquenched reporter dye into solution.

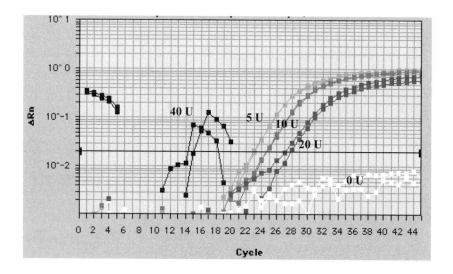

Figure 2.6. Effect of increasing AMV reverse transcriptase.

Fig. 2.7 demonstrates the effect of temperature. We amplified rat liver RNA at 100 and 1 ng, using the Platinum Quantitative RT-PCR Kit (Invitrogen). The RT enzyme, ThermoScript, is designed to work at a relatively high temperature (higher than 50°C). A definite trend in sensitivity was seen. At 37°C, 1 ng of RNA was not detected. At 47°C, detection was marginal while at 57°C definite amplification is seen. Amplification was seen equally well at all three temperatures with 100 ng of RNA.

Often, a particular enzyme is recommended for use at a particular temperature that is not the actual optimum. An example of this can be seen in **Fig. 2.8** with MMLV Reverse Transcriptase. Even though the half-life of this enzyme is less than 5 minutes at 60°C,[37] the assay sen-

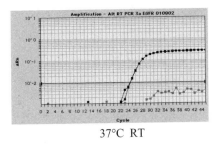

37°C RT

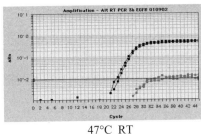

47°C RT

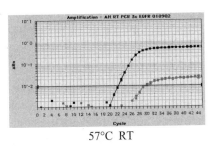

57°C RT

Figure 2.7. RT temperature optimization. 100 and 1 ng of rat liver RNA was amplified with the ThermoScript Platinum Quantitative RT-PCR Kit (Invitrogen). Three RT temperatures were examined: 37, 47, and 57°C.

sitivity is far superior to using an RT temperature at the recommended 47°C. This is probably due to the fact that, although the enzyme degrades quickly at the higher temperature, the secondary structure of the template, primer and probe at the lower temperature impedes the reaction to a greater extent.

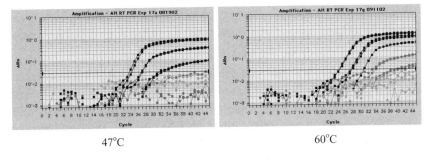

47°C   60°C

Figure 2.8. RT-PCR using MMLV at what is most often its suggested operating temperature (47°C) and at 60°C, a temperature at which the half-life of the enzyme is less than 5 minutes. Viral RNA template at 1000, 100, and 10 pfu (black), 1 and 0.1 pfu (dark gray), and no-template control (light gray).

2.4. Synthetic Molecules

2.4.1. Substituted Primers and Probes

Some researchers are placed in a situation where there is only a limited amount of sequence information available. The limitations could be that the available sequences are too short for rigorous primer/probe design, or that the sequences are too A/T rich for good primers and/or probes. The catch 22 is that as oligonucleotides become longer to meet the desired T_m goals while compensating for the lack of Gs and Cs, two things happen. First, the longer compensating oligos take up more of your available sequence, thus limiting choices for the oligos that will comprise an assay. Second, as the oligos become ever longer, there is a growing risk for intra- and inter-oligonucleotide interactions, which are the bane of an efficient, sensitive, and specific assay. One solution for these problems is to employ nucleotide analogs that serve the purpose of raising the T_m of an oligonucleotide, thereby allowing the oligo to be shorter and increasing the flexibility of design (which would also allow for the easier use of degenerate bases, which tend to lower the T_m.[76-79] Several nucleotide analogs exist that have the property of raising the T_m of an oligonucleotide. They include (1) 2-Amino-dA and 5-Methyl-cytosine (available from Glen Research, Sterling, Va.), (2) Super A, Super T, and Super G (available from Amersham, Piscataway, N.J.), and (3) A, G, T, C Locked Nucleic Acids (available from Proligo, Boulder, Colo.). Our laboratory and others have experience with 2-Amino-dA and 5-Methyl-cytosine.[80] Other laboratories have seen benefits with the other categories of T_m enhancing bases.[81,82]

In one exercise, we analyzed substitutions of modified nucleotides in one primer; four As being replaced with 2-amino deoxyadenosine, and six Cs being replaced with 5-methyl deoxycytidine. As can be seen in **Fig. 2.9, panel 1**, these substitutions greatly improve the performance of *Tth* DNA polymerase. These substitutions do not have any effect on the performance of Platinum *Taq* DNA polymerase, although amplifications were more robust and sensitive using Platinum *Taq* (**Fig. 2.9, panel 2**).

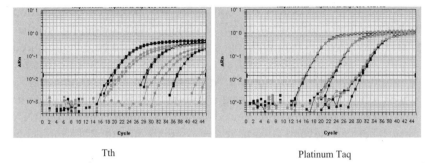

Figure 2.9. Effect of a modified primer on PCR with *Tth* and Platinum *Taq*. Gray = unmodified nucleotides. Black = 2-amino dA and 5-methyl dC substitutions. 100-fold dilutions of DNA template (RT-PCR product).

2.4.2. Synthetic RNA Controls

One of the major complications of developing standardized RT-PCR assays revolves around the lability of RNA. RNA is substantially less stable than DNA and the plethora of RNA degrading enzymes that seem to be ubiquitous in the environment also tend to be very rugged enzymes. Their persistence in the environment is largely due to their ability to be naturally lyophilized on surfaces where, upon rehydration, enzymatic activity is restored. Furthermore, RNases have high thermal stability; even standard autoclaving conditions will not fully inactivate some RNases.

An alternative to native and hence labile RNA, is synthetic RNA comprised either partially or entirely of 2'-O-methyl or phosphorothioate ribonucleotides. The phosphorothioate and 2'-O-methyl are chemical modifications on the backbone of the RNA molecule that renders the substituted molecule resistant to hydrolysis based nucleolytic attack. In the case of phosphorothioate RNA, a sulfur moiety replaces an oxygen molecule in the phosphate group. Conversely for 2'-O-methyl RNA the hydroxyl group at position 2 of the sugar ring is replaced by an OCH_3 group. Synthetic RNA molecules constructed entirely with 2'-O-methyl ribonucleotides are highly resistant to nucleases but are rather insoluble. Synthetic RNA that is partially constructed of 2'-O-methyl ribonucleotides, though not as nuclease resistant as fully substituted, is several orders of magnitude more resistant to nucleases than native RNA, and yet still maintains high water solubility.

Synthetic RNA molecules can consist of any sequence composition with a practical synthesized length of about 75 bases from the synthesizer. In addition to customization, synthetic RNA can be manufactured swiftly, in large quantities, and at a cost that is a fraction of that for Armored RNA (RNA packaged in MS2 protein).

Synthetic RNA molecules using a 2'-O-methyl backbone were engineered for our laboratory, to be used as positive controls in a viral RNA assay. There are several advantages to using a synthetic RNA molecule as the positive control instead of viral RNA. The synthetic RNA is quantifiable whereas the actual number of copies of the viral RNA is more difficult to quantify and will be variable between preparations. In addition, the viral RNA is inherently unstable and subject to degradation. Three molecules were synthesized: U and G substituted, A and C substituted, and fully substituted. **Fig. 2.10** shows the differing abilities of four RT enzymes to transcribe off of the substituted molecules. RT-PCR

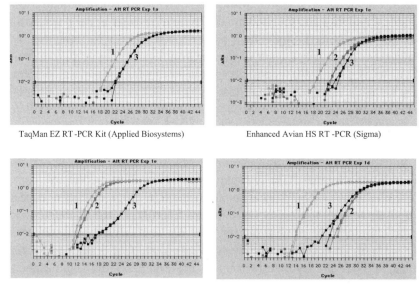

Figure 2.10. Synthetic RNA templates utilizing 2'-O-methyl ribonucleosides either fully substituted (2) or substituted at A and C sites only (1) versus viral RNA (3) template. For each experiment 10 pM of synthetic RNA template was used and 2×10^3 Pfu of viral RNA. Four different RT-Kits were tested to demonstrate the varying ability of different enzymes to amplify the synthetic molecules.

was performed following each individual kit's protocol using primer, probe, and metal concentrations optimized for the TaqMan EZ RT-PCR kit. The TaqMan EZ RT-PCR enzyme (*Tth*) was unable to amplify the fully substituted synthetic molecule, but it was able to amplify the A/C substituted molecule. In a previous experiment (data not shown), it was unable to transcribe the U/G substituted molecule. On the other hand MMLV (SuperScript Kit) and AMV (Sigma's Enhanced Avian and Invitrogen's ThermoScript Kits) were able to transcribe both the fully substituted and A/C substituted molecule, although at different efficiencies. MMLV appears to have no problem with either substitution as indicated by the similar amplification plots for both synthetics. On the other hand, neither AMV transcribes the fully substituted molecule as well as the A/C substituted molecule. In addition, the Invitrogen version of AMV is less able to handle the fully substituted molecule than the Sigma version. All were equally able to handle the viral RNA and A/C substituted molecule (taking in account that these were not fully optimized amplifications for several of the kits).

2.5. A Word about DNA Polymerases

2.5.1. DNA-Dependent DNA Polymerases

Without question, DNA polymerases derived from archaea are far superior to enzymes derived from eubacteria in terms of thermal stability, fidelity, and maximum amplifiable amplicon length. The two archaea genera from which enzymes have been commercialized are Thermococcus and Pyrococcus and include enzymes such as *Pfu* (Stratagene), *Tgo* (Roche), Vent (New England Biolabs), Deep Vent (New England Biolabs), and *Pfx*, also known as KOD (Invitrogen and EMD Biosciences, San Diego, Calif.). *Pfu* and Deep Vent enzymes are from *Pyrococcus furiosus* and *Pyrococcus sp. GB-D*, respectively. *Tgo*, Vent, and *Pfx* are from *Thermococcus gorgonarius*, *Thermococcus litoralis*, and *Thermococcus kodakaraensis*, respectively. Each of these enzymes possesses replication fidelities significantly higher than enzymes derived from other genera.[83-87] Each company makes the claim that they have the most faithful enzyme. However, after careful review of the data offered in support of these claims, one may realize that none of the manufacturers compares the full set of five enzymes listed above. This is only the first interesting observation. The second is that the enzymes are not compared on a per unit basis or under truly identical reaction conditions. A third observation is that different methods for determining error rates are employed by each manufacturer and, not surprisingly, the results show that the enzyme produced by the company making the comparisons comes out on top. A closer look reveals that whenever compared (regardless of the method or the company making the comparison), *Pfu* is always shown to be the most faithful DNA polymerase or by a slim margin, the second most faithful. Stratagene has recently isolated a clone of *Pfu* whose DNA polymerase has an error rate that is one third that of the original clone. If the data holds up, the new mutant derived *Pfu* would easily be the most faithful thermostable DNA polymerase yet discovered on the planet. At the time of this writing, we had not evaluated this enzyme, so no further comment can be made. It is important to note that the performance of each of the enzymes has steadily improved with the discovery of better buffers and reaction cofactors.

Most DNA template-dependent DNA polymerases have a definite divalent cation preference for Mg^{2+}, and some enzymes are so picky that they even have a preference for a certain salt form of Mg^{2+}, with $MgSO_4$ preferred over $Mg(OAc)_2$, which is preferred over the most commonly used salt form, $MgCl_2$. In general, enzymes from the hyperthermophilic archaea have a distinct preference for sulfur-based salts. Use of an inappropriate metal or conjugate results in lower reaction fidelity, which translates into decreased amplification efficiency. Moreover, if the fidelity drops below a certain level, the reaction could utterly fail.

2.5.2. RNA-Dependent DNA Polymerases

There is evidence that a mixture of two different reverse transcriptases (MMLV + AMV) perform better in combination than do the single enzymes when used alone. The reason for this is believed to be that each enzyme has different properties that complement one another when used in combination. Another consideration is the use of reverse transcriptases with higher thermal stability than AMV or MMLV. Two enzymes fitting this description are currently available. Of interest is the fact that both of these enzymes are derived from thermophilic bacteria, all other commercially available enzymes that catalyze reverse transcription in the presence of Mg^{2+} are derived from viruses. These two newcomers are from the unrelated bacteria *Carboxydothermus hydrogenoformans* (*Chy*) and *Bacillus caldotenax* (*Bca*). These enzymes are of particular interest for two reasons: (1) they were isolated from thermophiles and thus have high thermal stability, and (2) they almost certainly have higher fidelity than any reverse transcriptase isolated from a virus. The assertion that these enzymes are higher fidelity comes from two lines of evidence: (1) bacterial enzymes have higher fidelity than enzymes of viral origin, and (2) enzymes originating from thermophiles have higher fidelity than enzymes derived from nonthermophiles. High thermal stability means that RT reactions can be performed at temperatures sufficiently high to remove secondary structure from RNA.

Blends of RT enzymes may be the ultimate answer to producing prodigious quantities of cDNA from small amounts of target or from difficult targets (loaded with secondary structure or zones of high GC content). The higher thermal stability of the blends would erase any advantage that *Tth* has over viral derived RTs in cases where RT reaction temperature is a factor. It is also a good bet that blends of enzymes would perform well in a wider number of cases than single enzymes. A blend of reverse transcriptases is simply more robust (the same has been shown for blends of enzymes used for DNA amplification). These qualities would improve the chance of converting existing assays into "new and improved" assays as well as assist in the development of new highly sensitive assays.

2.6. Tips and Tricks

2.6.1. Probes

There are many variables that must be considered in order to maximize the sensitivity and specificity for any given quantitative real-time RT-PCR system. Some probe systems are better suited for certain applications. Other probes work best in other systems. The first question one should ask is "What am I trying to detect?" The answer to this question has a large bearing on which probe/enzyme system the reader should focus on. For the purpose of probe type selection, the major categories of target may be broken down into three groups: (1) targets with no known sequence variation, (2) targets with single nucleotide polymorphisms (SNPs), and (3) targets with unpredictable sequence variations (such as HIV-1). In the first category when there are no sequence variations, any probe type will function satisfactorily. It is simply a matter of the investigator's preference. In the case where one wants to detect SNPs, the best probe choices are Scorpions, Molecular Beacons, and displacement hybridization probes. With each of these probes, performance is a balance between a DNA duplex (hairpin for Scorpions and Molecular Beacons), linear duplex for displacement probes, and competition for a more energy favorable configuration (being bound to the perfectly complementary target). Since SNP detection probes are usually used in the reaction in two permutations (one for each choice of base at the SNP site), the reaction very strongly favors the perfect complementation. Scorpion probes have an advantage because of their unimolecular mode of action. However, it will often be the case where a good priming site is not within striking distance of the probe-binding site that, ideally, would be centered over the SNP. Molecular Beacons and displacement hybridization probes afford the freedom of positioning the probe optimally, and choosing a more favorable primer binding site. Great distances between primer and probe binding sites may negate the unimolecular advantage of Scorpions, thus hindering efficient probing of the SNP.

In cases where the expectation for sequence variation is high but this variation is unpredictable, the best probes are the ones that tolerate the greatest degree of mismatches. The best candidates for this situation are standard FRET hybridization probes (LightCycler Hyb probes) and standard exonuclease probes (TaqMan probes). These probe types usually have a T_m cushion built in (are designed to have T_ms 5–10°C higher than the primers) and this cushion can be readily increased to 20°C or more, thus accommodating fairly large degrees of mismatching. Probes such as Eclipse, which are from the TaqMan probe family, are not well suited for these applications due to the large changes in T_m that are characteristic of mismatches in short probes. However, because of this abnormal Tm behavior (a minor groove binder provides a large T_m increase), Eclipse probes are reasonably well suited for SNP detection.

2.6.2. The Right Enzyme for the Job

In order to encourage maximal sensitivity of detection, it would be prudent to optimally match the DNA polymerase to the probe type that was selected as described above in **Section 2.6.1. Table 2.1** indicates the suggested match-up for probe types and enzymes. Notice that under the optimal enzyme system column, there are always two enzymes listed. Further, in all cases, one of the enzymes of the pair has 3'–5' exonuclease activity. This activity is commonly referred to as "proofreading" ability. Adding a minor amount of proofreading enzyme to a real-time reaction almost invariably enhances assay sensitivity. The reason for the enhancement is two fold: (1) the proofreading enzyme minimizes pauses from the main enzyme (most commonly *Taq*) when a mismatch is encountered and (2) the proofreading enzyme increases the fidelity of the amplification product, which leads to more efficient amplification (no enzyme induced mutations under primer/probe binding sites).

With some probe types it is recommended that the primary enzyme (the one lacking 3'–5' exonuclease activity) be deficient in 5'–3' exonuclease activity. During DNA synthesis, the 5'-exonuclease activity enables the advancing enzyme to degrade nucleic acids in its path. For TaqMan chemistry this is a desirable characteristic. For many other probe technologies, this is suboptimal. For example, one of the fortes of Molecular Beacons is their very low background fluorescence when unbound to target. However, these probes can be degraded by enzymes possessing 5'-exonuclease activity, thereby raising the background fluorescence and reducing the signal-to-noise ratio. The alternatives are to use a polymerase that lacks 5'-exonuclease activity or protect the Molecular Beacon through its construction with a nuclease resistant backbone such as PNAs or thioate. In cases where the reporting mechanism is associated with the primer (or the probe is nuclease resistant), the recommendation is to use a polymerase with 5'-exonuclease activity. The reason for this is that this activity will not harm the primer or probe, yet retains the benefit of having the capacity to remove undesirable sequences in its path. In addition, enzymes with 5'–3' exonuclease activity usually have higher extension rates than enzymes with 3'–5' exonuclease activity. And higher extension rates generally translate into more PCR product.

2.7. Buffers

The buffer composition of many commercially available RT-PCR kits is considered a trade secret. Though I have not personally tested all buffer systems, I have tested many, and over the years I have had discussions with numerous scientists on this subject. I will discuss some of what I have learned but it is up to the investigators to decide what works best for them. I am merely tossing out a few hints that could be helpful. The reason for the secrecy of buffer composition by commercial vendors is that the buffer system seems to play a larger role in one-step RT-PCR than originally thought. There is a consensus opinion that it is important to have sulfate ions in the reaction buffer. However, there is some disagreement over the importance of how the sulfate is supplied. Some scientists prefer ammonium sulfate buffer with $MgCl_2$, other scientists will use *Tris* buffer with $MgSO_4$, and still others prefer ammonium sulfate with $MgSO_4$ as the Mg^{2+} source. The important feature is that in each case, sulfate ions have been identified as significant. Tangled in this web is the buffer salt itself. It was discovered long ago that enzymes from archaea have a strong preference for low ionic strength buffers using ammonium ions. It has recently been suggested that enzymes derived from eubacteria also prefer buffers containing ammonium ions. All RT-PCR systems require the presence of a divalent cation in order to function. In most cases, several species of cation can be utilized but with the exception of Mg^{2+}, they invariably lead to a decreased product yield with lower fidelity. Other ways of enhancing PCR amplifications include adding archaeal dUTPase, dimethylsulfoxide (DMSO), glycerol, betaine, polyethylene glycol, formamide, sulfolane, methyl sulfone, and tetramethylene sulfoxide.[88-90]

2.8. Concluding Remarks

It is my hope that after reading this chapter, the reader goes away with a greater appreciation for the complexities of developing a sensitive and robust real-time RT-PCR assay. Many parts must work in concert, in order to provide optimal results. One should first consider the target subject matter, then choose an appropriate probe technology, and finally, select an enzyme system to work optimally with the probe. There are many good reagents available for performing real-time RT-PCR and the user should not shy away from trying new things.

Acknowledgement

I would like to express my gratitude to Dr. Louis E. Holland, William S. Reed, Kenneth E. Robbins, and Amanda M. Rom for their assistance in the preparation of this chapter.

References

1. Powell LM, Wallis SC, Pease RJ, Edwards YH, Knott TJ, Scott J: **A novel form of tissue-specific RNA processing produces apolipoprotein-B48 in intestine.** *Cell* 1987, **50**(6):831–840.

2. Wilkinson DA: **Getting the message with RT-PCR.** *The Scientist 1998*, **12**(15):0 http://www.the-scientist.com/yr1998/august/profile2_980817.html.

3. Koos RD, Seidel RH: **Detection of acidic fibroblast growth factor mRNA in the rat ovary using reverse transcription-polymerase chain reaction amplification.** *Biochem Biophys Res Commun* 1989, **165**(1):82–88.

4. Grillo M, Margolis FL: **Use of reverse transcriptase polymerase chain reaction to monitor expression of intronless genes.** *Biotechniques* 1990, **9**(3):262, 264, 266–268.

5. Moriyama T, Murphy HR, Martin BM, Garcia-Perez A: **Detection of specific mRNAs in single nephron segments by use of the polymerase chain reaction.** *Am J Physiol* 1990, **258**(5 Pt 2):F1470–F1474.

6. Oikawa M, Dargan C, Ny T, Hsueh AJ: **Expression of gonadotropin-releasing hormone and prothymosin-alpha messenger ribonucleic acid in the ovary.** *Endocrinology* 1990, **127**(5):2350–2356.

7. Buesa J, Collado B, Lopez-Andujar P, Abu-Mallouh R, Rodriguez Diaz J, Garcia Diaz A, Prat J, Guix S, Llovet T, Prats G, Bosch A: **Molecular epidemiology of caliciviruses causing outbreaks and sporadic cases of acute gastroenteritis in Spain.** *J Clin Microbiol* 2002, **40**(8):2854–2859.

8. Drosten C, Gottig S, Schilling S, Asper M, Panning M, Schmitz H, Gunther S: **Rapid detection and quantification of RNA of Ebola and Marburg viruses, Lassa virus, Crimean-Congo hemorrhagic fever virus, Rift Valley fever virus, dengue virus, and yellow fever virus by real-time reverse transcription-PCR.** *J Clin Microbiol* 2002, **40**(7):2323–2330.

9. Elschner M, Prudlo J, Hotzel H, Otto P, Sachse K: **Nested reverse transcriptase-polymerase chain reaction for the detection of group A rotaviruses.** J *Vet Med B Infect Dis Vet Public Health* 2002, **49**(2):77–81.

10. Hirai M, Kiuchi M, Wang J, Ishii A, Matsuoka H: **cDNA cloning, functional expression and characterization of kynurenine 3-hydroxylase of Anopheles stephensi (Diptera: Culicidae).** *Insect Mol Biol* 2002, **11**(5):497–504.

11. Qi H, Chen HZ, Jin ZJ: **Caspase 3 gene expression and [Ca2+]i homeostasis underlying desipramine-induced C6 glioma cell apoptosis.** *Acta Pharmacol Sin* 2002, **23**(9):803–807.

12. Turunen M, Puhakka H, Koponen J, Hiltunen M, Rutanen J, Leppanen O, Turunen A, Narvanen A, Newby A, Baker A, Yla-Herttuala S: **Peptide-retargeted adenovirus encoding a tissue inhibitor of metalloproteinase-1 decreases restenosis after intravascular gene transfer.** *Mol Ther* 2002, **6**(3):306.

13. Wall SJ, Edwards DR: **Quantitative reverse transcription-polymerase chain reaction (RT-PCR): A comparison of primer-dropping, competitive, and real-time RT-PCRs.** *Anal Biochem* 2002, **300**(2):269–273.

14. Liss B: **Improved quantitative real-time RT-PCR for expression profiling of individual cells.** *Nucleic Acids Res* 2002, **30**(17):e89 (1-9).

15. Vandesompele J, De Preter K, Pattyn F, Poppe B, Van Roy N, De Paepe A, Speleman F: **Accurate normalization of real-time quantitative RT-PCR data by geometric averaging of multiple internal control genes.** *Genome Biol* 2002, **3**(7):RESEARCH0034.1-12.

16. Baltimore D, Smoler D: **Primer requirement and template specificity of the DNA polymerase of RNA tumor viruses.** *Proc Natl Acad Sci USA* 1971, **68**(7):1507–1511.

17. Goodman NC, Spiegelman S: **Distinguishing reverse transcriptase of an RNA tumor virus from other known DNA polymerases.** *Proc Natl Acad Sci USA* 1971, **68**(9):2203–2206.

18. Gallo RC: **RNA-dependent DNA polymerase in viruses and cells: Views on the current state.** *Blood* 1972, **39**(1):117–137.

19. Baltimore D: **RNA-dependent DNA polymerase in virions of RNA tumour viruses.** *Nature* 1970, **226**(252):1209–1211.

20. Temin HM, Mizutani S: **RNA-dependent DNA polymerase in virions of Rous sarcoma virus.** *Nature* 1970, **226**(252):1211–1213.

21. Williams KJ, Loeb LA: **Retroviral reverse transcriptases: error frequencies and mutagenesis.** *Curr Top Microbiol Immunol* 1992, **176**:165–180.

22. Singer MF: **Unusual reverse transcriptases.** *J Biol Chem* 1995, **270**(42):24623–24626.

23. Bebenek K. and Kunkel TA: **The fidelity of retroviral reverse transcriptases.** In: *Reverse Transcriptase* (Goff SP, Skalka AM, eds.). Cold Spring Harbor, New York: Cold Spring Harbor Laboratories, 1993, pp 85–102.

24. Overbaugh J, Bangham CR: **Selection forces and constraints on retroviral sequence variation.** *Science* 2001, **292**(5519):1106–1109.

25. Green M, Gerard GF: **RNA-directed DNA polymerase—Properties and functions in oncogenic RNA viruses and cells.** *Prog Nucleic Acid Res Mol Biol* 1974, **14**:187–334.

26. Wu AM, Gallo RC: **Reverse transcriptase.** *CRC Crit Rev Biochem* 1975, **3**(3):289–347.

27. Allaudeen HS, Sarngadharan MG, Gallo RC: **A comparative evaluation of methods for isolation of RNA-directed DNA polymerase from cells in a reconstituted system.** *Biochim Biophys Acta* 1976, **435**(1):45–62.

28. Whitcomb JM, Hughes SH: **Retroviral reverse transcription and integration: Progress and problems.** *Annu Rev Cell* Biol 1992, **8**:275–306.

29. Jeong JH, Kwak DS, Rho HM, Jung G: **The catalytic properties of human hepatitis B virus polymerase.** *Biochem Biophys Res Commun* 1996, **223**(2):264–271.

30. Taube R, Loya S, Avidan O, Perach M, Hizi A: **Reverse transcriptase of mouse mammary tumour virus: Expression in bacteria, purification and biochemical characterization.** *Biochem J* 1998, **329**(Pt 3):579–587; Erratum in: *Biochem J* 1998, **332**(Pt 3):808.

31. Tamblyn TM, Wells RD: **Comparative ability of RNA and DNA to prime DNA synthesis in vitro: Role of sequence, sugar, and structure of template-primer.** *Biochemistry* 1975, **14**(7):1412–1425.

32. Verma IM: **Studies on reverse transcriptase of RNA tumor viruses III. Properties of purified Moloney murine leukemia virus DNA polymerase and associated RNase H.** *J Virol* 1975, **15**(4):843–854.

33. Weinberg RA: **Structure of the intermediates leading to the integrated provirus.** *Biochim Biophys Acta* 1977, **473**(1):39–55.

34. Verma IM: **The reverse transcriptase.** *Biochim Biophys Acta* 1977, **473**(1):1–38.

35. Kumar G, Patel D, Naz RK: **c-MYC mRNA is present in human sperm cells.** *Cell Mol Biol Res* 1993, **39**(2):111–117.

36. Mallet F, Oriol G, Mary C, Verrier B, Mandrand B: **Continuous RT-PCR using AMV-RT and Taq DNA polymerase: Characterization and comparison to uncoupled procedures.** *Biotechniques* 1995, **18**(4):678–687.

37. Gerard GF, Potter RJ, Smith MD, Rosenthal K, Dhariwal G, Lee J, Chatterjee DK: **The role of template-primer in protection of reverse transcriptase from thermal inactivation.** *Nucleic Acids Res* 2002, **30**(14):3118–3129.

38. Cupo D: **The Evolution of RT-PCR Products.** *Focus* 2000, **22**(1):2.

39. Anonymous. **RT-PCR Systems Offer Unsurpassed Performance.** *Strategies* 2002, **15**(3):1.

40. Nathan M, Mertz LM, Fox DK: **Optimizing Long RT-PCR.** *Focus* 1995, **17**(3):78–80.

41. Polumuri SK, Ruknudin A, Schulze DH: **RNase H and Its Effects on PCR.** *Biotechniques* 2002, **32**:1224–1225.

42. Nevett C, Louwrier A: **A formulation of multiple reverse transcriptases for improved RT-PCR.** *Insights* 2002, **13**:12–13.

43. Kotewicz ML, Sampson CM, D'Alessio JM, Gerard GF: **Isolation of cloned Moloney murine leukemia virus reverse transcriptase lacking ribonuclease H activity.** *Nucleic Acids Res* 1988, **16**(1):265–277.

44. Schwabe W, Lee JL, Nathan M, Xu RH, Sitaraman K, Smith M, Potter RJ, Rosenthal K, Rashtchian A, Gerard GF: **ThermoScript RT, a new avian reverse transcriptase for high-temperature cDNA synthesis to improve RT-PCR.** *Focus* 1998, **20**(2):30–33.

45. Fuchs B, Zhang K, Rock MG, Bolander ME, Sarkar G: **High temperature cDNA synthesis by AMV reverse transcriptase improves the specificity of PCR.** *Mol Biotechnol* 1999, **12**(3):237–240.

46. Bustin SA: **Absolute quantification of mRNA using real-time reverse transcription polymerase chain reaction assays.** *J Mol Endocrinol* 2000, **25**(2):169–193.

47. Bustin SA: **Quantification of mRNA using real-time reverse transcription PCR (RT-PCR): Trends and problems.** *J Mol Endocrinol* 2002, **29**(1):23–39.

48. Kreuzer KA, Lass U, Landt O, Nitsche A, Laser J, Ellerbrok H, Pauli G, Huhn D, Schmidt CA: **Highly sensitive and specific fluorescence reverse transcription-PCR assay for the pseudogene-free detection of beta-actin transcripts as quantitative reference.** *Clin Chem* 1999, **45**(2):297–300.

49. Higuchi R, Dollinger G, Walsh PS, Griffith R: **Simultaneous amplification and detection of specific DNA sequences.** *Biotechnology (N Y)* 1992, **10**(4):413–417.

50. Higuchi R, Fockler C, Dollinger G, Watson R: Kinetic **PCR analysis: Real-time monitoring of DNA amplification reactions.** *Biotechnology (N Y)* 1993, **11**(9):1026–1030.

51. Wittwer CT, Herrmann MG, Moss AA, Rasmussen RP: **Continuous fluorescence monitoring of rapid cycle DNA amplification.** *Biotechniques* 1997, **22**(1):130–131, 134–138.

52. Wittwer CT, Ririe KM, Andrew RV, David DA, Gundry RA, Balis UJ: **The LightCycler: A microvolume multisample fluorimeter with rapid temperature control.** *Biotechniques* 1997, **22**(1):176–181.

53. Thellin O, Zorzi W, Lakaye B, De Borman B, Coumans B, Hennen G, Grisar T, Igout A, Heinen E: **Housekeeping genes as internal standards: Use and limits.** *J Biotechnol* 1999, **75**(2–3):291–295.

54. Bereta J, Bereta M: **Stimulation of glyceraldehyde-3-phosphate dehydrogenase mRNA levels by endogenous nitric oxide in cytokine-activated endothelium.** *Biochem Biophys Res Commun* 1995, **217**(1):363–369.

55. Chang TJ, Juan CC, Yin PH, Chi CW, Tsay HJ: **Upregulation of beta-actin, cyclophilin and GAPDH in N1S1 rat hepatoma.** *Oncol Rep* 1998, **5**(2):469–471.

56. Selvey S, Thompson EW, Matthaei K, Lea RA, Irving MG, Griffiths LR: **Beta-actin—An unsuitable internal control for RT-PCR.** *Mol Cell Probes* 2001, **15**(5):307–311.

57. Sinclair B, Wolf PG: **A thousand points of light: Novel fluorescent probes, tags, and Molecular Beacons.** *The Scientist* 2000, **14**(20):19–22.

58. Didenko VV: **DNA probes using fluorescence resonance energy transfer (FRET): Designs and applications.** *Biotechniques* 2001, **31**(5):1106–1116, 1118, 1120–1121.

59. Nazarenko IA, Bhatnagar SK, Hohman RJ: **A closed tube format for amplification and detection of DNA based on energy transfer.** *Nucleic Acids Res* 1997, **25**(12):2516–2521.

60. Kurata S, Kanagawa T, Yamada K, Torimura M, Yokomaku T, Kamagata Y, Kurane R: **Fluorescent quenching-based quantitative detection of specific DNA/RNA using a BODIPY((R)) FL-labeled probe or primer.** *Nucleic Acids Res* 2001, **29**(6):E34.

61. Kandimalla ER, Agrawal S: **'Cyclicons' as hybridization-based fluorescent primer-probes: Synthesis, properties and application in real-time PCR.** *Bioorg Med Chem* 2000, **8**(8):1911–1916.

62. Afonina IA, Reed MW, Lusby E, Shishkina IG, Belousov YS: **Minor groove binder-conjugated DNA probes for quantitative DNA detection by hybridization-triggered fluorescence.** *Biotechniques* 2002, **32**(4):940–944, 946–949.

63. Maxwell DJ, Taylor JR, Nie S: **Self-assembled nanoparticle probes for recognition and detection of biomolecules.** *J Am Chem Soc* 2002, **124**(32):9606–9612.

64. French DJ, Archard CL, Brown T, McDowell DG: **HyBeacon(TM) probes: A new tool for DNA sequence detection and allele discrimination.** *Mol Cell Probes* 2001, **15**(6):363–374.

65. Isacsson J, Cao H, Ohlsson L, Nordgren S, Svanvik N, Westman G, Kubista M, Sjoback R, Sehlstedt U: **Rapid and specific detection of PCR products using light-up probes.** *Mol Cell Probes* 2000, **14**(5):321–328.

66. Tyagi S, and Kramer FR: **Molecular beacons: Probes that fluoresce upon hybridization.** *Nat Biotechnol* 1996, **14**(3):303–308.

67. Kuhn H, Demidov VV, Gildea BD, Fiandaca MJ, Coull JC, Frank-Kamenetskii MD: **PNA beacons for duplex DNA.** *Antisense Nucleic Acid Drug Dev* 2001, **11**(4):265–270.

68. Kuhn H, Demidov VV, Coull JM, Fiandaca MJ, Gildea BD, Frank-Kamenetskii MD: **Hybridization of DNA and PNA molecular beacons to single-stranded and double-stranded DNA targets.** *J Am Chem Soc* 2002, **124**(6):1097–1103.

69. Fiandaca MJ, Hyldig-Nielsen JJ, Gildea BD, Coull JM: **Self-reporting PNA/DNA primers for PCR analysis.** *Genome Res* 2001, **11**(4):609–613.

70. Thelwell N, Millington S, Solinas A, Booth J, Brown T: **Mode of action and application of Scorpion primers to mutation detection.** *Nucleic Acids Res* 2000, **28**(19):3752–3761.

71. Solinas A, Brown LJ, McKeen C, Mellor JM, Nicol J, Thelwell N, Brown T: **Duplex Scorpion primers in SNP analysis and FRET applications.** *Nucleic Acids Res* 2001, **29**(20):E96.

72. Livak KJ, Flood SJ, Marmaro J, Giusti W, Deetz K: **Oligonucleotides with fluorescent dyes at opposite ends provide a quenched probe system useful for detecting PCR product and nucleic acid hybridization.** *PCR Methods Appl* 1995, **4**(6):357–362.

73. Nurmi J, Ylikoski A, Soukka T, Karp M, Lovgren T: **A new label technology for the detection of specific polymerase chain reaction products in a closed tube.** *Nucleic Acids Res* 2000, **28**(8):E28, i–vi.

74. Li Q, Luan G, Guo Q, Liang J: **A new class of homogeneous nucleic acid probes based on specific displacement hybridization.** *Nucleic Acids Res* 2002, **30**(2):E5.

75. Didenko VV: **Early shape-shifting FRET probe.** *Biotechniques* 2002, **32**(2):272.

76. Lin PK, Brown DM: **Synthesis of oligodeoxyribonucleotides containing degenerate bases and their use as primers in the polymerase chain reaction.** *Nucleic Acids Res* 1992, **20**(19):5149–5152.

77. Lin PK, Brown DM: **Oligonucleotides containing degenerate bases. Synthesis and uses.** *Methods Mol Biol* 1994, **26**:187–206.

78. Bailly C, Payet D, Travers AA, Waring MJ: **PCR-based development of DNA substrates containing modified bases: An efficient system for investigating the role of the exocyclic groups in chemical and structural recognition by minor groove binding drugs and proteins.** *Proc Natl Acad Sci USA* 1996, **93**(24):13623–13628.

79. Hill F, Loakes D, Brown DM: **Polymerase recognition of synthetic oligodeoxyribonucleotides incorporating degenerate pyrimidine and purine bases.** *Proc Natl Acad Sci USA* 1998, **95**(8):4258–4263.

80. Lebedev Y, Akopyants N, Azhikina T, Shevchenko Y, Potapov V, Stecenko D, Berg D, Sverdlov E: **Oligonucleotides containing 2-aminoadenine and 5-methylcytosine**

are more effective as primers for PCR amplification than their nonmodified counterparts. *Genet Anal* 1996, **13**(1):15–21.

81. Wahlestedt C, Salmi P, Good L, Kela J, Johnsson T, Hokfelt T, Broberger C, Porreca F, Lai J, Ren K, Ossipov M, Koshkin A, Jakobsen N, Skouv J, Oerum H, Jacobsen MH, Wengel J: **Potent and nontoxic antisense oligonucleotides containing locked nucleic acids.** *Proc Natl Acad Sci USA* 2000, **97**(10):5633–5638.

82. Kurreck J, Wyszko E, Gillen C, Erdmann VA: **Design of antisense oligonucleotides stabilized by locked nucleic acids.** *Nucleic Acids Res* 2002, **30**(9):1911–1918.

83. Cline J, Braman JC, Hogrefe HH: **PCR fidelity of pfu DNA polymerase and other thermostable DNA polymerases.** *Nucleic Acids Res* 1996, **24**(18):3546–3551.

84. Takagi M, Nishioka M, Kakihara H, Kitabayashi M, Inoue H, Kawakami B, Oka M, Imanaka T. **Characterization of DNA polymerase from *Pyrococcus sp.* strain KOD1 and its application to PCR.** *Appl Environ Microbiol* 1997, **63**(11):4504–4510.

85. Andre P, Kim A, Khrapko K, Thilly WG: **Fidelity and mutational spectrum of *Pfu* DNA polymerase on a human mitochondrial DNA sequence.** *Genome Res* 1997, **7**(8):843–852.

86. Bracho MA, Moya A, Barrio E: **Contribution of *Taq* polymerase-induced errors to the estimation of RNA virus diversity.** *J Gen Virol* 1998, **79**(Pt 12):2921–2928.

87. Diaz RS, Sabino EC: **Accuracy of replication in the polymerase chain reaction. Comparison between *Thermotoga maritima* DNA polymerase and *Thermus aquaticus* DNA polymerase.** *Braz J Med Biol Res* 1998, **31**(10):1239–1342.

88 Chakrabarti R, Schutt CE. **The enhancement of PCR amplification by low molecular-weight sulfones.** *Gene* 2001, **274**(1–2):293–298.

89. Hogrefe HH, Cline J, Lovejoy AE, Nielson KB: **DNA polymerases from hyperthermophiles.** *Methods Enzymol* 2001, **334**:91–116.

90. Chakrabarti R, Schutt CE: **Novel sulfoxides facilitate GC-rich template amplification.** *Biotechniques* 2002, **32**(4):866, 868, 870–872, 874.

3

Quantification Strategies in Real-Time PCR

Michael W. Pfaffl

Abstract

This chapter analyzes the quantification strategies in real-time RT-PCR and all corresponding *markers of a successful real-time RT-PCR*. The following aspects are describes in detail: RNA extraction, reverse transcription (RT), and general quantification strategies—absolute vs. relative quantification, real-time PCR efficiency calculation, data evaluation, automation of quantification, data normalization, and statistical comparison. The discussion turns into practical considerations with focus on specificity and sensitivity.

3

Quantification Strategies in Real-Time PCR

Michael W. Pfaffl

Institute of Physiology, Center of Life and Food Science, Weihenstephan, Freising, Germany

3.1. Introduction

Reverse transcription (RT) followed by polymerase chain reaction (PCR) represents a powerful tool for the detection and quantification of mRNA. Real-time RT-PCR (or kinetic RT-PCR) is widely and increasingly used because of its high sensitivity, good reproducibility, and wide dynamic quantification range.[1-4] The first practical kinetic PCR technology, the 5'-nuclease assay, was established 1993 and combines the exponential PCR amplification of a specific transcript with the monitoring of newly synthesized DNA in each performed PCR cycle[5-7] It is the most sensitive method for the detection and quantification of gene expression levels, in particular for low abundant transcripts in tissues with low RNA concentrations, from limited tissue sample and for the elucidation of small changes in mRNA expression levels.[1-4,8-12] While kinetic RT-PCR has a tremendous potential for analytical and quantitative applications, a comprehensive understanding of its underlying principles is important. Fidelity of real-time RT-PCR is associated with its "true" specificity, sensitivity, reproducibility, and robustness and, as a fully reliable quantitative method, it suffers from the problems inherent in RT and PCR, e.g., amplification of unspecific products, primer-dimers, amplification efficiencies, heteroduplex formation, etc.[13]

This chapter analyzes the quantification strategies in real-time RT-PCR and all corresponding markers of a successful real-time RT-PCR.

3.2. Markers of a Successful Real-Time RT-PCR Assay

3.2.1. RNA Extraction

The integrity of purified RNA is critical to all gene expression analysis techniques. The preparation of intact cellular total RNA or pure mRNA is the *first marker in gene quantification.* For successful and reliable diagnostic use, real-time RT-PCR needs high-quality, DNA-free, and undegraded RNA.[14,15] Accurate quantification and quality assessment[30] of the starting RNA sample is particularly important for absolute quantification methods that normalize specific mRNA expression levels against total RNA ("molecules/g total RNA" or "concentrations/g total RNA").[28,29] RNA, especially long mRNA up to 10 kb,[14] is easily degraded by cleavage of RNases during tissue sampling, RNA purification, and RNA storage. The source of RNA, sampling techniques (biopsy material, single-cell sampling, and laser microdissection),[2,16,17] as well as RNA isolation techniques (either total RNA or poly-adenylated RNA) often vary significantly between processing laboratories.[15] RNA extracted from adipose or collagen-rich tissues often has a lower yield and is of lesser quality, and contains partly degraded RNA sub-fractions (own unpublished results). Particular RNA extraction techniques can work more effectively in one specific tissue type compared with another one, and result in up to 10-fold variations in total RNA yield.[15] RNA may contain tissue enzyme inhibitors that result in reduced RT and PCR reaction efficiencies and generate unreliable and "wrong" quantification results.[14,15]

Most RNA preparations are contaminated with DNA and protein at very low levels. Even high-quality commercially obtained RNAs contain detectable amounts of DNA.[15] While this is not a problem for some applications, the tremendous amplification power of kinetic PCR may result in even the smallest amount of DNA contamination to interfering with the desired "specific amplification." To confirm the absence of residual DNA either a "minus-RT" or "water control" should always be included in the experimental design. It may be necessary to treat the RNA sample with commercially available RNase-free DNase, to get rid of residual DNA. However, unspecific side reactions of the DNase often result in RNA degradation (own unpublished results). It is always necessary to remove the DNase prior to any RT or PCR step.

Furthermore, the design of the PCR product should incorporate at least one exon-exon splice junction to allow a product obtained from the cDNA to be distinguished on electrophoresis from genomic DNA contamination. However, processed pseudogenes (e.g., β-actin, GAPDH, or 18S rRNA) can be present and lead to confusion in data interpretation. In addition, intron-lacking pseudogenes (e.g., β-actin) with equal sequence length to endogenous mRNA have been described.[18-24] They prevent a distinction between products originating from genomic DNA versus mRNA, which poses a significant problem in qualitative and quantitative gene quantification. Therefore, various housekeeping genes must be tested or multiplex assays of reference genes as internal controls for the assessment of RNA and cDNA quality must be performed.[25-27]

3.2.2. Reverse Transcription

The *second marker in quantitative RT-PCR* is the production of a single-stranded (ss) complementary DNA copy (cDNA) of the RNA through the reverse transcriptase (RT) and its dynamic range, sensitivity, and specificity are prime consideration for a successful kinetic RT-PCR assay.[31-34] For many quantitative applications, MMLV H⁻ RT is the enzyme of choice,[31,35,36] as its cDNA synthesis rate is up to 40-fold greater than that of AMV (own unpublished results). Newly available thermostable RNase H⁻ RT maintains its activity up to 70°C, thus permitting increased specificity and efficiency of first primer annealing. However, this enzyme may be less robust than more conventional ones as it appears to be more sensitive to inhibitors present in RNA preparation.[28,36,37]

The RT step is the source of most of the variability in a kinetic RT-PCR experiment and for each enzyme the specific reaction conditions has to be optimized. Salt contamination, alcohol, phenol, and other inhibitors carried over from the RNA isolation process can affect the apparent RT efficiency.[13,31,34] Another source of variability is the choice of priming method used to initiate cDNA synthesis, which can be either target gene-specific or nonspecific. Target gene-specific primers work well in conjunction with elevated RT-reaction temperatures to eliminate spurious transcripts.[36,37] The same reverse primer is used for the subsequent PCR assay in conjunction with the corresponding gene-specific sense primer (forward primer). However, the use of gene-specific primers necessitates a separate RT reaction for each gene of interest. It cannot be assumed that different reactions have the same cDNA synthesis efficiency; the result can be high variability during multiple RT reactions.

To circumvent these high inter-assay variations in RT, target gene unspecific primers, e.g., random hexamer, octamer, or decamer primers, can be used and a cDNA pool can be synthesized. Similarly, poly-T oligonucleotides (consisting solely of 16–25 deoxythymidine residues) can anneal to the polyadenylated 3' (poly-A) tail found on most mRNAs.[13,30] cDNA pools synthesized with unspecific primers can be split into a number of different target-specific kinetic PCR assays. This maximizes the number of genes that can be assayed from a single cDNA pool, derived from one small RNA sample. Therefore the gene expression results are directly comparable between the applied assays, at least within one and the same RT pool. In conclusion, a rank order of RT efficiency can be shown for the applied different primers for ONE specific gene: random hexamer primers > poly-dT primer > gene-specific primer (own unpublished results).

Importantly, not only RNA quantity and quality, but also yield and quality of cDNA can be highly variable. Certainly, there is evidence that cDNA yield from sequences near the 5' end of partially degraded mRNAs is significantly less than from sequences near the poly-A tail and assays aimed at identifying RNA degradation are being developed.[3,14,34,38] Thus, reliable internal quality control of cDNA synthesis is essential. Controls are generally performed by PCR amplification of reference genes, mostly common housekeeping genes (GAPDH, albumin, actins, tubulins, cyclophilin, microglobulins, 18S ribosomal RNA (rRNA), or 28S rRNA).[11,27,39-43] The chosen reference genes used as well as the expression levels vary between different laboratories, and only few of them have been critically evaluated (see **Section 3.4.** *Normalization*).

3.2.3. Comparison of Real-Time RT-PCR with Classical EndPoint Detection Method

The efficacy of kinetic RT-PCR is measured by its specificity, low background fluorescence, steep fluorescence increase, high amplification efficiency, and high level plateau.[44] Typically, the PCR reaction can be divided in four characteristic phases:[45] 1st phase is hidden under the background fluorescence where an exponential amplification is expected; 2nd phase with exponential amplification that can be detected and above the background; 3rd phase with linear amplification efficiency and a steep increase of fluorescence; and finally 4th phase or plateau phase, defined as the attenuation in the rate of exponential product accumulation, which is seen concomitantly in later cycles.[46,47] The amount of amplified target is directly proportional to the input amount of target only during the exponential phase of PCR amplification. Hence the key factor in the quantitative ability of kinetic RT-PCR is that it measures the product of the target gene within that phase.[10,45,48-51] Since data acquisition and analysis are performed in one and the same tube, this increases sample throughput, reduces the chances of carryover contamination, and removes post-PCR processing as a potential source of error.[52]

In contrast, during the plateau phase of the PCR there is no direct relation of "DNA input" to "amplified target," hence classical RT-PCR assays have to be stopped at least in linear phase.[44,53] The exponential range of amplification has to be determined for each transcript empirically by amplifying equivalent amounts of cDNA over various cycles of the PCR or by amplifying dilutions of cDNA over the same number of PCR cycles.[10,53] Amplified RT-PCR end product is later detected by ethidium bromide gel staining, radioactivity labeling, fluorescence labeling, high-performance liquid chromatography, southern blotting, densitometric analysis, or other post-amplification detection methods.[53-55] This step-wise accumulation of post-PCR variability[10,49,53] leads to semiquantitative results with high intra-assay (around 30–40%) and inter-assay variability (around 50–70%; own unpublished results) in endpoint detection assays. Finally, whereas real-time methods have a dynamic range of greater than eight orders of magnitude, the dynamic range of the endpoint assays is at best two.[10,49,56]

3.2.4. Chemistry Developments for Real-Time RT-PCR

The *third marker in kinetic RT-PCR* is the right detection chemistry. Two general methods for the quantitative detection of the amplicon have become established: gene-specific fluorescent probes or specific double-strand (ds) DNA binding agents[8,49,52,57,58] based on fluorescence resonance energy transfer (FRET).[11,48,59] The best-know probe-based system is ABI's TaqMan,[6,60,61] which makes use of the 5'–3' exonuclease activity of *Taq* polymerase to quantitate target sequences in the samples. Probe hydrolysis separates fluorophore and quencher and results in an increased fluorescence signal called "Förster type energy transfer."[62,63] The alternative is a nonsequence specific fluorescent intercalating dsDNA binding dye, e.g., SYBR Green I (Molecular Probes) or ethidium bromide.[58] For single PCR product reactions with well-designed primers, SYBR Green I can work extremely well, with spurious nonspecific background only showing up in very late cycles.[4,47,56] Among the real-time detection chemistry, SYBR Green I and TaqMan assays produced comparable dynamic range and sensitivity, while SYBR Green I detection was more precise and produced a more linear decay plot than the TaqMan probe detection.[10]

3.2.5. Real-Time RT-PCR Platforms

A detailed description of all real-time PCR platforms is available under http://www.wzw.tum.de/gene-quantification/platform.html. These PCR machines differ in sample capacity, up to 96-well and 384-well standard format, others process 72 (Rotor-Gene) or only 32 samples and require specialized glass capillaries (LightCycler), excitation method (lasers and others broad-spectrum light sources with various filters), and fluorescence acquisition channels. There are also platform-specific differences in how the software processes data with focus on absolute or relative quantification strategies.[61,64,65] For at least two systems and chemistries, the ABI PRISM 7700 using "TaqMan Probes" and Roche's LightCycler using "Hybridization Probes," there is little difference in accuracy and performance.[66]

3.2.6. Quantification Strategies in Kinetic RT-PCR

The quantification strategy is the principal marker in gene quantification. Generally, two strategies can be performed in real-time RT-PCR. The levels of expressed genes may be measured by absolute or relative quantitative real-time RT-PCR. Absolute quantification relates the PCR signal to input copy number using a calibration curve, while relative quantification measures the relative change in mRNA expression levels. The reliability of an absolute real-time RT-PCR assay depends on the condition of "identical" amplification efficiencies for both the native target and the calibration curve in RT reaction and in following kinetic PCR.[67-69] Relative quantification is easier to perform than absolute quantification because a calibration curve is not necessary. It is based on the expression levels of a target gene versus a housekeeping gene (reference or control gene) and in theory is adequate for most purposes to investigate physiological changes in gene expression levels.[61,64] The units used to express relative quantities are irrelevant, and the relative quantities can be compared across multiple real-time RT-PCR experiments.[1]

3.2.6.1. Absolute Quantification

Calibration curves are highly reproducible and allow the generation of highly specific, sensitive and reproducible data.[3,4,47,54,56] However, the external calibration curve model has to be thoroughly validated as the accuracy of absolute quantification in real-time RT-PCR depends entirely on the accuracy of the standards. Standard design, production, determination of the exact standard concentration, and stability over long storage time is not straightforward and can be problematic. The dynamic range of the performed calibration curve can be up to nine orders of magnitude from $< 10^1$ to $> 10^{10}$ start molecules, depending on the applied standard material.[4,56,71] The calibration curves used in absolute quantification can be based on known concentrations of DNA standard molecules, e.g., recombinant plasmid DNA (recDNA), genomic DNA, RT-PCR product, and commercially synthesized big oligonucleotide.[3,4,49,54,58,71] Stability and reproducibility in kinetic RT-PCR depends on the type of standard used and depends strongly on "good laboratory practice." Cloned recDNA and genomic DNA are very stable and generate highly reproducible standard curves even after a long storage time, in comparison to freshly synthesized DNA. Furthermore, the longer templates derived from recDNA and genomic DNA mimic the average native mRNA length of about 2 kb better than shorter templates derived from RT-PCR product or oligonucleotides. They are more resistant against unspecific cleavage and proofreading activity of polymerase during reaction setup and in kinetic PCR (own unpublished results). One advantage of the shorter templates and commercially available templates is an accurate knowledge of its concentration and length. A second advantage is that their use avoids the very time consuming process of having to produce standard material: standard synthesis, purification, cloning, transformation, plasmid preparation, linearization, verification, and exact determination of standard concentration.[4,47,49,56]

A problem with DNA-based calibration curves is that they are subject to the PCR step only, unlike the unknown mRNA samples that must first be reverse transcribed. This increases the potential for variability of the RT-PCR results and the amplification results may not be strictly comparable with the results from the unknown samples. However, the problem of the sensitivity of the RT-PCR to small variations in the reaction setup is always lurking in the background as a potential drawback to this simple procedure. Therefore, quantification with external standards requires careful optimization of its precision (replicates in the same kinetic PCR run—intra-assay variation) and reproducibility (replicates in separate kinetic PCR runs—inter-assay variation) in order to understand the limitations within the given application.[4,54,56]

A recombinant RNA (recRNA) standard that was synthesized *in vitro* from a cloned RT-PCR fragment in plasmid DNA is one option.[4,7,47,56,72]

However, identical RT efficiency, as well as real-time PCR amplification efficiencies for calibration curve and target cDNA must be tested and confirmed if the recRNA is to provide a valid standard for mRNA quantification.[4] This is because only the specific recRNA molecules are present during RT and the kinetics of cDNA synthesis are not like those in native RNA (the unknown sample) that also contain a high percentage of natural occurring subfractions, e.g., ribosomal RNA (rRNA, approximately 80%) and transfer RNA (tRNA, 10–15%). These missing RNA subfractions can influence the cDNA synthesis rate and in consequence RT efficiency rises and calibration curves are then overestimated in gene quantification.[36,73] To compensate for background effects and mimic a natural RNA distribution like in native total RNA, total RNA isolated from bacterial or insect cell lines can be used. Alternatively commercially available RNA sources can be used as RNA background, e.g., poly-A RNA or tRNA, but they do not represent a native RNA distribution over all RNA subspecies.[4] Earlier results suggest, that a minimum of RNA background is generally needed and that it enhances RT synthesis efficiency rate. Low concentrations of recRNA used in calibration curves should always be buffered with background or carrier RNA; otherwise the low amounts can be degraded easily by RNAses. Very high background concentrations had a more significant suppression effect in RT synthesis rate and in later real-time PCR efficiency.[4]

No matter how accurately the concentration of the standard material is known, the final result is always reported relatively compared to a defined unit of interest, e.g., copies per defined ng of total RNA, copies per genome (6.4-pg DNA), copies per cell, copies per gram of tissue, copies per ml blood, etc. If absolute changes in copy number are important, then the denominator still must be shown to be absolute stable across the comparison. This accuracy may only be needed in screening experiments (amount of microorganism in food), to measure the percentage of GMO (genetic modified organism) in food, to measure the viral load or bacterial load in immunology and microbiology. The quality of your gene quantification data cannot be better than the quality of the denominator. Any variation in the denominator will obscure real changes, produce artificial changes, and wrong quantification results. Careful use of controls is critical to demonstrate that your choice of denominator was a wise one.[49] Under certain circumstances, absolute quantification models can also be normalized using suitable and unregulated references or housekeeping genes (see **Section 3.4** *Normalization*).

3.2.6.2. Relative Quantification

Relative quantification determines the changes in steady-state mRNA levels of a gene across multiple samples and expresses it relative to the levels of an internal control RNA. This reference gene is often a house-keeping gene and can be coamplified in the same tube in a multiplex assay or can be amplified in a separate tube.[56,59] Therefore, relative quantification does not require standards with known concentrations and the reference can be any transcript, as long as its sequence is known.[29] Relative quantification is based on the expression levels of a tar-get gene versus a reference gene and in many experiments is adequate for investigating physiological changes in gene expression levels. To calculate the expression of a target gene in relation to an adequate ref-erence gene various mathematical models are established. Calculations are based on the comparison of the distinct cycle determined by various methods, e.g., crossing points (CP) and threshold values (C_t) at a con-stant level of fluorescence; or CP acquisition according to established mathematical algorithm.[50,51,69] To date, several mathematical models that determine the relative expression ratio have been developed. Two types of relative quantification models are available and published: (1) without efficiency correction (see **Eqs. 3.1–3.2**).[11,61,70]

$$R = 2^{-[\Delta CP_{sample} - \Delta CP_{control}]} \quad , \qquad (3.1)$$

$$R = 2^{-\Delta\Delta CP} \quad , \qquad (3.2)$$

and (2) with kinetic PCR efficiency correction (**Eqs.3.3–3.6**).[50,51,68,69,74-78] Further, the available models allow for the determination of single tran-scription difference between one control and one sample, assayed in triplicates ($n = 1/3$), e.g., LightCycler Relative Quantification Software[65] or Q-Gene[79] or for a group-wise comparison for more samples (up to 100), e.g., REST and REST-XL.[69] The relative expression ratio of a target gene is computed, based on its real-time PCR efficiencies (E) or a static efficiency of 2, and the crossing point (CP) difference (Δ) of one unknown sample (treatment) versus one control ($\Delta CP_{control - treatment}$). Using REST and REST-XL, the relative calculation procedure is based on the MEAN CP of the experimental groups (**Eq. 3.4**) (http://www.wzw.tum.de/gene-quantification/rest.html).

$$\text{ratio} = \frac{(E_{target})^{\Delta CP_{target} \, (control - sample)}}{(E_{ref})^{\Delta CP_{ref} \, (control - sample)}} \quad , \quad (3.3)$$

$$\text{ratio} = \frac{(E_{target})^{\Delta CP_{target} \, (MEAN \, control - MEAN \, sample)}}{(E_{ref})^{\Delta CP_{ref} \, (MEAN \, control - MEAN \, sample)}} \quad , \quad (3.4)$$

In these models the target gene expression is normalized by a non-regulated reference gene expression, e.g., derived from classical and frequently described housekeeping genes.[11,39-41,43] The crucial problem in this relative approach is that the most common reference-gene transcripts from so-called housekeeping genes, whose mRNA expression can be regulated and whose levels vary significantly with treatment or between individuals.[43,80-83] However, relative quantification can generate useful and biologically relevant information when used appropriately.

$$\text{ratio} = \frac{(E_{ref})^{CP_{sample}}}{(E_{target})^{CP_{sample}}} \div \frac{(E_{ref})^{CP_{calibrator}}}{(E_{target})^{CP_{calibrator}}} \quad , \quad (3.5)$$

$$\text{ratio} = \frac{conc_{(target \, sample)} / conc_{(ref \, sample)} * MF}{conc_{(target \, cal.)} / conc_{(ref \, cal.)} * CF} \quad , \quad (3.6)$$

3.2.7. Advantages and Disadvantages of External Standards

External standard quantification is the method of choice for the nucleic acid quantification, independent of any hardware platform used. The specificity, sensitivity, linearity, and reproducibility allow for the absolute and accurate quantification of molecules even in tissues with low mRNA abundance (less than 100 molecules/reaction setup) and detection down to a few molecules (less than 10 molecules/reaction setup).[4,12,56,71] The dynamic range of an optimal validated and optimized external standardized real-time RT-PCR assay can accurately detect target mRNA up to nine orders of magnitude or a billion-fold range with high assay linearity (correlation coefficient; $r > 0.99$).[4,12,49,56,84] In general, a mean intra-assay variation of 10–20% and a mean inter-assay variation of 15–30% on molecule basis (maximal 2–4% variability on CP basis, respectively) is realistic over the wide dynamic range.[6,12,47,56,71,85] At high (greater than 10^7) and low (less than 10^3) template copy input levels the assay variability is higher than in the range between the two.[4,47,49] At very low copy numbers, under 20 copies per tube, the random variation due to sampling error (Poisson's error law) becomes significant.[49,76]

A recDNA calibration curve model can quantify precisely only cDNA molecules derived from the RT step; it says nothing about the conversion to cDNA of the mRNA molecules present in the native total RNA sample. Variability in cDNA synthesis efficiency during reverse transcription must be always kept in mind. Therefore, a recRNA calibration curve model has the advantage that both RNA templates undergo parallel RT and real-time PCR steps. However, a direct comparison suggests that the recDNA quantification model shows higher sensitivity, exhibits a larger quantification range, has a higher reproducibility, and is more stable than the recRNA model.[4] Furthermore, recDNA external calibration curves exhibit lower variation (intra-assay variation less than 0.7%; inter-assay variation less than 2.6% on CP basis) than the recRNA model (less than 2.7% and 4.5%, respectively). Clearly, the RT step has a profound affect on the overall result obtained from an RT-PCR assay and more thorough consideration of RT efficiency is needed.

The main disadvantage of external standards is the lack of internal control for RT and PCR inhibitors. All quantitative PCR methods assume that the target and the sample amplify with similar efficiency.[61,70] The risk with external standards is that some of the unknown samples may contain substances that significantly reduce the efficiency of the PCR reaction in the unknown samples. As discussed, sporadic RT and PCR inhibitors or different RNA/cDNA distributions can occur. A dilution series can be run on the unknown samples and the inhibitory factors can often be diluted out, causing a nonlinear standard curve.[49,58,68,69]

Real-time assays using SYBR Green I can easily reveal the presence of primer dimers, which are the product of nonspecific annealing and primer elongation events.[58] These events take place as soon as PCR reagents are combined. During PCR, formation of primer dimers competes with formation of specific PCR product, leading to reduced amplification efficiency and a less successful specific RT-PCR product.[86] To distinguish primer dimers from the specific amplicon a melting curve analysis can be performed in all available quantification software.[61,64,65] The pure and homogeneous RT-PCR products produce a single, sharply defined melting curve with a narrow peak. In contrast, the primer dimers melt at relatively low temperatures and have broader peaks.[87] To avoid primer dimer formation, an intensive primer optimization is needed, by testing multiple primer pair using crosswise combinations.[51] Multiple optimization strategies have been developed and are published.[88-90] The easiest and most effective way to get rid of any dimer structures, at least during the quantification procedure, is to add an additional 4th segment to the classical three-segmented PCR procedure: 1st segment with denaturation at 95°C; 2nd segment with primer annealing at 55–65°C; 3rd segment with elongation at 72°C; and 4th segment with fluorescence acquisition at elevated temperatures.[47,56,91] The fluorescence acquisition in 4th segment is performed mainly in the range of 80–87°C, eliminates the nonspecific fluorescence signals derived by primer dimers or unspecific minor products, and ensures accurate quantification of the desired product. High temperature quantification keeps the background fluorescence and the "no-template control" fluorescence under 2–3% of maximal fluorescence at plateau.[47,56]

"Do we need to run a calibration curve in each run?"[49] and *"Do we need a calibration curve at all?"*[64,65,85] are frequently posed questions, together with *"What about the reproducibility between the runs?"* (http://www.idahotec.com/lightcycler_u/lectures/quantification_on_lc.htm). Repeated runs of the same standard curve give minor variations of a 2–3% in the slope (real-time PCR efficiency) and about 10% in the intercept of calibration curve. Since the variation in the standard curve

correlates with variation in the unknowns, a detection of a 2-fold difference over a wide range of target concentrations is possible.[49] The slope of the calibration curve is more reproducible than the intercept, hence only a single standard point will be required to "re-register" a previously performed calibration curve level for the new unknowns. The curve can be imported into any run, as done in the LightCycler software.[64] Never changing variations and 100% reproducibility are the big advantages of such a calibration curve import, but there are also disadvantages as variations of reagents, primers, and probe (sequence alterations and fluorescence intensity), day-to-day or sample-to-sample variations will not be covered in this "copy-and-paste" approach. Since these affect PCR efficiency, such an approach can introduce significant errors into the quantification.

3.2.8. Real-Time PCR Amplification Efficiency

Individual samples generate different and individual fluorescence histories in kinetic RT-PCR. The shapes of amplification curves differ in the steepness of any fluorescence increase and in the absolute fluorescence levels at plateau depending on background fluorescence levels. The PCR efficiency has a major impact on the fluorescence history and the accuracy of the calculated expression result and is critically influenced by PCR reaction components. Efficiency evaluation is an *essential marker in real-time gene quantification procedure.*[45,49-51,77,78] Constant amplification efficiency in all compared samples is one important criterion for reliable comparison between samples. This becomes crucially important when analyzing the relationship between an unknown sequence and a standard sequence, which is performed in all relative quantification models. In experimental designs employing standardization with housekeeping genes, the demand for invariable amplification efficiency between target and standard is often ignored, despite the fact that corrections have been suggested.[68,69,77,78] A correction for efficiency, as performed in efficiency corrected mathematical models (**Eqs. 3.3–3.6**), is strongly recommended and results in a more reliable estimation of the "real expression ratio" compared to no-efficiency correction. Small efficiency differences between target and reference gene generate false expression ratio, and the researcher over-

or underestimates the "real" initial mRNA amount. Difference in PCR efficiency (ΔE) of 3% ($\Delta E = 0.03$) between target gene and reference gene generate a falsely calculated differences in expression ratio of 47% in case of $E_{target} < E_{ref}$ and 209% in case of $E_{target} > E_{ref}$ after 25 performed cycles. This gap will increase dramatically by higher efficiency differences $\Delta E = 0.05$ (28% and 338%, respectively) and $\Delta E = 0.10$ (7.2% and 1083%, respectively) and higher cycle number performed.[49,69] Therefore efficiency corrected quantification should be included in the automation and calculation procedure in relative quantification models.

The assessment of the exact amplification efficiencies of target and reference genes must be carried out before any calculation of the normalized gene expression is done. LightCycler Relative Expression Software,[65] Q-Gene,[79] REST, and REST-XL software applications[69] allow the evaluation of amplification efficiency plots. A separate determination of real-time PCR efficiency in triplets for every tissue and each performed transcript is necessary.[64,68,69,79] Different tissues exhibit different PCR efficiencies, caused by RT inhibitors, PCR inhibitors, and by variations in the total RNA fraction pattern extracted. Several methods are described in the literature to calculate real-time PCR efficiency (http://www.wzw.tum.de/gene-quantification/efficiency.html):

A) Efficiency calculation from the slopes of the calibration curve according to the equation: $\mathbf{E = 10^{[-1/slope]}}$, as described earlier.[5,49,61] Determination of efficiency should be evaluated in a pool of all starting RNAs to accumulate all possible "negative impacts" on kinetic PCR efficiency. Usually, real-time PCR efficiency vary with high linearity ($r > 0.989$) from $E = 1.60$ to maximal values up to $E = 2.10$ for cDNA input ranges from a few pg to 75 ng cDNA input.[12,56,69,71] Typically, the relationship between CP and the logarithm of the starting copy number of the target sequence should remain linear for up to five orders of magnitude in the calibration curve as well as in the native sample RNA.[79] This calculation method results, in some cases, in efficiencies higher than ($E > 2.0$), which is practically impossible in the PCR amplification theory. But as shown in given results they are highly reproducible and constant within one transcript and tissue.[68,71] This probably indicates that this efficiency calculation method is not optimal and *overestimates* the "real efficiency."

B) Efficiency calculation from the fluorescence increase in 3rd linear phase of each logarithmic fluorescence history plot. The investigator has to decide which cycle number to include in the analysis and plot a linear regression (similarly to the *Fit Point Method* regression) where the slope of the regression line represents the PCR efficiency. Here efficiencies between E = 1.35 and E = 1.60 are realistic and differ dramatically from the results above.[47,92] This efficiency calculation method might *underestimate* the "real efficiency," because data evaluation is made in linear phase near the plateau where reaction trend to get restrictive.[46]

C) Efficiency calculation on the basis of all fluorescence data points (starting at cycle 1st up to the last cycle), according to a sigmoidal or logistic curve fit model. The advantage of such model is that all data points will be included in the calculation process. No background subtraction is necessary.[45,50,51,77,78] Slope value is "nearly" identical to method B and only measured at the point of inflexion at absolute maximum fluorescence increase (1.35 < E < 1.60). But the derived slope parameters generated by the sigmoidal or logistic models are not directly comparable with the "real PCR efficiency." This method is easy to perform and a good estimator for the maximum curve slope with high correlation coefficient ($r > 0.99$) and level of significance ($p < 0.001$).[45,50,51,77,78]

D) Efficiency calculation from the fluorescence increase only in the 2nd real exponential phase, according to a polynomial curve fit, as described earlier $\mathbf{Y}_n = \mathbf{Y}_0\,(\mathbf{E})^n$, where Y_n is fluorescence acquired at cycle n, and Y_0 initial fluorescence, so-called ground fluorescence.[45,74,92-94] This phase around the *Second Derivate Maximum* exhibit a real exponential amplification behavior.[45] Here in the exponential part of the PCR reaction, kinetic is still under "full power" with no restrictions.[46] In this method the calculation is performed on each reaction kinetic plot and the amplification efficiency can be determined exactly. They range from E = 1.75 to E = 1.90, hence are between the other methods.

Which efficiency calculation method is "the right one" and which one shows the realistic real-time PCR kinetic and thereby is highly reproducible, has to be evaluated in further experiments.

3.2.9. Data Evaluation

The *next marker in gene quantification* using real-time RT-PCR is the data evaluation. The calculation unit in real-time PCR is a sample specific and characteristic crossing points (CP). For CP determination various fluorescence acquisition methodologies are possible. The *Fit Point Method* and *Threshold Cycle Method* measure the CP at a constant fluorescence level.[5,7,61,64,74] These constant threshold methods assume that all samples have the same cDNA concentration at the threshold fluorescence. Measuring the level of background fluorescence can be a challenge in real-time PCR reactions with significant background fluorescence variations caused by drift-ups and drift-downs over the course of the reaction. Averaging over a drifting background will give an overestimation of variance and thus increase the threshold level.[61,49] The threshold level can be calculated by fitting the intersecting line upon the ten-times value of ground fluorescence standard deviation. This acquisition mode can be easily automated and is very robust.[61] In the *Fit Point Method* the user has discard the uninformative background points, exclude the plateau values by entering the number of log-linear points, and then fits a log-line to the linear portion of the amplification curves. These log lines are extrapolated back to a common threshold line and the intersection of the two lines provides the CP value. The strength of this method is that it is extremely robust. The weakness is that it is not easily automated and so requires a lot of user interaction.[49,64] *Fit Point Method* or *Threshold Cycle Method* can be used on all available platforms with different evaluation of background variability.

The problems of defining a constant background for all samples within one run, sample-to-sample differences in variance and absolute fluorescence values lead to develop a new acquisition modus according to mathematical algorithms. In the LightCycler software the *Second Derivative Maximum Method* is performed where CP is automatically identified and measured at the maximum acceleration of fluorescence.[49,64] The kinetic fluorescence histories of individual curves are different. They show individual background variability (1st phase), exponential and linear growth of fluorescence (2nd and 3rd phases), and finally reaction-specific plateau values (4th phase). The amplification reaction and the kinetic fluorescence history over various cycles is obviously not a smooth and easy function. The mathematical algorithm on which the *Second Derivative Maximum Method* in Roche Molecular Biochemicals software is based is unpublished. But it is possible to fit sigmoidal and polynomial curve models[45,50,51,77,78] with high significance ($p < 0.001$) and coefficient of correlation ($r > 0.99$), which can be differentiated, and the second-derivate maximum can be estimated.[45,50,51] This increase in the rate of fluorescence increase, or better called the acceleration of the fluorescence signal, slows down at the beginning of the 3rd linear phase. Therefore the cycle where the second derivative is at its maximum is always between 2nd exponential and 3rd linear phase.[45]

3.3. Automation of the Quantification Procedure

Automation of quantification with any kind of calibration curve using *Fit Point Method*, *Threshold Cycle Method*, or *Second Derivative Maximum Method* is fully supported by the software supplied with the real-time instruments. The investigator has to input his individual settings, e.g., threshold level and noise band, import an existing standard curve, and then click for calculation of the CPs and the corresponding concentrations. However, although relative expression is performed by researchers according to several established mathematical models (**Eqs. 3.1–3.6**),[61,68-70,75,79] up to now relative quantification software has been commercially available only from Roche Molecular Biochemicals *LightCycler Relative Quantification Software* (http://www.lightcycler-online.com/lc_sys/soft_ind.htm#quant). The software allows for a comparison of maximal triplets ($n = 3$) of a target versus a calibrator gene, both corrected via a reference-gene expression and calculates on the basis of the median of the performed triplets. Real-time PCR efficiency correction is possible within the software and calculated from the calibration curve slope, according to the established equation $\mathbf{E} = \mathbf{10}^{[-1/\text{slope}]}$, ranging from E = 1.0 (minimum value) to E = 2.0 (theoretical maximum and efficiency optimum). A given correction factor (CF) and a multiplication factor (MF), which are provided in the product specific applications (**Eq. 3.6**) by Roche Molecular Biochemicals, have to be attended in the equation calculation process.[65]

Importantly, until recently it was not possible to perform a reliable group-wise calculation of the relative expression ratios and a subsequent statistical comparison of the results by a statistical test with more than three repeats or more than three samples. This has changed when new software tools were established (e.g., REST and REST-XL), both Excel®-based and programmed in Visual Basic for Applications.[68,69] Both compare two treatment groups, with multiple data points in sample group versus control group, and calculate the relative expression ratio between them. Four target genes with up to 100 data points can be calculated in REST-XL. The mathematical model used is published;[69] it is based on the MEAN crossing point deviation between sample and control group of up to four target genes, normalized by the MEAN crossing point deviation of a reference gene (**Eq. 3.4**). Normalization via endogenous control can be performed according to the users demand, but it is recommended to compensate intra- and inter-RT-PCR variations.[68,69,95] Therefore the requirement for high reproducibility of RT and RT efficiency is not "that important" anymore. cDNA input concentration variation of ± 3-fold was evaluated to mimic these huge RT variations and resulted in no significant changes of relative expression ratio.[69] Specific amplification efficiencies of four target-gene genes can be estimated and included in the correction of the quantification ratio. If no real-time PCR efficiency assessment is performed, REST assumes an optimal efficiency of $E = 2.0$. The big advantage of the software tool is the subsequent statistical test. REST tests the group differences for significance with a newly developed randomization test—*Pair-Wise Fixed Reallocation Randomization Test*©. Variation depends only on CP variation of the investigated transcripts and remains stable between 3% and 12%.[69]

Nevertheless, successful application of real-time RT-PCR and REST depends on a clear understanding of the practical problems. Therefore a coherent experimental design, application, and validation of the individual real-time RT-PCR assay remains essential for accurate and fully quantitative measurement of mRNA transcripts (http://www.wzw.tum.de/gene-quantification/rest.html).

Recently a second software tool, named Q-Gene, was developed.[79] Q-Gene manages and expedites the planning, performance, and evaluation of quantitative real-time PCR experiments, as well as the mathematical and statistical analysis, storage, and graphical presentation of the data. An efficiency correction is possible. The Q-Gene software application is a tool to cope with complex quantitative real-time PCR experiments at a high-throughput scale (96-well and 384-well format) and considerably expedites and rationalizes the experimental setup, data analysis, and data management while ensuring highest reproducibility (http://www.biotechniques.com/softlib/qgene.html).

3.4. Normalization

Data normalization in real-time RT-PCR is a further *major marker in gene quantification analysis*. The reliability of any relative RT-PCR experiment can be improved by including an invariant endogenous control in the assay to correct for sample-to-sample variations in RT-PCR efficiency and errors in sample quantification. A biologically meaningful reporting of target mRNA copy numbers requires accurate and relevant normalization to some standard and is strongly recommended in kinetic RT-PCR.[28,29,68-70] But the quality of normalized quantitative expression data cannot be better than the quality of the normalizer itself. Any variation in the normalizer will obscure real changes and produce artifactual changes.[28,29] Real-time RT-PCR-specific errors in the quantification of mRNA transcripts are easily compounded with any variation in the amount of starting material between the samples, e.g., caused by sample-to-sample variation, variation in RNA integrity, RT efficiency differences, and cDNA sample loading variation.[15,31,95] This is especially relevant when the samples have been obtained from different individuals, different tissues, and different time courses and will result in the misinterpretation of the derived expression profile of the target genes. Therefore, normalization of target gene expression levels must be performed to compensate intra- and interkinetic RT-PCR variations (sample-to-sample and run-to-run variations).

Data normalization can be carried out against an endogenous unregulated reference gene transcript or against total cellular DNA or RNA content (molecules/g total DNA/RNA and concentrations/g total DNA/RNA). Normalization according the total cellular RNA content is increasingly used, but little is known about the total RNA content of cells or even about the mRNA concentrations. The content per cell or per gram tissue may vary in different tissues *in vivo*, in cell culture (*in vitro*), between individuals and under different experimental conditions. Nevertheless, it has been shown that normalization to total cellular RNA is the least unreliable method.[3,28,29] It requires an accurate quantification of the isolated total RNA or mRNA fraction by optical density at 260 nm (OD_{260}), Agilent Bioanalyzer 2100, or RiboGreen RNA Quantification Kit. Alternatively the rRNA content has been proposed as an optimal and stable basis for normalization, despite reservations concerning its expression levels, transcription by a different RNA polymerase, and possible imbalances in rRNA and mRNA fractions between different samples.[29,42,80,96,97]

To normalize the absolute quantification according to a single reference gene, a second set of kinetic PCR reactions has to be performed for the invariant endogenous control on all experimental samples and the relative abundance values are calculated for internal control as well as for the target gene. For each target gene sample, the relative abundance value obtained is divided by the value derived from the control sequence in the corresponding target gene. The normalized values for different samples can then be directly compared. The sets of CPs for the reference gene can be easily imported into the REST software application, according to the given equations (**Eqs. 3.3–3.4**). The calculation process considers them and allows for a normalization of the target genes with the reference gene.[64,68,69,79] Additionally, it will show whether normalization via the chosen reference is useful by showing the factor of regulation and level of significance as result of the randomization test. The investigators can decide if the reference is suitable in this experimental trial or not.

Here a central question arises: *"What is the appropriate reference gene for an experimental treatment and investigated tissue?"*[3,41,42,98] Commonly used housekeeping genes, e.g., GAPDH, albumin, actins, tubulins, cyclophilin, microglobulins, 18S rRNA, or 28S rRNA[27,39-42,50] may be suitable for reference genes, since they are present in all nucleated cell types and are necessary for basic cell survival. The mRNA synthesis of housekeeping genes is considered to be stable in various tissues, even under experimental treatments.[39-41,50] However, numerous treatments and studies have already shown that the mentioned housekeeping genes are regulated and vary under experimental conditions.[42,43,80-83,99] It remains up to the individual investigator to choose a reference gene that is best for reliable normalization in their particular experimental setting. In addition, the endogenous control should be expressed at roughly the same CP level as the target gene.[3,28] At the same CP level, reference and target experience the same condition and real-time RT-PCR kinetics with respect to polymerase activation (heat activation of polymerase), reaction inactivation, stochastic relation between target and primer concentration, and reaction end product inhibition by the generated RT-PCR product.

It cannot be emphasized enough that the choice of housekeeping or lineage specific genes is critical. For a number of commonly used reference genes processed pseudogenes have been shown to exist, e.g., β-actin or GAPDH.[22-24] These pseudogenes may be responsible for specific amplification products in an mRNA-independent fashion and result in specific amplification even in the absence of intact mRNA.[18-21,84] It is vital to develop universal, artificial, stable, internal standard materials that can be added prior to the RNA preparation to monitor the efficiency of RT as well as the kinetic PCR respectively.[29] Usually more than one housekeeping genes should be tested in a multiple pair wise correlation analysis and its behavior summarized to a housekeeping gene index called *BestKeeper*©.[105] According to this *BestKeeper*© index, which is based on the weighted expression of at least three housekeeping genes, a more reliable basis of normalization in relative quantification can be postulated[69,100,101] (http:www.wzw.tum.de/gene-quantification/bestkeeper.html).

There is increasing appreciation of these aspects of quantitative RT-PCR and recently a software tool was established for the evaluation of housekeeping genes expression levels. *geNorm*[27] allows for an accurate normalization of real-time quantitative RT-PCR data by geometric averaging of multiple internal control genes (http://allserv.rug.ac.be/~jvdesomp/genorm/). The *geNorm* VBA applet for Microsoft Excel determines the most stable housekeeping genes from a set of ten tested genes in a given cDNA sample panel, and calculates a gene expression normalization factor for each tissue sample based on the geometric mean of a user defined number of housekeeping genes. The normalization strategy used in *geNorm* is a prerequisite for accurate kinetic RT-PCR expression profiling, which opens up the possibility of studying the biological relevance of small expression differences.[27]

3.5. Statistical Comparison

Bioinformatics and biostatistics on real-time RT-PCR experiment data is a *new subject and a new challenge in gene quantification analysis.* This is because the coordination of the experiments and the efficient management of the collected data has become an additional major hurdle for kinetic RT-PCR experiments. The main challenge remains the evaluation and the mathematical and statistical analysis of the enormous amount of data gained by this technology, as these functions are not included in the software provided by the manufacturers of the detection systems.[79] Normally the statistical data analysis in gene quantification, independent of block, competitive or real-time RT-PCR experiments, are all performed on the basis of classical standard parametric tests, such as analysis of variance or *t*-tests.[102] Parametric tests depend on assumptions, such as normality of distributions, whose validity is unclear. In absolute or relative quantification analysis, where the quantities of interest are derived from ratios and variances can be high, normal distributions might not be expected, and it is unclear how a parametric test could best be constructed.[69]

Only two free available software packages support statistical analysis of expression results: Q-Gene[79] and REST.[69] The *Q-Gene Statistics Add-In* is a collection of several VBA programs for the rapid and menu-guided performance of frequently used parametric and nonparametric statistical tests. To assess the level of significance between any two-group expression values, it is possible to perform a paired or an unpaired Student's test, a Mann-Whitney U-test, or Wilcoxon signed-rank test.[102] In addition, the Pearson's correlation analysis can be applied between two matched groups of expression values. Furthermore, all statistical programs calculate the mean values of both groups analyzed and their difference in percent.[79]

Permutation or randomization tests are a useful alternative to more standard parametric tests for analyzing experimental data.[103,104] They have the advantage of making no distributional assumptions about the data, while remaining as powerful as conventional tests. Randomization tests are based on one we know to be true: that treatments were randomly allocated.[103,104] The randomization test is conducted as follows: A statistical test is based on the probability of an effect as large as that observed occurring under the null hypothesis of no treatment effect. If this hypothesis is true, the values in one treatment group were just as likely to have occurred in the other group. The randomization test repeatedly and randomly reallocates the observed values to the two groups and notes the apparent effect (expression ratio in REST) each time. The proportion of these effects, which are as great as that actually observed in the experiment, gives us the *p*-value of the test (http://www.bioss.ac.uk/smart/unix/mrandt/slides/frames.htm).

The REST software package makes full use of the advantages of a randomization test.[69] In the applied two-sided *Pair-Wise Fixed Reallocation Randomization Test* for each sample, the CP values for reference and target genes are jointly reallocated to control and sample groups (equal pair-wise fixed reallocation), and the expression ratios are calculated on the basis of the mean values. In practice, it is impractical to examine all possible allocations of data to treatment groups, and a random sample is drawn. If 2,000 or more samples are taken, a good estimate of *p*-value (standard error < 0.005 at $p = 0.05$) is obtained.[103,104] Randomization tests with a pair-wise reallocation are seen as the most appropriate approach for this type of application. They are more flexible than nonparametric tests based on ranks (Mann-Whitney, Kruskal-Wallis, etc.) and do not suffer a reduction in power relative to parametric tests (*t*-tests, ANOVA, etc.). They can be slightly conservative (i.e., type I error rates lower than the stated significance level) due to acceptance of randomizations with group differences identical to that observed, but this mainly occurs when used with discrete data.[103,104]

3.6. Conclusion

The recent advances in gene quantification strategies, fluorescence chemistries, and instrumentations have led to the development of various assays whereby mRNA transcripts can be quantified precisely in very short time. The benefits in terms of increased sensitivity, reduced variability, reduced risk of contamination, increased throughput by automation, and meaningful data interpretation are obvious. If done properly, kinetic RT-PCR is the most powerful method for quantifying cellular mRNA levels. The quantification strategy used should be designed according to the researchers demand, but must be highly optimized and precisely validated. In the future, there is a need for greater standardization of the applied assays to make the expression results comparable between runs, between real-time RT-PCR platforms, and between different laboratories worldwide.

Sharing any technical and practical information for sample preparation, assay design, standard materials, and data management will help to improve gene quantification analysis. Therefore various information platforms and discussion forums are available on the internet (summarized under http://www.wzw.tum.de/gene-quantification/link.html#news).

References

1. Orlando C, Pinzani P, Pazzagli M: **Developments in quantitative PCR.** *Clin Chem Lab Med* 1998, **36**:255–269.

2. Lockey C, Otto E, Long Z: **Real-time fluorescence detection of a single DNA molecule.** *Biotechniques* 1998, **24**:744–746.

3. Bustin SA: **Absolute quantification of mRNA using real-time reverse transcription polymerase chain reaction assays.** *J Mol Endocrinol* 2000, **25**:169–193.

4. Pfaffl MW, Hageleit M: **Validities of mRNA quantification using recombinant RNA and recombinant DNA external calibration curves in real-time RT-PCR.** *Biotechn Lett* 2001, **23**:275–282.

5. Higuchi R, Fockler C, Dollinger G, Watson R: **Kinetic PCR analysis: Real-time monitoring of DNA amplification reactions.** *Biotechnology* 1993, **11**(9):1026–1030.

6. Heid CA, Stevens J, Livak KJ, Williams PM: **Real time quantitative PCR.** *Genome Res* 1996, **6**:986–993.

7. Gibson UE, Heid CA, Williams PM: **A novel method for real time quantitative RT-PCR.** *Genome Res* 1996, 6:1095–1001.

8. Mackay IM, Arden KE, Nitsche A: **Real-time PCR in virology.** *Nucleic Acids Res* 2002, **30**:1292–1305.

9. Steuerwald N, Cohen J, Herrera RJ, Brenner CA: **Analysis of gene expression in single oocytes and embryos by real-time rapid cycle fluorescence monitored RT-PCR.** *Mol Hum Reprod* 1999, **5**:1034–1039.

10. Schmittgen TD, Zakrajsek BA, Mills AG, Gorn V, Singer MJ, Reed MW: **Quantitative reverse transcription-polymerase chain reaction to study mRNA**

decay: Comparison of endpoint and real-time methods. *Anal Biochem* 2000, **285**(2):194–204.

11. Winer J, Jung CK, Shackel I, Williams PM: Development and validation of real-time quantitative reverse transcriptase-polymerase chain reaction for monitoring gene expression in cardiac myocytes in vitro. *Anal Biochem* 1999, **270**(1):41–49.

12. Wittwer CT, Garling DJ: Rapid cycle DNA amplification: Time and temperature optimization. *BioTechniques* 1991, **10**:76–83.

13. Freeman WM, Walker SJ, Vrana KE: Quantitative RT-PCR: Pitfalls and potential. *Biotechniques* 1999, **26**(1):112–125.

14. Swift GH, Peyton MJ, MacDonald RJ: Assessment of RNA quality by semi-quantitative RT-PCR of multiple regions of a long ubiquitous mRNA. *Biotechniques* 2000, **28**(3):524–531.

15. Mannhalter C, Koizar D, Mitterbauer G: Evaluation of RNA isolation methods and reference genes for RT-PCR analyses of rare target RNA. *Clin Chem Lab Med* 2000, **38**:171–177.

16. Freeman TC, Lee K, Richardson PJ: Analysis of gene expression in single cells. *Curr Opin Biotechnol* 1999, **10**(6):579–582.

17. Dixon AK, Richardson PJ, Pinnock RD, Lee K: Gene-expression analysis at the single-cell level. *Trends Pharmacol Sci* 2000, **21**(2):65–70.

18. Moss M, Gallwitz D: Structure of two human beta-actin related processed genes, one of which is located next to a simple repetitive sequence. *EMBO* 1983, **2**:757–761.

19. Mutimer H, Deacon N, Crowe S, Sonza S: Pitfalls of processed pseudogenes in RT-PCR. *Biotechniques* 1998, **24**(4):585–588.

20. Neumaier M, Gerhard M, Wagener C: Diagnosis of micrometastases by the amplification of tissue-specific genes. *Gene* 1995, **159**(1):43–47.

21. Tschentscher P, Wagener C, Neumaier M: Sensitive and specific cytokeratin 18 reverse transcription-polymerase chain reaction that excludes amplification of processed pseudogenes from contaminating genomic DNA. *Clin Chem* 1997, **43**(12):2244–2250.

22. Dirnhofer S, Berger C, Untergasser G, Geley S, Berger P: Human beta-actin retro pseudogenes interfere with RT-PCR. *Trends Genet* 1995, **11**(10):380–381.

23. Ercolani L, Florence B, Denaro M, Alexander M: Isolation and complete sequence of a functional human glyceraldehyde-3-phosphate dehydrogenase gene. *J Biol Chem* 1988, **263**(30):15335–15341.

24. Garcia-Meunier P, Etienne-Julan M, Fort P, Piechaczyk M, Bonhomme F: Concerted evolution in the GAPDH family of retrotransposed pseudogenes. *Mamm Genome* 1993, **4**(12):695–703.

25. Watzinger F, Lion T: Multiplex PCR for quality control of template RNA/cDNA in RT-PCR assays. *Leukemia* 1998, **12**:1983–1986.

26. Burkardt HJ: **Standardization and quality control of PCR analyses.** *Clin Chem Lab Med* 2000, **38**(2):87–91.

27. Vandesompele J, De Preter K, Pattyn F, Poppe B, Van Roy N, De Paepe A, Speleman F: **Accurate normalization of real-time quantitative RT-PCR data by geometric averaging of multiple internal control genes.** *Genome Biology* 2002, **3**(7):0034.1–0034.11.

28. Bustin SA: **Quantification of mRNA using real-time reverse transcription PCR (RT-PCR): Trends and problems.** *J Mol Endocrinol* 2002, **29**(1):23–39.

29. Bustin SA: **Quantification of mRNA using real-time RT-PCR. Trends and problems.** *J Mol Endocrinol* 2002, **29**(1):23–39.

30. Glasel JA: **Validity of nucleic acid purities monitored by 260 nm/280 nm absorbance ratios.** *BioTechniques* 1994, **18**(1):62–63.

31. Wong L, Pearson H, Fletcher A, Marquis CP, Mahler S: **Comparison of the efficiency of Moloney Murine Leukaemia virus (M-MuLV) reverse transcriptase, RNase H—M-MuLV reverse transcriptase and Avian Myeloblastoma Leukaemia virus (AMV) reverse transcriptase for the amplification of human immunoglobulin genes.** *Biotechnology Techniques* 1998, **12**(6):485–489.

32. Fuchs B. Zhang K, Rock MG, Bolander ME, Sarkar G: **High temperature cDNA synthesis by AMV reverse transcriptase improves the specificity of PCR.** *Mol Biotechnol* 1999, **12**(3):237–240.

33. Fuchs B, Zhang K, Rock MG, Bolander ME, Sarkar G: **Repeat cDNA synthesis and RT-PCR with the same source of RNA.** *Mol Biotechnol* 1999, **12**(3):231–235.

34. Schwabe H, Stein U, Walther W: **High-copy cDNA amplification of minimal total RNA quantities for gene expression analyses.** *Mol Biotechnol* 2000, **14**(2):165–172.

35. Hayward AL, Oefner PJ, Sabatini S, Kainer DB, Hinojos CA, Doris PA: **Modelling and analysis of competitive RT-PCR.** *Nucleic Acids Res* 1998, **26**(11):2511–2518.

36. Freeman WM, Vrana SL, Vrana KE: **Use of elevated reverse transcription reaction temperatures in RT-PCR.** *Biotechniques* 1996, **20**(5):782–783.

37. Raja S, Luketich JD, Kelly LA, Ruff DW, Godfrey TE: **Increased sensitivity of one-tube, quantitative RT-PCR.** *Biotechniques* 2000, **29**:702–708.

38. Sugita M, Haney JL, Gemmill RM, Franklin WA: **One-step duplex reverse transcription-polymerase chain reaction for quantitative assessment of RNA degradation.** *Analytical Biochemistry* 2001, **295**:113–116.

39. Marten NW, Burke EJ, Hayden JM, Straus DS: **Effect of amino acid limitation on the expression of 19 genes in rat hepatoma cells.** *FASEB J* 1994, **8**:538–544.

40. Foss DL, Baarsch MJ, Murtaugh MP: **Regulation of hypoxanthine phosphoribosyl transferase, glyceraldehyde-3-phosphate dehydrogenase and beta-actin mRNA expression in porcine immune cells and tissues.** *Anim Biotechnol* 1998, **9**:67–78.

41. Thellin O, Zorzi W, Lakaye B, De Borman B, Coumans B, Hennen G, Grisar T, Igout A, Heinen E: **Housekeeping genes as internal standards: Use and limits.** *J Biotechnol* 1999, **75**:291–295.

42. Goidin D, Mamessier A, Staquet MJ, Schmitt D, Berthier-Vergnes O: **Ribosomal 18S RNA prevails over glyceraldehyde-3-phosphate dehydrogenase and beta-actin genes as internal standard for quantitative comparison of mRNA levels in invasive and noninvasive human melanoma cell subpopulations.** *Anal Biochem* 2001, **295**(1):17–21.

43. Schmittgen TD, Zakrajsek BA: **Effect of experimental treatment on housekeeping gene expression: Validation by real-time, quantitative RT-PCR.** *J Biochem Biophys Methods* 2000, **46**(1–2):69–81.

44. Cha RS, Thilly WG: **Specificity, efficiency, and fidelity of PCR.** *PCR Methods Appl* 1993, **3**(3):18–29.

45. Tichopad A, Dilger M, Schwarz G, Pfaffl MW: **Standardised determination of real-time PCR efficiency from a single reaction setup.** *Nucl Acids Res* 2003, **31**(20):e122.

46. Kainz P: The **PCR plateau phase—Towards an understanding of its limitations.** *Biochim Biophys Acta* 2000, **1494**:23–27.

47. Pfaffl MW: **Development and validation of an externally standardised quantitative Insulin like growth factor-1 (IGF-1) RT-PCR using LightCycler SYBR Green I technology.** In: Meuer S, Wittwer C, Nakagawara K, eds. *Rapid Cycle Real-time PCR, Methods and Applications* Springer Press, Heidelberg 2001:281–191.

48. Wittwer CT, Ririe KM, Andrew RV, David D.A, Gundry RA, Balis U.J: **The LightCycler: A microvolume multisample fluorimeter with rapid temperature control.** *BioTechniques* 1997, **22**:176–181.

49. Rasmussen R: **Quantification on the LightCycler**. In: Meuer S, Wittwer C, Nakagawara K, eds. *Rapid Cycle Real-time PCR, Methods and Applications* Springer Press, Heidelberg 2001:21–34.

50. Tichopad A, Didier A, Pfaffl MW: **Inhibition of real-time RT-PCR quantification due to tissue specific contaminants.** *Molecular and Cellular Probes* 2004, **18**:45–50.

51. Tichopad A, Dzidic A, Pfaffl MW: **Improving quantitative real-time RT-PCR reproducibility by boosting primer-linked amplification efficiency.** *Biotechn Lett* 2003, **24**: 2053–2056.

52. Foy CA, Parkes HC: Emerging Homogeneous **DNA-based Technologies in the Clinical Laboratory.** *Clinical Chemistry* 2001, **47**: 990–1000.

53. Pfaffl M, Meyer HHD, Sauerwein H: **Quantification of insulin-like growth factor-1 (IGF-1) mRNA: development and validation of an internally standardised competitive reverse transcription-polymerase chain reaction.** *Exp Clin Endocrinol Diabetes* 1998, **106**(6):506–513.

54. Reischl U, Kochanowski B: Quantitative PCR. **A survey of the present technology.** *Mol Biotechnol* 1995, **3**(1):55–71.

55. Ferre F: **Quantitative or semi-quantitative PCR: Reality versus myth.** *PCR Methods Appl* 1992, **2**(1):1–9.

56. Pfaffl MW, Georgieva TM, Georgiev IP, Ontsouka E, Hageleit M, Blum JW: **Real-time RT-PCR quantification of insulin-like growth factor (IGF)-1, IGF-1 receptor, IGF-2, IGF-2 receptor, insulin receptor, growth hormone receptor, IGF-binding proteins 1, 2 and 3 in the bovine species.** *Domest Anim Endocrinol* 2002, **22**(2):91–102.

57. Ginzinger DG: **Gene quantification using real-time quantitative PCR: An emerging technology hits the mainstream.** *Exp Hematol* 2002, **30**(6):503–512.

58. Morrison TB, Weis JJ, Wittwer CT: **Quantification of low-copy transcripts by continuous SYBR Green I monitoring during amplification.** *Biotechniques* 1998, **24**(6):954–962.

59. Wittwer CT, Herrmann MG, Gundry CN, Elenitoba-Johnson KS: **Real-time multiplex PCR assays.** *Methods* 2001, **25**(4):430–442.

60. Holland PM, Abramson RD, Watson R, Gelfand DH: **Detection of specific polymerase chain reaction product by utilizing the 5'–3' exonuclease activity of *Thermus aquaticus* DNA polymerase.** *Proc Natl Acad Sci USA* 1991, **88**(16):7276–7280.

61. Livak KJ: ABI Prism 7700 **Sequence detection System User Bulletin #2 Relative quantification of gene expression**; 1997 & 2001.
http://docs.appliedbiosystems.com/pebiodocs/04303859.pdf

62. Förster VT: **Zwischenmolekulare Energiewanderung und Fluorescence.** *Annals of Physics,* Leipzig, 1948.

63. Lakowicz JR: **Energy transfer.** In: *Principles of Fluorescent Spectroscopy*, New York: Plenum Press 1983:303–339.

64. *LightCycler Software®*, Version 3.5; Roche Molecular Biochemicals, 2001.

65. *LightCycler Relative Quantification Software*, Version 1.0, Roche Molecular Biochemicals, 2001.

66. Nitsche A, Steuer N, Schmidt CA, Landt O, Siegert W: **Different real-time PCR formats compared for the quantitative detection of human cytomegalovirus DNA.** *Clin Chem* 1999, **45**(11):1932–1937.

67. Souaze F, Ntodou-Thome A, Tran CY, Rostene W, Forgez P: **Quantitative RT-PCR: Limits and accuracy.** *Biotechniques* 1996, **21**(2):280–285.

68. Pfaffl MW: **A new mathematical model for relative quantification in real-time RT-PCR.** *Nucleic Acids Res* 2001, **29**(9):e45.

69. Pfaffl MW, Horgan GW, Dempfle L: **Relative expression software tool (REST) for group-wise comparison and statistical analysis of relative expression results in real-time PCR.** *Nucleic Acids Res* 2002, **30**(9):e36.

70. Livak KJ, Schmittgen TD: **Analysis of relative gene expression data using real-time quantitative PCR and the 2^[-delta delta C(T)] method.** *Methods* 2001, **25**(4):402–408.

71. Pfaffl MW, Lange IG, Daxenberger A, Meyer HHD: **Tissue-specific expression pattern of estrogen receptors (ER): quantification of ER alpha and ER beta mRNA with real-time RT-PCR.** *APMIS* 2001, **109**(5):345–355.

72. Fronhoffs S, Totzke G, Stier S, Wernert N, Rothe M, Bruning T, Koch B, Sachinidis A, Vetter H, Ko Y: **A method for the rapid construction of cRNA standard curves in quantitative real-time reverse transcription polymerase chain reaction.** *Mol Cell Probes* 2002, **16**(2):99–110.

73. Zimmermann K, Mannhalter JW: **Technical aspects of quantitative competitive PCR.** *Biotechniques* 1996, **21**(2):268–279.

74. Meijerink J, Mandigers C, van de Locht L, Tonnissen E, Goodsaid F, Raemaekers J: **A novel method to compensate for different amplification efficiencies between patient DNA samples in quantitative real-time PCR.** *J Mol Diagn* 2001, **3**(2):55–61.

75. Soong R, Ruschoff J, Tabiti K: **Detection of colorectal micrometastasis by quantitative RT-PCR of cytokeratin 20 mRNA.** Roche Molecular Biochemicals internal Publication, 2000.

76. Peccoud J, Jacob C: **Theoretical uncertainty of measurements using quantitative polymerase chain reaction.** *Biophys J* 1996, **71**(1):101–108.

77. Liu W, Saint DA: **Validation of a quantitative method for real time PCR kinetics.** *Biochem Biophys Res Commun* 2002, **294**(2):347–353.

78. Liu W, Saint DA: **A new quantitative method of real time reverse transcription polymerase chain reaction assay based on simulation of polymerase chain reaction kinetics.** *Anal Biochem* 2002, **302**(1):52–59.

79. Muller PY, Janovjak H, Miserez AR, Dobbie Z: **Processing of gene expression data generated by quantitative real-time RT-PCR.** *Biotechniques* 2002, **32**(6):1372–1378.

80. Bhatia P, Taylor WR, Greenberg AH, Wright JA: **Comparison of glyceraldehyde-3-phosphate dehydrogenase and 28S-ribosomal RNA gene expression as RNA loading controls for northern blot analysis of cell lines of varying malignant potential.** *Anal Biochem* 1994, **216**:223–226.

81. Bereta J, Bereta M: **Stimulation of glyceraldehyde-3-phosphate dehydrogenase mRNA levels by endogenous nitric oxide in cytokine-activated endothelium.** *Biochem Biophys Res Commun* 1995, **217**:363–369.

82. Chang TJ, Juan CC, Yin PH, Chi CW, Tsay HJ: **Up-regulation of beta-actin, cyclophilin and GAPDH in N1S1 rat hepatoma.** *Oncol Rep* 1998, **5**:469–471.

83. Zhang J, Snyder SH: **Nitric oxide stimulates auto-ADP-ribosylation of glyceraldehydes 3 phosphate dehydrogenase.** *Proc Natl Acad Sci USA* 1992, **89**:9382–9385.

84. Jung R, Soondrum K, Neumaier M: **Quantitative PCR.** *Clin Chem Lab Med* 2000, **38**(9):833–836.

85. Gentle A, Anastasopoulos F, McBrien NA: **High-resolution semi-quantitative real-time PCR without the use of a standard curve.** *Biotechniques* 2001, **31**(3):502–508.

86. Das S, Mohapatra SC, Hsu JC: **Studies on primer-dimer formation in polymerase chain reaction (PCR).** *Biotechnology Techniques* 1999, **13**(10):643–646.

87. Ririe KM, Rasmussen RP, Wittwer CT: **Product differentiation by analysis of DNA melting curves during the polymerase chain reaction.** *Anal Biochem* 1997, **245**(2):154–160.

88. Vandesompele J, De Paepe A, Speleman F: **Elimination of primer-dimer artifacts and genomic coamplification using a two-step SYBR Green I real-time RT-PCR.** *Anal Biochem* 2002, **303**(1):95–98.

89. Brownie J, Shawcross S, Theaker J, Whitcombe D, Ferrie R, Newton C, Little S: **The elimination of primer-dimer accumulation in PCR.** *Nucleic Acids Res* 1997, **25**(16):3235–3241.

90. Sturzenbaum SR: **Transfer RNA reduces the formation of primer artifacts during quantitative PCR.** *Biotechniques* 1999, **27**(1): 50–52.

91. *How to Reduce Primer Dimers in a LightCycler PCR.* Roche Diagnostics Technical Note No. 1, 1999.

92. Raeymaekers L: **Basic principles of quantitative PCR.** *Mol Biotechnol* 2000, **15**(2):115–122.

93. Chelly J, Kaplan JC, Maire P, Gautron S, Kahn A: **Transcription of the dystrophin gene in human muscle and non-muscle tissue.** *Nature* 1988, **333**(6176):858–860.

94. Schnell S, Mendoza C: **Theoretical description of the polymerase chain reaction.** *J Theor Biol* 1997, **188**(3):313–318.

95. Karge WH, Schaefer EJ, Ordovas JM: **Quantification of mRNA by polymerase chain reaction (PCR) using an internal standard and a non-radioactive detection method.** *Methods Mol Biol* 1998, **110**:43–61.

96. Zhong H, Simons JW: **Direct comparison of GAPDH, beta-actin, cyclophilin, and 28S rRNA as internal standards for quantifying RNA levels under hypoxia.** *Biochem Biophys Res Commun* 1999, **259**(3):523–526.

97. Solanas M, Moral R, Escrich E: **Unsuitability of using ribosomal RNA as loading control for Northern blot analyses related to the imbalance between mes-**

senger and ribosomal RNA content in rat mammary tumors. *Anal Biochem* 2001, **288**(1):99–102.

98. Haberhausen G, Pinsl J, Kuhn CC, Markert-Hahn C: **Comparative study of different standardization concepts in quantitative competitive reverse transcription-PCR assays.** *J Clin Microbiol* 1988, 3:628–633.

99. Zhu G, Chang Y, Zuo J, Dong X, Zhang M, Hu G, Fang F: **Fudenine, a C-terminal truncated rat homologue of mouse prominin, is blood glucose-regulated and can up-regulate the expression of GAPDH.** *Biochem Biophys Res Commun* 2001, **281**(4):951–956.

100. Inderwies T, Pfaffl MW, Meyer HHD, Bruckmaier RM: **Detection and quantification of mRNA expression of α- and β-adrenergic receptor subtypes in the bovine mammary gland of dairy cows.** *Domestic Animal Endocrinology* 2003, **24**(2):123–135.

101. Reist M, Pfaffl MW, Morel C, Meylan M, Hirsbrunner G, Blum JW, Steiner A: **Quantitative mRNA analysis of bovine 5-HT receptor subtypes in brain, abomasum, and intestine by real-time PCR.** *Journal of Receptors and Signal Transduction* 2003, **23**(4):271–287.

102. Sheskin D: *Handbook of Parametric and Nonparametric Statistical Procedures.* CRC Press LLC : Boca Raton, Florida, 2000.

103. Manly B: *Randomization, Bootstrap and Monte Carlo. Methods in Biology.* Chapman & Hall, 1997.

104. Horgan GW, Rouault J: *Introduction to randomization tests, Biomathematics and Statistics.* Scotland, 2000.

105. Pfaffl MW, Tichopád A, Prgomet C, Neuvians TP: **Determination of stable housekeeping genes, differentially regulated target genesand sample integrity: *BestKeeper*—Excel-based tool using pair-wise correlations.** *Biotechnology Letters* 2004, **26**:509–515

PART II

BASICS

4

Good Laboratory Practice!

Stephen A. Bustin and Tania Nolan

4

Good Laboratory Practice!

Stephen A. Bustin[*] and Tania Nolan[†]

*Barts and The London, Queen Mary's School of Medicine
and Dentistry, University of London, London, United Kingdom
†Stratagene Europe, Amsterdam, The Netherlands*

4.1. Introduction

One can always spot a molecular biology laboratory: it is characteristically messy, with tubes, tips, and dishes all lying around the place, contaminated bottles festering away, old Petri dishes with bacterial or yeast colonies, plus penicillium, and even the principal investigator's sandwiches blocking up the refrigerators. The freezers are a frightful sight, with boxes and tubes stuffed everywhere with the remnants of the last twenty years worth of enzymes and kits clogging up the place. First aid kits, eye-wash station, and local safety rules are honored by their absence, and the occasional cup of coffee and sandwich also finds its way into the laboratory, if not into any reaction tube open at the time.

The information in this chapter is provided to point out a few, basic procedures that might help not just to generate more reproducible results, but also to make the laboratory environment a more pleasant *and safe* place for everyone. Even collaborating biochemists who will be appalled by the state of the unreconstructed molecular biology laboratory need to feel a minimal sense of security.

4.2. General Precautions

Some of the instruments and reagents used for the purification of nucleic acids are very hazardous. This is especially so for phenol, hydrochloric, sulfuric, and glacial acetic acids, but chloroform, isoamyl alcohol, and even (or especially) ethanol (EtOH) must also be handled with caution. A Russian professor working in Oxford who regularly drank EtOH as an alcohol substitute killed himself after drinking methanol by mistake. Although warned by colleagues that drinking EtOH was not encouraged, the professor claimed this was common in Russian laboratories. The 44-year-old professor was said to have had poor vision, and probably misread the label (http://darwinawards.com/darwin/darwin2001-22.html?email). Another hazardous substance is ethidium bromide (EtBr), a dye that is used to visualize nucleic acids under UV light. It is a powerful mutagen, hence contact with it should be minimal and gloves should always be worn whenever handling it.

Every reagent is supplied with relevant information on any hazards associated with its use in the form of Material Safety Data Sheets (MSDS). These contain detailed information on special precautions needed when handling such a chemical and what to do in case of spillage, including first aid treatment. When working with hazardous reagents, you should as a matter of course:

- ☑ Wear a lab coat, gloves, and sturdy shoes covering toes.
- ☑ Wear eye protection.
- ☑ Check chemical labels to make sure you have the correct substance.
- ☑ Pay attention to the hazard classifications shown on the label.
- ☑ Never mouth pipette.

☑ Know the locations of all emergency equipment:
- First Aid Kits,
- chemical spill kits,
- safety showers,
- eye-wash stations,
- telephone and emergency telephone number.

4.2.1. Phenol

Phenol warrants a separate section on safety since it can pose a severe health hazard and is part of many reagents used for the extraction of nucleic acids. It and any reagent containing phenol, e.g., TRIzol®, must be handled with extreme caution. Phenol is readily absorbed through the skin, and it can affect the central nervous system and cause damage to the liver and kidneys. It is also a mutagen, and there is some evidence that phenol may be a reproductive hazard. When heated, phenol will produce flammable vapors that are highly toxic (at just a few parts per million) and explosive (at concentrations of 3% to 10% in air). It is vital that you familiarize yourself with these hazards and are aware of the protective measures you must take, for your own sake, but also for the sake of your colleagues, students, and the cleaning staff.

☑ Review a Phenol MSDS before handling the material.

☑ Phenol should always be handled in a fume cupboard to ensure the short-term exposure limit is not exceeded.

☑ Phenol is flammable. Ensure no naked flames are in use nearby.

☑ Phenol must be contained in shatter-proof vessels (e.g., polypropylene) as it plasticizes polycarbonate and polystyrene.

☑ Wear butyl rubber or neoprene gloves; latex, but not nitrile, will suffice for short periods.

☑ Sturdy footwear should be worn to prevent splashes to feet in the event of a spillage.

☑ Colleagues working nearby should be made aware that phenol is being used.

☑ Always wash hands thoroughly after handling phenol, even if gloves are used.

Emergency procedures in case of skin contact

Phenol is irritating and corrosive to the skin. Because it has a local anesthetic effect, little or no pain may be felt on initial contact. However, skin in contact with phenol will turn white; later, severe burns may develop. Phenol is rapidly absorbed through the skin, and toxic or even fatal amounts can be absorbed through relatively small areas. Ingestion of as little as 1 gram can be fatal to humans. Phenol can also cause severe damage to eyes, including blindness. Repeated or prolonged exposure to phenol or its vapors may cause headache, nausea, dizziness, difficulty swallowing, diarrhea, vomiting, shock, convulsions, or death.

In case of spillage:

1. Remove the victim from the source of contamination.

2. Take the victim to the nearest eye-wash, shower, or other source of clean water. Immediately flush the contaminated area with soap and water for at least fifteen minutes before applying polyethylene glycol 300 (PEG300) solution. This should always be readily available for use in the event of a spill on skin since phenol partitions preferably into PEG300. Organic solvents should not be used to remove contaminating phenol, as they will tend to assist the transport of phenol into the skin.

3. Do not scrub the contaminated area, as this will tend to both spread the contamination and drive any phenol further into the skin.

4. Remove contaminated clothing.

5. In case of eye contact, promptly flush the eyes with copious amounts of water (not PEG300) for 15 minutes, lifting upper and lower eyelids occasionally, and obtain medical attention.

6. If phenol is ingested, obtain medical attention immediately.

7. If large amounts of phenol are inhaled, move the person to fresh air and seek medical attention at once. Both the victim and anybody assisting must avoid secondary contamination from the washings and contaminated clothing—gloves should be worn.

8. Spillages should be absorbed with vermiculite (which should be readily available in laboratories where phenol is used routinely) and disposed of as for normal phenol waste.

In order to minimize contact with phenol wastes, do not accumulate stocks of liquid phenol waste for disposal, i.e., do not decant small quantities from microfuge tubes, etc., into larger containers. Instead, a suitable leak-proof container (i.e., one designed to hold liquids, not solids) should be chosen into which the phenol solutions complete with contaminated glass- or plasticware can be placed. The full container should be sealed and placed in a large leak proof container along with a larger phenol-contaminated or phenol-containing plasticware (e.g., centrifuge tubes, pipettes, etc.). Also bear in mind that phenol is a combustible solid; hence it must be stored so that it cannot come in contact with strong oxidizers (such as chlorine and bromine) because a violent reaction could result.

Wide-mouthed red-topped kegs suitable for such disposal are available from Merck/BDH and should be used by every lab where phenol is used routinely (wide-mouthed HDPE 6.4 liter, *Cat. No. 215/0380/00*, wide-mouthed HDPE 15.4 liter, *Cat. No. 215/0380/02*). When the kegs are full, they must be disposed of through the hazardous chemical waste route.

4.2.2. Liquid Nitrogen (N_2)

Liquid N_2 is a colorless, odorless gas, with a boiling point of $-196°C$. The extreme low temperature of liquid N_2 means that frostbite can occur rapidly on contact with gas or significant levels of vapor. In the laboratory, the most serious danger is likely to be caused by liquid N_2 spattering while being poured. The resultant burns are similar to thermal burns and can result in severe blistering. Contact with liquid N_2 will cause embrittlement of exposed areas, due to the high water content of the human body—the eyes are particularly vulnerable. On vaporization liquid N_2 expands by a factor of 700; one liter of liquid N_2 becomes 24.6 cubic feet of N_2 gas. This can cause explosion of a sealed container, e.g., a cryogenic vial or it can displace oxygen in the room and cause suffocation without warning.

☑ Neither frozen objects nor liquid N_2 must be touched.

☑ Goggles must be worn whenever pouring liquid N_2.

☑ A thermal glove and tongs must be used to handle any object being placed into or taken out of liquid N_2 and while carrying any containment vessel.

☑ Use only approved unsealed containers.

☑ Never seal it in any container (it will explode).

☑ Never dip a hollow tube into liquid N_2; it may spurt liquid.

☑ Pierce the ends of sample tubes prior to submersion.

☑ Use permanent markers for labeling tubes.

☑ Never use in a small poorly ventilated room, and never dispose of liquid N_2 by pouring it on the floor. It could displace enough oxygen to cause suffocation.

☑ Do not store liquid N_2 for long periods in an uncovered container (on the other hand, never totally seal a container). Because the boiling point of oxygen (O_2) is above that of N_2, O_2 can condense from the air into the liquid N_2. If the air over the N_2 circulates, this liquid O_2 can build up to levels which may cause violent reactions with organic materials; even materials which are ordinarily nonflammable. For example, a severe clothing fire could result from ignition in the presence of liquid oxygen.

☑ If cryogenic liquid or cold boil off contacts a worker's skin or eyes, frozen tissues should be flooded or soaked with tepid water (40°C). **DO NOT USE HOT WATER.** The frozen part must not be rubbed either before or after rewarming. Cryogenic burns, which result in blistering or deeper tissue freezing, should be seen promptly by a medical doctor.

4.2.3. Waste Disposal

Although each institution or laboratory has its own procedures for storing and disposing of waste, some general rules can be applied:

1. Biohazard waste: place in designated biohazard waste cans that are autoclaved prior to being discarded in the general rubbish.

2. Sharp objects: in clearly labeled sharps containers *only*.

3. Broken glass: in separate, clearly labeled broken glass containers *only*.

4. Pipette tips/microfuge tubes: in plastic beakers on the bench. When full, empty contents into biohazard waste cans.

4.3. Equipment

4.3.1. Electrophoresis

The high voltage used during electrophoresis constitutes a serious hazard. Always turn off the power supply before touching agarose gel boxes, and always keep the box, leads, and power supply away from the edge of the bench. Make sure your power supply is turned off before connecting and disconnecting gel boxes.

4.3.2. Freezer

Make sure you label everything clearly with all relevant information, including your name, before you put anything in the freezer. Use a permanent marker for this since sticky labels fail to adhere at very low temperatures. Also keep a record of where you have placed your tubes. Use an insulated glove when handling frozen samples.

4.3.3. UV Transilluminators

Ultraviolet light boxes, or transilluminators, are commonly used to view electrophoretic gels and other objects. The light output, mainly 254 nm or 312 nm, is in the UVC and UVB bands which are biologically active and capable of damaging skin and eyes.

☑ Locate UV boxes in low occupancy areas, preferably in separate rooms.

☑ Minimize contact times with UV light sources; maximize distance by working at arms' length and avoiding stooping over the work surface. Use shielding and personal protective equipment.

☑ When purchasing new transilluminators, only consider units with retractable or hinged plastic safety covers since these can filter a significant amount of biologically active UV. Since intense exposure to UV light degrades plastic over time, it is important to replace these covers every few years and even sooner if discoloration or cracking occurs.

☑ Keep basic personal protective equipment available and ready for use at light box workstations. This should include a full-face shield designed for UVB and UVC filtration (typically polycarbonate) and several sizes of plastic gloves. Wearing ordinary prescription or safety glasses under the face shield provides even greater eye protection. A fully buttoned lab coat provides good arm, wrist, chest and, neck protection. Since protective equipment is least likely to be worn when it is damaged or soiled, assign responsibility for ensuring that equipment is available and kept in good condition.

☑ Users should wipe down UV light work surfaces and control knobs after each use, discarding used wipes as hazardous waste. Despite regular cleaning, the routine use of EtBr in gels and electrophoresis running buffers means that contamination from this known mutagen should be anticipated and UV light box work areas approached accordingly. If radioactive materials are also used in nucleic acid work, this kind of contamination should also be expected and dealt with appropriately. Storing cleaning supplies and a waste receptacle near the workstation can help promote regular surface cleaning.

☑ Remind lab workers of the symptoms of UV overexposure (i.e., skin reddening, sandy or gritty feeling in the eyes) and encourage anyone who experiences them to obtain medical attention and report the incident as soon as possible. Since these symptoms are often delayed by several hours, making prompt diagnosis and medical treatment more difficult, prevention is especially important.

4.3.4. Micropipettes

Micropipettes present a major source of contamination to nucleic acid samples, restriction enzymes, PCR reactions, etc., because they can aerosolize the liquid you are measuring. Therefore draw up any liquid slowly and use filtered tips.

Pipetting is a routine laboratory technique that is performed everyday for a good portion of the day. It requires concentration, accuracy, and precision; and its capacity to cause serious damage to the operator is not well publicized. Mechanical micropipettes introduce a repetitive movement that can result in cumulative trauma disorders in anyone pipetting for more than 300 hours a year. This equates to a daily routine of only 1–2 hours a day of pipetting tasks. The features of the pipette, such as the design of the plunger, weight and length of the pipette, force needed to operate the pipette, and how the pipette fits into the hand, may also increase the risk of cumulative trauma disorder. Therefore, it is important that some preventative measures are applied:

- ☑ Take short micro pauses of a few seconds, when you can't take a longer break.

- ☑ Correct posture and body position can reduce the stress caused by continuous pipetting. Use adjustable chairs or stools with built in solid foot stools.

- ☑ Do not elevate your arm, without support, for lengthy periods of time. Work with arms close to the body to reduce the strain on shoulders. Keep hands and shoulders in a neutral position.

- ☑ Use electronic pipettes, which are programmable and reduce the need for excessive thumb force and repetition.

- ☑ If using manual pipettes, choose those requiring the least pressure and use only the force, necessary to operate the pipette. Use shorter pipettes as this decreases the arm and hand elevation and consequent awkward positions.

- ☑ Use low profile waste receptacles, no higher than the height of the tubes that you are using.

Any volume error is likely to have a significant effect on the accuracy of real-time PCR quantification. Therefore, the volume error for a pipette should be determined when the pipette is new and at regular time intervals thereafter. Calibration of pipettes can be done fairly easily by carrying out the following procedure:

1. Adjust pipette to desired volume in μl (e.g., a Gilson P10 should be measured at 10 μl).

2. Place an empty microfuge tube upright on an analytical balance and weigh.

3. Dispense 10 times 10 μl water which is at room temperature and whose temperature has been recorded carefully, into the microfuge tube, recording the weight at the end of the pipetting.

4. Record the temperature of the water and determine the water density. Knowing the weight of the water pipetted and the water density allows the calculation of the volume error (**Table 4.1**).

Table 4.1. Measuring the volume error of a micropipette.

Water Temperature in °C	Density in g/ml
20°C	0.99823
21°C	0.99802
22°C	0.99780
23°C	0.99756
24°C	0.99732
25°C	0.99707

Mean volume in ml = (mean weight of aliquot in grams) / (density of water for °C)

Volume error in ml = (mean volume in ml) – (expected volume in ml)

Volume error in percent = (volume error in ml) × 100/(expected volume in ml)

The acceptable volume error should be <= 3%.

4.3.5. Gloves

There are at least two good reasons for wearing gloves as a matter of course while in the laboratory: they can form an effective barrier between the skin and any harmful chemical or pathogen and they are also useful for preventing sample contamination.

4.3.5.1. Vinyl Gloves

These are the least expensive option, they come in powdered and powder-free varieties, are better than latex at protecting hands against DMSO, and pose only a small allergy risk. The chemical resistance of vinyl is about equal to that of latex, but fit and comfort are not as good.

4.3.5.2. Latex Gloves

Latex is the most popular type of glove that fits well and has a high resistance to cuts and tears. The most problematic aspect of Latex is that Latex allergy can be developed after prolonged exposure, with severe consequences (even death from shock). Talc-powdered Latex gloves can cause microscopic cuts to the hands, contributing to any allergy and irritation. Medical-grade cornstarch powder has become the standard for most gloves, eliminating the talc problem. Unfortunately, cornstarch absorbs the protein antigens in Latex responsible for the Latex allergy, making the gloves even more allergenic. Alternatively, powder-free Latex gloves avoid the powder difficulty altogether. Since Latex gloves are coated with the powder before they are removed from the mould, they must be treated with chlorine before they can be considered powder free. Chlorine is also used to preserve the Latex's light color and poses another potential health hazard to the wearer. However, chlorine-treated gloves last only for about six months before the chlorine starts to affect the quality of the glove. The best way to avoid a Latex allergy is simply to use non-Latex alternatives.

4.3.5.3. Nitrile Gloves

Nitrile gloves are more expensive than Latex, but usually are a superior non-Latex choice (**but not for phenol**) as they have increased chemical resistance, strength, longevity, and sensitivity. They have very low allergenicity and tear and puncture resistance equivalent to Latex, and are nearly as comfortable as Latex gloves.

4.3.6. Eye Protection

Eyes are very vascular and can quickly absorb many chemicals; furthermore, there are obvious hazards of flying objects, splashing chemicals, and corrosive vapors. Hence eye protection should be mandatory and safety glasses/goggles should be provided for each individual.

Safety glasses with clear side shields are adequate protection for general laboratory use, but goggles must be worn when there is danger of splashing chemicals or flying particles, such as when chemicals are poured or glassware is used under elevated or reduced pressure. A face shield with goggles offers maximum protection (for example, with vacuum systems that may implode).

Corrective lenses in spectacles do not in themselves provide sufficient protection and goggles should be worn over the eyeglasses. This is also recommended for persons who customarily wear contact lenses. If contact lenses are worn, they should not be handled in the laboratory and should be worn with regularly required eye protection, such as plastic goggles.

4.3.7. Legal Information

Many aspects of the PCR process are covered by patents owned by Hoffmann-La Roche, Inc. and F. Hoffmann-La Roche Ltd. (collectively called Roche). These include the actual amplification process, DNA polymerase reagents used in the PCR process, and automated instruments for performing PCR. Roche has granted exclusive and non-exclusive licenses for various applications of PCR, and Roche and its licensees provide end-user licensing within their designated field. These licenses have different terms depending on the field, and different rules may apply in different countries. In the U.S. and most other nations, the user should always have proper license to perform PCR.

Applied Biosystems is the exclusive licensee for the field of research and development, and applied fields such as quality assurance and control, environmental testing, food testing, agricultural testing (including plant disease diagnostics), forensics and identity testing in humans (other than parentage testing), and animal identity testing. (Applied Biosystems' applied fields do not include human and animal diagnostics.) Applied Biosystems is the owner of basic PCR instrument patents, as well as other related patents.

Commonly required rights are made automatically available through the purchase of PCR-related products from many manufacturers that have been licensed by Applied Biosystems to pass on end-user rights. This applies both to consumable reagents as well as to thermal cyclers.

PCR rights can be purchased from Applied Biosystems, whether the use of PCR is for internal research, for providing services, or for an organization's internal testing in the applied fields. However, it is usually more convenient to obtain at least some necessary rights through the purchase of reagents and thermal cyclers from Applied Biosystems or other licensed suppliers.

The literature accompanying reagents and thermal cyclers from licensed suppliers spells out the specific rights included.

In addition to the basic PCR process patent rights, other patent rights will also be needed in most cases. You can obtain rights under Applied Biosystems thermal cycler instrument patents by purchasing a thermal cycler from a licensed manufacturer or by an agreement from Applied Biosystems. Make sure that your thermal cycler manual from manufacturer XYX contains the following statement:

> "Practice of the patented polymerase chain reaction (PCR) process requires a license. The XYZ system is an Authorized Thermal Cycler and may be used with PCR licenses available from Applied Biosystems. Its use with Authorized Reagents also provides a limited PCR license in accordance with the label rights accompanying such reagents. For Research Use Only. Not for use in diagnostic procedures."

A license under U.S. patents 4,683,202, 4,683,195, and 4,965,188 or their foreign counterparts owned by Roche Molecular Systems, Inc. and F. Hoffmann-La Roche Ltd. ("Roche") for use in research and development, has an up-front fee component and a running-royalty component. By purchasing certain Applied Biosystems PCR reagents, purchasers obtain limited, nontransferable rights under the running royalty component to use the purchased amount of reagents to practice the Polymerase Chain Reaction (PCR) and related processes described in said patents only for research and development activities of the purchaser. Such use is fully licensed under these patents only when the reagents are used in conjunction with a thermal cycler whose use is covered by the up-front fee component. Rights under the up-front fee component of a PCR license may be purchased from Applied Biosystems or obtained by purchasing an Authorized Thermal Cycler. No right to perform or offer commercial services of any kind using PCR, including, for example, reporting the results of purchaser's activities for a fee or other commercial consideration, is granted unless the purchaser obtains a further license from either Applied Biosystems or Roche. Additional information on purchasing licenses to practice the PCR process may be obtained by contacting the Director of Licensing at Applied Biosystems, 850 Lincoln Centre Drive, Foster City, California 94404 or Roche Molecular Systems, 1145 Atlantic Avenue, Alameda, California 94501.

The PCR Process is covered by U.S. Patent Nos. 4,683,202, 4,683,195, 4,800,159, and 4,965,188 owned by Roche Molecular Systems, Inc., and other pending and issued patents in non-U.S. countries owned by F. Hoffmann-La Roche Ltd., all of which are licensed for certain uses to Applied Biosystems. *Taq* DNA Polymerase and AmpliTaq DNA Polymerase are covered by U.S. Patent Nos. 4,889,818, 5,075,216, and 5,079,352 owned by Roche Molecular Systems, Inc., and other pending and issued patents in non-U.S. countries owned by F. Hoffmann-La Roche Ltd., all of which are licensed for certain uses to Applied Biosystems. GeneAmplimer HIV-1 Control Reagents are covered by U.S. Patent No. 5,008,182 owned by Roche Molecular Systems, Inc., and other pending patents in non-U.S. countries owned by F. Hoffmann-La Roche Ltd., all of which are licensed for certain uses to Applied Biosystems.

Note that registered names, trademarks, etc., used in this book, even when not specifically marked as such, are not to be considered unprotected by law.

Relevant Websites

General health and safety guidelines:

http://web.uvic.ca/ohs/labsafety.html

http://www.btk.utu.fi/Research_Services/Laboratory_safety_rules/
laboratory_safety_rules.html

http://www.northwestern.edu/research-safety/labsafe/cbsl/
cbsl5.htm#5.2.2

Phenol:

http://users.ox.ac.uk/~phar0036/biomedsafety/labsafety/chemicalsafe-
ty/phenol.html

Liquid N_2:

http://webs.wichita.edu/facsme/nitro/safe.htm

Safe disposal:

http://www.hse.ubc.ca/v.2/innerPubsAndProcs.php?ct=pc

Agarose gel electrophoresis:

http://www.ich.ucl.ac.uk/cmgs/agarcosh.htm

Polyacrylamide gel elcrophoresis:

http://www.uwcm.ac.uk/study/medicine/medical_microbiology/Postgrad/
page.htm

Electrophoresis electrical safety:

http://www.ab.ust.hk/sepo/tips/ls/ls008.htm

Micropipettes:

http://www.the-scientist.com/yr1997/nov/review1_971110.html

http://www.rainin.com/lit_ergopaper.asp

Gloves:

http://www.anesth.com/gloves.htm

Legal information:

http://www.appliedbiosystems.com/legal/roche_release.cfm

5

Template Handling, Preparation, and Quantification

Stephen A. Bustin and Tania Nolan

5

Template Handling, Preparation, and Quantification

Stephen A. Bustin* and Tania Nolan†

*Barts and The London, Queen Mary's School of Medicine and Dentistry, University of London, London, United Kingdom
†Stratagene Europe, Amsterdam, The Netherlands

5.1. Introduction

Garbage-in, garbage-out. Sample acquisition and purification of the nucleic acid mark the initial step of every qPCR/RT-PCR assay, and it is worth emphasizing near the beginning of this book that the quality of the template is an important and, for RT-PCR assays, arguably ***the most*** important determinant of the reproducibility and biological relevance of subsequent qPCR results. Any problems that affect reproducibility, and hence the relevance of results, are likely to have originated here.[1] Template quality depends on the procedures used for:

- Sample acquisition and handling;
- Template preparation;
- Template storage.

Many samples, especially biopsies of human tissue, are unique; hence a wasted nucleic acid preparation means that the opportunity to record data from that sample is irretrievably lost. A separate consideration concerns the waste of money, as one of the distinguishing features of real-time PCR assays is their significant running cost. Hence it is prudent to expend extensive efforts on getting every stage of this process absolutely right, starting with consistency when collecting, transporting, and storing samples. This continues with rigorous adherence to protocols when extracting nucleic acids and with the appropriate storage of purified material; continued care must be exercised every time the sample is taken out of storage for analysis.

A detailed description of the steps involved in starting with a biological sample and ending up with a high quality nucleic acid preparation is provided in this chapter. Most importantly, the commentaries and protocols are designed to result in samples that will generate reproducible and meaningful results in any qPCR/RT-PCR assay. The protocols listed here are not the only ones that will produce such results. Indeed, there are probably as many protocol variants as there are researchers carrying out nucleic acid extractions. New protocols are constantly being published, and commercial kits are improving all the time. The websites of the commercial suppliers provide a wealth of information about their products, and the reader is encouraged to browse these.

5.1.1. General Precautions

☑ Prepare DNA and RNA in separate fume hoods, if possible.

☑ Use disposable, RNase-free plasticware for everything. This avoids confusion.

☑ Use separate solutions for the preparation of DNA and RNA.

☑ Do not share your solutions and do not use anyone else's.

☑ Use dedicated micropipettes for DNA and RNA *only*.

☑ Avoid contamination by rigorously cleaning micropipettes and rinsing their exterior and interior shafts with 70% ethanol (EtOH).

☑ Use sterile pipette tips that contain a physical barrier to prevent entrance of aerosols into the barrel.

Note: Most filter tips contain pure, polyethylene filter matrices, but self-sealing filters also employ cellulose gum additives, which "seal" on contact with liquids. These additives are not bound to the filter, can easily be deposited into samples and inhibit the PCR reaction.

☑ Regularly calibrate micropipettes (at least once a year; see **Chapter 4**).

☑ Dedicate one set of micropipette for use with DNase, and another one for use with RNase. Keep all RNases as far away from any RNA preparation as possible.

☑ Always have a supply of liquid N_2 available before disrupting tissue.

Although everyone dreads contamination of the PCR assay by amplified DNA from previous reactions, either one's own or one's colleagues, the actual extent of contamination may not be as prevalent as expected.[2] Nevertheless, once a laboratory has become contaminated with amplified DNA, it takes a major effort to get rid of it. Hence there are many strategies and protocols that are designed to minimize the risk of contamination. How useful they are is, of course, another matter. Preexposure of all PCR reagents to UV irradiation is one recommended solution.[3-5] UV irradiation of DNA results in the formation of pyrimidine dimers and thus prevents it from being an effective template in subsequent PCR assays. However, the practical value of UV irradiation is by no means clear.[6] A detailed characterization of the effects of UV irradiation suggests that whilst it can be effective in reducing contamination, it also has significant effects on the sensitivity of the PCR assay. Precisely how significant depends on target sequence[7,8] as well as on primer concentration and sequence.[9] Note that *Taq* polymerase is very sensitive to UV irradiation.[9] Furthermore, UV irradiation of polypropylene microfuge tubes[10] and polystyrene pipettes[11] can also cause an inhibition of DNA amplification. Therefore, (1) routine UV irradiation of reagents may cause more damage than prevent any contamination and (2) all plasticware should be removed from fume hoods and workspaces prior to routine overnight UV irradiation.

Plastics play a very important role in affecting the results of qPCR experiments. Microfuge tubes and micropipette tips are made of polypropylene. It has been known for a long time that the manufacturing process of polypropylene reagents can lead to the incorporation of contaminating chemicals that are extracted by aqueous or organic solvents.[12] However, there have been more recent reports that suggest that certain polypropylene surfaces are able to cause denaturation of DNA fragments[13] and cause it to adhere to the walls of microfuge tubes and pipette tips.[14] This is a particular problem at high ionic strength where polypropylene tubes can adsorb up to 92% of DNA present. Even in solutions of low or medium ionic strength, some polypropylene tubes can bind up to 25% of DNA, although 5% is more usual. The only tubes that do not have these undesirable properties are polyallomer tubes (Beckman) and Axygen MAXYmum Recovery polypropylene tubes. No contaminating ion releasing fluids are used during the manufacturing process and Axygen has made modification to the original polypropylene resin and improvements to the molding process. This results in polypropylene plasticware that is free from occlusions and cavities which can cause sample retention and denaturation in standard polypropylene. Instead, fluid retention is 5–6-fold lower than with standard tips. This is important to anyone who has prepared sufficient master mix for 98 reactions only to find that there is only enough for 94 assays, with the remainder taken up with pipetting error and/or fluid retention. Axygen also manufactures tips using MAXYmum recovery polypropylene.

5.2. DNA

5.2.1. Preanalytical Steps

DNA is the heritable repository of an organism's genetic make-up, and the rapid isolation and analysis of DNA is a fundamental requirement for numerous diagnostic, forensic biotechnology, and research applications. DNA is remarkably stable, and amplifiable DNA is obtainable from virtually any source,[15] although, obviously, the quality of a DNA preparation from a freshly lysed tissue culture cannot be compared to the quality of DNA obtained from an ancient Egyptian mummy. Luckily, the type of question asked from a PCR assay, e.g., is there a translocation event, pathogen, transgene, etc., or not, does not depend on maintaining the integrity of large molecules of genomic DNA. However, it does depend on extracting the DNA without copurifying any contaminant that could inhibit the PCR reaction or indeed result in amplification bias.[16] The extensive optimization required to obtain DNA preparations without inhibitors of the PCR reaction is illustrated by a recent report[17] in which considerable modification of existing clinical extraction protocols are described. This is of course particularly important when considering multiplex analyses.[18]

There are numerous components within blood and tissue that can inhibit PCR assays. Inhibition has been reported when extracting DNA from ancient human remains,[19] possibly caused by the copurification of collagen.[20] Mammalian blood, especially the heme compound,[21] is well known for containing inhibitors of the PCR assay[22,23] with as little as 1% v/v blood inhibiting *Taq* polymerase.[24] This, apart from being a nuisance for research applications, creates serious practical problems in forensic investigations where PCR reactions are carried out on extracts of dried blood stains or for clinical diagnostic assays where the aim is to detect pathogens.[25] The "FoLT" (formamide low temperature) PCR protocol for amplification of DNA directly from whole blood without any preparative steps is designed to overcome these problems.[26] This protocol relies on the use of an appropriate anticoagulant, preferably sodium heparin or EDTA, which are superior to lithium or fluoride heparin, and of formamide at 18% v/v as well as reduced incubation temperatures (cycles of 85°C, 40°C, 60°C). This allows up to 10% (v/v) whole blood to be added directly into the tube containing the PCR mixture. FoLT PCR probably works by reducing the amount of protein coagulation and allowing more DNA template to be accessible for amplification. Another protocol allows the amplification by PCR of human chromosomal DNA sequences from whole blood samples (up to 80% v/v), with EDTA, citrate, or heparin used as the anticoagulant.[27] Amplification requires the freeze/thawing of the sample (to lyse the leukocytes) and optimization of salt (K^+ and Mg^{2+}) according to sample volume and type of anticoagulant used. In addition, EDTA-treated blood samples require a heat treatment before PCR for maximal amplification.

One interesting and on the face of it surprising, protocol reports the use of TaqMan™ chemistry to genotype single nucleotide polymorphisms (SNP) in unprocessed whole blood and serum samples.[28] The key to success is that blood or serum samples are deposited at the bottom of standard 96-well microtiter plates used for real-time PCR and are allowed to dry at room temperature. Plates can be stored at 4°C for several months before analysis. PCR reactions were carried out by adding PCR master mix to the in-well dried samples and using DNA polymerase from *Thermus brockianus* (DynAZyme II; Finnzymes). The reaction buffer was standard buffer containing Triton X-100. FAM and TET were used as reporters for the wild-type and variant alleles respectively, with DABCYL as the quencher. The authors demonstrate the detection of accurate and reproducible allele-specific fluorescence signals, suggesting that DNA in the dried blood and serum spots is available for PCR amplification and that inhibitory substances, or material quenching the fluorescence signal, are not efficiently released into the PCR mixture. Under these conditions even the more fussy *Taq* polymerase can amplify DNA.[29] When these results were compared to those obtained with whole blood, or if serum was mixed in with the PCR master mix, complete inhibition of the reaction was observed.

Humic acid is a common inhibitor of PCR reactions carried out on DNA extracted from soil,[30] and inhibitors are present in DNA extracted from food,[31] with calcium an important culprit,[32] although it is perfectly possible to perform qPCR assays on nucleic acid extracted from cells in milk.[33] One important aspect of any inhibition of the PCR assay is this may compromise PCR as a diagnostic tool. For example, chain-terminating drugs such as acyclovir used in the treatment of retro viruses inhibit *Taq* DNA polymerase, producing a false-negative result in some patients.[34] High levels of copurified RNA can also result in failure of the PCR assay.[35] Culture media, components of DNA extraction reagents,[31] and even the use of wooden toothpicks to pick bacterial colonies have been reported as inhibiting the PCR reaction.[36] Last, but not least, inhibitors can be selective: Skeletal muscle has been reported to contain inhibitors that inhibit one polymerase, e.g., *Taq*, but not *Tth* polymerase.[37] Indeed, for many applications *Taq* polymerase may be less robust than other enzymes.

Therefore, a useful DNA purification protocol has to fulfill three criteria:

1. It must result in a reproducible yield.
2. It must avoid the copurification of PCR inhibitors.

3. It must generate DNA that can be stored safely for extended periods of time.

Obtaining reproducible DNA yields from tissue samples can be difficult, since yield is affected not just by the protocol used to extract the DNA but depends also on the amount, type, age, and quality of the starting material. Any conclusions following its amplification may also be dependent on the precise source of the DNA template. DNA is found in the blood of many cancer patients:[38-40] DNA levels are higher in serum than plasma, but levels are not correlated. Only serum DNA levels are associated with the presence of liver metastases, whereas only plasma DNA is predictive for recurrence.[41] Furthermore, tumors and cell lines are often polyploid[42] which will also affect DNA yield. It is worth remembering that a purification method that works well for one particular tissue type may result in the copurification of PCR inhibitors if applied to another tissue type.[43,44] Furthermore, many infectious agents are fastidious and are grown on blood culture material that usually contains the anticoagulant and anticomplementary agent sodium polyanetholesulfonate, a potent PCR inhibitor,[45] as well as contaminating microbial DNA.[46] Extraction of DNA from plant cells can present a particular challenge as the methods used for growing plants can influence subsequent nucleic acid purification by affecting the production and accumulation of plant metabolites such as polysaccharides, polyphenolics, and flavones.[47] The efficiency of many DNA isolation techniques is affected by the presence of such metabolites, and the presence of these compounds can reduce the performance of PCR assays.

The best DNA yield and quality is usually achieved from fresh material. However, if samples cannot be processed immediately, they must be snap frozen and stored at $-70°C$. Repeated freezing and thawing should be avoided, as this can lead to a reduced yield, especially of viral DNA from clinical samples. Apart from this, no special precautions need to be taken, and as long as protocols are followed faithfully and good laboratory practice is followed, DNA extraction will always be successful. For the moment, the main question remaining is whether it is better to use well-loved homegrown protocols or trust one of the numerous commercial purification kits on the market. Soon, automated extraction protocols will be sufficiently reliable for the researcher to entrust his precious samples to a robot and expect to obtain high-quality, high-yield DNA preparations.[48]

5.2.2. Sample Collection

5.2.2.1. Tissue Culture

☑ Harvest cells, centrifuge, remove supernatant, and store cells at $-70°C$.

5.2.2.2. Bacteria/Yeast/Solid Tissue

☑ Snap freeze in liquid N_2, store at $-70°C$, and process within 3 months.

☑ Animal and human tissue can also be fixed for storage using alcohol and formalin. Long-term storage of tissues in formalin will result in chemical modification of the DNA. Fixatives that cause cross-linking, such as osmic acid, should not be used. It is also possible to isolate DNA from paraffin-embedded tissue[49-52] and use it for promoter methylation studies.[53]

5.2.2.3. Blood

☑ Blood samples should be collected in EDTA tubes to prevent coagulation and can then be stored for up to 48 h at 5°C.[1] The inhibition of the PCR reaction by Heparin[54-56] can be reversed by incubating DNA with heparinase II prior to PCR.[57]

☑ For long-term storage, blood nuclei can be prepared and stored at $-20°C$.

☑ Freezing is not recommended as the disruption of the red blood cells results in the release of vast amounts of PCR-inhibiting heme.

☑ It is easiest to use a commercial kit as DNA prepared from blood often contains inhibitors of the PCR reaction.

5.2.2.4. Plants

☑ Place plants in darkness for up to 48 h before harvesting to prevent the accumulation of metabolites.

☑ Nucleic acid yields from young tissue are often higher than from old tissue because young tissue generally contains more cells than the same amount of older tissue. In addition, young tissue of the same weight contains fewer metabolites.

☑ When using fresh leaves, tissue can be harvested by cutting discs (e.g., with a hole puncher) and collecting the disks in the lid of a microfuge tube. A leaf disk with a 1.5 cm diameter weighs 25–75 mg.

☑ Leaves and needles from most species can be stored for up to 24 hours at 4°C without affecting yield or quality. Tree buds can be stored for several days at 4°C. Tissues stored at 4°C should be kept in a closed container to prevent dehydration.

☑ If it is not practical to store frozen samples for DNA preparation, a number of methods are available for lyophilizing plant tissue. To prevent DNA degradation, material should be completely desiccated in less than 24 hours and kept in darkness at room temperature under desiccating or hermetic conditions.

5.2.3. Disruption

Efficient disruption of cells or tissue is an obvious requirement for maximizing DNA yield from what is often a unique sample. There is a bewildering array of methods, both homegrown and commercial, and DNA yield and quality are optimized by choosing the protocol most appropriate to the target nucleic acid and type of starting material. Disruption is usually achieved by a combination of mechanical (e.g., grinding, bead mill, or sonication), chemical treatment (e.g., detergent lysis), and enzymatic digestion (e.g., lysozyme, zymolase, and lysostaphin digestion of bacterial or yeast cell walls and Proteinase K to digest proteins). The aim is to disrupt the cell, inactivate any nucleases present, and remove some of the contaminating proteins that can interfere with the efficient purification of the DNA. The final step involves filtration or precipitation to remove cellular debris.

Note: Small amounts of proteinase K activity can survive phenol extraction and heat inactivation and will subsequently inactivate RT-PCR enzymes.[58]

Rotor-stator homogenizers disrupt animal and plant tissues in 5–90 seconds by a combination of turbulence and mechanical shearing. Foaming of the sample should be kept to a minimum by using properly sized vessels, by keeping the tip of the homogenizer submerged, and by holding the immersed tip to one side of the tube. Rotor-stator homogenizers are available in different sizes and operate with probes of different sizes. Probes with diameters of 5 mm and 7 mm are suitable for volumes up to 300 µl and can be used for homogenization in microfuge tubes. Probes with a diameter of 10 mm or above require larger tubes.

When using a bead mill for disruption, the sample is agitated at high speed in the presence of beads. Disruption occurs by the shearing and crushing action of the beads as they collide with the cells. Disruption efficiency is influenced by the size and composition of beads, speed, and configuration of agitator, the ratio of buffer to beads, disintegration time, and the amount of starting material. Results can be quite variable, and the efficiency of disruption of normal tissue biopsies is significantly better than with cancer biopsies. The optimal beads to use are 0.1-mm (mean diameter) glass beads for bacteria, 0.5-mm glass beads for yeast and unicellular animal cells, 3–7 mm stainless steel beads for animal tissues, and 3–7 mm stainless steel or tungsten carbide beads for plant and fungal tissues. It is essential that glass beads are pretreated by washing in concentrated nitric acid (see **Subsection 5.3.4.5**). Alternatively, use commercially available acid-washed glass beads (Sigma-Aldrich, *Cat. No. G8772*).

5.2.3.1. Tissue Culture

Tissue cultures cells are lysed efficiently using lysis buffer and protease or proteinase K.

5.2.3.2. Bacteria

Many bacterial cell cultures can be efficiently lysed using lysis buffer and protease or proteinase K. Some bacteria, particularly Gram-positive bacteria, require preincubation with specific enzymes (e.g., lysozyme or lysostaphin) to lyse the rigid, multilayered cell wall. Bacterial DNA can also be isolated from a wide variety of clinical samples. Bacterial cells should be pelleted from biological fluids, and the DNA should be isolated as described for bacterial cell cultures. Swab samples should be pretreated with fungicide before centrifugation of bacterial cells.

5.2.3.3. Yeast

Yeast cell cultures must first be treated with lyticase or zymolase to digest the cell wall. The resulting spheroplasts are collected by centrifugation and then lysed using lysis buffer and proteinase K or protease.

5.2.3.4. Virus

Virus particles may need to be concentrated before DNA isolation by ultracentrifugation, ultrafiltration or precipitation. Addition of carrier DNA may also be necessary during DNA isolation when the expected yield of DNA is low. Integrated viral DNA is prepared using the same procedure as for isolation of genomic DNA from the relevant sample.

5.2.3.5. Solid Biopsies

Fresh or frozen tissue samples should be cut into small pieces to aid lysis prior to mechanical disruption using a homogenizer, mixer mill, or mortar and pestle. Skeletal muscle, heart, and skin tissue have an abundance of contractile proteins, connective tissue, and collagen, and care should be taken to ensure complete digestion with protease or proteinase K. For fixed tissues, the fixative must be removed prior to lysis.[49-52] Formalin can be removed by washing the tissue in PBS. Paraffin should similarly be removed from paraffin-embedded tissues by extraction with xylene followed by washing with ethanol. Viral DNA is typically isolated from cell-free body fluids, where their titer can be very low.

5.2.3.6. Blood

Erythrocytes from birds, fish, and frogs contain nuclei and hence genomic DNA, while those from mammals do not. Since there are approximately 103 times more erythrocytes than nuclei-containing leukocytes, removing the erythrocytes prior to DNA isolation can give higher DNA yields. This can be accomplished by several methods. One is selective lysis of erythrocytes, which are more susceptible than leukocytes to hypotonic shock and burst rapidly in the presence of a hypotonic buffer. Alternatively, Ficoll® density-gradient centrifugation can be performed to recover mononuclear cells and remove erythrocytes. This technique also removes granulocytes. A third method is to prepare a leukocyte-enriched fraction of whole blood, "buffy coat," by centrifuging whole blood at $3,300 \times g$ for 10 minutes at room temperature. After centrifugation, three different fractions are distinguishable: the upper clear layer is plasma; the intermediate layer is buffy coat; and the bottom layer contains concentrated erythrocytes. Blood samples, including those treated to remove erythrocytes, can be efficiently lysed using lysis buffer and protease or proteinase K.

5.2.3.7. Plants

The cell walls of plants make disruption of plant cells very difficult. However, complete disruption of cell walls, plasma membranes, and organelle membranes is essential to release the entire DNA contained in the tissue as insufficient disruption result in low yields. Cell wall properties vary widely between different species and different methods are required to achieve complete disruption. The most common disruption method involves freezing samples in liquid nitrogen and grinding with a mortar and pestle. Alternative protocols are available, usually adapted for a specific tissue (e.g., young leaves) and involve crushing the tissue with a glass rod, plastic pestle, or wooden stick and result in DNA yields which are 20–80% of the yields obtained using standard disruption using a mortar and pestle. Tissue powder can be used directly for nucleic acid purification. After disruption and lysis, the lysate may be viscous and must be homogenized.

5.2.4. Purification

5.2.4.1. Commercial Kits

There are numerous kits available from large and small manufacturers. Many are based on the Tri reagent protocol[59] (Invitrogen DNAzol®, *Cat. No. 10503-027*; Molecular Research Center TRI REAGENT®, *Cat. No. TR-118*); others use a combination of proprietary lysis and extraction methods followed by gel filtration to prepare DNA free from salts, unincorporated nucleotides or excess primers and involve minimal hands-on time (Qiagen's separate DNeasy kits for tissue, bacteria, and yeasts (*Cat. No. 69504*), plants (*Cat. No. 69103*), blood (*Cat. No. 51104*), stool (*Cat. No. 51504*); Sigma Aldrich's GenElute™ for mammalian cells (*Cat. No. G1N10*), plants (*Cat. No. G2N10*), blood (*Cat. No. NA2000*), and bacteria (*Cat. No. NA2100*)). A third protocol (Stratagene RecoverEase™, *Cat. No. 720202*) separates the nuclei isolated after disaggregation of the tissue, releases the DNA following incubation with proteinases and overnight dialysis to remove any protein. On the plus side, these kits are quick and easy and take the tedium out of extracting DNA. On the minus side, yields may be a little lower; they are less flexible than homegrown protocols and certainly more expensive.

Note: Failure to extract DNA from tissue or biological fluids using a commercial kit is not necessarily due to the investigator's incompetence. It might simply be that the particular kit being used is not appropriate for the tissue.[60]

5.2.4.2. Homegrown Protocols

Most laboratory-developed protocols involve the use of organic solvents, usually phenol and chloroform and/or selective precipitation with high concentrations of salt to remove proteins. They tend to be time consuming and tedious; nevertheless they are cheap and produce large amounts of DNA of a quality that is more than sufficient for qPCR applications. The following protocol works well with animal tissue biopsies, but is easily modified for extraction of DNA from other sources. Its main disadvantage is that in its full form it takes a long time to complete. However, note that the various short cuts indicated significantly reduce the time required.

1. Precool mortar to $-20°C$ and keep on dry ice. Pour liquid N_2 into the mortar and precool pestle by placing the grinding end in the liquid N_2.

2. Use 5–50 mg frozen tissue biopsy for each DNA extraction.

3. Cut larger samples into small pieces (approximately 5 mg each) on plastic dish covered with parafilm using a clean scalpel. Keep sample as cool as possible.

4. Place tissue in precooled mortar and grind until a fine, whitish powder results.

5. Grind tissue in liquid N_2 to a fine powder using mortar and pestle. Add more liquid N_2 as required to keep frozen.

Tip: In our hands this produces the best yields. A bead mills or a rotor-stator homogenizers are alternatives when the amount of tissue is a limiting factor and they certainly are more convenient, especially when processing several samples at the same time; although they do tend to yield less DNA.

6. Allow the liquid N_2 to evaporate and use a precooled spatula to add the powdered tissue to a microfuge tube containing 100 μl of extraction buffer (10 mM *Tris* pH 8, 100 mM EDTA pH 8, 20 μg/ml pancreatic RNase, 0.5% SDS. Ensure the liquid N_2 has evaporated completely before vortexing briefly and placing the sample at 37°C for 1 h.

 Tips: RNase treatment is recommended since RNA contamination in a DNA preparation can chelate Mg^{2+} and reduce the yield of the PCR. Make certain any DNases have been inactivated by boiling the RNase for 10 min. Alternatively, trust the manufacturer and buy DNase-free RNase.

7. Add 400 μl of lysis buffer (50 mM *Tris* HCl pH 8, 200 mM NaCl, and 20 mM EDTA, pH 8, 1% SDS).

8. Add 80 μl of proteinase K (10 mg/ml) and incubate up to 4 h at 55°C (ideally with gentle rotation).

 Tips: Make up proteinase K stock and freeze in aliquots. A rotating hybridization oven is ideal for the incubation step.

9. Add 500 μl of phenol neutralized with TE buffer (10 mM *Tris*-HCl, pH 7.5, 0.1 mM EDTA). This is best purchased preequilibriated and stored at 4°C for use or aliquoted and stored at –20°C. Mix by inverting repeatedly. Rotate for at least 2 h at room temperature.

 Tips: Phenol extraction removes proteins from nucleic acid samples. **Phenol is harmful in contact with skin and if swallowed. Contact with acids liberates toxic gas.** Inadequate removal of protein contamination by inadequate mixing is the most common source of protein contamination. It is important to create an emulsion between the organic and aqueous phases, either by vortexing or if the aim is to generate very high-quality DNA, by extended rocking.

10. Centrifuge in a refrigerated microfuge at 5°C and maximum speed (approximately 12,000 rpm) for 15 min.

 Tip: The low temperature helps form a clearly defined organic/aqueous interface.

11. Carefully draw off 400 µl of aqueous (***upper***) phase and place in new 2-ml microfuge tube.

    Tips: Use 1-ml pipette tips with the ends cut off. It is tempting to remove too much of the aqueous phase after centrifugation, thus running the risk of contaminating the DNA with some of the flocculent material (which contains cell debris) at the aqueous/phenol interface. It is better to back extract by adding half a volume of lysis buffer to the spent phenol solution, which is vortexed or rocked and centrifuged. Following removal of the aqueous layer, both aqueous solutions can be pooled.

12. Add 200 µl of lysis buffer, mix by inverting, and repeat **step 10**.

13. Draw off 200 µl of aqueous (***upper***) phase and combine with the 400 µl from **step 11**.

14. Add 600 µl of chloroform-isoamyl alcohol (24:1). Mix by inverting tubes.

15. Centrifuge in a refrigerated microfuge at 5°C and maximum speed for 15 min.

16. Carefully draw off 500 µl of aqueous (***lower***) phase and place in new 2-ml tube.

    Tip: Use 1-ml pipette tips with the ends cut off.

17. Add 100 µl of TE buffer, vortex briefly and repeat **step 15**.

18. Draw off 100 µl of aqueous (***upper***) phase and combine with the 500 µl from **step 16**.

    Tip: Repeat **steps 14** through **18** until the interface is clear.

19. Add 3 M sodium acetate, pH 5.2, to 10% (v/v) and mix tube contents.

A. High-quality DNA

20a. For highest quality DNA, carefully layer two volumes of cold (–20°C) 95% EtOH from the freezer onto the DNA solution. Do not invert. There is no need to place the tube in the freezer.

    Tip: Not freezing the tubes prevents co-precipitation of salt.

21a. The buffer/EtOH interface may become cloudy with high molecular weight DNA. DNA can be spooled using a curved

Pasteur pipette and placed into a new tube containing 500 μl of 70% EtOH.

Tip: To make a curved Pasteur pipettes, place it horizontally, 10 cm from the end, into the pilot light of a Bunsen burner. When the glass softens and the tip drops, remove it and let it cool. Then re-heat and seal the tip of the pipette.

22a. Swirl the DNA in the 70% EtOH to displace it from the Pasteur pipette. **Go to step 23**.

B. Small quantities/quick DNA preparation

20b. Small quantities of DNA cannot be spooled; therefore, if the yield is likely to be less than 10-15 μg, you must centrifuge.

21b. Add two volumes of cold (–20°C) 95% EtOH from the freezer onto the DNA solution. Mix well by inverting tube several times. There is no need to place the tube in the freezer. Centrifuge in a refrigerated microfuge at maximum speed for 15 min. Decant or pipette off EtOH taking care not to disturb the pellet.

22b. Wash with 500 μl of 70% EtOH.

Tip: The 70% EtOH wash is very important as it removes residual salts from the DNA pellet. Salt carried over into the final DNA preparation can interfere with PCR assays. DNA is not soluble in 70% EtOH, so there is no need to worry about losing the pellet in too large a volume. Cover the pellet and vortex briefly or place in shaking water bath for 15 min. It is important that the pellet comes loose from the side of the tube so that the EtOH can penetrate the sample. Centrifuge in a microfuge at top speed for 15 min. Aspirate off the EtOH and recentrifuge in a microfuge at top speed for 2 min. Aspirate off the remainder of the EtOH with a drawn-out Pasteur pipette. (To make drawn-out Pasteur pipettes, soften the pipette tip with a flame and draw the tip out with forceps, then break the tip at the narrowest point).

23. Centrifuge in a refrigerated microfuge at maximum speed for 15 min. Decant or pipette off EtOH taking care not to disturb the pellet.

24. Place tubes at between 37°C and 65°C to dry off the remaining EtOH.

25. Dissolve in 20 μl to 100 μl TE buffer (10 mM *Tris*-HCl, pH 7.5, 0.1 mM EDTA), place at 50°C for 1 h, then in the refrigerator overnight.

    Tip: DNA should be stored in TE buffer to prevent acid hydrolysis that can occur when stored in water.

26. Quantify DNA concentration in each tube. It is probably best not to dilute the DNA at this stage.

    Tip: Expect 1–5 μg DNA/mg tissue.

5.2.5. Long-Term Storage

Divide DNA samples into eight 50-μl aliquots microfuge tubes and freeze seven aliquots at –80°C, keeping one for immediate use. This sample can be diluted to a standard concentration (100–250 ng/μl).

Note: Some viral DNA levels can remain stable whether the DNA is stored as purified DNA or unextracted DNA in a whole specimen.[61]

5.3. RNA

The quantification of mRNA copy numbers has become an indispensable tool for anyone interested in gene expression profiling. This is because the ability of a cell to adjust mRNA copy numbers is one crucial component of the regulation of gene expression in response to changes in the cellular environment. In addition, a wide spectrum of biological and pathological processes is associated with alterations in gene expression at the mRNA level. Alterations in mRNA levels are regulated by numerous endogenous and exogenous stimuli and are the result of at least two processes: (1) increased or reduced transcription caused by highly complex combinatorial control mechanisms[62] and (2) changes to mRNA stability, with the degradation rates of different mRNAs varying over a broad range.[63]

Unlike DNA, which is as tough as old boots, RNA is extremely delicate. Therefore, RNA purification is much trickier than that of DNA and must fulfill the following criteria:

1. It must be of the highest quality; unlike with DNA, this is essential if quantitative results are to be relevant.

2. It should be free of DNA, especially if the target is an intron-less gene

3. There must be no copurification of potential inhibitors of the RT step.

4. RNA must be free of nucleases for extended storage.

mRNA, the target of many qPCR experiments, is present as a small percentage of total RNA, generally 1–5% and can be divided into three general classes based upon relative abundance (the average number of molecules of that RNA species per cell). **Table 5.1** gives an indication of the extent of the problem when attempting to quantitate a low abundance mRNA target from a tiny biopsy. Manufacturer's model systems claim easy and reproducible detection of single copies of mRNA. In reality, detection—never mind accurate quantification—of such mRNAs is very difficult to achieve. The source of mRNA is disparate and includes not just easy *in vitro* material such as tissue culture cells, but *in vivo* biopsies obtained during endoscopy, post-surgery, postmortem, and from archival materials. Each has unique problems and the following pages contain guidance on how to maximize the chances of reliably quantifying low abundance mRNA targets.

Table 5.1. Abundance of mRNAs.

Abundance	No. of copies/cell	No. of Different messages/cell	Abundance of each message
Low	~ 10	~ 11,000	< 0.004%
Intermediate	~ 200	~ 500	< 0.1%
High	~ 12,000	~ 10	3%

5.3.1. Preanalytical Steps

Naked RNA is extremely susceptible to degradation by endogenous ribonucleases (RNases) that are present in all living cells. Surprisingly, there are several reports that suggest an unexpected degree of *in vivo* stability in unfavorable circumstances such as in tissue obtained from post-mortems. In these cases, there can be very little degradation of total RNA or mRNA for up to 96 h post-mortem and tissue can remain frozen for 15 years without evidence of deterioration from storage.[64-67] Not surprisingly, there is some variation in the observed degradation depending on the tissue type being sampled, but it tends to suggest that degradation by endogenous RNases, i.e., those present on hands and on the surfaces of any material likely to come into contact with these precious samples, might be most to blame for poor quality RNA preparations. Therefore, while it is important to ensure the rapid and efficient inhibition of the action of endogenous RNases, the key to the successful isolation of high quality RNA and to the reliable and meaningful comparison of qRT-PCR data is to ensure that no exogenous RNases are introduced during the extraction procedure.[68] A second problem in the design of experiments for quantification of mRNA levels is that mRNA expression profiles can change rapidly after cells or tissue samples have been collected, but before they have been frozen. Most researchers obtain their tissue or cell samples from a wide variety of sources and the ease and speed with which it can be collected and processed will differ widely. Frequently, samples are collected by operating theatre staff; hence it is important that any protocol is simple and can be carried out without too much hassle and inconvenience to the surgeon or theatre nurse. Therefore, appropriate sample acquisition has a major influence on the quality of the RNA and subsequently on any result of qRT-PCR assays[69] and it is essential to develop routine protocols that standardize the pre-analytical steps for different sources of biological material.

5.3.2. General Considerations

RNases are extremely stable, found everywhere and are very active. They are difficult to inactivate and even minute amounts are sufficient to destroy RNA, especially over extended storage periods. Since some RNases do not require cofactors, chelating agents such as EDTA that protect DNA from DNases by binding divalent cations, have no effect on the activity of these RNases.

☑ Always aliquot RNA, keep the aliquot in use on ice, with tubes closed for as long as possible. When finished using a tube, close lid and refreeze as soon as possible.

Tip: Always keep a microfuge rack in a dry ice/EtOH bath next to you and as soon as you are finished with your tube, place it into that rack. Stratagene's Stratacooler (*Cat. No. 400008*) is a very useful device for keeping samples cold.

☑ Proper microbiological, aseptic technique should always be used when working with RNA.

Tip: Paranoia is an essential attribute for anyone hoping to avoid inadvertently introducing RNases into the RNA sample during or after the isolation procedure.

☑ Gloves are an absolute must when carrying out any experiment involving RNA as RNases are present on the skin and the most obvious introduction of RNases into the sample occurs when pressing one's thumb inside a microfuge cap (Ambion have coined the term "fingerase").

Tip: Use unpowdered gloves.

☑ Presterilized, disposable plasticware and pipette tips should be used at all times, but it is important to confirm that they are certified to be RNase-free.

Tip: Pipette tips must be of the filter-variety. Most filter tips contain pure, polyethylene filter matrices, but self-sealing filters also employ cellulose gum additives, which "seal" on contact with liquids. These additives are not bound to the filter, can easily be deposited into samples and inhibit the RT-PCR reaction.

☑ Daily swabs of work surfaces and centrifuges are not necessary.

Tip: Daily swabbing can actually help spread RNases. If you must swab, use RNase*Zap* from Ambion (*Cat. No. 9784*).

☑ The use of diethylpyrocarbonate (DEPC)-treated reagents is not essential.

Note: This may be an unexpected statement but as well as being toxic, DEPC degrades RNA if not removed completely from solutions by autoclaving.

5.3.3. Tissue Handling and Storage

Once a biological sample has been obtained, immediate stabilization of RNA is the most important consideration.[70]

Note: The time cells or tissue spend in ice-cold PBS prior to disruption/homogenization should be minimized as RNases remain active and expression profiles may be altered. However, note the observations with respect to RNA stability discussed above. Conventionally, solid tissue biopsies are snap frozen in liquid N_2 and stored at −80°C. Once frozen, they must be kept frozen. However, sometimes it is not possible to freeze tissue immediately or a sample has to be shipped to a different location. Here RNA*later*™ (Ambion, *Cat. No. 7021* or Qiagen, *Cat. No. 76106*) can provide a convenient solution. It has been used successfully to extract RNA from ocular tissue,[71] skin,[72] cancers,[73] and from flow cytometrically purified epithelial cells.[74] RNA*later* solution is a collection of salts (mainly ammonium sulfate) that salts out proteins (i.e., RNases) inside the cell. Placing samples in RNA*later* is meant to obviate the need for elaborate precautions when obtaining the tissue and allow tissue to be transported more conveniently. It is important to cut the sample into slices no thicker than 0.5 cm, so that RNA*later* can rapidly penetrate the sample. It is also important to add sufficient RNA*later* (approximately 100 μl per 10 mg of tissue) for the tissue to be completely submerged.

Note: Researchers' experience with RNA*later* separates them into two camps: one that swears by its use, another that finds it totally useless ("RNA*never*"). It is possible that there is some tissue-specific variation in its effectiveness but we obtain more consistently high-quality RNA preparations from human breast, colon, and lymph node biopsies when these are resuspended in RNA*later* prior to freezing. RNA*Later Ice* (Ambion) has recently been introduced into the portfolio of RNA protecting solutions and is designed for protecting frozen tissue samples as they defrost, prior to RNA extraction.

Tip: Since RNA*later* is a concentrated salt solution; small chunks of tissue may actually float on top. Briefly vortex the sample before placing in refrigerator.

The preservation of the original cellular RNA profile is a particular problem with cells extracted from whole blood[75] and mRNA profiles can change over several orders of magnitude even in the short time it can take from collecting the blood to processing it in the laboratory. The causes for this are RNA degradation, the induction of certain genes, e.g., Cox-2, as well as the method of RNA preparation.[76] Furthermore, blood is notorious for containing numerous inhibitors of the PCR reaction.[21,22,45] The PAXgene™ Blood RNA System (PreAnalytiX) allows the collection, storage, stabilization, and isolation of RNA from whole-blood samples.[77] The system consists of proprietary tubes that contain a stabilizing reagent that permits blood samples to be stored for several days whilst maintaining the mRNA expression profile and an RNA extraction kit that is based on spin columns. An interesting report describes a different distribution of splice variants of the Neuro-fibromatosis 1 (*NF1*) gene in samples collected in PAX gene and EDTA vacutainers,[78] emphasizing the need to be very careful when interpreting results.

There is another problem with isolating RNA from blood: Increasing evidence shows that tumor-derived RNA is present in the plasma/serum of cancer patients. The variety of RNA targets that have been detected include tyrosinase mRNA in 6/8 serum samples from patients with melanoma,[79] telomerase RNA template (5/18 serum samples) and hTERT (6/16 serum samples) in breast cancer patients,[80] hTERT in plasma from controls and patients with colorectal cancer and follicular lymphoma,[81] cytokeratin 19 in plasma samples from both controls and breast cancer patients,[82] and viral RNA in the plasma of 55/57 patients with nasopharyngeal carcinoma[83,84] and even GAPDH.[85] This RNA is particle-associated[85] and very stable and can be detected after serum has been stored frozen for many years.[79] Some of the markers are present in control samples, while others are found at higher levels in cancer patients. Whilst this may well be significant for early detection of cancer, it suggests that quantitative RT-PCR assays carried out using whole blood samples may generate false results. If significant levels of GAPDH are found in plasma, it is likely that most other mRNAs are also present.

5.3.4. Disruption/Homogenization

Efficient tissue homogenization is a key step in extracting RNA from in vivo tissue samples[86] and the speed and efficiency of cell disruption and subsequent homogenization has a direct effect on both RNA yield and quality. Cell disruption releases endogenous RNases that must be inactivated quickly and completely. Storage in RNA*later* and immediate homogenization in a chaotropic-based cell lysis solution such as TRIzol® (Invitrogen) or RNAzol® (Molecular Research Center) will effectively prevent degradation of RNA.

Note: Chaotropic agents denature proteins by disrupting hydrophobic interactions, thus affecting their secondary structures and increasing their solubility in water.

The exact disruption/homogenization method used depends on the cell or tissue type, and tissues high in fat, such as those obtained from mammary tissue, require additional pretreatment such as extraction with chloroform to remove lipids. The recommended procedures are listed in **Table 5.2**.

Table 5.2. Summary of recommended disruption/homogenization procedures.

Sample	Disruption/Homogenization
Tissue culture cells	Lysis buffer or Omni Rotor-Stator with disposable probes or Qiashredder
Tissue biopsies	Omni Rotor-Stator with disposable probes or 5-mm steel beads in bead mill/Mortar & Pestle
Plant	Mortar and pestle or 5-mm tungsten carbide beads in bead mill
Yeast	Lyticase/zymolase or 0.5-mm glass beads in bead mill
Bacteria	Lysozyme/syringe and needle or sonication

5.3.4.1. Tissue Culture Cells

Cells grown in suspension:

1. Count the number of cells.
2. Collect cells by centrifugation at 300 g and remove supernatant.

Note: Do not wash cells to minimize RNase degradation. If samples are frozen, add TRIzol®/RNAzol® to the frozen pellet.

3. Immediately snap freeze or add 1 ml lysis solution, e.g., TRIzol® or RNAzol®, per 10^7 cells.

4. Vortex and pipette to ensure complete lysis.

Cells grown in monolayer:

1. Determine the area of the culture dish (see **Table 5.3**).

2. Carefully aspirate tissue culture medium.

Note: Do not disrupt cells with trypsin as this releases RNases.

3. ***Immediately*** add 1 ml lysis solution, e.g., TRIzol®/RNAzol®, per 10-cm² area of culture dish.

Note: Calculate the volume of reagent needed based on the area of a culture dish and not on cell number as the use of an insufficient amount of TRIzol®/RNAzol® may result in contamination of the isolated RNA with DNA.

Table 5.3. Relationship between tissue culture vessel and cell number.

Tissue culture vessel	Growth area (cm²)	Approximate cell number
Flasks		
50 ml	25	3×10^6
250 ml	75	1×10^7
650 ml	175	2×10^7
Dishes		
35 mm	10	1×10^6
60 mm	21	3×10^6
100 mm	56	7×10^6
150 mm	145	2×10^7
Multiwell plates		
6-well	10	1×10^6
12-well	4	5×10^5
24-well	2	3×10^5
48-well	1	1×10^5
96-well	0.5	5×10^4

4. Use a spatula to scrape cells and debris into a collection tube.
5. Vortex and pipette to ensure complete lysis.

5.3.4.2. Animal Tissues

The best RNA yield is obtained from tissue that has been diced into small fragments with a scalpel prior to being frozen by submerging in liquid N_2. It can then be disrupted using a prechilled pestle and mortar under liquid N_2, with the powdered tissue added to lysis buffer. The samples must be homogenized using a bead mill or a mechanical homogenizer followed by further enzymatic digestion. Adipose tissue is best disrupted and homogenized using a polytron homogenizer.

Note: A 3-mm cube of animal tissue weighs approximately 30 mg.

5.4.3.3. Blood

The method of RNA isolation from blood has a significant impact on the sensitivity and reproducibility of qRT-PCR assays.[87] Freezing blood lyses all cells and reduces yield and quality of RNA. The removal of red blood cells, which contain RNases, is required to maximize RNA yield from the nucleated white blood cell population. Also, heme or porphyrin coextracted with RNA inhibits *Taq* polymerase. It is best to use a commercial kit optimized for RNA purification from blood. There is some evidence that RNAzol® extraction provides highest yield as well as least DNA contamination.[88] However, in our experience the optimal method is very much de-pendent on the operator, with some finding spin column-based methods more reliable and convenient. Heparin inhibits the RT step in a dose-dependent manner above a concentration of 1×10^{-4} U/ml.[89,90] It is not just used as an anticoagulant but is present in peritoneal mast cells at levels sufficient to case complete inhibition of the RT-PCR assay; heparinase treatment can restore RT activity.[91]

Note: There are several reports that suggest that RT-PCR assays carried out on RNA prepared from whole blood can be as sensitive as assays carried out on rigorously purified RNA[90,93] and successful amplification even from frozen whole blood using a two-enzyme/two-tube assay (MMLV-RT and *Taq* polymerase) has been reported.[94] Another surprising, recent report describes the successful detection of measles virus RNA from whole blood spotted and dried on to filter paper.[95]

5.3.4.4. Plant Tissues

Effective purification of RNA from most plant cells is significantly more difficult than from animal cells. In addition to being encased in a durable cell wall made from cellulose and pectins,[96] plant tissues contain a high abundance of polysaccharides and phenolics, terpenes, tannins, and other secondary metabolites that can co-precipitate with RNA.[97] The additional manipulations required to extract high-quality RNA from plant tissue exacerbate the problems arising from the presence of both endogenous and exogenous RNases. The levels of endogenous RNases can be enhanced under certain conditions, e.g., wounding, pathogen attack or phosphate starvation. The use of chaotropic agent-based extraction buffers is essential to help denature those RNases and the addition of proteinase K will digest them. The two major problems, then, are (1) that variability in the ability to completely disrupt cellular integrity will result in variable RNA yields and (2) that copurification of inhibitors will affect subsequent RT-PCR assays. The extent to which these cellular constituents interfere with the isolation of RNA varies significantly between plant species, tissue types, environmental conditions, and developmental stages. Of course, this is less important when performing qualitative assays, but it becomes crucial when attempting to quantitate mRNA copy numbers. Grinding tissue snap frozen in liquid N_2 using a pestle and mortar is the most effective way of disrupting plant tissue, especially when lignified from secondary growth. Sometimes, even that is not sufficient and woody or fibrous tissue may require the use of a grinding mill, such as a hammer mill.[98]

Tubers, fruit seeds or cotyledons accumulate relatively high levels of polysaccharides, many of which have chemical properties similar to those of nucleic acids. Therefore, they may copurify with RNA, hinder the resuspension of precipitated RNA, interfere with absorbance-based quantification, and affect the RT-PCR assay itself.[99] Excess polysaccharides can be removed either by selective precipitation of the polysaccharide or by selective precipitation of the RNA. Polysaccharides can be precipitated selectively by using 30% EtOH with low salt concentration,[100] 20% EtOH with 500 mM potassium acetate,[101] 70% EtOH with 2 M NaCl[99] or by adding KOAc to 200 mM.[102] RNA is selectively precipitated in the presence of 2 M LiCl[101] or extensive washing of an RNA pellet with 3M NaOAc.[103]

The *in vivo* compartmentalization of phenolics and other secondary metabolites is totally disrupted by homogenization and is a second factor complicating the extraction of RNA from plant tissue. Again, phenolics will co-purify with RNA, interfere with absorbance-based quantification, and affect the RT-PCR assay.[97,104] Furthermore, phenolics can cross-link to RNA and interfere with RNA purification protocols.[105] Treatment of a plant tissue lysate with polyvinylpyrrolidone (PVP), which acts by hydrogen bonding and precipitating such compounds, before the RNA isolation is carried out can prevent such chemical interactions with released RNA. Furthermore, the addition of a reducing agent such as β-mercaptoethanol or dithiothreitol prevents oxidation of phenolics by limiting the free-radical-dependent cross-linking.[101,103] Alkaline buffers or buffers with a high concentration of borate are another way to limit potential problems with polyphenolics during the RNA isolation step.[105]

Note: The use of "Plant RNA isolation aid," Ambion *Cat. No. 9690*, is highly recommended.

5.3.4.5. Yeasts

Yeast can form nearly indestructible spores that are very resistant to disruption. Hence it is important to use actively growing cells for RNA extraction. Three methods are in common use: (1) hot-phenol, which disrupts cells by vigorous mixing of cells with acidic phenol in the presence of SDS at 65°C; (2) use of a bead mill with small glass beads allows extraction of the RNA with phenol at room temperature; (3) yeast cell walls can be digested with zymolase, glucalase, and /or lyticase to produce spheroplasts that are readily lysed by vortexing in a guanidinium-based lysis buffer.

Note: Enzymatic digestion is less advisable because it is likely that the mRNA expression profile will be altered.

To obtain RNA from yeast:

1. Soak 0.5-mm glass beads in concentrated nitric acid for 1 h, wash thoroughly with ddH$_2$O and dry at 80°C overnight.

   Note: Carry this step out in a fume hood, as nitric acid can cause severe burns.

2. Harvest approximately 10^7 yeast cells (late log phase) from about 20 ml of appropriate medium and transfer cells to 50-ml Falcon tube. Spin 3,000 rpm in refrigerated table-top centrifuge for 5 min at RT.

3. Wash pellet with RNase-free water at RT.

Note: The pellet can be stored at –70°C for extended periods of time.

4. Vortex, transfer to 50-ml corex tube, and repellet at 3,000 rpm for 5 min.

5. Add 1 ml of TRIzol® reagent to the sample and vortex vigorously to resuspend cell pellet.

Note:

Yeast cells	Beads (ml)
$< 10^7$	2
$< 5 \times 10^7$	3
$< 10^8$	4

Add glass beads to around 3/4 of the level of the organic phase meniscus. Vortex 2 min at max speed.

Transfer solution to 1.5-ml microfuge tubes. Separate phases by centrifugation. After centrifugation, the phenol layer plus the interphase should be just below the surface of the beads, allowing easy retrieval of the aqueous phase without disturbing the interphase.

5.3.4.6. Bacteria

Bead milling will lyse most bacteria, and bacterial cell walls can be digested with lysozyme to form spheroplasts. Gram-positive bacteria usually require more rigorous digestion (increased incubation time, increased incubation temperature, etc.) than Gram-negative organisms. The spheroplasts are then easily lysed with vigorous vortexing or sonication in lysis buffer. Ambion's Gramcracker (*Cat. No. 1904*) reagent is a commercial alternative for the degradation of bacterial cell walls.

1. Harvest approximately 10^7 bacterial cells and carefully remove supernatant by aspiration.

Note: Accurate determination of bacterial cell number is not straightforward since different bacterial species show different OD values at the same wavelength. Also, there is significant variation in RNA content between species. As a very rough guide, 10^7 cells contain between 0.5–2 μg of RNA.

2. Resuspend the bacterial pellet in 100 μl of TE buffer containing lysozyme and incubate at 25°C.

Note: Gram-positive bacteria: use 3 mg/ml lysozyme and incubate for 10 min. Gram-negative bacteria: use 200 μg/ml and incubate for 5 min. For best results make up lysozyme fresh and do not freeze/thaw.

3. Add 1 ml of TRIzol® reagent to the sample and vortex vigorously.

4. Homogenize the lysate by repeated passing through a syringe and 20-gauge needle.

Alternative protocol

A rapid and simple method for total RNA extraction from Gram-negative bacteria, some Gram-positive bacteria, and yeasts was published recently. It generates high RNA yields while avoiding the use of phenol or other toxic reagents.[106]

1. Inoculate a bacterial or yeast colony in liquid YED medium (0.5% yeast extract, 0.5% glucose) or Nutrient Broth (Difco Laboratories, Detroit, Mich.) +0.4% lactose from a fresh plate culture and grow at 28°C for 24 h.

2. Harvest cells from 1 ml of the culture in exponential growth phase (approximately 1×10^8 cells/ml) by centrifugation at 10,000 × g for 5 min at room temperature.

3. Freeze at –20°C.

4. Resuspend thawed cells in 200 μl of 0.1% N-lauroyl sarcosine sodium salt and collect by centrifugation at 10,000 × g for 5 min at room temperature.

5. Add 100 μl of acetate/SDS solution (1% SDS in 10 mM EDTA, 50 mM sodium acetate, pH 5.1 adjusted with acetic acid) to the cells and heat the mixture at 100°C for 5 min.

6. Adjust the acetate/SDS solution to pH 5.1 to obtain DNA-free RNA.

7. Dilute the suspension with 900 µl of H_2O and centrifuge at 7,000 × g for 5 min at room temperature.

8. Store RNA samples at –80°C.

5.3.4.7. Disruption/Homogenization Aids

Qiagen's QIAshredder (*Cat. No. 79654*) and Invitrogen's Homogenizer (*Cat. No. 12183-026*) spin columns take some of the tedium out of homogenizing tissue culture cells and tissue biopsies. The Retsch Grinding Mixer Mills work by agitating the sample at high speed in the presence of beads. The MM200 can process sample volumes from as little as 0.2 ml in batches of up to 10 samples with tandem grinding containers, and the more expensive MM301 can process up to 20 samples. Disruption and simultaneous homogenization occur by the shearing and crushing action of the beads as they collide with the cells. Disruption efficiency is influenced by: size and composition of beads, speed and configuration of agitator, ratio of buffer to beads, disintegration time, and the amount of starting material.

When using a mortar and pestle, it is best to place the (fresh or frozen) sample in liquid N_2 and grind to a fine powder ensuring the liquid N_2 does not evaporate. Once the tissue has been ground to a suitable consistency, pour the powder/liquid N_2 suspension into a tube cooled in a dry ice/ethanol bath. As soon as the liquid N_2 is evaporated, lysis buffer can be added. Note that grinding will disrupt the tissue, but not homogenize it.

The luxury option, and the one yielding the best results with minimal effort, makes use of Omni's Rotor-Stator. The Omni TH, which can be post-mounted and the Omni µH, which is battery or a.c. power operated, are the two most useful microhomogenizers for high-quality RNA preparations. They can deliver speeds up to 25,000 rpm with pulse operation up to 30,000 rpm. Probes can either be made from stainless steel or plastic and be autoclavable and reusable. In addition, there are disposable probes of 7 mm diameter and 65 mm or 110 mm in length that fit directly into microfuge or test tubes.

Stainless steel generator probes are offered in many configurations tailored for specific sample types, and various probe sizes can process samples from 0.1–100 ml. Flat bottom probes are recommended for liquid or soft tissues while saw teeth and extended blades are best for processing fibrous tissues. For situations where pre-processing or cutting the tissue prior to homogenization is inconvenient, widened window openings allow for larger pieces of sample to effectively pass through the processing head where shearing occurs. Plastic Omni Tip generator probes are ideal for situations where molecular contamination between samples cannot be tolerated. They have good chemical resistance to weak acids, chlorides, hypochlorites, and many other chemicals, including phenol. Omni lists several factors that can affect processing efficiency:

1. The size and type of material being processed—Solid particles, in any dimension, should be no more than half the diameter of the generator probe for optimal processing.

2. The higher the processing speed, the more the efficiency of both plastic and stainless steel generator probes is enhanced.

3. Container geometry and size—Round vessels encourage swirling while fluted or cornered vessels disrupt flow patterns, thus allowing for more effective mixing to occur. The vessel length and diameter must be considered when selecting the generator probe, as this will determine the size of the generator probe chosen.

5.3.5. RNA Extraction

RNA extraction protocols use either organic extraction to remove DNA, proteins, lipids, and fats from the RNA, followed by alcohol precipitation, or they use solid phase purification in an aqueous environment. The main disadvantages of any organic extraction protocol are that the reagents are hazardous and any contamination of the final RNA preparation can interfere with the accuracy of quantification and further downstream processing. Solid phase purification protocols have no real disadvantages, except for cost. Selection for mRNA is not usually necessary, and indeed the extra steps involved may lead to additional variability between samples. It is the quality of the RNA preparation, rather than the use of total or mRNA that has the most significant effect on the result.

Note: Total RNA preparations contain variable amounts of "junk" RNA such as unspliced or partially spliced RNA that might interfere with accurate quantification. It is still unclear how much of a problem this can really cause, but one way of avoiding this is to prepare cytoplasmic RNA extracts, even from tissue biopsies.[107] On the other hand, it has been demonstrated recently that ribosomes are present in the nucleus and localize to transcription sites, associating with newly transcribed RNA polymerase II transcripts.[108] This association is not limited to a few loci, but is a global phenomenon in which essentially all transcriptionally active regions of the chromosome have coupled ribosomal subunit and translation factors. Therefore, preparation of RNA from cytoplasmic fractions may avoid one set of problems only to generate another that will also result in inaccurate quantification

5.3.5.1. Commercial Kits

As with DNA, there are homegrown as well as commercial alternatives to isolating A. Numerous suppliers offer a bewildering selection of kits, many based on the guanidine thiocyanate, phenol:chloroform principle (Invitrogen's TRIzol®, *Cat. No. 15596-026*, Sigma-Aldrich's Tri Reagent, *Cat. No. T9424*, Ambion's Totally RNA™, *Cat. No. 1910*, and Stratagene's MicroRNA extraction kit, *Cat. No. 200344*). Alternatives use RNA-adsorbing silica/glass-based spin-columns that depend on the tendency of nucleic acids to adsorb to silica/glass in the presence of a chaotropic salt.[109] Columns fit into microfuge tubes and cell lysate is forced through the filters either by centrifugation or under vacuum. The best known of these are Ambion's RNAqueous™ kits, *Cat. No. 1912*, Qiagen's RNeasy™ system, *Cat. No. 74104*, Roche's High Pure™ RNA Isolation Kit, *Cat. No. 2033674*, Invitrogen's "Micro-to-Midi Total RNA purification System," *Cat. No. 12183-018*, and Stratagene's Absolutely RNA™ kit, *Cat. No. 400805*. Ambion's "RNAqueous™-4 PCR" kit (*Cat. No. 1914*) is very useful since it includes DNase I and the DNA-free™ removal agent (*Cat. No. 1906*) that we have found to be a highly convenient and reliable method for removing DNA contamination from RNA preparations.

Commercial kits are increasingly tailored for specific applications and tissues and are ideal if there is very little starting material.[110] They are usually significantly more expensive per sample than homemade solutions; however, since RNases are always lurking around the corner, and the manufacturer will have quality controlled their kits (one hopes) it often makes sense to use commercial reagents and/or kits. Certainly, it allows concentration on the scientific problems under investigation, rather than wasting time ensuring consistently high RNA quality preparations of buffers and reagents sourced from numerous suppliers or colleagues. Use of commercial suppliers *should* ensure adequately pure and consistent reagents that actually work.

5.3.5.2. TRIzol® Protocol

In our experience, the best combination of RNA yield and quality is obtained using TRIzol (Invitrogen Gibco-BRL reagent, *Cat. No. 15596-026*) or RNAzol (Molecular Research Center, *Cat. No. TR 118*), monophasic solutions of phenol and guanidine isothiocyanate although this method is not nearly as convenient as spin column-based methods and care must be taken to avoid contamination with reagent. These reagents are improved versions of the single-step method for total RNA isolation.[111] In the presence of chloroform or bromochloropropane, the solution separates into an aqueous phase and an organic phase. RNA remains exclusively in the aqueous phase and most proteins and DNA fragments are in the organic phase. RNA is recovered by precipitation with isopropyl alcohol and DNA can be recovered by precipitation with EtOH from the interphase. This is very useful, since this allows quantitative recovery of RNA and DNA from the same tissue sample. Following the homogenization step, the entire procedure can be completed in about one hour and up to 10 samples can be handled comfortably at any one time.

1. Cut out piece of aluminium foil 2 cm^2 and weigh. Precool a mortar to $-20°C$ and keep on dry ice. Pour liquid N_2 into the mortar, and precool a pestle by placing the grinding end in the liquid N_2.

2. Cut tissue biopsies (up to 30 mg) into small pieces (approximately 5 mg each) on glass plate covered with parafilm. Place on foil, fold foil securely, and submerge in liquid N_2.

Tip: Any handling of cells prior to the addition of TRIzol™ increases the risk of mRNA degradation. Use clean scalpel and parafilm for each new sample.

3. Weigh and replace in liquid N_2 for 30 min. Record the weight of the tissue.

 Tip: Use long forceps to hold foil parcel above liquid N_2 to allow it to drain off.

4. Carefully open aluminium foil and rinse the tissue into the pre-chilled mortar with stream of liquid N_2.

5. Grind tissue in liquid N_2 to a fine powder using a mortar and pestle. Use a spatula and liquid N_2 to collect the tissue at the bottom of the mortar, then pipette into a microfuge tube.

 Tip: Poor yield is often associated with incomplete disruption. Use Rotor-Stator if budget allows.

6. Allow the liquid N_2 to evaporate and add 500 µl of TRIzol™ (10 v/v of sample) to the powdered tissue.

 Tip: Keep a careful eye on proceedings. Do not add TRIzol™ too soon, as it may bubble over; do not add it too late, since the tissue must not be allowed to defrost.

7. Homogenize the tissue for 1–5 min using a bead mill.

 Tip: Alternatively you can pass the solution several times through a 20-gauge needle. Large molecular weight DNA left intact by incomplete homogenization reduces RNA yield. At this stage, if absolutely necessary, samples can be stored at –80°C for at least one month.

8. Incubate the sample at 30°C for 5 min. This permits the complete dissociation of nucleoprotein complexes.

 Tip: Samples with high protein, fat, polysaccharide or ligneous content require an additional purification step. A red color in the aqueous phase suggests the presence of residual fat that picks up red color from the TRIzol™. Following homogenization, insoluble material is removed from the homogenate by centrifugation at $12,000 \times g$ for 10 minutes at 5°C. The resulting pellet contains membranes, polysac-

charides, and high molecular weight DNA, while the supernatant contains RNA. In samples from fat tissue, an excess
of fat collects as a top layer, which should be removed. In
each case, transfer the cleared homogenate solution to a fresh
tube before continuing with the next step. For RNA extractions from blood, any traces of iron or hemoglobin can
give a yellow/maroon color. This inhibits the PCR reaction and suggests an insufficient TRIzol™ /sample ratio.

9. Add 1 ml of chloroform, cap tightly, and shake vigorously for up
    to 1 min. Incubate at 30°C for 5 min.

Tip: Chloroform used for phase separation must not contain
isoamyl alcohol or any other additive. Alternatively, add
50 μl of bromochloropropane (Molecular Research Center,
Cat. No. BP151), which is less toxic than chloroform and
its use may reduce the possibility of contaminating RNA
with DNA.[112]

10. Centrifuge the sample at 12,000 × *g* for 15 min at 5°C.

Tip: Centrifugation must be performed at 5°C, otherwise a residual amount of DNA may sequester in the aqueous phase.
Following centrifugation, the mixture separates into a lower
red phenol-chloroform phase, cloudy interphase, and the
colorless aqueous (*upper*) phase. RNA remains exclusively in the aqueous phase whereas DNA and proteins
are in the interphase and organic phase, respectively. The
volume of the aqueous (*upper*) phase will be about 300 μl.
A precipitate forming in the bottom of the tube suggests
the presence of polysaccharides or proteoglycans. This is
solved by removing the aqueous phase and modifying
the isopropanol step to 0.25 volumes of 1.2 M sodium citrate, 0.8 M NaCl, and 0.25 volumes of isopropanol.

11. Transfer the aqueous (*upper*) phase to a fresh microfuge tube.
    Save the organic phase for extraction of DNA (see **Section 5.3.6**).

12. Reextract the aqueous (*upper*) phase with 200 μl of chloroform at
    least once, preferably twice, until the interface is clear.

Tip: This step is critical, as any contamination of the aqueous
(*upper*) phase will result in the introduction of RNases.

13. Spin the combined, reextracted aqueous (***upper***) phases at maximum speed for 5 min. This ensures that any remaining chloroform is at the bottom of the tube and will not contaminate the aqueous (***upper***) phase. Remove the upper phase, making absolutely sure you do not touch the chloroform phase, measure its volume.

14. Add an equal volume of isopropanol to the tube, mix by inverting tube, then leave at room temperature for 10 min. This is the RNA precipitation step.

   Tip: Efficient precipitation of nucleic acids is one of those topics where every researcher has their own idea of what works best.[113] Most accept that they will lose as much as 50%, especially when working with very dilute samples. The presence of a pellet is always reassuring, but this is only visible when extracting significant amounts of nucleic acid. Some protocols suggest the addition of glycogen or tRNA as carriers to maximize RNA yield. However, glycogen may be contaminated with DNA and, less critically, can prevent RNA from solubilizing. The addition of RNA, to RNA that will be used for qRT-PCR, does not seem advisable, either. If a carrier is required, linear acrylamide is a better and less expensive option. It can be prepared by adding 5 mg of acrylamide (***not bis-acrylamide***) to 200 µl of TE, followed by 1 µl of 10% APS and 1 µl of TEMED. Allow polymerization at room temperature (it will take anything up to 30 min). Add 500 µl of EtOH and microfuge for 10 min. Take off EtOH, dry in a Speed Vac and resuspend in 500 µl of ddH$_2$O. The acrylamide will take several hours (overnight) to resuspend and the solution will turn clear. Aliquot and store in refrigerator for up to a year. Use 1–2 µl per precipitation.

15. Pellet the RNA by centrifuging the samples in a microfuge at 12,000 × g for 15 min at 5°C. Pour off the supernatant.

   Tip: The pellet forms a gel-like or white pellet on the side and bottom of the tube. Some tissue, e.g., liver, has high glycogen content. Glycogen can be removed by adding 500 µl of 4M LiCl, vortexing briefly and precipitating the RNA by centrifuging in a microfuge at maximum speed for 15 min.

16. Resuspend the RNA pellet in 500 µl of ddH$_2$O and transfer to a clean microfuge tube.

17. Add 50 µl of 3 M Na-Acetate, pH 5.2 and 1,100 µl of isopropanol, mix by inverting tube, then leave at room temperature for 10 min.

18. Centrifuge in a microfuge at 12,000 × g for 15 min at 5°C. Remove supernatant.

19. Wash with 1 ml 70% EtOH. Vortex to resuspend the RNA pellet.

Tip: Take care not to contaminate the sides while washing the precipitate.

20. Centrifuge in a microfuge at 12,000 × g for 15 min at 5°C. Remove supernatant.

21. Repeat **steps 19** and **20**.

22. Remove residual liquid with a drawn-out Pasteur pipette.

23. Air-dry for 15 min.

Tip: The pellet should not be clear, as this indicates overdrying. If RNA has been overdried, place the RNA pellet and TE buffer overnight together at –80°C. The freeze–thaw process helps in subsequent solubilization. Partly solubilized RNA has an A$_{260}$/A$_{280}$ ratio of less than 1.6. To improve solubility, heat to 60°C with intermittent vortexing or by passing the RNA through a pipette tip.

24. Dissolve in 50–200 µl of TE buffer and place at 50°C for 10 min to aid resuspension. Typical RNA yields are shown in **Table 5.4**.

Tip: Prepare a 50-ml stock of TE, aliquot into microfuge tubes and freeze. Discard each aliquot after each use. Alternatively use Ambion's RNA Storage Solution (*Cat. No. 7000*), which minimizes strand scission of RNA that can occur if RNA is heated in the presence of divalent cations such as Mg^{2+} or Ca^{2+}.

25. Store at –80°C.

Tip: For long-term, archival storage of RNA, it should be kept as an NH$_4$OAc/ethanol precipitate in several aliquots at –80°C. The low pH will stabilize the RNA and the high alcohol content and low temperature will completely inhibit all enzymatic activity. RNA can be stored in this fashion for years.

Table 5.4. RNA yield from different samples.
Note that actual yield is very variable. However the table provides
a typical expected yield.

Source	Yield of total RNA	Source	Yield of total RNA
Cultured Cells		**Human**	
Amniocytes	7–10 µg/10^6 cells	Whole blood	15–50 µg/ml
Chorionic villi	3–20 µg/10^6 cells	NBC	10–15 µg/10^6 cells
K562 cells	10–20 µg /10^6 cells	bone marrow	0.3–0.8 µg/10^6 cells
HeLa	15–25 µg/10^6 cells	normal colon	0.2–2.0 µg/mg
T84	5–15 µg/10^6 cells	colon cancer	1.0–5.0 µg/mg
HT-29	10–20 µg/10^6 cells	normal breast	< 0.05 µg/mg
Caco-2	5–10 µg/10^6 cells	breast cancer	2.0 µg/mg
Dog cells	5–25 µg/10^6 cells	**Plants**	
Bacteria/yeast		*Alfalfa* (cotyledons)	0.1–0.5 µg/mg
Escherichia coli	0.5–1 µg/10^7 cells	*Arabidopsis* (leaves)	0.1–0.5 µg/mg
Bacillus subtili s	0.3–0.5 µg/10^7 cells	*Chlamydomonas*	2–20 µg/ml
Actinomyces viscosus	0.05–0.1 µg/10^7 cells	Soybean (leaves)	1.5–2.0 µg/mg
Saccharomyces cerevisiae	1–2 µg/10^7 cells	Corn (leaves)	0.2–1.5 µg/mg
Rodent		Garlic (leaves)	0.5 µg/mg
brain	0.6–1 µg/mg	Grass (s eeds)	0.5–1.5 µg/mg
bladder	0.05–0.1 µg/mg	Lettuce (leaves)	0.01–1.5 µg/mg
heart	0.6–1 µg/mg	Onion (leaves)	0.5 µg/mg
kidney	1–4 µg/mg	Oats leaf (leaves)	0.5 µg/mg
liver	3–8 µg/mg	Rice (leaves)	0.2–0.5 µg/mg
lung	0.4–1 µg/mg	Soybean (leaves)	0.3–0.7 µg/mg
muscle	0.5–1 µg/mg	Sugarbeet (leaves)	0.05–0.02 µg/mg
ovary	1.0–1.5 µg/mg	Sunflower (leaves)	2–3 µg/mg
pancreas	1.0–4.0 µg/mg	Tomato (leaves)	0.6 µg/mg
spleen	3.0–4.5 µg/mg	Tobacco (leaves)	0.6 µg/mg
tail	2.0–4.0 µg/mg	Wheat (root)	0.5 µg/mg
thymus	1.0–3.0 µg/mg	**Others**	
Avian		*Caenorhabditis elegans*	0.1–1.0 µg/mg
liver	3–8 µg/mg	*Drosophila*	0.3–1.5 µg/fly
lung	1–6 µg/mg	Paraffin-embedded tissue	0.1–2 µg/mg
muscle	0.2–0.5 µg/mg	Alcohol fixed tissue	2.5–4.5 µg/mg
		Formalin fixed tissue	0.03–0.20 µg/mg

5.3.6. Simultaneous DNA Extraction

DNA in the interphase and phenol phase from the initial homogenate
can be recovered quantitatively when using TRIzol™ and this allows
for the determination of the DNA content in analyzed samples.[114] This
has the advantage of allowing the normalization of the results of qPCR

assays per genomic DNA instead of the more variable total RNA or tissue weight.

1. Precipitate the DNA from the interphase and organic phase with EtOH. Add 0.3 ml of 100% EtOH per 1 ml of TRIzol™ used for the initial homogenization and mix samples by inversion.

2. Place the samples at 30°C for 2 min and sediment DNA by centrifugation at no more than 2,000 × *g* for 5 min at 5°C.

3. Remove the phenol–EtOH supernatant and wash the DNA pellet twice in a solution containing 0.1 M sodium citrate in 10% EtOH. Use 1 ml of the solution per 1 ml of TRIzol™ used for the initial homogenization. At each wash, leave the DNA pellet in the washing solution for 30 min at 30°C with periodic mixing and centrifuge at 2,000 × *g* for 5 min at 5°C.

   Note: An additional wash in 0.1 M sodium citrate/10% EtOH solution is required for large pellets containing more than 200 μg DNA or large amounts of a non-DNA material.

4. Suspend the DNA pellet in 75% EtOH (1.5 ml of 75% EtOH per 1 ml TRIzol™), place at 30°C with periodic mixing for 10 min, and centrifuge at 2,000 × *g* for 5 min at 5°C.

5. Air-dry the DNA for 15 min in an open tube. Do not dry under centrifugation, as it will be more difficult to dissolve.

6. Dissolve DNA in 8 mM of NaOH to a concentration of DNA of 0.2–0.3 μg/μl. Typically add 300–600 μl of 8 mM NaOH to DNA isolated from 10^7 cells or 50–70 mg of tissue.

   Note: Resuspending in weak base is highly recommended since isolated DNA does not resuspend well in water or in *Tris* buffers. The pH of the 8 mM NaOH is only around 9 and can be easily adjusted with HEPES once the DNA is in solution.

7. If the DNA preparation contains insoluble gel-like material such as membrane fragments, etc., centrifuge at more than 12,000 × *g* for 10 minutes at 5°C.

8. Transfer the supernatant containing the DNA to a new tube. Adjust samples with HEPES to pH 8 (add 101 μl of 0.1 M HEPES

to 1 ml DNA in 8 M NaOH) and supplement with 1 mM EDTA. Once the pH is adjusted, DNA can be stored at 4°C or –20°C.

5.3.7. DNA Contamination

RNA should be essentially free from contaminating DNA as this will produce the most reliable qPCR results.[115] However, some degree of DNA contamination can easily occur either if too little TRIzol™ was added to the sample at the beginning of the extraction or if some of the interphase was removed with the aqueous phase after the initial chloroform extraction. This raises the question of whether or how to remove traces of contaminating DNA. Undoubtedly the simplest solution is to use Ambion's DNase-free DNA Treatment and Removal reagent (*Cat. No. 1906*). Less expensive, but more likely to result in loss of RNA is to DNase-I treat and then remove the enzyme using a phenol extraction followed by EtOH precipitation.

Tip: Do not believe any manufacturer's claim that their reagent is RNase-free.[116] Whilst it is always agreeable to BOGOF (**b**uy **o**ne, **g**et **o**ne **f**ree), this is one instance when you should not avail yourself of the manufacturer's generosity. Always test the DNase on an expendable sample and use as little DNase for as short a time as you can get away with.

5.3.7.1. DNase I Digest

1. Incubate up to 10 µg of RNA in DNase buffer (10 mM *Tris* pH 7.5, 2.5 mM $MgCl_2$, 0.5 mM $CaCl_2$) using 2–5 units of DNase I in a 100-µl reaction. Incubate for 30 min at 37°C.
2. Add 100 µl of phenol/chloroform to the DNase digest.

Note: It has been reported that the use of Mg^{2+} containing buffer for DNase I cleavage of DNA contaminants in RNA samples leads to DNA artifacts after RT-PCR. These are absent if Mn^{2+} buffer (1 mM final concentration) is substituted.[117]

3. Vortex intermittently and centrifuge at top speed in a refrigerated microfuge at 5°C for 2 min.
4. Transfer the aqueous (***upper***) phase into a new tube.
5. Back extract the organic phase with 50 µl of TE buffer.
6. Repeat step 3 and combine the two aqueous phases.

7. Add 15 µl 3M NaCl and 300 ml of 100% EtOH (ethanol). Mix well.
8. Store for 15 min in dry ice/EtOH bath.
9. Centrifuge in refrigerated microfuge at 5°C at top speed for 15 min. Discard supernatant.
10. Cover the pellet with a layer of 500 µl of 70% ethanol. Vortex to resuspend pellet.
11. Centrifuge in refrigerated microfuge at 5°C at top speed for 15 min. Discard supernatant.
12. Air-dry the pellet. Resuspend the RNA in 50 µl of TE-buffer.

Note: If you are a gambling person, you might consider this regime to be over-the-top, and believe that it is possible that 10 min incubation at 75°C is sufficient to destroy all DNase activity and preserve 100% of RNA integrity.[118]

5.3.8. Preparation of RNA from Flow Cytometrically Sorted Cells

Flow cytometry is a powerful technique for analyzing large populations of single cells that are labeled with fluorescent stains selecting user-specified traits such as their position in the cell cycle, their apoptotic state, or it allows the evaluation and purification of neoplastic cells. Clearly, the isolation of RNA from flow-sorted cells would be extremely valuable for expression profiling of defined cell populations. However, whole-cell sorting typically involves treating cells in organic fixatives, followed by staining with tissue specific antibodies in an aqueous solution. Therefore, at first sight it does not appear ideally suited to the purification of high-quality RNA. Nevertheless, there have been several reports that suggest that high-quality RNA, as judged by *in vitro* translation assays, can be obtained from such cells.[119-122] However, these are, by molecular biology standards, positively antique old protocols whose usefulness is limited by the need for extensive precautions against RNase activity and the rapid loss of RNA in the post-fixation aqueous solutions. A recent protocol that uses RNA*later* has been described for the isolation of high-quality RNA suitable for microarray analysis from flow cytometrically purified whole epithelial cells.[74] It allows the preservation of RNA during fixation, immunofluorescent cytokeratin labeling, and subsequent sorting of whole cells. A549 lung adenocarcinoma cells and cells obtained from mastectomy samples were fixed in RNA*later*. Single cell suspensions were stained with fluorescent antibodies to cytokeratin and a nuclear counterstain and were sorted by DNA content and cytokeratin staining intensity using a flow cytometer. RNA was isolated using the Totally RNA Kit (Ambion, *Cat. No. 1910*) according to standard protocols and the integrity of RNA was assessed by measuring the relative 3' and 5' levels of GAPDH mRNA in a one-enzyme/one-tube real-time RT-PCR assay using ABI's EZ kit. The samples prepared in RNA*later* retain high 3'/5' C_t ratios for GAPDH, whereas those not prepared in RNA*later* are rapidly degraded. By this criterion, the quality of the RNA obtained from RNA*later*-treated cells and tissues was equivalent to control RNA and superior to RNA obtained from cells fixed in the traditional manner (EtOH/acetic acid fixation). Agarose gel analysis confirmed these results.

5.3.9. Extraction from Formalin-Fixed and Paraffin-Embedded Biopsies

Every hospital contains vast archives of morphologically defined biopsies derived from normal and pathologically altered tissues for which extensive clinical data are available. Some types of biopsies taken for routine diagnostic purposes exist almost exclusively as fixed and embedded samples because the processing of fresh biopsies does not yield satisfying morphology. Retrospective analysis of this archival tissue could enable the correlation of molecular findings with the response to treatment and the clinical outcome. Hence a possible quantification of nucleic acids in these biopsies offers a promising extension of current methodology to study the pathogenesis of many different diseases.

Initially it was thought that the ability to extract RNA from such tissue would be of limited utility for retrospective analysis of archival tissue.[123] It is interesting that whilst every text book, manual, and protocol exhorts the user to ensure that RNA used for RT-PCR be of the highest quality, there are several reports that describe the isolation of RNA from, on occasion, decades-old formalin-fixed and paraffin-embedded archival material.[124-128] Following the successful use of such RNA in "quantitative" dot blot analyses,[129] it has proved to be useful for the detection of viral (high copy number) RNA.[130-134] The use of RNA extracted from archival material has been given a boost by the development of real-time assays[135] and methods have progressed so that it is possible to obtain RNA from LCM protocols.[136] The main problem is that fixation results in substantially degraded RNA due to cross-links between nucleic acids and proteins and covalently modifies RNA,[137] although there are differences of degree.[138] Not surprisingly, this makes subsequent RNA extraction, reverse transcription, and quantification analysis problematic.[139] However, recently methods have been developed where between 60%[140] and 84% (100% of samples less than 10 years old)[141] of templates can be amplified by RT-PCR, and it is remarkable that it is now apparently possible to quantitate accurately and reproducibly mRNA expression levels,[58,142-145] even after immuno-histochemical staining.[146]

Naturally there are some caveats. (1) Absolute quantification is not accurate, because absolute C_t values on fixed tissues are an average of 5 cycles higher than on matched fresh tissues.[58] This indicates that only one-thirtieth of the RNA in the reaction is accessible to cDNA synthesis. Presumably the remaining RNA is chemically altered by the formalin-fixation and paraffin-embedding and cannot be reverse transcribed. (2) Formalin fixation and paraffin embedding differentially affects different mRNAs and indeed different fragments of the same mRNA species. This may be a result of regulatory proteins binding to and then being cross-linked to different parts of the mRNA. (3) Since the RNA obtained from fixed tissues is highly degraded, the best RT-PCR results are obtained with amplicon sizes less than 130 bp. The C_t value increases in proportion to larger amplicon sizes. This decrease in sensitivity is much greater with RNA from fixed tissue than with control RNA from fresh tissue. This agrees with other estimate of an average size of 200–250 nucleotides for RNA extracted from archival biopsies.[135,147]

Note: The authors make the astute suggestion to carry out three separate cDNA synthesis reactions with different RNA input amounts (75–300 ng) for all quantitative analyses from archival material.[58] An analysis of three points should result in a linear decrease in C_t that corresponds to increasing RNA input in the RT reaction. If linearity is not observed, then the RT step is not quantitative, and therefore the results are questionable. Furthermore, the use of three RT points produces an estimate of the error associated with the measurement.

Another thought-provoking result suggests that pre-fixation time is not necessarily the major factor influencing the ability to quantitate gene expression in fixed tissues. *A priori*, one might expect mRNAs with short half-lives to disappear more quickly, and be more affected by longer pre-fixation times. However, it was found that leaving samples up to 12 hours in PBS before fixation and embedding did not change the relative expression of several genes studied, including c-*myc*. This is probably due to the fact that qPCR assays only require a small fragment of intact RNA, so the RNA can be substantially degraded and still be detected. But, more intriguingly, it suggests that while a biopsy remains intact, steady-state mRNA levels do not necessarily change. This agrees with the post-mortem studies previously described in this section. In support of this assumption, c-*myc* mRNA levels in a biopsy that had been stored frozen at −70°C dropped significantly over an 8-hour pre-fixation time course. This implies that, once frozen, tissue metabolism is stopped and steady-state levels of mRNA are then influenced only by degradation rates. On the other hand, many genes are affected by stress, hypoxia, depletion of nutrients, etc. One of such examples is Cox-2. For such gene expression measurements, if samples are not handled carefully, inappropriate significant changes may be reported and may preclude meaningful quantification from any tissues collected in an uncontrolled manner. For example, placing a colonic tissue biopsy into medium results in an immediate increase of Cox-2 mRNA levels. Clearly this is an area worth further investigation.

The problem with isolating RNA from formalin-fixed, paraffin-embedded tissue is that most samples will not have been processed for ease of RNA extraction at all, but to retain tissue morphology. Several protocols have been developed involving different fixatives and times of fixation that crucially affect the success of RNA extraction[138] with different fixatives that make it significantly easier to extract and amplify RNA.[148,149] Natural buffered formalin is the standard fixative used in histology because it preserves tissue morphology. However, overfixation (more than 24 h) may interfere with the extraction of amplifiable RNA due to the extensive modifications introduced, as discussed previously in this section; however, what constitutes overfixation depends on the fixative used.[133,150,151] The optimal time for RNA extraction and reproducible amplification varies and depends on the marker under investigation.[152] Ambion recommends no more than 24 h, although it is possible to amplify RNA from tissue that has been fixed for longer.

Ambion's Paraffin Block RNA Isolation procedure (*Cat. No. 1902*), recently replaced by Optimum FFPE RNA Isolation Kit (*Cat. No. 47000*) involves numerous steps, yet remains fairly simple. It starts by incubating paraffin-embedded tissue sections in xylene to remove the paraffin. Next, the xylene is removed by washing in alcohol. The tissue is then digested with Proteinase K, and solubilized in a guanidinium-based RNA Extraction Buffer to extricate the RNA and to inactivate RNases. Finally, the RNA is separated from other cellular components using Acid Phenol:Chloroform, and is precipitated with isopropanol, using linear acrylamide as a carrier. After DNase I treatment, the samples are ready for RT-PCR.

5.3.10. Specialized Expression Analysis

5.3.10.1. Nuclear poly(A)+ RNA

Quantification of mRNA levels from total RNA or mRNA samples prepared from cells or tissue biopsies represents the balance of mRNA transcription and degradation. Changes in target mRNA levels may be due to an altered rate of transcription, degradation or both. The problem is that it is impossible to tell which is responsible. Conventionally, nuclear run-on assays are used to measure the level of transcription of specific genes.[153] A recent report describes a rapid, sensitive, and high-throughput technique for extracting polyA+ RNA from the nuclei of tissue culture cells and analyzing mRNA levels via the reduction of the cytosolic components.[154] Cells are first trapped on the glass fiber membranes of 96-well filter plates and subsequently exposed to non-ionic detergent to achieve cell membrane permeation. The cytosolic components, which contain preexisting mRNA, are removed by washing with the appropriate buffer, while nuclei remained in the filter plates. Lysis buffer is then used to release nuclear mRNA, which is collected on oligo(dT)-immobilized PCR plates for the capture of poly(A)+ RNA, on which RT-PCR can be performed. Results obtained using this method relate to newly synthesized, rather than to preexisting mRNA and may provide a better guide to transcriptional changes. On the downside, it is not possible to carry out this enrichment on *in vivo* biopsies, recovery is limited to polyA-tailed mRNA, and the additional manipulations involved could induce or repress the transcription of target genes.

5.3.10.2. Polysomal RNA

Not every mRNA is translated, but if it is, it must be associated with ribosomes. In eukaryotic cells, translated mRNA is complexed with one or more ribosomes and such polysomes constitute the sites of protein synthesis. Polysomes can be size fractionated and separated from sub-polysomal material by centrifugation of cytoplasmic extracts through a sucrose density gradient. mRNA can be extracted from both the polysomes and the subpolysomal fraction and subjected to qRT-PCR assays. The distribution of any mRNA among the polysomal and sub-polysomal fractions provides information about whether a given mRNA is translated and if it is, about its translational efficiency.

5.4. Quantification of Nucleic Acids

Accurate quantification of nucleic acids is important for qPCR assays, since (1) the aim is to use as little template as possible to achieve a reproducible result as the template is often acquired from a irreplaceable sample, (2) addition of too much template can interfere with the PCR assay, and (3) sometimes normalization is carried out against DNA or total RNA.

5.4.1. Absorbance Spectrometry

The traditional method for measuring DNA concentration is the determination of the absorbance of UV light at 260 nm (A_{260}) in a spectrophotometer using a quartz cuvette. The amount of light absorbed by a sample is directly proportional to the concentration of protein and/or nucleic acid in the sample. Both DNA and RNA absorb maximally at 260 nm, and most proteins absorb strongest at 280 nm (A_{280}). However, nucleic acids also absorb significantly at 280 nm (50–55% of the absorbance at 260 nm), and most proteins can absorb strongly at 260 nm, with the absorbance varying depending on the protein. Obviously, for this method to produce accurate results, there must be no nucleotide, ssDNA, RNA, protein or phenol contaminants in the solution, the measurements must be made at neutral pH, and the concentration of the nucleic acid should be greater than 250 ng/ml. In addition, the absorbance method is relatively insensitive. For greatest accuracy absorbance readings should be no lower than 0.1, which corresponds to 5 µg/ml of dsDNA.

Note: The A_{260} value for oligonucleotides depends very much on the base composition since the extinction coefficients for G and A are much higher than those for T and C.

Spectrophotometric conversions for nucleic acids are shown in **Table 5.5**.

Table 5.5. Spectrophotometric conversions for nucleic acids.

$A_{260} = 1$	Concentration (µg/ml)
Double stranded DNA	50
Single stranded DNA	33
Single stranded RNA	40
Oligonucleotides	20–30

However, for ssDNA, this conversion applies only to longer nucleic acid molecules. For oligonucleotides, it is best to use the following formula:

concentration (pmol/µl) = $A_{260}/(100/(1.5{\times}A_n+0.71{\times}C_n+1.2{\times} G_n+0.84 {\times}T_n))$,

where n = number of each of the four bases.

Note: Transmission spectrophotometers use quartz cuvettes with two opposite optical windows, with the sides frosted for easy handling. Cuvettes must be matched if more than one cuvette is used and it is important to check that the optical faces of cuvettes are free of fingerprints and scratches.

Tips: Use www.geocities.com/CapeCanaveral/Lab/9965/ calculator-dnaconc.html to calculate concentration. We have long used the GeneQuant (Amersham Biosciences, *Cat. No. 80-2111-98*) to quantify nucleic acids.[155] It is reliable down to nucleic acid concentrations of about 30–50 ng, and automatically calculates concentrations and purity. It is a little cumbersome to use, especially when quantitating a large number of samples.

5.4.2. Fluorescence

Fluorescence assays are less prone to interference than A_{260} measurements and are also simple to perform. As with absorbance measurement, a reading from the reagent blank is taken prior to adding the DNA. PicoGreen™ (Molecular Probes, *Cat. No. P-7589*), a fluorescent dye that shows fluorescence enhancement when binding to dsDNA, provides an alternative to absorbance spectrometry for quantitating DNA. Following excitation at 485 nm, emission at 535 nm is measured in a fluorimeter. Its main advantages are the potential for high throughput, its wide linear response over four orders of magnitude and sensitivity that it is 100–1,000 times more than absorbance measurement. This allows the quantification of as little as 50 pg of dsDNA in a 200 μl volume. The assay can be carried out in the presence of ssDNA or RNA; however, the intensity of the signal is affected by salt, phenol, EtOH, detergent, and protein contamination of the DNA sample.

OliGreen™ (Molecular Probes, *Cat. No. O-7582*) has been specifically developed for the quantification of ssDNA in a fluorimeter and it can detect as little as 200 pg of ssDNA in a 200 μl volume. Quantification is accurate even in the presence of free nucleotides and the assay is suitable not only for quantitating pure oligonucleotides, but also for accurately quantitating oligonucleotides in mixtures as complex as blood plasma.[156] However, the OliGreen™ reagent does exhibit fluorescence enhancement when bound to dsDNA and RNA. Furthermore, OliGreen™ exhibits significant base selectivity and shows a large fluorescence enhancement when bound to poly(dT), but only a relatively small fluorescence enhancement when bound to poly(dG) and little signal with poly(dA) and poly(dC).

Tip: Fluorimeters use cuvettes with four optically clear faces, as excitation and emitting light enters and leaves the cuvette through directly adjacent sides. Thus, fluorometric cuvettes must be held by the upper edges only.

5.4.3. Purity

The usual method for measuring purity uses the ratio of A_{260} to A_{280} (R-value). For pure DNA, that ratio should be greater than 1.8. The absorbance maximum of phenol is 270–275 nm and for proteins 280 nm, hence contamination with phenol and proteins can mimic higher yield and purity. Proteins have A_{280} readings considerably lower than nucleic acids on an equivalent weight basis. Thus, even a small lowering of the A_{260}/A_{280} ratio can indicate severe protein contamination. Commonly used buffer components absorb strongly at 260 nm and can cause interference if present in high enough concentrations. EDTA, for example, should not be present at more than 10 mM. Absorbance at 325 nm indicates particulates in the solution or dirty cuvettes; contaminants containing peptide bonds or aromatic moieties such as protein and phenol absorb at 230 nm. The ratio is also influenced by pH as the A_{280} decreases with increasing pH, whereas the A_{260} is unaffected. Hence DNA resuspended in (unbuffered) water can result in a lower R-value and suggest a better DNA quality.

Tip: When diluting DNA, make sure it results in a reading that is within the linear range of the spectrophotometer (usually no less than 0.1 and no more than 1.0). The lower the concentration, the greater the error.

The absorbance minima of nucleotides are around 230 nm. Nucleic acid preparations should have an A_{260}/A_{230} ratio greater than 2.0, hence *Tris*, EDTA, organic solvents, and buffer salts can be detected by an abnormally higher than A_{230} absorbance.

Tip: Some impurities, which interfere with UV absorbance readings, can be removed by extraction of the preparation with *n*-butanol.

5.4.4. Quantification of RNA

Accurate quantification of mRNA levels by qRT-PCR depends crucially on the ability to measure the initial amount of RNA in the sample with high accuracy. This remains a real challenge, with all methods commonly used to do this suffering from some disadvantages.

5.4.4.1. Spectrophotometer

The concentration of RNA can be determined by measuring the A_{260} in a spectrophotometer using quartz cuvettes. Most accurate readings are obtained when the absorbance is between 0.15 and 1.0. An absorbance of 1 unit at 260 nm measured at neutral pH corresponds to 40 µg of RNA per ml. Therefore, if it is necessary to dilute the RNA sample, this should be done in a low-salt buffer with neutral pH (e.g., 10 mM *Tris* HCl, pH 7.0).

Tip: Cuvettes must be RNase-free, especially if the RNA is to be recovered after spectrophotometry. Wash cuvettes with 100 mM NaOH, 1 mM EDTA followed by washing with ddH$_2$O.

Another problem with relying on A$_{260}$ measurement is that absorbance increases in the presence of free nucleotides, leading to overestimation of the amount of RNA in a degraded sample.

The A$_{260}$/A$_{280}$ ratio (R-value) provides an estimate of RNA purity. The above protocol yields RNA that is essentially free of DNA and proteins and has an R-value of 1.6–1.9. An R-value of greater than 1.7 suggests that residual organic solvents have been carried over into the aqueous phase. In this case it is best to carry out an additional EtOH precipitation with several 70% EtOH washes.

Note: The accuracy of the A$_{260}$/A$_{280}$ method has been questioned, with a value of 1.8 corresponding to only 40% RNA, with the remainder accounted for by protein.[157] It is important to compare samples with similar values, as otherwise significantly different amounts of RNA may be analyzed.

5.4.4.2. Fluorescence

The RiboGreen® (Molecular Probes, *Cat. No. R-11491*) RNA quantification assay is undoubtedly the Gold Standard for RNA quantification. It is similar to the PicoGreen™ DNA assay and is based on the RiboGreen® RNA quantification reagent, an unsymmetrical cyanine dye that is essentially nonfluorescent when free in solution. Upon binding to RNA, the fluorescence of the reagent increases more than 1000-fold. RiboGreen® has an excitation maximum of approximately 500 nm and an emission maximum of about 525 nm, similar to Fluorescein. RiboGreen®-based assays are significantly more sensitive than A$_{260}$ measurements and have a linear dynamic range extending from 1 ng/ml to 1 µg/ml RNA using two different dye concentrations. RiboGreen® does not bind to free nucleotides, hence does not generate false reading due to RNA degradation.[158]

Note: False readings can be obtained if RiboGreen® absorbs to the sides of the tube. This can be avoided by using non-stick, nuclease-free polypropylene tubes (e.g., Axygen's MAXYmum).

Tip: Protect RiboGreen® from photodegradation by wrapping the container in aluminium foil and using it promptly.

5.4.4.3. Use of RiboGreen® and a Combined Fluorimeter/Thermal Cycler to Quantitate RNA

A real-time PCR instrument that has the facility to make a quantitative plate read, such as the ABI Prism 7700 or the Mx4000 or Mx3000p (Stratagene), is ideal for use as a fluorimeter to quantitate nucleic acids. When using the Stratagene instruments, there is a software feature that is designed specifically for this application making this a simple and rapid procedure to define the standard curve, perform a plate read and read off the unknown sample concentrations. The protocol described in this section also includes details on how to persuade the SDS software, v. 1.6.3 to produce this data. In either case the construction of the standard curve and sample material are identical. For RNA and RiboGreen®, its detection range is between 0.01 ng/μl and 1 ng/μl in an assay volume of 30 μl made up of 15 μl diluted sample and 15 μl of a 1:200 dilution of RiboGreen®.

1. For the assay, RiboGreen® is used at 1:400 stock concentration. Make up a master mix of 1:200 RiboGreen®, which will be diluted 1:2 in the RNA sample. All dilutions in this assay are carried out in TE, which comes in a 20× stock with the RiboGreen® kit (*Cat. No. R-11490*).

2. First a standard curve covering the expected concentration range of the RNA is prepared. The RiboGreen® kit includes a rRNA standard at a concentration of 100 ng/μl. After an initial dilution of 1:100, prepare a two-fold serial dilution series starting at 1 ng/μl.

3. Analyze each standard in triplicate for greatest reliability. This requires at least 45 μl of each standard; so 50 μl of serial dilutions are suggested. Note that, once the RiboGreen® dye is added, the actual concentrations of RNA in the assay will be half of those in the above table.

4. On the ABI Prism 7700 select the appropriate Spectra Components folder for use in this assay. NB: only for MAC compatible. Go

to Mac HD/System Folder/Preferences/SDS and rename Spectra Components as Spectra Components.original. Rename Spectra Components.ribo as Spectra Components (this will set the Pure Dye Spectra file that includes RiboGreen® as the default pure spectra file that the SDS software will use).

Dilution	Input RNA concentration
1:1	1.0 ng/µl
1:2	0.5 ng/µl
1:4	0.25 ng/µl
1:8	0.125 ng/µl
1:16	0.0625 ng/µl
1:32	0.0313 ng/µl
1:64	0.0156 ng/µl
1:128	0.0078 ng/µl

5. Start Sequence Detector v.1.6.3 software. Exit the existing blank plate and create a new one, selecting under the Run pull-down menu Plate Read instead of the default Real-Time. From the Setup view of this new plate, select Ribo from the Dye Layer pull-down menu. Under Sample Type pull-down, select Sample Type Setup. Create a new sample type, named appropriately for your sample, select a color and choose Ribo as the reporter from the pull-down menu.

6. Go back to the Setup view, highlight wells of interest, and from Sample Type menu and select the newly created type.

7. Click Show Analysis.
   Under Instrument/Diagnostics/Advanced Options, unclick Reference (set to ROX). Under the analysis view, click Post-PCR Read; the instrument will take a reading.

8. Under Analysis menu, click Analyze. To view Fluorescence, under Analysis/Display select Rn/ΔRn. To export to a tab-delineated text file, choose File/Export/Experimental Report. This file can be opened by Excel for plotting graphs. Mean fluorescence values will appear in the column titled "Mean."

9. Remember to change back the Spectra Components folders and ROX reference settings when you are finished!

5.4.4.4. Agilent 2100 Bioanalyzer

Just as real-time chemistries have revolutionized the PCR reaction, so the development of the Agilent Bioanalyzer together with the RNA 6000 LabChip® (*Cat. No. 5065-4476*) and the more recent Pico LabChip® (*Cat. No. 5065-4473*) has revolutionized the ability to analyze RNA samples for quality. The Agilent 2100 Bioanalyzer and the RNA 6000 LabChips are undoubtedly the method of choice for analyzing RNA preparations destined to be used in qRT-PCR assays. The Agilent 2100 Bioanalyzer is a small benchtop system that integrates sample detection, quantification, and quality assessment. It does this by using a combination of microfluidics, capillary electrophoresis, and fluorescent dye that binds to nucleic acid. An RNA-reference standard (Ambion, *Cat. No. 7152*) made up of six RNAs of different sizes is loaded in a designated well on the RNA LabChip®. Size and mass information is generated by the fluorescence of the nucleic acid molecules as they migrate through the channels of the chip. The instrument software quantitates unknown RNA samples by comparing their peak areas to the combined area of the six reference RNAs. It has a wide dynamic range and can quantitate as little as 200 pg/μl (Pico LabChip®), while the standard LabChip® is most accurate at concentrations above 50 ng/μl.

> **Note:** Since only 1 μl of sample is loaded, accurate pipetting is crucial for obtaining accurate quantification. Quantification will also be inaccurate if the entire sample does not enter the gel, something that is difficult to ascertain.

An electropherogram of fluorescence vs. time and a virtual gel image are generated and the software assesses RNA quality by using the areas under the 28S and 18S rRNA peaks to calculate their ratios. The analysis of total RNA sample from human colon biopsies is shown in **Fig. 5.1.**

The 18S and 28S ribosomal RNA peaks are identified by the Agilent 2100 Bioanalyzer software in the electropherogram. The amount of small RNA (peak 1), which can include 5.8S and 5S ribosomal peaks and transfer RNA, is highly dependent on the preparation protocol. The sample in **Fig. 5.1** contains little material in the small RNA region, whereas other preparations may contain significant levels of small

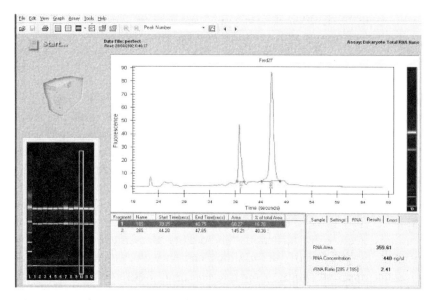

Figure 5.1. Electropherogram of a good total RNA preparation from a normal human colon biopsy. Total RNA from colon biopsies was isolated using the RNeasy Mini Kit from Qiagen (Hilden, Germany). 1 µl aliquots were analyzed using the RNA 6000 LabChip kit.

RNA. Each disposable LabChip® can be used to determine the concentration and purity/integrity of 12 RNA samples with a total analysis time of about 25 minutes.

Note: Poor LabChip® loading and formation of salt bridges between electrodes are common causes of poor assay performance. Overloading the chip with RNA (more than 500 ng) generates unreliable results.

Tip: The sample's ionic strength affects the accuracy of quantification, as it can quench fluorescence. The RNA loaded onto the LabChip® should be diluted in RNase-free water, as otherwise its concentration may be under estimated.

RNase degradation of total RNA samples produces a shift in the RNA size distribution toward smaller fragments and a decrease in fluorescence signal (**Fig. 5.2**). The 18S and 28S peaks can no longer be identified with certainty and the spectrum shifts toward early migration times. The overall signal becomes weak as dye intercalation sites are destroyed.

5.4.4.5. Other Quality Assessment Techniques

Since not everyone has access to RNA LabChips and an Agilent Bioanalyzer, the following three procedures can be used instead.

Formaldehyde agarose gel electrophoresis

Assessment of RNA quality by gel electrophoresis and analysis of 28S and 18S rRNA bands uses up a lot of precious RNA. Nevertheless, it is the traditional way of checking the integrity of an RNA preparation. The high degree of secondary structure of RNA makes it necessary to run the RNA on denaturing gels; the formaldehyde in the gel disrupts secondary RNA structure so that RNA molecules can be separated by their charge migration.

Qiagen have developed a streamlined protocol for running formamide gels. It uses a concentrated RNA loading buffer that allows a larger volume of RNA sample to be loaded onto the gel.

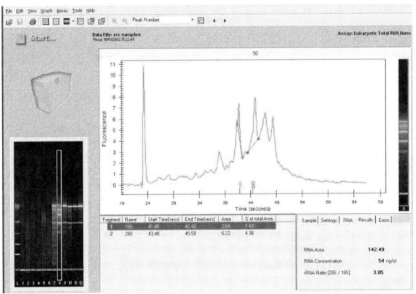

Figure 5.2. Electropherogram of a poor total RNA preparation from a normal human colon biopsy. Total RNA from colon biopsies was isolated using the RNeasy Mini Kit from Qiagen (Hilden, Germany). 1 μl aliquots were analyzed using the RNA 6000 LabChip kit. The indications for RNA degradation are the decreased ratio of ribosomal RNA bands, the additional peaks, the decrease in overall RNA signal, and the shift towards shorter fragments.

Ingredients

- 37% (12.3 M) formaldehyde;
- 10 mg/ml EtBr;
- agarose;
- 10× FA buffer (200 mM 3-[morpholino] propanesulphonic acid (MOPS) free acid, 50 mM; NaOAc, 10 mM EDTA, pH to 7 with NaOH);
- RNase-free H_2O.

Gel preparation

1. Prepare a 1.2% gel by mixing the agarose, 10× buffer, and RNase-free water in a loosely stoppered Erlenmeyer flask and heat (microwave is the easiest) to melt the agarose.

    Tip: Cotton wool makes the best plug.

    Note: To prepare a standard gel of 14 × 0.7 cm, use 1.2 g of agarose, 10 ml of 10× buffer and make up the volume to 100 ml.

2. Make sure that the agarose is completely melted and place flask in a 56°C water bath.

    Tip: The agarose is ready to use if you can just hold the flask with your bare hands.

3. Add formamide and ErBr.

    Note: Use 1.8 ml of formaldehyde and 1 µl of EtBr for the above gel. Both are toxic and/or mutagenic. Handle carefully.

4. Mix carefully and pour onto gel support tray.

Running the gel

5. Equilibrate the gel by prerunning it in 1× running buffer (100 ml of 10× FA buffer, 20 ml of 37% formaldehyde, and 880 ml H_2O) at 5–7 V/cm for 30 min.

6. Add one volume of 5× gel loading buffer (16 μl of saturated aqueous bromophenol blue, 80 μl of 500 mM EDTA, pH 8, 720 μl of 37% formaldehyde, 2 ml of 10% glycerol, 3.08 μl of formamide, 4 ml of 10× FA gel buffer, and RNase-free water to 10 ml) to 4 volumes of sample.

7. Mix and incubate at 65°C for 5 min, then place on ice.

8. Load onto the equilibrated agarose gel and run at 5–7 V/cm in 1× FA buffer until the lead dye is ¾ of the way down the gel.

9. Take picture of the gel. Place a ruler next to the gel for calibrating the gel following hybridization.

The 28S and 18S rRNA bands should appear as sharp bands on the stained gel, with the 28S rRNA band approximately twice the intensity of the 18S rRNA band. Any apparent smearing is likely to be caused either by DNA contamination or, more likely, by degraded RNA.

However, running gels is not an option for many *in vitro* biopsies, since there is barely sufficient RNA to carry out reproducible RT-PCR experiments. There are two additional approaches that provide some information about RNA quality and could be used for such samples.

Multiplex analysis of multiple reporter mRNAs

This method of RNA analysis uses conventional multiplex RT-PCR to assess RNA integrity by coamplification of sequences from four mRNA molecules—BCR, ABL, β2-microglobulin, and Porphobilinogen decarboxylase (PBGD)—all of which are expressed at different levels.[159] Coamplification of the four target sequences yields PCR products ranging from 128 to 377 bp that are visualized on agarose gels. RNA preparations of suboptimal quality are characterized by loss of the BCR signal, while further deterioration of sample quality results in an additional loss of either the ABL or the β2-microglobulin signal. In samples of very poor mRNA quality the multiplex amplification reveals a PBGD signal only. Of course there is no reason why this assay could not be converted to a real-time format. Primer sequences, genomic location, and predicted size of amplified cDNA and gDNA fragments are indicated in **Table 5.6**. Alternatively, it is possible to use probe-based chemistries to develop real-time modifications of this protocol.

Table 5.6. Primer sequences for multiplex method of assessing RNA quality.

Marker	Forward	Reverse	Location	Size (bp)
ABL M14752	AGCATCTGACTTTGAGCC	CCCATTGTGATTATAGCCTAAGAC	463–480 (F) 632–655 (R)	193
beta-MG M17987	ATTTCCTGAATTGCTATGTG	GAATTCACTCAATCCAAATG	177–196 (F) 2304–2323 (R)	287
BCR M24603	GAGAAGAGGGCGAACAAG	CTCTGCTTAAATCCAGTGGC	2889–2906 (F) 3246–3265 (R)	377
PBGD D12722 X04217	TGAGAGTGATTCGCGTGGGTAC	CCCTGTGGTGGACATAGCAAT	264–285 (F) 189–210 (R)	128

Analysis of multiple amplicons from a reporter mRNA

A further method of RNA analysis is based on the increasing probability of RNA cleavage with increasing length of an RNA molecule. The rationale is that since transcript amplification occurs primarily at the 3' end of the gene, degraded RNA will have less detectable message from the 5' end of the gene. Under ideal conditions, reverse transcription of the 10-kb fatty acid synthase (FAS) mRNA using oligo-dT as the primer generates a population of cDNAs that terminates at the 5' end of the mRNA. If the mRNA is not intact, the 5' end of the mRNA will be under represented in the cDNA population. Four sets of primers are used that amplify sequences 2, 6, 8, or 9 kb from the polyA tail and a comparison of the relative yields of the amplified fragments from regions distal and proximal to the 3' end of the mRNA provide a relative measure of the fraction of intact FAS mRNA in the RNA preparation[160] (**Fig. 5.3**). One difficulty with this approach is that problems with the RT-PCR could also result in different yields quite independently of RNA quality. Again, it would be easy to use SYBR-Green I or probe-based chemistries to develop real-time modifications of this protocol.

Relevant Websites

General protocols:

http://iprotocol.mit.edu/

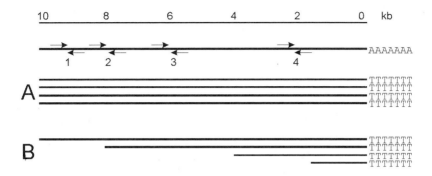

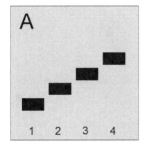
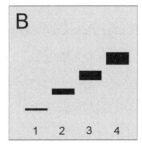

Figure 5.3. Use of FAS mRNA to assess RNA quality. The four primer pairs are used to amplify oligo-dT primed cDNA. (**A**) A PCR reaction of intact RNA will result in roughly equal amounts of all fragments. (**B**) If the RNA is partially degraded, cDNA synthesis will generate shorter transcripts in proportion to the degree of degradation. The yield of DNA from each primer pair will decrease with increased distance from the polyA site in proportion to the degree of degradation.

Issues surrounding polypropylene:

http://www.axygen.com/NewFiles/Encoll.pdf
http://www.axygen.com/NewFiles/Teknova.pdf
http://www.axygen.com/NewFiles/Strauss.pdf

Yeast RNA preparation:

http://plantdev.bio.wzw.tum.de/methods/protocolsRNA/
        yeastTotalRNA.html
http://iprotocol.mit.edu/protocol/103.htm

Grinding mixer mills:

http://www.retsch.de/

Rotor Stator:

http://www.omni-inc.com/

RNA purification:

http://www.ambion.com/
http://www.rnature.com/
http://www.qiagen.com/literature/rnalit.asp
http://www.qiagen.com/literature/clinlit.asp
http://www.qiagen.com/literature/genomlit.asp

RNAzol: Molecular Research Center

http://www.mrcgene.com/tri.htm

Agilent:

www.agilent.com/chem/labonachip

References

1. Bomjen G, Raina A, Sulaiman IM, Hasnain SE, Dogra TD: **Effect of storage of blood samples on DNA yield, quality and fingerprinting: A forensic approach.** *Indian J Exp Biol* 1996, **34**:384–386.

2. Scherczinger CA, Ladd C, Bourke MT, Adamowicz MS, Johannes PM, Scherczinger R, Beesley T, Lee HC: **A systematic analysis of PCR contamination.** *J Forensic Sci* 1999, **44**:1042–1045.

3. Sarkar G, Sommer SS: **Shedding light on PCR contamination.** *Nature* 1990, **343**:27.

4. Sarkar G, Sommer S: **More light on PCR contamination.** *Nature* 1990, **347**:340–341,.

5. Cone RW, Fairfax MR: **Protocol for ultraviolet irradiation of surfaces to reduce PCR contamination.** *PCR Methods Appl* 1993, **3**:S15–S17.

6. Dwyer, DE, Saksena, N: **Failure of ultra-violet irradiation and autoclaving to eliminate PCR contamination.** *Mol.Cell Probes* 1992, **6**:87–88.

7. Fox JC, Ait-Khaled M, Webster A, Emery, VC: **Eliminating PCR contamination: Is UV irradiation the answer?** *J Virol Meth* 1991, **33**:375–382.

8. Sarkar, G, Sommer, SS: **Parameters affecting susceptibility of PCR contamination to UV inactivation.** *Biotechniques* 1991, **10**:590–594.

9. Ou CY, Moore JL, Schochetman G: **Use of UV irradiation to reduce false positivity in polymerase chain reaction.** *Biotechniques* 1991, **10**:442, 444, 446.

10. Burgess LC, Hall JO: **UV light irradiation of plastic reaction tubes inhibits PCR.** *Biotechniques* 1999, **27**:252, 254–254, 256.

11. Linquist V, Stoddart CA, McCune JM: **UV irradiation of polystyrene pipets releases PCR inhibitors.** *Biotechniques* 1998, **24**:50–52.

12. Glossmann H, Hering S, Savchenko A, Berger W, Friedrich K, Garcia ML, Goetz MA, Liesch JM, Zink DL, Kaczorowski GJ: **A light stabilizer (Tinuvin 770) that elutes from polypropylene plastic tubes is a potent L-type Ca^{2+}-channel blocker.** *Proc Natl Acad Sci USA* 1993, **90**:9523–9527.

13. Belotserkovskii BP, Johnston BH: **Polypropylene tube surfaces may induce denaturation and multimerization of DNA.** *Science* 1996, **271**:222–223.

14. Belotserkovskii BP, Johnston BH: **Denaturation and association of DNA sequences by certain polypropylene surfaces.** *Anal.Biochem* 1997, **251**:251–262.

15. Rollo F, Ubaldi M, Ermini L, Marota I: **Otzi's last meals: DNA analysis of the intestinal content of the Neolithic glacier mummy from the Alps.** *Proc Natl Acad Sci USA* 2002, **99**:12594–12599.

16. Mutter GL, Boynton KA: **PCR bias in amplification of androgen receptor alleles, a trinucleotide repeat marker used in clonality studies.** *Nucleic Acids Res* 1995, **23**:1411–1418.

17. Cuschieri KS, Seagar AL, Moore C, Gilkison G., Kornegay J, Cubie HA: **Development of an automated extraction procedure for detection of human papillomavirus DNA in liquid based cytology samples.** *J Virol.Methods* 2003, **107**:107–113.

18. Weissensteiner T, Lanchbury JS: **Strategy for controlling preferential amplification and avoiding false negatives in PCR typing.** *Biotechniques* 1996, **21**:1102–1108.

19. Goodyear PD, MacLaughlin-Black S, Mason IJ: **A reliable method for the removal of co-purifying PCR inhibitors from ancient DNA.** *Biotechniques* 1994, **16**:232–235.

20. Scholz M, Giddings I Pusch CM: **A polymerase chain reaction inhibitor of ancient hard and soft tissue DNA extracts is determined as human collagen type I.** *Anal Biochem* 1998, **259**:283–286.

21. Akane A., Matsubara K., Nakamura H, Takahashi S, Kimura K: **Identification of the heme compound copurified with deoxyribonucleic acid (DNA) from blood-**

stains, a major inhibitor of polymerase chain reaction (PCR) amplification. *J Forensic Sci* 1994, **39**:362–372.

22. Al Soud WA, Radstrom P: **Purification and characterization of PCR-inhibitory components in blood cells.** *J Clin Microbiol* 2001, **39**:485–493.

23. Al Soud WA, Jonsson LJ, Radstrom P: **Identification and characterization of immunoglobulin G in blood as a major inhibitor of diagnostic PCR.** *J Clin Microbiol* 2000, **38**:345–350.

24. Panaccio M, Lew A: **PCR based diagnosis in the presence of 8% (v/v) blood.** *Nucleic Acids Res* 1991, **19**:1151.

25. Schwartz I., Varde S., Nadelman RB., Wormser GP, Fish D. **Inhibition of efficient polymerase chain reaction amplification of *Borrelia burgdorferi* DNA in blood-fed ticks.** *Am J Trop Med Hyg* 1997, **56**: 339–342.

26. Panaccio M., Georgesz M, Lew AM: **FoLT PCR: A simple PCR protocol for amplifying DNA directly from whole blood.** *Biotechniques* 1993, **14**:238–243.

27. Burckhardt J: **Amplification of DNA from whole blood. PCR.** *Methods Appl* 1994, **3**:239–243.

28. Ulvik A, Ueland PM: **Single nucleotide polymorphism (SNP) genotyping in unprocessed whole blood and serum by real-time PCR: Application to SNPs affecting homocysteine and folate metabolism.** *Clin Chem* 2001, **47**:2050–2053.

29. Ulvik A, Evensen ET, Lien EA, Hoff G, Vollset SE, Majak BM, Ueland PM: **Smoking, folate and methylenetetrahydrofolate reductase status as interactive determinants of adenomatous and hyperplastic polyps of colorectum.** *Am J Med Genet* 2001, **101**:246–254.

30. Zhou J, Bruns MA, Tiedje JM: **DNA recovery from soils of diverse composition.** *Appl Environ Microbiol* 1996, **62**:316–322.

31. Rossen L, Norskov P, Holmstrom K, Rasmussen OF: **Inhibition of PCR by components of food samples, microbial diagnostic assays and DNA-extraction solutions.** *Int J Food Microbiol* 1992, **17**:37–45.

32. Bickley J, Short JK, McDowell DG, Parkes HC: **Polymerase chain reaction (PCR) detection of Listeria monocytogenes in diluted milk and reversal of PCR inhibition caused by calcium ions.** *Lett Appl Microbiol* 1996, **22**:153–158.

33. Leutenegger CM, Alluwaimi AM, Smith WL, Perani L, Cullor JS: **Quantitation of bovine cytokine mRNA in milk cells of healthy cattle by real-time TaqMan polymerase chain reaction.** *Vet Immunol Immunopathol* 2000, **77**:275–287,

34. Yedidag EN, Koffron AJ, Mueller KH, Kaplan B, Kaufman DB, Fryer JP, Stuart FP, Abecassis M: **Acyclovir triphosphate inhibits the diagnostic polymerase chain reaction for cytomegalovirus.** *Transplantation* 1996, **62**:238–242.

35. Pikaart MJ, Villeponteau B: **Suppression of PCR amplification by high levels of RNA.** *Biotechniques* 1993, **14**:24–25.

36. Lee AB, Cooper TA: **Improved direct PCR screen for bacterial colonies: Wooden toothpicks inhibit PCR amplification.** *Biotechniques* 1995, **18**:225–226.

37. Belec L, Authier J, Eliezer-Vanerot MC, Piedouillet C, Mohamed AS, Gherardi RK: **Myoglobin as a polymerase chain reaction (PCR) inhibitor: A limitation for PCR from skeletal muscle tissue avoided by the use of Thermus thermophilus polymerase.** *Muscle Nerve* 1998, **21**:1064–1067.

38. Mulcahy HE, Croke DT, Farthing MJ: **Cancer and mutant DNA in blood plasma.** *Lancet* 1996, **348**:628.

39. Giacona MB, Ruben GC, Iczkowski KA, Roos TB, Porter DM, Sorenson GD: **Cell-free DNA in human blood plasma: Length measurements in patients with pancreatic cancer and healthy controls.** *Pancreas* 1998, **17**:89–97.

40. Jahr S, Hentze H, Englisch S, Hardt D, Fackelmayer FO, Hesch RD, Knippers R: **DNA fragments in the blood plasma of cancer patients: Quantitations and evidence for their origin from apoptotic and necrotic cells.** *Cancer Res* 2001, **61**:1659–1665.

41. Thijssen MA, Swinkels DW, Ruers TJ, de Kok JB: **Difference between free circulating plasma and serum DNA in patients with colorectal liver metastases.** *Anticancer Res* 2002, **22**:421–425.

42. Pathak S, Dave BJ, Gagos S: **Chromosome alterations in cancer development and apoptosis.** *In Vivo* 1994, **8**:843–850.

43. Haugland RA, Brinkman N, Vesper SJ: **Evaluation of rapid DNA extraction methods for the quantitative detection of fungi using real-time PCR analysis.** *J Microbiol Methods* 2002, **50**:319–323.

44. Burkhart C, Norris M, Haber M: **A simple method for the isolation of genomic DNA from mouse tail free of real-time PCR inhibitors.** *J Biochem Biophys Methods* 2002, **52**:145.

45. Fredricks DN, Relman DA: **Improved amplification of microbial DNA from blood cultures by removal of the PCR inhibitor sodium polyanetholesulfonate.** *J Clin Microbiol* 1998, **36**:2810–2816.

46. Millar BC, Jiru X, Moore JE, Earle JA: **A simple and sensitive method to extract bacterial, yeast and fungal DNA from blood culture material.** *J Microbiol Methods* 2000, **42**:139–147.

47. de Castillo AL, Gavidia I, Perez-Bermudez P, Segura J: **PEG precipitation, a required step for PCR amplification of DNA from wild plants of *Digitalis obscura* L.** *Biotechniques* 1995, **18**:766–768.

48. Loeffler J, Schmidt K, Hebart H., Schumacher UH: **Automated extraction of genomic DNA from medically important yeast species and filamentous fungi by using the MagNA Pure LC system.** *J Clin Microbiol* 2002, **40**:2240–2243.

49. Chan PK, Chan DP, To KF, Yu MY, Cheung JL, Cheng AF: **Evaluation of extraction methods from paraffin wax embedded tissues for PCR amplification of human and viral DNA.** J Clin Pathol 2001, **54**:401–403.

50. Frank TS, Svoboda-Newman SM, Hsi ED: **Comparison of methods for extracting DNA from formalin-fixed paraffin sections for nonisotopic PCR.** *Diagn Mol Pathol* 1996, **5**:220–224.

51. Kallio P, Syrjanen S, Tervahauta A, Syrjanen K: **A simple method for isolation of DNA from formalin-fixed paraffin-embedded samples for PCR.** *J Virol Methods* 1991, **35**:39–47.

52. Ren ZP, Sallstrom J, Sundstrom C, Nister M, Olsson Y: **Recovering DNA and optimizing PCR conditions from microdissected formalin-fixed and paraffin-embedded materials.** *Pathobiology* 2000, **68**:215–217.

53. Lehmann U, Bock O, Glockner S, Kreipe H: **Quantitative molecular analysis of laser-microdissected paraffin-embedded human tissues.** *Pathobiology* 2000 **68**:202–208.

54. Poli F, Cattaneo R, Crespiatico L, Nocco A, Sirchia G: **A rapid and simple method for reversing the inhibitory effect of heparin on PCR for HLA class II typing.** *PCR Methods Appl* 1993, **2**:356–358.

55. Satsangi J, Jewell DP, Welsh K, Bunce M, Bell JI: **Effect of heparin on polymerase chain reaction.** *Lancet* 1994, **343**:1509–1510.

56. Jung R, Lubcke C, Wagener C, Neumaier M: **Reversal of RT-PCR inhibition observed in heparinized clinical specimens.** *Biotechniques* 1997, **23**:24, 26, 28.

57. Beutler E, Gelbart T, Kuhl W: **Interference of heparin with the polymerase chain reaction.** *Biotechniques* 1990, **9**:166.

58. Godfrey TE, Kim SH, Chavira M, Ruff DW, Warren RS, Gray JW, Jensen RH: **Quantitative mRNA expression analysis from formalin-fixed, paraffin-embedded tissues using 5' nuclease quantitative reverse transcription-polymerase chain reaction.** *J Mol Diagn* 2000, **2**:84–91.

59. Chomczynski P, Mackey K., Drews R, Wilfinger W: **DNAzol: A reagent for the rapid isolation of genomic DNA.** *Biotechniques* 1997, **22**:550–553.

60. Suffys P, Vanderborght PR, Santos PB, Correa LA, Bravin Y, Kritski AL: **Inhibition of the polymerase chain reaction by sputum samples from tuberculosis patients after processing using a silica-guanidiniumthiocyanate DNA isolation procedure.** *Mem Inst Oswaldo Cruz* 2001, **96**:1137–1139.

61. Jerome KR, Huang ML, Wald A, Selke S, Corey L: **Quantitative stability of DNA after extended storage of clinical specimens as determined by real-time PCR.** *J Clin Microbiol* 2002, **40**:2609–2611.

62. Hill CS, Treisman R: **Transcriptional regulation by extracellular signals: Mechanisms and specificity.** *Cell* 1995, **80**:199–211.

63. Ross J: **mRNA stability in mammalian cells.** *Microbiol Rev* 1995, **59**: 423–450.

64. Marchuk L, Sciore P, Reno C, Frank CB, Hart DA: **Postmortem stability of total RNA isolated from rabbit ligament, tendon and cartilage.** *Biochim Biophys Acta* 1998, **1379**:171–177.

65. Schramm M, Falkai P, Tepest R, Schneider-Axmann T, Przkora R, Waha A, Pietsch T, Bonte W, Bayer TA: **Stability of RNA transcripts in post-mortem psychiatric brains.** *J Neural Transm* 1999, **106**:329–335.

66. Fitzpatrick R, Casey OM, Morris D, Smith T, Powell R, Sreenan JM: **Postmortem stability of RNA isolated from bovine reproductive tissues.** *Biochim Biophys Acta* 2002, **1574**:10–14.

67. Yasojima K, McGeer EG, McGeer PL: **High stability of mRNAs postmortem and protocols for their assessment by RT-PCR.** *Brain Res Brain Res Protoc* 2001, **8**:212–218.

68. Lee KH, McKenna MJ, Sewell WF, Ung F: **Ribonucleases may limit recovery of ribonucleic acids from archival human temporal bones.** *Laryngoscope* 1997, **107**:1228–1234.

69. Vlems F, Soong R, Diepstra H, Punt C, Wobbes T, Tabiti K, Van Muijen G: **Effect of blood sample handling and reverse transcriptase-plymerase chain reaction assay sensitivity on detection of CK20 expression in healthy donors.** *Blood Diagn Mol Pathol* 2002, **11**:90–97.

70. Madejon A, Manzano ML, Arocena C, Castillo I, Carreno V: **Effect of delayed freezing of liver biopsies on the detection of hepititis C virus RNA strands.** *J Hepatol* 2000, **32**:1019–1025.

71. Wang WH, McNatt LG, Shepard AR, Jacobson N, Nishimura DY, Stone EM, Sheffield VC, Clark AF: **Optimal procedure for extracting RNA from human ocular tissues and expression profiling of the congenital glaucoma gene FOXC1 using quantitative RT-PCR.** *Mol Vis* 2001, **7**:89–94.

72. Florell SR, Coffin CM, Holden JA, Zimmermann JW, Gerwels JW, Summers BK, Jones DA, Leachman SA: **Preservation of RNA for functional genomic studies: A multidisciplinary tumor bank protocol.** *Mod Pathol* 2001, **14**:116–128.

73. Grotzer MA, Patti R, Geoerger B, Eggert A, Chou TT, Phillips PC. **Biological stability of RNA isolated from RNAlater-treated brain tumor and neuroblastoma xenografts.** *Med Pediatr Oncol* 2000, **34**:438–442.

74. Barrett MT, Glogovac J, Prevo LJ, Reid BJ, Porter P, Rabinovitch PS: **High-quality RNA and DNA from flow cytometrically sorted human epithelial cells and tissues.** *Biotechniques* 2002, **32**:888–890, 892, 894, 896.

75. Keilholz U, Willhauck M, Rimoldi D, Brasseur F, Dummer W, Rass K, de Vries T, Blaheta J, Voit C, Lethe B, Burchill S: **Reliability of reverse transcription-polymerase chain reaction (RT-PCR)-based assays for the detection of circulating tumour cells: A quality-assurance initiative of the EORTC Melanoma Cooperative Group.** *Eur J Cancer* 1998, **34**:750–753.

76. de Vries TJ, Fourkour A, Punt CJ, Ruiter DJ, van Muijen GN: **Analysis of melanoma cells in peripheral blood by reverse transcription-polymerase chain reaction for tyrosinase and MART-1 after mononuclear cell collection with cell preparation tubes: A comparison with the whole blood guanidinium isothiocyanate RNA isolation method.** *Melanoma Res* 2000, **10**:119-126.

77. Rainen L, Oelmueller U, Jurgensen S, Wyrich R, Ballas C, Schram J, Herdman C, Bankaitis–Davis D, Nicholls N, Trollinger D, Tryon V: **Stabilization of mRNA expression in whole blood samples.** *Clin Chem* 2002, **48**:1883–1890.

78. Thomson SA, Wallace MR: **RT-PCR splicing analysis of the NF1 open reading frame.** *Hum Genet* 2002, **110**:495–502.

79. Kopreski MS, Benko FA, Kwak LW, Gocke CD: **Detection of tumor messenger RNA in the serum of patients with malignant melanoma.** *Clin Cancer Res* 1999, **5**:1961–1965.

80. Chen, XQ, Bonnefoi H, Pelte MF, Lyautey J, Lederrey C, Movarekhi S, Schaeffer P, Mulcahy HE, Meyer P, Stroun M, Anker P: **Telomerase RNA as a detection marker in the serum of breast cancer patients.** *Clin Cancer Res* 2000, **6**:3823–3826.

81. Dasi F, Lledo S, Garcia-Granero E, Ripoll R, Marugan M, Tormo M, Garcia-Conde J, Alino SF: **Real-time quantification in plasma of human telomerase reverse transcriptase (hTERT) mRNA: a simple blood test to monitor disease in cancer patients.** *Lab Invest* 2001, **81**:767–769.

82. Silva JM, Dominguez G, Silva J, Garcia JM, Sanchez A, Rodriguez O, Provencio M, Espana P, Bonilla F: **Detection of epithelial messenger RNA in the plasma of breast cancer patients is associated with poor prognosis tumor characteristics.** *Clin Cancer Res* 2001, **7**:2821–2825.

83. Lo KW, Lo YM, Leung SF, Tsang YS, Chan LY, Johnson PJ, Hjelm NM, Lee JC, Huang DP: **Analysis of cell-free Epstein-Barr virus associated RNA in the plasma of patients with nasopharyngeal carcinoma.** *Clin Chem* 1999, **45**:1292–1294.

84. Lo YM, Chan LY, Lo KW, Leung SF, Zhang J, Chan AT, Lee JC, Hjelm NM, Johnson PJ, Huang DP: **Quantitative analysis of cell-free Epstein-Barr virus DNA in plasma of patients with nasopharyngeal carcinoma.** *Cancer Res* 1999, **59**:1188–1191.

85. Ng EK, Tsui NB, Lam NY, Chiu RW, Yu SC, Wong SC, Lo ES, Rainer TH, Johnson PJ, Lo YM: **Presence of filterable and nonfilterable mRNA in the plasma of cancer patients and healthy individuals.** *Clin Chem* 2002, **48**:1212–1217.

86. Sparmann G, Jaschke A, Loehr M, Liebe S, Emmrich J: **Tissue homogenization as a key step in extracting RNA from human and rat pancreatic tissue.** *Biotechniques* 1997, **22**:408–10, 412.

87. Schittek B, Blaheta HJ, Urchinger G, Sauer B, Garbe C: **Increased sensitivity for the detection of malignant melanoma cells in peripheral blood using an improved protocol for reverse transcription-polymerase chain reaction.** *Br J Dermatol* 1999, **141**:37–43.

88. Mannhalter C, Koizar D, Mitterbauer G: **Evaluation of RNA isolation methods and reference genes for RT-PCR analyses of rare target RNA.** *Clin Chem Lab Med* 2000, **38**:171–177.

89. Imai H, Yamada O, Morita S, Suehiro S, Kurimura T: **Detection of HIV-1 RNA in heparinized plasma of HIV-1 seropositive individuals.** *J Virol Methods* 1992, **36**:181–184.

90. Izraeli S, Pfleiderer C, Lion T: **Detection of gene expression by PCR amplification of RNA derived from frozen heparinized whole blood.** *Nucleic Acids Research* 1991, **19**:6051.

91. Tsai M, Miyamoto M, Tam SY, Wang ZS, Galli SJ: **Detection of mouse mast cell-associated protease mRNA. Heparinase treatment greatly improves RT-PCR of tissues containing mast cell heparin.** *Am J Pathol* 1995, **146**:335–343.

92. Shi YJ, Liu JZ: **Direct reverse transcription—Polymerase chain reaction from whole blood without RNA extraction.** *Genet Anal Tech Appl* 1992, **9**:149–150.

93. Lozano ME, Grau O, Romanowski V: **Isolation of RNA from whole blood for reliable use in RT-PCR amplification.** *Trends Genet* 1993, **9**:296.

94. Kruse N, Pette M, Toyka K, Rieckmann P: **Quantification of cytokine mRNA expression by RT PCR in samples of previously frozen blood.** *J Immunol Methods* 1997, **210**:195–203.

95. Katz RS, Premenko-Lanier M, McChesney MB, Rota PA, Bellini WJ: **Detection of measles virus RNA in whole blood stored on filter paper.** *J Med Virol* 2002, **67**:596–602.

96. Carpita NC, Gibeaut DM: **Structural models of primary cell walls in flowering plants: Consistency of molecular structure with the physical properties of the walls during growth.** *Plant J* 1993, **3**:1–30.

97. Schneiderbauer A, Sandermann H Jr, Ernst D: **Isolation of functional RNA from plant tissues rich in phenolic compounds.** *Anal Biochem* 1991, **197**:91–95.

98. Lewinsohn E, Steele CL, Croteau R: **Simple isolation of functional RNA from woody stems of gymnosperms.** *Plant Mol Biol Rep* 1994, **12**:20–25.

99. Fang G, Hammar S, Grumet R: **A quick and inexpensive method for removing polysaccharides from plant genomic DNA.** Biotechniques 1992, **13**:52–54, 56.

100. Tesniere C, Vayda ME: **Method for the isolation of high-quality RNA from grape berry tisues without contaminating tannins or carbohydrates.** *Plant Mol Biol Rep* 1991, **9**:242–251.

101. Su X, Gibor A: **A method for RNA isolation from marine macro-algae.** *Anal Biochem* 1988, **174**:650–657.

102. Ainsworth C: **Isolation of RNA from floral tissue of *Rumex acetosa* (Sorrel).** *Plant Mol Biol Rep* 1994, **12**:198–203.

103. Logemann J, Schell J, Willmitzer L: **Improved method for the isolation of RNA from plant tissues.** *Anal Biochem* 1987, **163**:16–20.

104. Katterman FR, Shattuck VI: **An effective method of DNA isolation from the mature leaves of *Gossypium* species that contain large amounts of phenolic terpenoids and tannins.** *Prep Biochem* 1983, **13**:347–359.

105. Loomis WD: **Overcoming problems of phenolics and quinones in the isolation of plant enzymes and organelles.** *Methods Enzymol* 1974, **31**:528–544.

106. Rivas R, Vizcaino N, Buey RM, Mateos PF, Martinez-Molina E, Velazquez E: **An effective, rapid and simple method for total RNA extraction from bacteria and yeast.** *J Microbiol Methods* 2001, **47**:59–63.

107. Carninci P, Nakamura M, Sato K, Hayashizaki Y, Brownstein MJ: **Cytoplasmic RNA extraction from fresh and frozen mammalian tissues.** *Biotechniques* 2002, **33**:306–309.

108. Brogna S, Sato TA, Rosbash M: **Ribosome components are associated with sites of transcription.** *Mol Cell* 2002, **10**:93–104.

109. Vogelstein B, Gillespie D: **Preparative and analytical purification of DNA from agarose.** *Proc Natl Acad Sci USA* 1979, **76**:615–619.

110. Gehrsitz A, McKenna LA, Soder S, Kirchner T, Aigner T: **Isolation of RNA from small human articular cartilage specimens allows quantification of mRNA expression levels in local articular cartilage defects.** *J Orthop Res* 2001, **19**:478–481.

111. Chomczynski P, Sacchi N: **Single-step method of RNA isolation by acid guanidinium thiocyanate-phenol-chloroform extraction.** *Anal Biochem* 1987, **162**:156–159.

112. Chomczynski P, Mackey K: **Substitution of chloroform by bromo-chloropropane in the single-step method of RNA isolation.** *Anal Biochem* 1995, **225**:163–164.

113. Hengen PN: **Carriers for precipitating nucleic acids.** *Trends Biochem Sci* 1996, **21**:224–225.

114. Chomczynski P: **A reagent for the single-step simultaneous isolation of RNA, DNA and proteins from cell and tissue samples.** *Biotechniques* 1993, **15**:532–537.

115. Vandesompele J, De Paepe A, Speleman F: **Elimination of primer-dimer artifacts and genomic coamplification using a two-step SYBR Green I real-time RT-PCR.** *Anal Biochem 2002, 303:95–98.*

116. Hengen PN: Is **RNase-free really RNase for free?** *Trends Biochem Sci* 1996, **21**:112–113.

117. Bauer P, Rolfs A, Regitz-Zagrosek V, Hildebrandt A, Fleck E: **Use of manganese in RT-PCR eliminates PCR artifacts resulting from DNase I digestion.** *Biotechniques* 1997, **22**:1128–1132.

118. Huang Z, Fasco MJ, Kaminsky LS: **Optimization of Dnase I removal of contaminating DNA from RNA for use in quantitative RNA-PCR.** *Biotechniques* 1996, **20**:1012–1020.

119. Dunne JF, Thomas J, Lee S: **Detection of mRNA in flow-sorted cells.** *Cytometry* 1989, **10**:199–204.

120. Khochbin S, Grunwald D, Pabion M, Lawrence JJ: **Recovery of RNA from flow-sorted fixed cells.** *Cytometry* 1990, **11**:869–874.

121. Longley J, Ding TG, Cuono C, Durden F, Crooks C, Hufeisen S, Eckert R, Wood GS: **Isolation, detection, and amplification of intact mRNA from dermatome strips, epidermal sheets, and sorted epidermal cells.** *J Invest Dermatol* 1991, **97**:974–979.

122. Church JG, Stapleton EA, Reilly BD: **Isolation of high quality mRNA from a discrete cell cycle population identified using a nonvital dye and fluorescence activated sorting.** *Cytometry* 1993, **14**:271–275.

123. Foss RD, Guha-Thakurta N, Conran RM, Gutman P: **Effects of fixative and fixation time on the extraction and polymerase chain reaction amplification of RNA from paraffin-embedded tissue. Comparison of two housekeeping gene mRNA controls.** *Diagn Mol Pathol* 1994, **3**:148–155.

124. Jiang YH, Davidson LA, Lupton JR, Chapkin RS: **A rapid RT-PCR method for detection of intact RNA in formalin-fixed paraffin-embedded tissues.** *Nucleic Acids Res* 1995, **23**:3071–3072.

125. Jackson DP, Lewis FA, Taylor GR, Boylston AW, Quirke P: **Tissue extraction of DNA and RNA and analysis by the polymerase chain reaction.** *J Clin Pathol* 1990, **43**: 499–504.

126. Finke J, Fritzen R, Ternes P, Lange W, Dolken G: **An improved strategy and a useful housekeeping gene for RNA analysis from formalin-fixed, paraffin-embedded tissues by PCR.** *Biotechniques* 1993, **14**:448–453.

127. Stanta G., Bonin S, Perin R: **RNA extraction from formalin-fixed and paraffin-embedded tissues.** *Methods Mol Biol* 1998, **86**:23–26.

128. Stanta G, Schneider C. **RNA extracted from paraffin-embedded human tissues is amenable to analysis by PCR amplification.** *Biotechniques* 1991, **11**:304, 306, 308.

129. Rupp GM, Locker J. **Purification and analysis of RNA from paraffin-embedded tissues.** *Biotechniques* 1988, **6**:56–60.

130. Akyol G, Dash S, Shieh YS, Malter JS, Gerber MA: **Detection of hepatitis C virus RNA sequences by polymerase chain reaction in fixed liver tissue.** *Mod Pathol* 1992, **5**:501–504.

131. Diamond DA, Davis GL, Qian KP, Lau JY: **Detection of hepatitis C viral sequences in formalin-fixed, paraffin-embedded liver tissue: Effect of interferon alpha therapy.** *J Med Virol* 1994, **42**:294–298.

132. Gruber AD, Greiser-Wilke IM, Haas L, Hewicker-Trautwein M, Moennig V: **Detection of bovine viral diarrhea virus RNA in formalin-fixed, paraffin-embedded brain tissue by nested polymerase chain reaction.** *J Virol Methods* 1993, **43**:309–319.

133. Guerrero RB, Batts KP, Brandhagen DJ, Germer JJ, Perez RG Persing DH: **Effects of formalin fixation and prolonged block storage on detection of hepatitis C virus RNA in liver tissue.** *Diagn.Mol Pathol* 1997, **6**:277–281.

134. Svoboda-Newman SM., Greenson JK, Singleton TP, Sun R, Frank TS: **Detection of hepatitis C by RT-PCR in formalin-fixed paraffin-embedded tissue from liver transplant patients.** *Diagn Mol Pathol* 1997, **6**:123–129.

135. Lehmann U, Kreipe H: **Real-time PCR analysis of DNA and RNA extracted from formalin-fixed and paraffin-embedded biopsies.** *Methods* 2001, **25**:409–418.

136. Lehmann U, Hasemeier B, Lilischkis R, Kreipe H: **Quantitative analysis of promoter hypermethylation in laser-microdissected archival specimens.** *Lab Invest* 2001, **81**:635–638.

137. Klimecki WT, Futscher BW, Dalton WS: **Effects of ethanol and paraformaldehyde on RNA yield and quality.** *Biotechniques* 1994, **16**:1021–1023.

138. Goldsworthy SM, Stockton PS, Trempus CS, Foley JF, Maronpot RR: **Effects of fixation on RNA extraction and amplification from laser capture microdissected tissue.** *Mol Carcino* 1999, **25**:86–91.

139. Masuda N, Ohnishi T, Kawamoto S, Monden M, Okubo K. **Analysis of chemical modification of RNA from formalin-fixed samples and optimization of molecular biology applications for such samples.** *Nucleic Acids Res* 1999, **27**:4436–4443.

140. Mizuno T, Nagamura H, Iwamoto KS, Ito T, Fukuhara T, Tokunaga M, Tokuoka S, Mabuchi K, Seyama T: **RNA from decades-old archival tissue blocks for retrospective studies.** *Diagn Mol Pathol* 1998, **7**:202–208.

141. Coombs NJ, Gough AC, Primrose JN: **Optimisation of DNA and RNA extraction from archival formalin-fixed tissue.** *Nucleic Acids Res* 1999, **27**:e12,.

142. Specht K, Richter T, Muller U, Walch A, Werner M, Hofler H: **Quantitative gene expression analysis in microdissected archival formalin-fixed and paraffin-embedded tumor tissue.** *Am J Pathol* 2001, **158**:419–429.

143. Cohen CD, Grone HJ, Grone, EF, Nelson PJ, Schlondorff D, Kretzler M: **Laser microdissection and gene expression analysis on formaldehyde-fixed archival tissue.** *Kidney Int* 2002, **61**:125–132.

144. Stanta G, Bonin S: **RNA quantitative analysis from fixed and paraffin-embedded tissues: Membrane hybridization and capillary electrophoresis.** *Biotechniques* 1998, **24**:271–276.

145. Stanta G, Bonin S, Utrera R: **RNA quantitative analysis from fixed and paraffin-embedded tissues.** *Methods Mol Biol* 1998, **86**:113–119.

146. Fink L, Kinfe T, Stein MM, Ermert L, Hanze J, Kummer W, Seeger W, Bohle RM: **Immunostaining and laser-assisted cell picking for mRNA analysis.** *Lab Invest* 2000, **80**:327–333

147. Bock O, Kreipe H, Lehmann U: **One-step extraction of RNA from archival biopsies.** *Anal Biochem* 2001, **295**:116–117.

148. Shibutani M, Uneyama C, Miyazaki K, Toyoda K, Hirose M: **Methacarn fixation: A novel tool for analysis of gene expressions in paraffin-embedded tissue specimens.** *Lab Invest* 2000, **80**:199–208.

149. Goldmann T, Wiedorn KH, Kuhl H, Olert J, Branscheid D, Pechkovsky D, Zissel G, Galle J, Muller-Quernheim J, Vollmer E: **Assessment of transcriptional gene activity *in situ* by application of HOPE–fixed, paraffin-embedded tissues.** *Pathol Res Pract* 2002, **198**:91–95.

150. Gruber AD, Moennig V, Hewicker-Trautwein M, Trautwein G: **Effect of formalin fixation and long-term storage on the detectability of bovine viral-diarrhoea-virus (BVDV) RNA in archival brain tissue using polymerase chain reaction.** *Zentralbl Veterinarmed* 1994 [B], **41**:654–661.

151. Koopmans M, Monroe SS, Coffield LM, Zaki SR: **Optimization of extraction and PCR amplification of RNA extracts from paraffin-embedded tissue in different fixatives.** *J Virol Methods* 1993, **43**:189–204.

152. Macabeo-Ong M, Ginzinger DG, Dekker N, McMillan A, Regezi JA, Wong DT, Jordan RC: **Effect of duration of fixation on quantitative reverse transcription polymerase chain reaction analyses.** *Mod Pathol* 2002, **15**:979–987.

153. Okamoto T, Mitsuhashi M, Kikkawa Y: **Fluorometric nuclear run-on assay with oligonucleotide probe immobilized on plastic plates.** *Anal.Biochem* 1994, **221**:202–204.

154. Matsuda K, Tomozawa S, Fukusho S, Yoshino T, Murakami T, Mitsuhashi M: **Gene expression analysis from nuclear Poly(A) RNA.** *Biotechniques* 2002, **32**:1014–6, 1018, 1020.

155. Teare JM, Islam R, Flanagan R, Gallagher S, Davies MG, Grabau C: **Measurement of nucleic acid concentrations using the DyNA Quant and the GeneQuant.** *Biotechniques* 1997, **22**:1170–1174.

156. Gray GD, Wickstrom E: **Rapid measurement of modified oligonucleotide levels in plasma samples with a fluorophore specific for single-stranded DNA.** *Antisense Nucleic Acid Drug Dev* 1997, **7**:133–140.

157. Glasel JA: **Validity of nucleic acid purities monitored by 260nm/280nm absorbance ratios.** *Biotechniques* 1995, **18**:62–63.

158. Jones LJ, Yue ST, Cheung CY, Singer VL: **RNA quantitation by fluorescence-based solution assay: RiboGreen reagent characterization.** *Anal Biochem* 1998, **265**:368–374.

159. Watzinger F, Lion T: **Multiplex PCR for quality control of template RNA/cDNA in RT-PCR assays.** *Leukemia* 1998, **12**:1984–1986.

160. Swift GH, Peyton MJ, MacDonald RJ: **Assessment of RNA quality by semi-quantitative RT–PCR of multiple regions of a long ubiquitous mRNA.** *Biotechniques* 2000, **28**:524–531.

6

Chemistries

Stephen A. Bustin and Tania Nolan

6

Chemistries

Stephen A. Bustin* and Tania Nolan†

*Barts and The London, Queen Mary's School of Medicine
and Dentistry, University of London, London, United Kingdom
†Stratagene Europe, Amsterdam, The Netherlands*

6.1. Introduction

The principle of fluorescence-based real-time PCR (qPCR) is simple: The presence of amplification products results in fluorescence, which is detected and monitored as amplification occurs.[1] Since the fluorescence output is linear to sample concentration over a very broad range, this linear correlation between PCR product and fluorescence intensity is used to calculate the amount of template present at the beginning of the reaction[2] (**Fig. 6.1A**). Rather than having to look at the amount of PCR product accumulated after a fixed number of cycles, real-time assays determine the number of cycles after which amplification of a PCR product is first detected. The higher the starting copy number of the nucleic acid target, the sooner a significant increase in fluorescence is observed (**Fig. 6.1B**). Three key innovations paved the way for this technology:

1. A process had to be developed that permitted the simultaneous amplification and detection of specific DNA sequences. The original procedure involved the addition of an intercalator, ethidium bromide (EtBr) to the PCR reaction with continuous monitoring during four-minute amplification cycles.[3] An inverse correlation of EtBr fluorescence and temperature was noted, with PCR-associated product accumulation accounting for increased fluorescence during the annealing/extension phase of each cycle. This approach was refined through the use of a thermal cycler with an ultraviolet light source and a computer-controlled CCD cam-

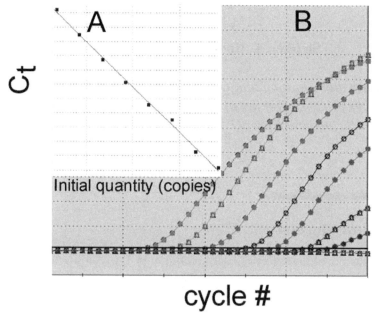

Figure 6.1. (**A**) Standard curve: a plot of initial template quantity against C_t shows the linear relationship between the two. (**B**) Amplification plot used to generate the standard curve.

era.[2] A plot of increased fluorescence, caused by EtBr binding to newly synthesized DNA, against PCR cycle allowed the calculation of the quantity of starting material. The major drawback of this approach was that this measurement could not be easily used to distinguish between specific and nonspecific products.

2. The second innovation provided that specificity by adding a separate oligonucleotide probe, labeled with ^{32}P at the 5' end and designed to hybridize within the target amplicon during the annealing reaction. This generated a substrate suitable for the double-strand-specific 5'–3' exonuclease activity of *Taq* DNA polymerase,[4] resulting in cleavage of the probe if the target sequence was present. However, measurement of the ^{32}P-labeled cleavage products was not straightforward and required their separation by thin layer chromatography.

3. The introduction of fluorogenic probes[5] provided the third innovation and made it possible to amalgamate the two protocols in the 5'-nuclease assay—the first practical real-time fluorescence-based quantitative PCR method.[6] The identity of the target DNA could now easily be determined from the post-PCR fluorescence emission spectrum.

The use of fluorescent dyes allows the amplification and detection steps of the PCR assay to be combined. However, not all dye chemistries are created equal and the fluorescent reagents used with homogeneous fluorescent reporting chemistries can be grouped into two types (see **Table 6.1**):

1. *Nonspecific detection:* Here the best-known reagents are intercalating dyes that are nonspecific in that they bind to any double stranded DNA (dsDNA) generated during the PCR reaction and emit enhanced fluorescence.[7-9] Several dyes are commercially available including the dye that established the proof-of-principle, ethidium bromide, pioneering dyes such as YOYO[®10,11] and YO-PRO-1[®7]dyes, and today's most commonly used dyes-SYBR Green[®] I[9,12] and the more stable SYBR Gold[®]. Intercalating dyes are simply added as a reagent to the PCR cocktail of standard reactions. Other types of nonspecific detection chemistry are the Amplifluor™ and the two quencher-labeled primer methods (see **Sections 6.3.4** and **6.3.5**). Although intrinsically nonspecific, these chemistries can yield quasi-template specific data if DNA melting curves are used to identify specific amplification products.[13]

Table 6.1. Currently available chemistries.

Nonspecific chemistries	Specific chemistries
SYBR™ Green	TaqMan™
SYBR™ Gold	Hybridisation
YoYo™-1	Molecular Beacons
Yo-Pro™-1	Scorpions™
Amplifluor™	Lanthanide
Quencher-labelled primers I	ResonSense™
Quencher-labelled primers II	Angler™
LUX™ primers	Hybeacons™
	Cationic conjugated PNA
	Light-up™
	Eclipse™
	Ds complex probes
	Cyclicons™
	Nanoparticles

2. *Specific detection:* Template-specific analysis requires the design and synthesis of one or more custom-made fluorescent probes for each PCR assay. Most reporting systems utilize fluorescent resonance energy transfer (FRET)[14] or similar interactions between donor and quencher molecules as the basis of detection. The types of reporters used for these probes include fluorescein, rhodamine, and cyanine dyes, and derivatives thereof; some also have either fluorescent or nonfluorescent acceptors on the same or on a complementary molecule. There is a huge selection of fluorescent dyes, mainly because the chemistries for label incorporation into nucleic acid probes are well developed since they are used in other molecular biology procedures such as DNA sequencing. All chemistries follow the same principle: a fluorescent signal is only generated if the amplicon-specific probe hybridizes to its complementary target. The increase in fluorescence may be reported at the annealing step, when the probe is hybridized or at the end of the polymerization step (TaqMan), when probe hydrolysis has resulted in the physical separation of fluorophore and quencher. In addition, some probes may also be used in melt point analyses to provide additional identification of amplified product.

New chemistries and detection systems are constantly being developed, although it is difficult to see how they might improve on the sensitivity and specificity provided by the numerous chemistries currently available.

6.2. Fluorescence

Since all qPCR assays are fluorescence-based, it is as well to have some rudimentary knowledge of what fluorescence is and how it is detected. The intensity of light (I) is a measure of the number of photons emitted per second. In fluorescence analysis this can be defined as the amount of energy falling upon a defined area within a defined wavelength region per unit time. In practice the photon energy is usually expressed in joules, the area in square meters (m^2) and the wavelength region (or spectral bandwidth) in nanometers (nm). Thus the intensity is expressed as Watts (joules per second) per m^2 per nm. Fluorescence results from the molecular absorption of light energy by fluorescent compounds (fluorophores) at one wavelength and its nearly instantaneous re-emission at another, longer wavelength of lower energy (**Fig. 6.2**). The wavelengths and amounts of light absorbed and emitted (known as the fluorescence signature) are characteristic of each individual fluorophore and allow their specific detection by combined thermal cyclers/fluorimeters during the real-time PCR assay. Excitation of a fluorophore at different wavelengths does not change the emission profile but does produce variations in fluorescence emission intensity that corresponds to the amplitude of the excitation spectrum.

Fluorescence is a three-stage process and the fluorescence output of a fluorophore depends on the efficiency with which it absorbs and emits photons. (1) The absorption of light by the fluorophore excites electrons to a higher electronic state. (2) The electrons remain in the excited state for about $(1–10)\times10^{-8}$ seconds. (3) The fluorophore is returned to the ground state following the emission of a photon of energy (**Fig. 6.3**). Since energy is dissipated during the excited-state lifetime, the energy of this photon is always lower (i.e., of a longer wavelength) than that of the absorbed light (the difference in wavelength is termed the *Stokes shift*). The fluorescence process is a cyclical one, where the fluor is repeatedly raised to an excited state and relaxes back to the ground state

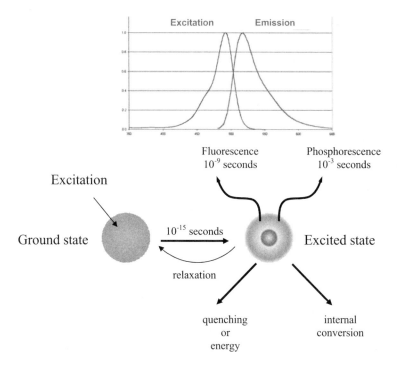

Figure 6.2. Fluorescence results from the absorption of light energy by fluorophores at one wavelength and its nearly instantaneous re-emission at another, longer wavelength of lower energy.

with emission of a fluorescent photon. This process can occur many times and is an important contributory factor to the sensitivity of fluorescence detection systems. However, one of the consequences of this repeated excitation and emission is the loss of fluorescence from the molecule, resulting in the irreversible destruction of the excited fluorophore, a process referred to as photobleaching. Fluorescence detection is affected by reagent background fluorescence originating from unbound, nonspecifically bound or insufficiently quenched probe.

6.2.1. Fluorophores

Most fluorescent dyes are heterocyclic or polyaromatic hydrocarbons and their fluorescence output depends on the efficiency with which they absorb and emit photons and their ability to undergo repeated excita-

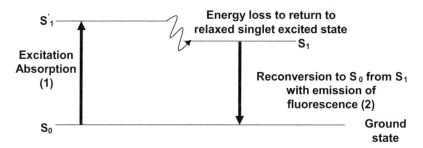

Figure 6.3. Excitation/emission: A photon of energy $h\nu_{EX}$ (1) is supplied by an external source such as a halogen lamp, LED, or laser and absorbed by the fluorophore, creating an excited electronic singlet state (S_1'). The excited state exists for a finite time, during which the fluorophore undergoes conformational changes and is also subject to a multitude of possible interactions with its molecular environment. The energy of S_1' is partially dissipated, yielding a relaxed singlet excited state (S_1) from which photon of energy $h\nu_{EM}$ (2) is emitted, returning the fluorophore to its ground state S_0. Due to energy dissipation during the excited-state lifetime, the energy of this photon is lower, and therefore of longer wavelength, than the excitation photon $h\nu_{EX}$. The difference in energy or wavelength represented by $h\nu_{EX}-h\nu_{EM}$ is the Stokes shift. Not all molecules return to the ground state (S_0) by fluorescence emission. Other processes, especially collisional quenching and FRET, may also depopulate S_1. The fluorescence quantum yield is a measure of the relative extent to which these processes occur.

tion/emission cycles. For multiplex reactions, signal isolation and data analysis are facilitated by maximizing the spectral separation of the multiple emissions. Consequently, fluorophores with narrow, well-resolved spectral bandwidths are particularly useful in multicolor applications (**Fig. 6.4**). An ideal combination of dyes for multiplexing would exhibit strong absorption at a coincident excitation wavelength and well-separated emission spectra. The emitted fluorescence intensity and spectrum of a fluorescent dye is strongly temperature-dependent. Thus the temperature chosen for data acquisition (fluorescence measurement) during a PCR run significantly influences the crosstalk between fluorophores. This is particularly important for applications where measurements are performed at different temperatures (e.g., during melting curve analysis). Unfortunately, it is not easy to find single dyes with the requisite combination of a large extinction coefficient for absorption

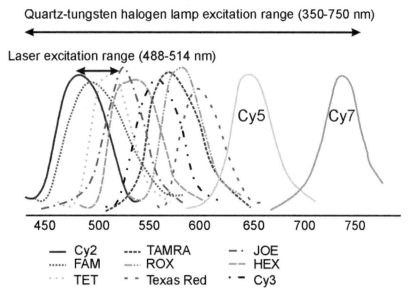

Quartz-tungsten halogen lamp excitation range (350-750 nm)

Laser excitation range (488-514 nm)

| 450 | 500 | 550 | 600 | 650 | 700 | 750 |

— Cy2   ···· TAMRA   – · JOE
······ FAM   —·· ROX   — — HEX
··· TET   ‑ ‑ Texas Red   · ‑ Cy3

Figure 6.4. Fluorophore spectra and excitation wavelengths of laser and halogen lamps.

and a large Stokes shift. The energy capture efficiency of a fluorescent dye is expressed as the extinction coefficient, e, and usually ranges from 10,000 to 250,000 $cm^{-1} M^{-1}$. Its emission efficiency is expressed as the quantum yield, Φ, and is defined as the ratio of the number of fluorescence photons emitted to the number of photons absorbed by a fluorophore. The maximal absorption and emission wavelengths and the extinction coefficients of the most common fluorophores are listed in **Table 6.2**. Since the fluorescence of many fluorophores is strongly influenced by local environment, the resulting quantum yields will vary. For example, although the quantum yield, Φ for TAMRA is less than that of fluorescein, it is less susceptible to photobleaching, and its fluorescence will often appear brighter than that of fluorescein. Brightness refers to the intensity of fluorescence of a fluorophore and the higher this is the more sensitive the dye. Brightness is proportional to the product of the extinction coefficient (ε) and the quantum yield (Φ). Since both of these factors are important in the overall brightness, both properties must be considered when evaluating a new fluorophore. Use of a high-sensitivity detector with broad band-pass filters can improve performance of fluorescein, although in real life photobleaching is proba-

Table 6.2. The maximal absorption wavelength, extinction coefficient, and the maximal emission wavelength of common fluorophores in the form of activated NHS-ester with a linker arm.

Dye	Ab_{max} (nm)	Extinction Coefficient (l mole^{-1} cm^{-1})	Em_{max} (nm)
Acridine™	362	11,000	462
AMCA	353	19,000	442
BODIPY FL-Br2®	531	75,000	545
BODIPY 530/550®	534	77,000	554
BODIPY TMR®	544	56,000	570
BODIPY 558/568®	558	97,000	569
BODIPY 564/570®	563	142,000	569
BODIPY 576/589®	575	83,000	588
BODIPY 581/591®	581	136,000	591
BODIPY TR®	588	68,000	616
BODIPY 630/650®	625	101,000	640
BODIPY 650/665®	646	102,000	660
Cascade Blue®	396	29,000	410
Cy2™	489	150,000	506
Cy3™	552	150,000	570
Cy3.5™	581	150,000	596
Cy5™	643	250,000	667
Cy5.5™	675	250,000	694
Cy7™	743	250,000	767
DABCYL™	453	32,000	none
EDANS™	335	5,900	493
Eosin™	521	95,000	544
Erythrosin™	529	90,000	553
Fluorescein™	492	78,000	520
6-FAM™	494	83,000	518
TET™	521	–	536
JOE™	520	71,000	548
HEX™	535	–	556
LightCycler 640™	625	110,000	640
LightCycler 705™	685	–	705
NBD™	466	22,000	535
Oregon Green 488®	492	88,000	517
Oregon Green 500®	499	78,000	519
Oregon Green 514®	506	85,000	526
Rhodamine 6G™	524	102,000	550
Rhodamine Green™	504	78,000	532
Rhodamine Red™	560	129,000	580
Rhodol Green™	496	63,000	523
TAMRA™	565	91,000	580
ROX™	585	82,000	605
Texas Red™	583	116,000	603
NED™	546	not available	575
VIC™	538	not available	554
Yakima Yellow™	526	84,000	448

bly not a major impediment to a sensitive qPCR assay as the fluorophores are exposed to the excitation wavelength only for a short time. However, fluorescein can be replaced with a more photostable dye with similar absorbance/emission spectra, such as FAM (the world's best fluorophore) or Oregon Green (Molecular Probes, *Cat. No. O-6806*).

The spectral properties of some fluorescent dyes are pH sensitive. For example, fluorescein has a pKa of approximately 6.4 and its Φ and fluorescence intensity rapidly fall off as pH drops below 7. Rhodamine-based dyes, such as ROX or TAMRA, are relatively pH-insensitive. Cy5 is physically unstable in acid conditions and should be stored and used in buffers above pH 7.

The fluorescence of fluorophores conjugated to oligonucleotide probes is sensitive to the environment around the point of attachment.[15-17] Many are quenched upon incorporation into double-stranded DNA, with a resulting 50% drop in Φ. The degree of quenching depends on the fluorophore's proximity to purines and on its position in the oligonucleotide[18-20] and this property is exploited by some probe-based chemistries (see **Section 6.5.2**). The assumption is that photo-induced charge transfer between the dye and a nucleotide residue plays a crucial role in this quenching process. Most of the dyes are quenched by guanosine, which may be explained by the good electron donating properties of this nucleotide. Importantly, hybridization of end-labeled single-stranded oligonucleotides to their complementary sequence can also quench the conjugated fluorophore[21] and again this effect is attributed to the presence of a guanosine in the complementary strand in close proximity to the dye.[22] However, any quenching effect also depends on secondary structure, local sequence, and the proximity of the 3' end or the 5' end of the oligonucleotide,[23] and depending on these factors, the fluorescence of a labeled oligonucleotide can increase or decrease upon hybridization. One important consequence of this is that the fluorescence intensity of many conjugated dyes can be modulated up to 10-fold, which has important consequences not just on probe design but also on the choice of chemistry.

6.2.2. Quenchers

Quenching refers to any process that causes a reduction in the quantum yield of a given fluorescence process. Sometimes, nearby molecules, e.g., heterocyclic ring structures that are present when the dye is conjugated to a nucleic acid or protein can absorb or dissipate energy from an excited fluorophore. This can return the fluorophore to its ground state without any fluorescent emission. Capture and transfer of light energy in this fashion is referred to as quenching. Quenchers accept energy from a fluorophore and dissipate it by one of two mechanisms:

1. Proximal quenching (also known as collisional quenching) occurs when the fluorophore is in close proximity to a quencher molecule, allowing energy transfer from the fluorophore to the quencher. The energy is dissipated as heat and no fluorescence is observed. Collisional quenchers include molecular oxygen and electron scavengers such as Cu^{2+}, Mn^{2+}, and nitrate ion. Since collisional quenching primarily occurs when these ions are present in the mM range or higher, it is usually negligible under most experimental conditions.

2. Fluorescence resonance energy transfer (FRET) is widely used as a reporter method[24] and involves a process that shifts energy from an excited donor fluorophore to a neighboring acceptor molecule, returning the donor to its ground state without fluorescence emission. The efficiency of the process is strongly dependent on (1) the spectral properties, (2) intermolecular distance (Förster distance, $1/r^6$) of donor and acceptor molecules which is unique to each reporter/quencher pair, and (3) the energy lost by the return to ground state of the donor that must be matched to the energy required for the acceptor's excitation, i.e., the absorption spectrum of the acceptor molecule must overlap the emission spectrum of the donor molecule. The degree of spectral overlap is given the symbol J and is sometimes called the "Förster overlap integral." This factor is dependent on both the fluorescent intensity of the donor at a given wavelength and also on the molar extinction coefficient of the acceptor at the same wavelength.

FRET occurs when donor and acceptor molecules are within a specified range, usually no more than 100 Å. Outside of that range the efficiency of quenching falls off rapidly. Since a helix rise occupies approximately 3.4 Å, the maximum distance between a reporter and its quencher on a linear probe should not exceed approximately 30 bases. The acceptor can be another fluorophore, in which case the transfer releases the energy from the quencher as fluorescence at a longer wavelength. For example, a combination of FAM and TAMRA will absorb at 492 nm (excitation peak for FAM) and emit at 580 nm (emission peak for TAMRA).

The inherent fluorescence and broad emission spectrum of the quencher (TAMRA) results in a relatively poor signal-to-noise ratio, which makes multiplexing very tricky. This issue has been addressed by the introduction of dark quenchers that absorb the energy emitted by the fluorophore but release it as heat rather than fluorescence. The fluorophore absorption spectrum remains unchanged. The early ones, such as 4-(49-dimethylaminophenylazo)benzoic acid (DABCYL), suffered from poor spectral overlap between the fluorescent dye and quencher molecule. Several new ones are now available, including Biosearch Technology's Black Hole Quenchers (BHQ™-1 and BHQ™-2), Iowa Black, Eurogentec/Oswell's ElleQuencher, and Epoch's Eclipse Dark Quencher. They tend to have lower background fluorescence, hence providing greater sensitivity and with their broad effective range of absorption, permit the simultaneous use of a wide range of reporter dyes, expanding the options available for multiplex assays.

Note: Unlike most quenchers, DABCYL must be in close proximity to the reporter molecule for efficient quenching. Therefore, DABCYL quenchers are best used in oligonucleotides probes where secondary structure brings the reporter and quencher into close contact, most obviously in Molecular Beacons (see **Section 6.6.1**), where the reporter group and DABCYL are brought together by hairpin-stem formation.

Improving the fluorescence quenching efficiency remains a considerable challenge. However, two new developments are taking place: (1) novel metal quenchers are beginning to appear with properties superior to those of more conventional quenchers and (2) chemistries that make use of the quenching properties of DNA itself and do not rely on a separate quencher are beginning to appear (see **Section 6.5.1**).

6.3. Nonspecific Chemistries

6.3.1. DNA Intercalators

DNA intercalators bind reversibly but tightly to DNA by slotting the chromophore in between the stacked base pairs.[25] The sequence selectivity of these compounds is generally very poor, although many contain side chains that interact with limited specificity in one of the grooves.

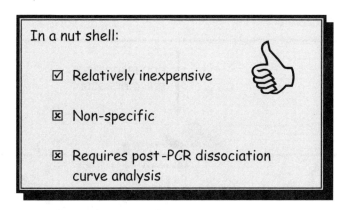

In a nut shell:

☑ Relatively inexpensive

☒ Non-specific

☒ Requires post-PCR dissociation curve analysis

Most real-time PCR assays that use DNA-binding dyes detect the binding of the fluorescent minor groove binding dye SYBR™ Green I or its more stable alternative, SYBR™ Gold) to DNA[9] (**Fig. 6.5**). One reason for their popularity is that their fluorescent peak emission spectrum closely matches that of fluorescein. This is convenient because PCR fluorimeter designs are often optimized for fluorescein. The unbound dyes exhibit little fluorescence in solution, but during elongation increasing amounts of dye bind to the nascent double-stranded DNA. When monitored in real-time by excitation at 497 nm (SYBR Gold 495 nm) this results in the emission of a fluorescence signal at 520 nm (SYBR Gold 537 nm) that can be observed during the polymerization step, and that falls off when the DNA is denatured. Consequently, fluorescence measurements taken at the end of the elongation step of every PCR cycle allow the monitoring of the increasing amounts of amplified DNA in that cycle.

6.3.2. Advantages

Assays using DNA-binding dyes have two advantages over probe-based ones: (1) they can be incorporated into optimized and long-established protocols that use legacy primers and experimental conditions and (2) they are significantly cheaper, as there is no probe-associated cost. This

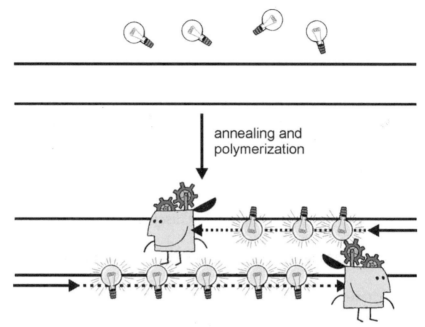

Figure 6.5. Schematic representation of real-time PCR with the SYBR Green I dye. When excited, SYBR Green I dye fluoresces upon binding to double-stranded DNA, providing a direct method for quantitating PCR products in real time.

makes them very useful for optimizing a PCR reaction, e.g., testing any interaction between the primers by melting curve analysis, and carrying out initial, exploratory screens of multiple amplicons before using a probe-based protocol. Indeed, despite the nonspecific nature of amplification detection, DNA-binding dye-based assays need not be less reliable than probe-based ones. Interestingly, there is at least one report that suggests that SYBR Green I detection is more precise and produces a more linear decay plot than TaqMan detection.[26] Not surprisingly, real-time PCR using SYBR Green chemistry is very popular with its use reported for quantification of mRNA levels,[27-31] detection of mRNA splice variants,[32] viral[33-39] and bacterial[40-46] pathogens, genotyping,[47,48] and the detection of minimal residual disease in cancer patients.[49] The recent publication of a protocol that allows the end user to make up a SYBR Green I-based real-time PCR kit[50] makes the use of this dye even more attractive, not least in terms of money saved.

Other intercalating dyes are available and have been used successfully for detection and/or quantification of nucleic acids. A rather labor-intensive, pioneering experiment used dimers of oxazole orange (Molecular Probes YOYO-1® and a laser-induced fluorescence detector in conjunction with a capillary electrophoresis system to detect femtogram amounts of dsDNA.[10] The same dye was also used to quantitate the fluorescence intensity of DNA in 96-well plates following a PCR assay, although the sensitivity achieved with this early experiment was only comparable to that obtained with EtBr-stained gel electrophoresis.[11] A combination of the oxazole yellow derivative YO-PRO-1® (Molecular Probes) and a homemade "PCR monitor" instrument consisting of a modified excitation fluorescence HPLC detector, an Argon laser and a photomultiplier was used early on to quantitate as few as 100 copies of Hepatitis C Virus RNA in serum samples from patients with hepatitis.[7]

6.3.3. Disadvantages

DNA-binding dye assays have several significant disadvantages. First, some of the dyes will bind to single-stranded DNA (ssDNA)[11] and their indiscriminate binding to any double-stranded DNA (dsDNA) results in nonspecific fluorescence. Characteristically, this results in fluorescence readings in the "No-Template Controls" (NTC) due to dye molecules binding to primer dimers and misprimed sequences.

> **Note:** For RT-PCR assays, a change from a combined RT and PCR step to separate ones can dramatically reduce problems due to primer dimerization, and DNase treatment is a prerequisite for accurate SYBR Green quantification.[51]

A second problem is that, as with conventional PCR, the specificity of the reaction is determined entirely by its primers. Therefore, this assay is no more specific than conventional PCR. However, all is not lost as additional specificity can be achieved and the PCR verified by melting curves[13;52] that allow a comparison of the melting temperatures of the specific and any suspected nonspecific products.[53] This is because different dsDNA molecules melt at different temperatures that are dependent upon a number of factors including their GC content, amplicon length, secondary and tertiary structure, and the chemical formulation of the reaction chemistry. Melting curves are obtained by slowly ramping the temperature of the PCR solution from about 50°C to 95°C while continuously collecting fluorescence readouts. This results in the denaturation of all dsDNA, and the point at which the dsDNA melts into ssDNA is observed as a drop in fluorescence as the intercalator dissociates. A plot of raw fluorescence against temperature results in characteristic melting profiles for the specific and nonspecific amplification products (**Fig. 6.6A**). The melting curves are converted to distinct melting peaks by plotting the first negative derivative of the fluorescence as a function of temperature (–dF/dT) (**Fig. 6.6B**). Different length products and products of different sequences will melt at different temperatures and will be observed as distinct peaks. Upon renaturation, SYBR Green I stain fluorescence exhibits a large increase upon DNA binding that can be used to obtain thermal denaturation profiles from complex nucleic acid mixtures such as those generated during PCR amplification. Typically, two semidiscrete populations with different transition temperatures can be identified in the first derivative plots. Populations with a T_m of 80°C or higher correspond to the larger PCR products, and can usually be assigned to the specific DNA product; DNA products displaying melting temperatures of more than 75°C usually correspond to nonspecific DNA products. It is important to note that these populations are not necessarily homogeneous and may contain multiple PCR product species. However, if the PCR reaction is fully optimized, it is possible to produce a melting peak profile that contains only a single peak that represents the specific .product expected from the primer pair. In this situation SYBR Green I may be useful for mutation detection[54] as amplicons that differ by a single nucleotide will melt at slightly different temperatures and can be distinguished by their melting peaks. This makes it possible to distinguish homozygotes (single peak) from heterozygotes (two peaks). However, in general, probe-based discrimination is likely to be more specific.[55]

A third drawback of this chemistry is that multiple dye molecules bind to a single amplified molecule and consequently the amount of signal generated following irradiation is dependent on the mass of double-stranded DNA produced in the reaction. Assuming the same amplification efficiencies, amplification of a longer product will generate more signal than a shorter one. If amplification efficiencies are different, quantification will be even more inaccurate.

Note: The concentration of SYBR has an important effect on the T_m of an amplicon: If it is too high, the amplicon will not melt.

Lastly, for anyone using Roche's LightCycler, the very short denaturation times used with this instrument can result in incomplete denaturation of genomic DNA. If the amplification target is present in very

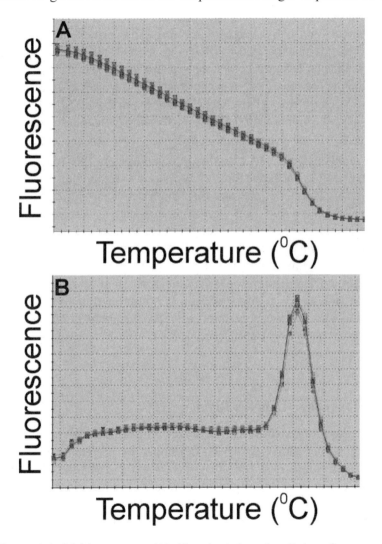

Figure 6.6. Melting curves. (**A**) The plot is based on R (raw fluorescence). (**B**) The plot is based on the first derivative of the normalized fluorescence reading multiplied by −1.

low amounts, the use of SYBR Green results in high levels of basal fluorescence, which can mask the increase in fluorescence generated by the amplification product.[56]

6.3.4. Quencher-Labeled Primer (I)

This system uses two labeled molecules: (1) a 13-residue quencher-labeled peptide nucleic acid (Q-PNA) probe with a C-terminal DABCYL group and (2) a primer with a target-specific sequence at its 3' end and a fluorophore and a Q-PNA-complementary sequence tag at its 5' end[57] (**Fig. 6.7**). The length of the Q-PNA ensures that the Q-PNA/primer duplex has a T_m higher than the primer annealing temperature, but lower than the T_m of the primer/amplicon duplex. This ensures that excess primer is quenched at the annealing temperature and the fluorescence measured during the annealing step indicates the amount of primer hybridized to amplicon, plus any full-length double-stranded amplicon, as the end result is a fluorescently label ds amplicon. A 13-residue Q-PNA is most suitable for real time as it hybridizes with sufficient strength to provide rapid and efficient quenching of excess primer at the temperature used for primer annealing. For endpoint measurements that are made at room temperature post-PCR, it is possible to use a Q-PNAs molecule with as few as nine residues. It is also possible to reverse the labels and monitor the generation of fluorescent PNA. This has the advantage of requiring significantly less PNA probe; however, its sensitivity is not as great.

6.3.5. Quencher-Labeled Primer (II)

Another ingenious solution to the nonspecific contribution to quantification of primer dimers has been developed by Molecular Probes. A QSY 7 (*Cat. No. Q-10193*) or QSY 9 (*Cat. No. Q-20131*) dye attached to the 5' terminus of an oligonucleotide primer (more than 25 bases) effectively quenches the fluorescence of intercalating dyes that bind to the primer or its dimers (**Fig. 6.8**). As the chain elongates, the dye that binds at sites sufficiently remote from the quencher exhibits fluorescence. Thus, the signal in PCR measurements more accurately indicates initial target numbers, and the background fluorescence is reduced.

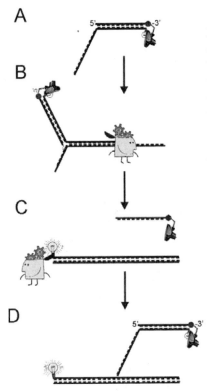

Figure 6.7. Quencher-labeled primers (I). (**A**) Quencher labeled Q-PNA hybridized to the 5'-tag sequence of a fluor-labeled forward primer quenches the fluorescence of the primer. (**B**) In the first cycle of the PCR assay, the 3' end of the forward primer hybridizes to denatured target and DNA polymerase extends the primer. (**C**) In the second cycle, the reverse primer initiates extension of the reverse strand, resulting in displacement of the Q-PNA and incorporation of the 13-base Q-PNA-binding region into the amplicon. (**D**) In subsequent annealing steps, the forward primer anneals fully to the reverse strand, reporting its presence for real time analysis because excess primer is quenched by the Q-PNA. E. The end product of the reaction is a ds amplicon, of which one strand is fluorescently labeled.

6.3.6. LUX™ Primers

The LUX system (Light Upon eXtension, Invitrogen) is another imaginative invention designed to address the limitations of DNA labeling dyes without having to go to the expense of using hybridization probes. One of the target-specific primers is labeled with a single fluorophore close to the 3' end in a hairpin structure (**Fig. 6.9**). This fluorogenic primer has a short sequence tail of 4–6 nucleotides at the 5' end that is complementary to the 3' end of the primer. The resulting hairpin configuration effectively quenches the fluorophore (relative fluorescence 0.1) and no separate quenching moiety is needed. When the primer is single-stranded, e.g., during the denaturation step, fluorescence increases a little (relative fluorescence 0.4); however, once it becomes incorporated into the double-stranded PCR product, quenching is relieved

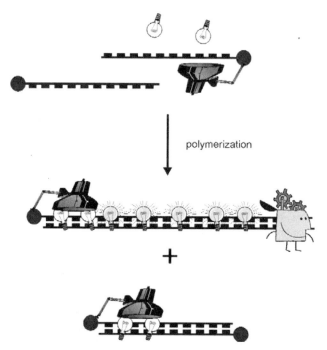

Figure 6.8. Quencher labeled primers (II). Schematic representation of real-time PCR with quencher-labeled primers and the SYBR Green I dye. When excited, the SYBR Green I dye fluoresces upon binding to double-stranded DNA. However, a quencher bound to one of the primers suppresses the fluorescence of nearby SYBR Green I dye molecules. In this way, the fluorescence signal of the dye bound to PCR products is maintained while background fluorescence from the dye bound to primer dimers is minimized.

and a significant increase in fluorescent signal (approximately 10-fold) is observed. Melting curve analyses can be performed to distinguish genuine amplicons from primer-dimer artifacts and different fluorescent labels can be used for multiplexing.

6.3.7. Amplifluor™

A fourth alternative to SYBR dyes is the Amplifluor Universal Amplification and Detection System (Serologicals) (see **Fig. 6.10**). This system uses three primers: two target-specific ones and a so-called UniPrimer™.[58] The first target-specific primer has a universal (Z) sequence

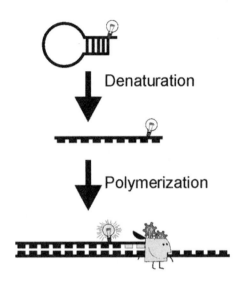

Figure 6.9. LUX primers. One primer contains a fluorophore, the other one is unlabeled. The fluorogenic primer has a short sequence tail of 4–6 nucleotides on the 5' end that is complementary to the 3' end of the primer. The resulting hairpin secondary structure provides optimal quenching of the attached fluorophore. When the primer is incorporated into the double-stranded PCR product, the fluorophore is dequenched and a signal is reported.

at its 5' end, which provides a universal polymerization template for the UniPrimer. The second target-specific primer is not modified in any way. Any PCR reaction can be adapted to the Amplifluor system by synthesizing one of the target-specific primers with the Z sequence added to its 5' end. The 3' end of the UniPrimer is complementary to the Z sequence of the first primer, thus providing a universal PCR priming site. The 5' end contains a hairpin region that is labeled with a fluorophore, e.g., fluorescein, and a quencher, e.g., DABSYL. The hairpin is similar in structure to a Molecular Beacon (see **Section 6.6.1**), but the single-stranded loop sequence is not specific to the amplicon sequence and does not bind to the amplicon. During the first cycle, the primer with the Z sequence becomes incorporated into the newly synthesized strand. During the second cycle, polymerization from the other primer incorporates the complement to the Z sequence into the newly synthesized strand. In the third cycle, the UniPrimer tail can anneal to the Z sequence, prime polymerization by *Taq* polymerase, and the UniPrimer itself becomes incorporated into the new strand, albeit retaining the hairpin conformation. During the fourth cycle, the polymerase unfolds the hairpin structure, and the whole UniPrimer becomes incorporated into the lower strand, thus separating fluorophore and quencher. This increase in distance results in a reduction of quenching, permitting the generation of fluorescence emission. From this cycle on the UniPrimer

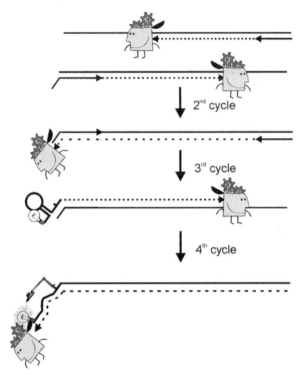

Figure 6.10. Amplifluor. In the first round of amplification, the reverse primer, containing a special sequence tag, primes synthesis along the template. In the second round, the forward primer primes synthesis that extends through the special sequence tag, forming a complementary sequence to the tag. In the third round, the UniPrimer hybridizes to this complementary sequence via the special sequence tag. The hairpin structure of the UniPrimer ensures that the quencher suppresses the fluorescence of the fluorophore. Finally, in the fourth round, synthesis extends through the hairpin loop, relieving the quenching of the fluorophore.

becomes part of the amplicon and the fluorescent signal produced with each PCR cycle and collected during the annealing step correlates with the amount of amplified DNA generated. Unincorporated UniPrimer remains in the hairpin conformation and does not fluoresce due to the proximity of the fluorophore and quencher.

It is possible to use two UniPrimers with different tail sequences and labeled with different fluorophores to perform SNP/mutation discrimination experiments. A single common reverse primer and two allele-specific primers are designed to amplify across the SNP. Each allele-specific primer contains a 5'-tail sequence identical to the tail sequence of one of the two UniPrimers. The UniPrimer, in conjunction with the common reverse primer, amplifies and fluorescently labels the PCR product. Depending on the genotype of the sample, a mixed signal from both fluorophores is observed for a heterozygote while a single signal is observed for a homozygote. The use of LNAs at the SNP/mutation site allows specific discrimination. A major advantage of this system is that the use of the UniPrimer eliminates the need for a unique fluorescent probe or primer set for each SNP/mutation. The major disadvantage is that the assay is not as specific as an assay based on amplicon-specific probes. There are still few reports of its use, but it has been shown to be more sensitive than the ELISA-based telomeric repeat amplification protocol (TRAP) for the detection of telomerase in breast cancer samples.[59,60]

6.4. Specific Chemistries

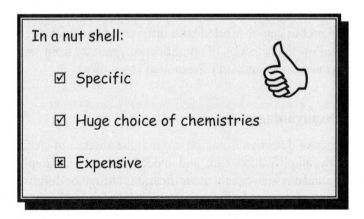

In a nut shell:

☑ Specific

☑ Huge choice of chemistries

☒ Expensive

Although all specific detection systems are variations on a single theme, there are significant differences in their complexity, cost, and the type of results obtained. Therefore, the intended applications should be considered carefully before any particular chemistry is chosen. Specific detection systems fall into two categories: those that use nonstructured linear probes and those that use structurally constrained constructs. All chemistries depend on the hybridization of that amplicon-specific hybridization probe (or two) and numerous different arrangements of fluorophore and quencher. Indeed, some chemistries do not require any quencher at all.

6.4.1. Advantages

In contrast to nonspecific chemistries, specificity no longer resides in the primers; instead an additional level of specificity is introduced that is the equivalent of a Southern blot. In the absence of specific target, the fluorescent probe is quenched and little or no fluorescence is emitted. If the probe(s) hybridize to a complementary sequence, quenching is relieved and fluorescence can be measured. This provides the most significant advantage of fluorogenic probes over the detection methods described previously: Specific hybridization between probe and target is required to generate fluorescent signals. Nonspecific amplification due to mispriming or primer-dimer artifacts does not generate a signal and is ignored by the fluorescence detector. This obviates the need for post-PCR Southern blotting, sequence analysis, or melting curves to confirm the identity of the amplicon. Another advantage over intercalating dyes is that the probes can be labeled with different, distinguishable reporter dyes that allow the detection of amplification products from several distinct sequences in a single qPCR reaction (multiplex).

6.4.2. Disadvantages

The absence of detection is not the same as the absence of artifacts, and nonspecific amplification can, and indeed does, affect amplification efficiency and any subsequent quantification. The major disadvantage is that because of its specificity, artifacts that interfere with amplification efficiency cannot be detected. Therefore, intercalating dyes should be used to optimize primers and reaction conditions prior to any quantification experiments in order to ensure the absence of amplification artifacts. Another disadvantage is the cost associated with these chemistries: Each target requires its own specific probe. This becomes particularly painful when quantifying multiple targets as costs escalate very rapidly.

6.5. Linear Probes

The number of available qPCR chemistries is increasing all the time, especially those involving linear probes. One advantage of linear probes is that the absence of secondary structure allows for optimum hybridization efficiency, as they are not impeded by competition with intramolecular hybridization that is characteristic of, e.g., Molecular Beacons (see **Section 6.6.1**).

6.5.1. ResonSense® and Angler® Probes

ResonSense chemistry was developed at the Defence, Science and Technology Laboratory at Porton Down, United Kingdom, to speed up the qPCR assay and was demonstrated to produce optimum signal after 5 s at the annealing step.[61] The assay uses a DNA intercalator, e.g., SYBR Gold as a donor FRET moiety, as well as a single amplicon-specific probe that is labeled with an acceptor fluorophore (e.g., Cy5) at the 5' end and contains a protected 3' end to prevent its extension by an exonuclease deficient mutant DNA polymerase, which ensures that the probe is not consumed during the reaction (**Fig. 6.11**). In the absence of target, or when dissociated from the target, no fluorescence is emitted because SYBR Gold donor molecules are not within the distance required for energy transfer. Sequence-specific binding of the probe provides a double-stranded DNA molecule that also binds SYBR Gold. Following excitation at 495 nm, energy is transferred from SYBR Gold to Cy5 via FRET and emitted at 695 nm. The Angler system is based on the same principle, but uses a probe that is attached to the downstream primer by a linker and results in more efficient probing of the amplification product. All PCR reactions are carried out in a homogeneous assay on the LightCycler (Roche), which is at present the fastest commercial combined thermal cycler/fluorimeter, and fluorescent signals are monitored using its color compensation algorithm. Analysis of two fluorescent signals allows the detection of both specific and nonspecific amplification. This technology works for both quantitative PCR and allelic discrimination.

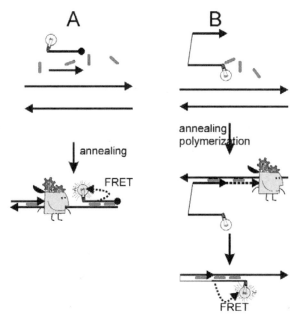

Figure 6.11. (**A**) ResonSense: The probe is labeled with an fluorescence acceptor moiety (e.g., Cy5.5) at its 5' end and a protective label at its 3' end. In the absence of target, or during the denaturation step, there is no donor fluorescence moiety, e.g., SYBR Gold, within the distance required for energy transfer. However, in the presence of a complementary amplification product, both donor and acceptor can bind and fluoresce by FRET. (**B**) Angler: The probe is attached to one of the primers by a chemical linker that brings it spatially close to the extended amplification product for efficient self-probing.

6.5.2. HyBeacons™

HyBeacons were developed by the Laboratory of the Government Chemist (LGC), UK, and make clever use of the quenching properties of DNA.[62] This approach also uses single labeled oligonucleotides; however with HyBeacons a fluorescent dye label is attached to an internal nucleotide and a blocking group at the a 3' end to prevent PCR extension (**Fig. 6.12**). Probes emit greater amounts of fluorescence when hybridized to complementary target sequences than when single-stranded. Following amplification, the identity of target sequences is confirmed by melting curve analysis. HyBeacon probes can also be

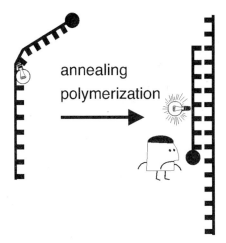

Figure 6.12. Hybeacons: Probes comprise specific linear oligonucleotides that possess a fluorescent dye label attached to an internal nucleotide and a 3' phosphate to prevent PCR extension. They emit greater amounts of fluorescence when hybridised to complementary target sequences than when single-stranded.

used for SNP/mutation analyses with the polymorphic nucleotides best located towards the center of the HyBeacon probe.[63] Major advantages of using this chemistry include simple mode of action, relatively inexpensive synthesis, and as functionality does not require FRET, enzymatic cleavage or secondary structures; probe design is uncomplicated.

6.5.3. Light-up Probes

Light-up probes are composed of thiazole orange (TO) conjugated to PNA and combine the excellent hybridization properties of PNA[64] which allows the use of shorter probes, with the extraordinary fluorescence enhancement of asymmetric cyanine dyes upon binding to nucleic acids.[65] The linker in the light-up probe is flexible, allowing the dye to interact with the target nucleic acid upon hybridization (**Fig. 6.13**). When the thiazole orange moiety interacts with the nucleic acid bases, the aromatic moieties are fixed in a co-planar geometry and the dye becomes strongly fluorescent and is readily detected.[66] The degree of fluorescence enhancement depends on the probe sequence.[67] The dye can, however, also fold back interacting with the bases in the free probe, which can give rise to residual free-probe fluorescence. In fact, one reason the light-up probes are based on PNA instead of normal oligodeoxyribonucleotides is that this eliminates electrostatic attraction

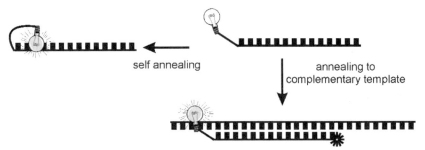

Figure 6.13. Light-up probes. The light-up probe consists of a sequence-recognizing element linked to a reporter group, here peptide nucleic acid (PNA), coupled to a thiazole orange derivative. When free in solution, the probe has low fluorescence due to the intrinsic properties of the reporter dye. Binding of the sequence-recognizing element to its complementary target allows interaction between the dye and the nucleobases, which causes the light-up probe to fluoresce brightly. Due to the flexibility of the linker, some of the reporter can back bind to the probe, resulting in background fluorescence.

of the cationic TO dye, minimizing this back-binding.[68] The probes do not interfere with the PCR reaction and can either be included in the sample mixture with fluorescence measured during the annealing step or added after completed amplification.[69] The sensitivity of Light-up-based assays is similar to that of other real-time chemistries but is claimed to be significantly better than that of PNA-based Molecular Beacons.[70] The specificity of the probe allows discrimination of a single-base mismatch in the target sequence.[71]

6.5.4. Hydrolysis (TaqMan®) Probes

This assay, popularly known as TaqMan, was first described in 1991[4] and relies on the 5'-3' exonuclease activity of *Taq* polymerase which cleaves a labeled probe when hybridized to a complementary target (**Fig. 6.14**). It is the most popular qPCR chemistry by far,[72-81] and may even be the best.[82] A fluorophore (typically FAM) is attached to the 5' end of the probe and a quencher (traditionally TAMRA) to the 3' end. Other arrangements are possible,[5] but having reporter and quencher at the ends of the oligonucleotide simplifies the design and synthesis of the hydrolysis probe.[83] More recently, dark quenchers have started to replace fluorescent quenchers, thus freeing up TAMRA as a reporter in multiplex analyses. The excited reporter fluorophore passes its energy, via FRET, to the quencher, which fluoresces. As this fluorescence is detected at a different wavelength to the reporter, its background level is low. If no amplicon complementary to the probe is present, the probe remains intact, and low fluorescence is detected. If the PCR reaction results in a complementary target, the probe binds to it during each annealing step of the PCR. The enzyme's double-strand-specific 5'–3' nuclease activity displaces the 5' end of the probe and then degrades it (**Fig. 6.14**). Note that most thermostable polymerases do not possess this activity.[84] Cleavage continues until the remaining probe melts off the amplicon. This process releases the fluorophore and quencher into solution, spatially separating them relative to when the probe held them together. This leads to an irreversible increase in fluorescence from the reporter and a decrease in the quencher. Since the polymerase will cleave the probe only while it remains hybridized to its complementary strand, the temperature conditions of the polymerization phase of the PCR must be adjusted to ensure probe binding. It is usually carried out 8–10°C below the T_m of the probe and this also ensures maximum 5'–3' exonuclease activity of the polymerase, although it also reduces its processivity.

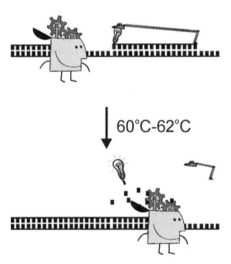

Figure 6.14. Hydrolysis probes. The 5–3' nuclease activity of the *Taq* polymerase cleaves a TaqMan probe during PCR. The TaqMan probe contains a reporter dye at the 5' end of the probe and a quencher at the 3' end of the probe. During the reaction, the reporter dye and quencher dye become separated, resulting in increased fluorescence of the reporter. Accumulation of PCR products is detected indirectly by monitoring the increase in fluorescence of the reporter dye.

This assay can also be used for SNP/mutation analysis[85] where probes for each allele are labeled with a different fluorophore, e.g., with FAM and HEX. If the amplification conditions are chosen correctly, each probe will remain bound to its perfect complement only during the polymerization step, resulting in efficient cleavage and release of the reporter dye. The mismatched probe, on the other hand, hybridizes with decreased efficiency, and is more readily displaced without cleavage of the probe (**Fig. 6.15**). Therefore, a substantial increase of one dye or the other indicates homozygosity for the FAM- or HEX-specific alleles. If both signals increase, the sample is likely to be from a heterozygote.

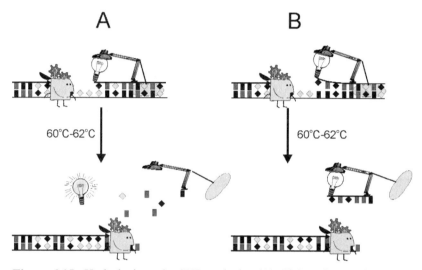

Figure 6.15. Hydrolysis probe SNP analysis. (**A**) If there is a perfect match between probe and target, the hybridized probe is displaced and cleaved by the exonuclease activity of *Taq* polymerase. (**B**) If there is a single mismatch, the hybridized probe is displaced, but not cleaved. It remains intact and the reporter fluorophore remains quenched.

6.5.5. Lanthanide Probes

An interesting variation on hydrolysis probes is the recent description of a new label technology based on lanthanide chelates and their use in time-resolved multiplex real-time qPCR.[86] Time resolved fluorescence resonance energy transfer (TR-FRET) is a standard spectroscopic technique and is based on FRET and the use of long-lived fluorescent molecules, such a lanthanides, as energy donors. The emission of these metals is characterized by narrow band emission and long fluorescent lifetime. If these metals are chelated with certain light absorbing ligands then the emission is enhanced by many orders of magnitude. The ligand field around the metal center serves to prevent quenching by water molecules and the consequent nonradiative loss of energy. The energy can then be transferred to the metal. In effect the ligand is enhancing the absorptivity of the lanthanide. Fluorescent lanthanide chelates have long excited state lifetimes, which allow the use of time-resolved fluorimetry where the signal is not recorded immediately after the excitation pulse but after a certain delay. During this delay, nonspecific background fluorescence and fluorescence from rapid labels such as FAM disappear. An additional advantage is that time-resolved fluorimetry assays have superior signal-to-noise ratios compared to conventional, short excited state lifetime reporters.

The qPCR assay uses terbium or europium chelates, whose fluorescence is quenched when coupled to a single-stranded DNA probe without the need for a separate quencher. Therefore, this method obviates the need for expensive dual-labeled probe incorporating a fluorophore and a quencher. The coupling has a significant effect on the lanthanide decay time and thus on the quantum yield of the reporter. As with hydrolysis probes, a signal with a wide dynamic range is generated when the 5'-3' exonuclease activity of *Taq* polymerase cleaves the hybridized probe.

Lanthanides are excited by light in the UV range, hence do not cause any background signal for conventional reporters that are excited by light in the visible range. Signal amplification is achieved by repeating the measurement several times in a short period of time. Therefore it is possible to combine conventional and lanthanide labels whose emission spectra overlap considerably, e.g., terbium and FAM, in one assay and discriminate between their signals, thus maximizing the specificity of a homogeneous multianalyte assay. It is also possible to use two lanthanide labels, terbium and europium, in one assay for efficient duplexing; temporal separation of their fluorescent signals from those of conventional, short emission lifetime reporters should increase the maximum number of amplicons detectable and considerably extend the multiplex capability of this assay. However, as with any multiplex reaction involving more than two sets of primers and probes, careful optimization is a must. A recent modification[87] reduces background fluorescence even further by cleverly adding a short quencher probe to the assay, which hybridizes to any unbound, nonhydrolyzed reporter probe at a low temperature, with reporting taking place at that low temperature. Fluorescence is measured when reporter and quencher probes have hybridized (**Fig. 6.16**). Placement of the quencher on a separate oligonucleotide significantly increases its quenching efficiency compared to TaqMan probes.

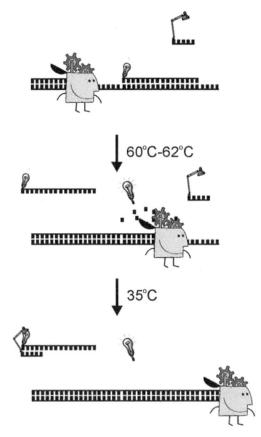

Figure 6.16. Lanthanide probes. The assay is carried out as a three-step reaction, with a denaturation step at 95°C, a primer/probe/template annealing and polymerization step at 62°C, and a unbound reporter probe/quencher probe hybridization and fluorescent data collecting step at 35°C. The *Taq* polymerase digests any reporter oligonucleotide probe labeled at the 5' end with lanthanide chelates, which has hybridized with amplicons generated during the PCR reaction. This results in a higher fluorescence intensity of the label. The reaction mixture is then rapidly cooled and the undigested probe is hybridized with a complementary, probe that incorporates a quencher at its 3' end. This probe is shorter and has a T_m lower than the annealing/polymerization temperature. Any remaining background fluorescence from intact fluorescent probe molecules is completely quenched, resulting in minimal background fluorescence. Since the signal-to-noise ratios are significantly higher, threshold cycles are lower than those obtained using conventional hydrolysis probes.

6.5.6. Hybridization Probes

These probes were developed specifically for use with the Idaho Technology/Roche capillary-based instrument,[1] but can be used with most current real-time instruments (**Fig. 6.17**). Two probes are designed to bind adjacent to one another on the amplicon. One has a donor dye at its 3' end (e.g., FAM), and the other has an acceptor dye on its 5' end (e.g., LC red 640 or 705) and is blocked at its 3' end to prevent its extension during the annealing step. In solution, the two dyes are apart and the donor emits only background fluorescence. Following the denaturation step, both probes hybridize to their target sequence in a head-to-tail arrangement during the annealing step. The reporter is excited and passes its energy to the acceptor dye through FRET. The intensity of the light of longer wavelength emitted by the second dye is measured, with the increase in fluorescence proportional to the increase in the amount of target amplicon. Since the probes are not hydrolyzed, fluorescence is reversible and allows the generation of melting curves. This technology can be also be used for SNP/mutation detection, where one probe is positioned over the polymorphic site and the mismatch causes the probe to dissociate at a different temperature to the fully complementary amplicon.[88] Melting curve analysis after the PCR reveals which alleles are present since one probe dissociating from the amplicon causes a decrease in fluorescence as FRET can no longer occur.[89] It should be noted that careful choice of FRET pairs is necessary: FRET is not efficient between FAM and the LC red 705 dye, due to the small overlap between the spectra.

6.5.7. Eclipse™

Eclipse probes are linear probes that have a minor groove binder (MGB) and quencher on the 5' end and the fluorophore on the 3' end.[90] This is the other way round compared with hydrolysis probes and the presence of the MGB at the 5' end prevents cleavage of the Eclipse probe by *Taq* polymerase. In solution and in the absence of target the probe is in a random coil conformation, which brings reporter and quencher close together. If the probe hybridizes to a complementary sequence, the probe is linearized, quenching is decreased, and the fluorescent signal is increased. The combination of MBG and quencher reduces the back-

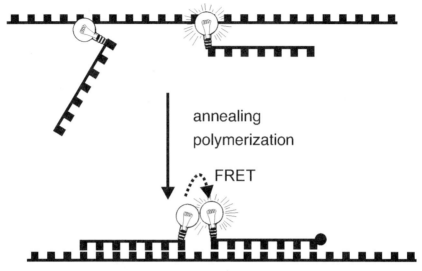

Figure 6.17. Hybridization probes. During the PCR annealing step, two different oligonucleotides hybridize, head-to-tail, to adjacent regions of the target DNA. The fluorophores, which are directly coupled to the oligonucleotides, are very close in the hybrid structure. The donor fluorophore (e.g., fluorescein) is excited by an external light source, then passes on part of its excitation energy to the adjacent acceptor via FRET. The excited acceptor fluorophore emits measurable light at a different wavelength.

ground level of fluorescence by enhancing the quenching. The use of MGB results in short probes which helps improve the specificity of allelic discrimination assays and the sensitivity of the detection with these probes is comparable to the other chemistries.

6.5.8. Displacement Hybridization/Complex Probe

Although hybridization between two single-stranded nucleic acids is highly specific, measurable physical changes are rather small. Moreover, it can be difficult to achieve accurate mismatch discrimination, necessitating the design and synthesis of probes containing hairpins, minor groove-binding (MGB) groups or nucleic acid analogues such as PNA and LNA. Displacement hybridization,[91] or the "complex probe method,"[92] differs from direct hybridization in that it has an additional competitor in the probe-target reaction system, as the probe is

double-stranded (**Fig. 6.18**). The role of this competitor is to be sufficiently competitive to block nonspecific hybridization but not to interfere with the formation of perfectly matched probe-target hybrids. The
competitor is a single-stranded oligonucleotide that has the same
sequence as the target in the binding region but is shorter than the probe
(15–21 nucleotides). In this way, the competitor will form a stable
duplex with the probe in the absence of a perfectly matched target but
can be displaced in the presence of a matched target. The target-binding
probe contains a fluorophore at its 5' end and the competitor contains a
quencher at its 3' end. After probe-target hybridization, the distance
between the fluorophore and the quencher changes from close proximity to totally free separation. The double-stranded molecule is named
a "Yin-Yang" probe, as the two strands interact synergistically to
enhance specificity. Hybridization of this double-stranded probe to a perfectly complementary target occurs between 10 and 20 times faster than
mismatched targets of hybridization. Measuring fluorescence as a function of temperature shows that at higher temperatures the double-stranded probes dissociates into single strands. When the temperature is decreased,
the double-stranded probes renature and only perfectly complementary
targets take part in displacement hybridization. There is complete discrimination between perfectly matched target and single nucleotide mismatch targets in the temperature range 30–60°C. Fluorescence intensity
is measured during the annealing stage of every PCR cycle.

6.6. Structured Probes

Thermodynamic analysis reveals that structurally constrained probes,
e.g., those with stem-loop structures, display a significantly higher
hybridization specificity than linear probes.[93,94] Furthermore, they have
a much greater specificity for mismatch discrimination because in the
absence of target they form fewer conformations than unstructured
probes. This increases entropy and, consequently, the free energy of
hybridization. On the other hand, secondary structure does impose
some kinetic and thermodynamic penalties, as probe/target complex
formation is slower and results in products with lower T_ms and free
energies.[95] Nevertheless natural evolution has produced micro-RNAs,

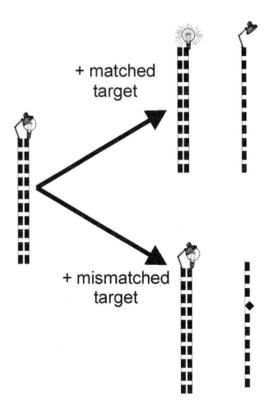

+ matched target

+ mismatched target

Figure 6.18. Displacement probes. Schematic drawings of a double-stranded probe and the working principle. The double-stranded probe is composed of two complementary oligonucleotides of different length. The longer positive strand is labeled with a fluorophore and the shorter negative strand is labeled with a quencher molecule.

a family of single-stranded RNA molecules that function as antisense regulators of other RNAs and form characteristic hairpin structures. Human ingenuity has invented Molecular Beacons, Scorpions™, and Cyclicons™.

Of these, Molecular Beacons and Scorpions are the best known, and one question that is often asked is which one is better or more specific. This question is difficult to answer, since it depends on the experimental conditions, e.g., temperature, on sequence context,[96] and whether absolute specificity is required or whether signal strength is the most important parameter. Scorpions are supposed to be a little more specific than Molecular Beacons, especially when detecting allelic variants or mutations, but, unlike Scorpions, Molecular Beacons can be cleaved by *Taq* polymerase. Scorpions generate huge signals, but the window of specificity tends to be narrower than with Beacons, i.e., the temperature of annealing is more critical.

6.6.1. Molecular Beacons

Molecular Beacons[97] have become increasingly popular not just for standard analyses such as quantification of DNA and RNA[98] but their use for numerous unique application gives them great and exciting potential. They can be used for the investigation of DNA/protein interactions,[99] detection of enzymatic cleavage of ssDNA,[100] demonstration and quantitation of hybridization,[101] real-time monitoring of intracellular mRNA hybridization,[102] RNA processing,[103] and transcription[104] in living cells in real-time. Molecular Beacons are also ideally suited to SNP/mutation analysis,[105] as they can readily detect single nucleotide differences,[106,107] and have been reported as being more reliable for G/C-rich sequences and having increased discriminatory power when compared to hydrolysis probes.[108] This may be because they allow quantitative detection of minority sequences over a wider range than hydrolysis probes. The incorporation of nucleotide analogues such as PNA results in Molecular Beacons that are less sensitive to salt concentration and able to hybridize more effectively than DNA based Molecular Beacons to crude DNA preparations.[109,110] Mismatched targets will form a probe/target duplex but this will dissociate at a lower temperature than a perfectly matched duplex. The associated differences in the melting curves will show this by revealing a temperature where the probe binds to the perfectly matched target but has dissociated from a mismatched target. The sensitivity of Molecular Beacons permits their use for the accurate detection of Y-chromosomes in blastomeres[111] and of mRNA from single cells.[112] They are showing great promise in multiplex assays, where they allow exquisite discrimination in a fourplex assay between as few as 10 copies of one retrovirus in the presence of 1×10^5 copies of another retrovirus.[113]

Molecular Beacons consist of a hairpin loop structure, with the loop complementary to a target nucleic acid and the stem formed by the annealing of complementary termini (**Fig. 6.19A**). One end of the stem has a reporter fluorophore attached and the other a quencher. In solution, free Molecular Beacons adopt a hairpin structure and the stem keeps the arms in close proximity, resulting in efficient proximal quenching of the fluorophore. During the denaturation step, the Molecular Beacons assume a random-coil configuration and fluoresce. At the annealing temperature, Molecular Beacons bind to any target amplicons as the probe/target duplex is designed to be thermodynami-

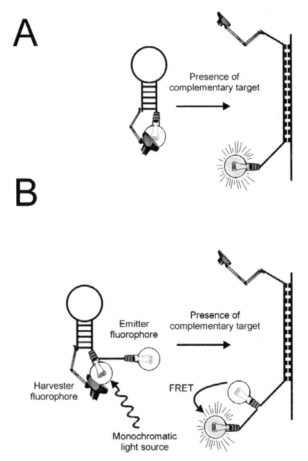

Figure 6.19. Molecular Beacons. (**A**) In the hairpin loop structure, the quencher forms a nonfluorescent complex with the fluorophore. Upon hybridization of the molecular beacon to a complementary sequence, the fluorophore and quencher are separated, restoring the fluorescence. (**B**) Wavelength shifting Molecular Beacons. This Molecular Beacon has two fluorophores on one end, a "harvester" and an "emitter," and a quencher on the other end. In the hairpin loop structure, the quencher forms a nonfluorescent complex with the harvester. Upon hybridization of the molecular beacon to a complementary sequence, quenching of the harvester fluorophore is relieved, and it transfers energy (via FRET) to the emitter, which emits fluorescence.

cally more stable than the hairpin structure at that temperature.[93] Once the probe binds to its target the hairpin is opened out and the fluorophore and quencher are separated, resulting in fluorescence. If the target DNA sequence does not exactly match the Molecular Beacon sequence, hybridization and fluorescence will not occur. This is because the thermodynamic properties of the Molecular Beacons favor the formation of a hairpin form rather than continued hybridization to a less than perfectly matched target sequence. When the temperature is raised to allow primer extension, the Molecular Beacons dissociate from their targets and do not interfere with polymerization. A new hybridization takes place in the annealing step of every cycle, and the intensity of the resulting fluorescence indicates the amount of accumulated amplicon. Again, since this is a reversible process, melting curves can be used to analyze the dynamics of the reaction and determine the best temperature for fluorescent acquisition.

The temperature during this analysis is increased to or reduced from 95°C, as the fluorescence is monitored in two separate reactions: one containing the Molecular Beacon alone and the other containing the Molecular Beacon with target DNA. At high temperatures, the Molecular Beacons will assume the open conformation. As temperature decreases in the absence of the single-stranded oligonucleotide target, the Molecular Beacons will assume a closed conformation. As temperature decreases in the presence of the single-stranded oligonucleotide target, the Molecular Beacons will hybridize to the target assuming an open confirmation, thus emitting fluorescence. The temperature at which half-maximum fluorescence is obtained gives the T_m for that Molecular Beacons.

An annealing temperature should be chosen at which the Molecular Beacon will bind efficiently to its complementary target, if present, and at which the Molecular Beacon will adopt a stem-loop conformation if it is not bound to target. Also, if such discrimination is desired, an annealing temperature should be chosen at which the Molecular Beacon would bind to its completely complementary target but not to a mismatched target, assuring assay specificity. **Fig. 6.20** illustrates a typical Molecular Beacon melting profile and shows that an annealing temperature of 60°C will provide low background fluorescence, high fluorescence if the perfectly matched target is present, and only background fluorescence when a target containing a single mismatched nucleotide is present.

The main drawback with Molecular Beacons is associated with the design of the hybridization probe. Optimal design of the Molecular Beacon stem is crucial since the Molecular Beacon may fold into alternate conformations that do not place the fluorophore in the immediate

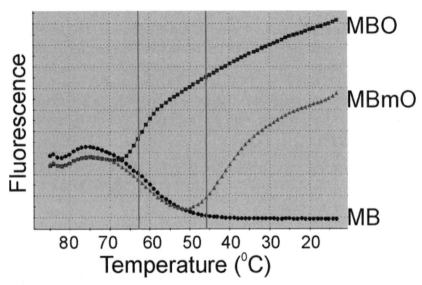

Figure 6.20. Typical Molecular Beacon melting profile for allele discrimination. Three melting curves are shown; one for Molecular Beacon alone (MB), a second one for Molecular Beacon plus its perfectly complementary single-stranded oligonucleotide target (MBO), and a third one for Molecular Beacon plus a single-strand target that produces a probe-target hybrid containing a single mismatched base pair (MBMO). To assure PCR assay specificity in discrimination, an annealing temperature at which the Molecular Beacon will bind to its completely complementary target but not to a mismatched target should be chosen. In this example, an annealing temperature of 60°C will provide high fluorescence when the perfectly matched target is present and low fluorescence when a target containing a single mismatched nucleotide is present.

vicinity of the quencher, resulting in a sub-population that is not quenched well and in large background signals. Alternatively, if the stem of a Molecular Beacon is too strong, it can interfere with the hybridization and the fluorescence of the beacon annealed to its target may be incompletely restored. Therefore, accurate thermal denaturation profiles to determine their melting characteristics have to be established for each Molecular Beacon, and different target sequences will have to be matched with different stem sequences.

Multiplexing with Molecular Beacons on laser-based detection systems poses another problem. The signal strength of the non-FAM fluorophores is relatively poor compared to FAM. This is because the laser excitation wavelength is optimized for FAM, hence excitation for most other fluorophores will be suboptimal. For halogen- or LED-based instruments this problem does not arise, of course, as wavelength and individual fluorophore can be matched. One solution is to use wavelength-shifting Molecular Beacons[114] (**Fig. 6.19B**). These Molecular Beacons have a nonfluorescent quencher and use FAM as a harvester fluorophore that absorbs strongly in the wavelength range of the monochromatic light source. In addition, they contain in close proximity an emitter fluorophore of the desired emission color. In the absence of complementary nucleic acid targets, the probes are nonfluorescent, whereas in the presence of targets, they fluoresce, not in the emission range of FAM, but rather in the emission range of the emitter fluorophore. This shift in emission spectrum is due to the transfer of the absorbed energy from FAM to the emitter fluorophore by FRET, and it only takes place in probes that are bound to targets. Wavelength-shifting Molecular Beacons are substantially brighter than conventional Molecular Beacons that contain a fluorophore that cannot efficiently absorb energy from the available monochromatic light source.

Catalytic Molecular Beacons represent another interesting development.[115] This approach does not require PCR at all, and makes use of signal amplification rather than target amplification by coupling the specific oligonucleotide recognition event of a Molecular Beacon to an enzymatic activity with a fluorogenic end point. Thus, the target oligonucleotide serves as an effector of enzymatic activity. A deoxyribozyme (DNAzyme)[116,117] module is combined with a Molecular Beacon stem-loop module. The substrate for the DNAzyme is a linear oligonucleotide with a reporter fluorophore at one end and a quencher at the other. In the absence of target, the Molecular Beacon forms a hairpin by hybridizing intramolecularly with the DNAzyme module and functions as an allosteric inhibitor of its activity (**Fig. 6.21**). Therefore, the substrate oligonucleotide remains intact and fluorescence is quenched. If a target complementary to the Molecular Beacon loop is present, it changes its conformation and hybridizes to that target. The doubly labeled fluorescent substrate can now hybridize to the DNAzyme module and is cleaved, resulting in fluorescence. The substrate dissociates on cleavage, the Molecular Beacon can re-hybridize to the DNAzyme module and the cycle can be repeated. The customized modular design

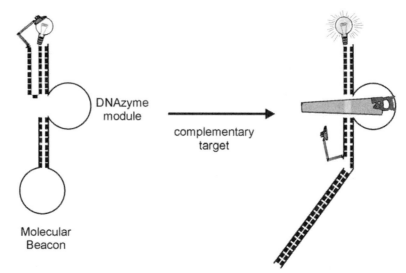

Figure 6.21. Catalytic Molecular Beacon. In the absence of target the stem loop Molecular Beacon structure masks the DNAzyme module. In the presence of target, the Molecular Beacon opens up and the DNAzyme can cleave its dual-labeled substrate, resulting in fluorescence.

of catalytic Molecular Beacons allows for any two single-stranded oligonucleotide sequences to be distinguished in homogenous solution in a single step.

Beacons come in all shapes and varieties: Traditional stem-forming DNA Molecular Beacons hybridize relatively fast to complementary ssDNA targets at high salt concentration, but much more slowly at low salt concentration. The signal-to-background ratio for this type of Molecular Beacon is variable but grows with increasing salt concentration. Hybridization of stemless DNA Molecular Beacons is very fast at any salt concentration, but the signal-to-background ratio is low, whereas stemless PNA Molecular Beacons hybridize to complementary targets both rapidly and with a high (around 10) signal-to-background ratio. Moreover, this Molecular Beacons is essentially insensitive to the change of salt thus allowing effective detection of nucleic acid targets under various conditions. Stemless Molecular Beacons are held in a closed form in the absence of target due to the flexibility of the sugar-phosphate and polyamide backbones of DNA and PNA, respectively, in combination with a string hydrophobic interaction between the fluorophore and the quencher.[110,118] They do not contain any sequences unrelated to the target, which results in faster kinetics of hybridization and better discrimination of mismatches. Other advantages of stemless PNA Molecular Beacons are: (1) the design is straightforward, (2) they are resistant to nucleases, (3) their insensitivity to the presence of DNA-binding proteins which normally affects the performance of DNA beacons,[119] and (4) they show a more rapid and highly selective response to the presence of nucleic acid targets at low salt concentrations and elevated temperatures. On the downside, they do exhibit higher background fluorescence.

6.6.2. Scorpions™

Scorpions combine primer and probe in one molecule, thus converting priming and probing into unimolecular a event, which is kinetically favorable and highly efficient as the covalent attachment of the probe to the target amplicon ensures that each probe has a target in the near vicinity.[120] Since no enzymatic cleavage is required, the time needed for signaling is reduced compared to TaqMan probes where a fluorescent signal is not generated until the polymerase has hydrolyzed the dual-labeled probe. Furthermore, unlike with hybridization probes, there is a one-to-one relationship between the number of amplicons generated and the amount of fluorescence produced. The original Scorpion consisted of a specific probe sequence held in a hairpin loop configuration by complementary stem sequences on the 5' and 3' sides of the probe, which is complementary to the extension product of the primer. However, some quenching can occur even in the open form, since the quencher is always in the proximity of the fluorophore. Therefore, a modification, duplex Scorpions, was developed that separates the fluorophore and the quencher onto different oligonucleotides (**Fig. 6.22**). The specific primer, PCR stopper (a nonamplifiable monomer, which prevents copying of the probe sequences during the polymerization step of the PCR reaction), probe, and fluorophore make up one oligonucleotide, while the quencher is linked to the 3' end of an oligonucleotide that is complementary to the probe sequence. After extension of the Scorpion primer, the specific probe sequence is able to bind to its complement within the same strand of DNA. Since this arrangement retains the intramolecular probing mechanism, it is favored over quencher oligonucleotide reannealing with the Scorpion and results in better sig-

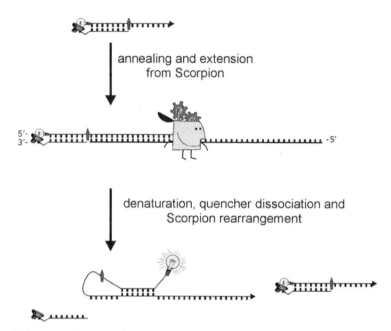

Figure 6.22. Scorpions. In the hairpin loop structure, the quencher forms a nonfluorescent complex with the fluorophore. Upon extension of the amplicon, the Scorpion probe hybridizes to the newly formed complementary sequence, separating the fluorophore from the quencher and restoring the fluorescence.

nal intensity than the normal Scorpion format.[121] Unimolecular hybridization is kinetically more favorable as it does not depend on a chance meeting between the probe, present at relatively low concentration, and the amplicon. This allows the introduction of more rapid cycling conditions together with a significantly stronger signal strength compared to both TaqMan and Molecular Beacons.[122] Another advantage over TaqMan assays is that the PCR reaction is carried out at the optimal temperature for the polymerase, rather than at the reduced temperature required for the 5'-nuclease assay to displace and cleave the probe.

Scorpions are ideally suited to SNP/mutation detection and have been used successfully to detect, type and quantitate human papillomaviruses,[123] to distinguish closely related plant fungal pathogens.[124,125] SNP detection can be carried out either by allele-specific hybridization or by allele-specific extension. If the probe sequence is allele specific, allelic variants of a SNP can be detected in a single reaction by labeling the two versions of the probe with different fluorophores. Alternatively, the PCR primer can be designed to selectively amplify only one allele of a SNP. A mutant allele-specific reaction converts the presence or absence of a polymorphic variant in a genomic sample into the presence or absence of a PCR product. Results with Scorpions compare favorably with the high signal/high background ratio of the TaqMan and low signal/low background ratio of Molecular Beacons (**Fig. 6.23**). An additional advantage of the modified Scorpion is that it is easier to design and synthesize, as there is no hairpin loop structure and only the fluorescent dye need be attached.

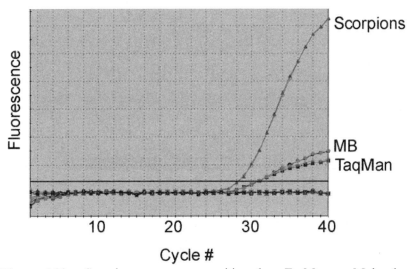

Figure 6.23. Scorpions are more sensitive than TaqMan or Molecular Beacons. Identical targets were probed using the three chemistries.

6.6.3. Cyclicons™

Pseudo-cyclic oligonucleotides (PCOs) consist of two oligonucleotide segments attached through their 3'–3' or 5'–5' ends (**Fig. 24A**).[126] One of the segments of the PCO is an oligonucleotide complementary to a target nucleic acid, which can be either mRNA or DNA. The other is a short protective oligonucleotide that is 5–8 nucleotides long and complementary to the 3' or 5' end of the antisense oligonucleotide. In the absence of target, PCOs form intramolecular pseudo-cyclic structures as a result

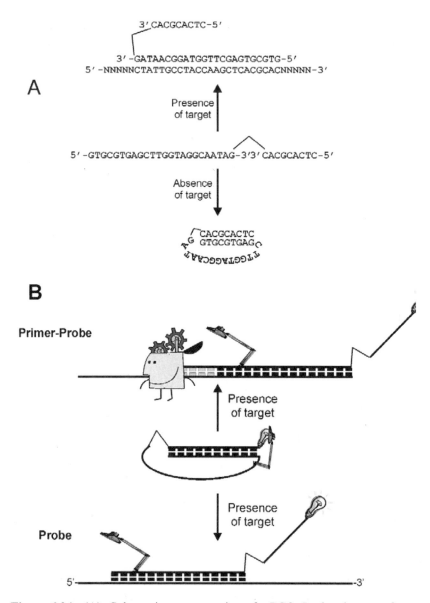

Figure 6.24. (**A**) Schematic representation of a PCO. In the absence of target, the antisense and protective oligonucleotides hybridize to one another. In the presence of target formation· of the heteroduplex between antisense oligonucleotide and target is favored. (**B**) Schematic representation of Cyclicon™ structure and its use as a primer-probe (above) and hybridization probe (below) to a complementary nucleic acid.

of complementarity between the antisense and protective oligonucleotide segments. In the presence of target the pseudo-cyclic structures dissociate, bind to the target and form heteroduplexes. The 3'–3' linkage between protective and antisense oligonucleotides provides increased nuclease stability from the 3' end, whereas the pseudo-cyclic structure formation at the 5' end provides additional nuclease stability against 5' nucleases. The PCOs may stay in linear or hybridized form depending on the temperature, salt concentration, and length of the protective oligonucleotide.

PCOs labeled with a fluorescence molecule and a quencher molecule (Cyclicons™ can be used both as fluorescent probes (5'–5' with blocked 3' end or 3'–3' linkage) as well as unimolecular primer-probes (5'–5' linkage).[127] If the protective (or "modifier") oligonucleotide is complementary to the 5' end of the antisense (or "primer-probe") oligonucleotide, the two oligonucleotides are attached through a 3'–3' linkage. If the modifier is complementary to the 3' end of the primer-probe, they are attached through a 5'–5' linkage. The FRET donor is attached to the free end of the modifier oligonucleotide (either 5' or 3'), and the acceptor is attached to a base within the primer-probe oligonucleotide. In the absence of the target, the PCO's intramolecular pseudo-cyclic structure brings the fluorophore and the quencher close together and this results in fluorescence quenching by FRET (**Fig. 6.24B**). In the presence of complementary target, the intramolecular cyclic structure of the Cyclicons™ is destabilized and opened up, separating the fluorophore and quencher groups, resulting in spontaneous fluorescence emission. Experiments with a 5'–5'-attached Cyclicons™ suggest that this design does not inhibit chain elongation by *Taq* polymerase and that this assay can use polymerases without a 5'–3' nuclease activity. The Cyclicon™ can discriminate between single-base mismatches.

6.7. Future Technology

6.7.1. Nanoparticle Probes

Hybrid materials composed of biomolecules, e.g., oligonucleotides, and nonbiological inorganic objects, e.g., colloidal gold nanoparticles, have been available for some time.[128,129] Two recent developments hold out the prospect that one of the major advances coming out of this integration of nanotechnology with biology is likely to result in significantly improved real-time PCR chemistries.

The quenching of fluorescence by metals results primarily from non-radiative energy transfer from the dye to the metal and the first innovation demonstrates that metal clusters can be used as efficient quenchers of fluorescence in a biological assay. This involves the assembly of a hybrid conjugate of a ssDNA oligonucleotide, a 1.4 nm gold nanoparticle, and a fluorescent dye.[130] The 5' and 3' ends of the oligonucleotide are self-complementary, allowing the DNA to form a Molecular Beacon-like hairpin-shaped structure that brings the fluorophore and the gold nanoparticle into close proximity and results in quenching of the fluorophore by the nanoparticle (**Fig. 6.25A**). Gold nanoparticles quench fluorescence as much as 100 times better than DABCYL and have higher quenching efficiency (up to 99.96%) for dyes emitting near the infrared region such as Texas Red or Cy5. In the presence of a target complementary to the ss oligonucleotide, the hairpin structure changes to a rod-like structure, which separates the fluorophore and the gold nanoparticle quencher and restores fluorescence. The hybrid conjugate can distinguish a perfect match from a single mismatch, but at present the mismatch detection sensitivity is significantly less. Furthermore, absorption spectrum of the 1.4 nm gold clusters decreases monotonically with increasing wavelength, since they are too small to develop surface plasmon resonances (SPRs). However, the optical properties of metal clusters can be altered through change of size and for larger particles the absorption spectrum increases in intensity and shows a local maximum at 520 nm characteristic of SPR. Therefore, the use of larger nanoparticles is likely to result in a coupling of fluorescence detection and SPR to provide additional sensitivity. A third problem relates to the gold-DNA linkage, which is unstable under the temperature cycling conditions of a PCR assay. However, undoubtedly this will be solved in the near future.

The second innovation takes the nanoparticle probe concept one step further by using a 2.5-nm gold nanoparticle that can develop SPR. Attached to this nanoparticle are oligonucleotide molecules labeled with a thiol group at one end and a fluorophore at the other (**Fig. 6.25B**). Two T_6 spacers are inserted at the 5' and 3' ends to reduce steric hin-

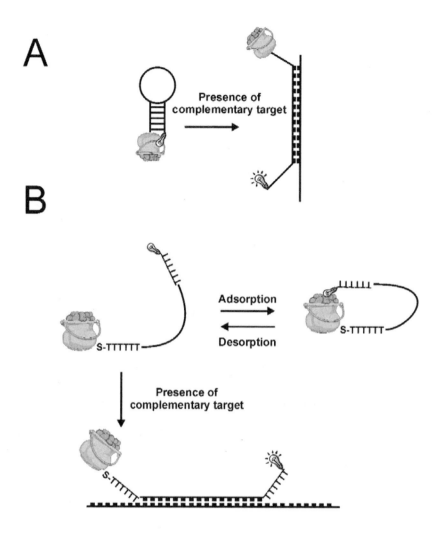

Figure 6.25. (**A**) nanoparticle quenching of Molecular Beacon. (**B**) The oligonucleotide is firmly tethered to the gold particle via a thiol group. Since fluorescent dyes can reversibly adsorb on the surface of colloidal gold nanoparticles, the fluorophore at the distal end can loop back and adsorb onto the same particle, leaving both the 5' and 3' ends of the oligonucleotide attached to the gold particle. The conformationally flexible backbone of ssDNA lets the oligonucleotide assume an arch-like structure with the DNA not contacting the gold surface, leaving it free to hybridize to any complementary sequences.

drance. This hybrid conjugate spontaneously self-assembles into a constrained arch-like conformation on the gold particle surface with the fluorophore efficiently quenched by efficient nonradiative energy transfer to the gold particle. Therefore, in addition to their role as a quencher, the gold nanoparticles serve an essential structural role, i.e., they act both as a "nano-scaffold" and as a "nano-quencher." The presence of a complementary target results in a conformational change, since the surface absorption energy of organic dyes on gold is much smaller than the energy involved in DNA hybridization. Therefore, once the oligonucleotide pairs with its complement, the structural rigidity of the dsDNA[97,131] forces the fluorophore to leave the surface and fluorescence is restored. Unlike conventional Molecular Beacons, the nanoparticle probes do not require a stem, and there is little increase with temperature in their background fluorescence. The hybridization specificity of the oligonucleotide is higher than that of linear probes, a characteristic of conformationally constrained probes.[93] The hybridization kinetics of the nanoparticle probes are slow, possibly because the surface-bound oligonucleotides are less accessible for hybridization. The introduction of surface modifications such as alkene thiols that force the oligonucleotide to adopt a single conformation is likely to improve the binding kinetics.

For the time being this technology is not yet ready to be applied to qPCR assays. However, there can be no doubt whatever that chemistries based on nanotechnology will be added to the real-time PCR arsenal and, with additional advances, may even take over from PCR-based assays altogether. But not just yet!

6.7.2. Conjugated Polymers and Peptide Nucleic Acid Probes

A major consideration with any chemistry concerns the ease with which its reagents can be synthesized, as this has a direct bearing on the economics of any assay based on it. This is a major driving force behind the development of the numerous chemistries described above. An interesting new chemistry has been described recently that makes use of the properties of cationic conjugated polymers (CCPs) and peptide nucleic acid (PNA).[132] CCPs are characterized by a delocalized electronic structure and since the effective conjugation length is substantially shorter than the number of repeat units, the backbone can hold a series of conjugated segments in close proximity. This makes them efficient for light harvesting and enables signal amplification via FRET. In solution, CCPs and negatively charged DNA form spontaneous complexes as a consequence of their cooperative electrostatic forces. PNA molecules lack a negatively charged backbone, resulting in more rapid and stronger PNA/DNA complexes than analogous DNA/DNA ones. The novel detection system is a homogeneous assay, where DNA, a fluorescently labeled PNA probe, and a CCP are mixed in solution (**Fig. 6.26**). Following denaturation of the DNA, the PNA probe can hybridize to any complementary target, if present. Electrostatic interactions cause the formation of a complex between the DNA/PNA hybrid and the CCP. This reduces the distance between the CCP and the fluorophore, allowing FRET to occur. Therefore, PNA/ssDNA hybridization can be detected by FRET efficiency, measured by fluorophore emission using a standard fluorimeter.

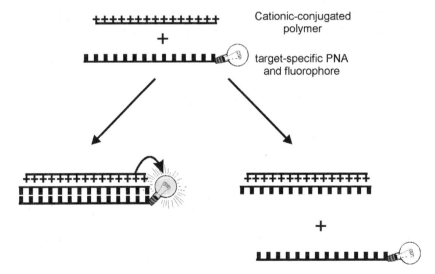

Figure 6.26. CCP and PNA. When DNA, a fluorescently-labeled PNA, and a CCP are mixed in solution, two outcomes are possible. (1) If the PNA is complementary to the DNA, it can hybridize to its target. Electrostatic attractions between the negatively charged DNA and the cationic polymer bring the polymer and the fluorophore close together. At short distances, FRET from the polymer to the fluorphore causes the dye unit to fluoresce efficiently when the solution is excited. (2) If the strands are noncomplementary, the CCP and fluorophore remain too far apart for energy transfer and no signal is detected.

Websites

Fluorescence:

http://www.probes.com/handbook/print/0001.html

SYBR Green/Gold:

www.molecularprobes.com

Amplifluor:

http://www.serologicals.com/products/int_prod/pcr.html

LUX primers:

www.invitrogen.com/LUX

Hybeacons and Quencher-labeled primers (I):

http://patft.uspto.gov/netacgi/
nph-Parser?Sect1=PTO1&Sect2=HITOFF&d=PALL&p=1&u=/netahtml/
srchnum.htm&r=1&f=G&l=50&s1=6,323,337.WKU.&OS=PN/6,323,337&
RS=PN/6,323,337

Molecular Beacons:

http://www.molecular-beacons.org/

Scorpions:

http://www.dxsgenotyping.com/technology_main.htm

Nanoprobes:

http://www.nanoprobes.com/

Collection of real-time papers as pdf files:

http://130.241.73.140/archive/

General information of fluorescent techniques:

http://www.probes.com/handbook/

General information on quenchers:

http://www.idtdna.com/program/techbulletins/Dark_Quenchers.asp
www.eurogentec.com or www.oswel.com

Black Hole Quencher:

http://www.biosearchtech.com/bhq/default.asp

ElleQuencher:

http://www.oswel.com/code/en/product_easy_qq.htm

Eclipse Dark Quencher:

http://www.epochbio.com/products/Dyes%20Quenchers_Dark.htm

References

1. Wittwer CT, Herrmann MG, Moss AA, Rasmussen RP: **Continuous fluorescence monitoring of rapid cycle DNA amplification.** *Biotechniques* 1997, **22**:130–138.

2. Higuchi R, Fockler C, Dollinger G, Watson R: Kinetic **PCR analysis: Real-time monitoring of DNA amplification reactions.** *Biotechnology (NY)* 1993, **11**:1026–1030.

3. Higuchi R, Dollinger G, Walsh PS, Griffith R: **Simultaneous amplification and detection of specific DNA sequences.** *Biotechnology (N.Y.)* 1992, **10**:413–417.

4. Holland PM, Abramson RD, Watson R, Gelfand DH: **Detection of specific polymerase chain reaction product by utilizing the 5'----3' exonuclease activity of Thermus aquaticus DNA polymerase.** *Proc Natl Acad Sci USA* 1991, **88**:7276–7280.

5. Lee LG, Connell CR, Bloch W: **Allelic discrimination by nick-translation PCR with fluorogenic probes.** *Nucleic Acids Res* 1993, **21**:3761–3766.

6. Heid CA, Stevens J, Livak KJ, Williams PM: **Real time quantitative PCR.** *Genome Res* 1996, **6**:986–994.

7. Ishiguro T, Saitoh J, Yawata H, Yamagishi H, Iwasaki S, Mitoma Y: **Homogeneous quantitative assay of hepatitis C virus RNA by polymerase chain reaction in the presence of a fluorescent intercalater.** *Anal Biochem* 1995, **229**:207–213.

8. Wittwer CT, Ririe KM, Andrew RV, David DA, Gundry RA, Balis UJ: **The LightCycler: A microvolume multisample fluorimeter with rapid temperature control.** *Biotechniques* 1997, **22**:176–181.

9. Morrison TB, Weis JJ, Wittwer CT: **Quantification of low-copy transcripts by continuous SYBR Green I monitoring during amplification.** *Biotechniques* 1998, **24**:954–958, 960, 962.

10. Srinivasan K, Morris SC, Girard JE, Kline MC, Reeder DJ: **Enhanced detection of PCR products through use of TOTO and YOYO intercalating dyes with laser induced fluorescence—Capillary electrophoresis.** *Appl Theor Electrophor* 1993, **3**:235–239.

11. Ogura M, Mitsuhashi M: **Screening method for a large quantity of polymerase chain reaction products by measuring YOYO-1 fluorescence on 96-well polypropylene plates.** *Anal Biochem* 1994, **218**:458–459.

12. Karlsen F, Steen HB, Nesland JM: **SYBR Green I DNA staining increases the detection sensitivity of viruses by polymerase chain reaction.** *J Virol Methods* 1995, **55**:153–156.

13. Ririe KM, Rasmussen RP, Wittwer CT: **Product differentiation by analysis of DNA melting curves during the polymerase chain reaction.** *Anal Biochem* 1997, **245**:154–160.

14. Selvin PR: **Fluorescence resonance energy transfer.** *Meth Enzymol* 1995, **246**:300–334.

15. Cardullo RA, Agrawal S, Flores C, Zamecnik PC, Wolf DE: **Detection of nucleic acid hybridization by nonradiative fluorescence resonance energy transfer.** *Proc Natl Acad Sci USA* 1988, **85**:8790–8794.

16. Cooper JP, Hagerman PJ: **Analysis of fluorescence energy transfer in duplex and branched DNA molecules.** *Biochemistry* 1990, **29**:9261–9268.

17. Walter NG, Burke JM: **Real-time monitoring of hairpin ribozyme kinetics through base-specific quenching of fluorescein-labeled substrates.** *RNA* 1997, **3**:392–404.

18. Nordlund TM, Andersson S, Nilsson L, Rigler R, Graslund A, McLaughlin LW: **Structure and dynamics of a fluorescent DNA oligomer containing the EcoRI recognition sequence: Fluorescence, molecular dynamics, and NMR studies.** *Biochemistry* 1989, **28**:9095–9103.

19. Hawkins ME, Pfleiderer W, Balis FM, Porter D, Knutson JR: **Fluorescence properties of pteridine nucleoside analogs as monomers and incorporated into oligonucleotides.** *Anal Biochem* 1997, **244**:86–95.

20. Randolph JB, Waggoner AS: **Stability, specificity and fluorescence brightness of multiply-labeled fluorescent DNA probes.** *Nucleic Acids Res* 1997, **25**:2923–2929.

21. Knemeyer JP, Marme N, Sauer M: **Probes for detection of specific DNA sequences at the single-molecule level.** *Anal Chem* 2000, **72**:3717–3724.

22. Crockett AO, Wittwer CT: **Fluorescein-labeled oligonucleotides for real-time PCR: Using the inherent quenching of deoxyguanosine nucleotides.** *Anal Biochem* 2001, **290**:89–97.

23. Nazarenko I, Pires R, Lowe B, Obaidy M, Rashtchian A: **Effect of primary and secondary structure of oligodeoxyribonucleotides on the fluorescent properties of conjugated dyes.** *Nucleic Acids Res* 2002, **30**:2089–2195.

24. Didenko VV: **DNA probes using fluorescence resonance energy transfer (FRET): Designs and applications.** *Biotechniques* 2001, **31**:1106–1111.

25. Neidle S, Abraham Z: **Structural and sequence-dependent aspects of drug intercalation into nucleic acids.** *CRC Crit Rev Biochem* 1984, **17**:73–121.

26. Schmittgen TD, Zakrajsek BA, Mills AG, Gorn V, Singe, MJ, Reed MW: **Quantitative reverse transcription-polymerase chain reaction to study mRNA decay: Comparison of endpoint and real-time methods.** *Anal Biochem* 2000, **285**:194–204.

27. Pfaffl MW, Georgieva TM, Georgiev IP, Ontsouka E, Hageleit M, Blum JW: **Real-time RT-PCR quantification of insulin-like growth factor (IGF)-1, IGF-1 receptor, IGF-2, IGF-2 receptor, insulin receptor, growth hormone receptor, IGF-binding proteins 1, 2 and 3 in the bovine species.** *Domest Anim Endocrinol* 2002, **22**:91–102.

28. Alfonso J, Pollevick GD, Castensson A, Jazin E, Frasch AC: **Analysis of gene expression in the rat hippocampus using Real Time PCR reveals high interindividual variation in mRNA expression levels.** *J Neurosci Res* 2002, **67**:225–234.

29. Castello R, Estelles A, Vazquez C, Falco C, Espana F, Almenar SM, Fuster C, Aznar J: **Quantitative real-time reverse transcription-PCR assay for urokinase plasminogen activator, plasminogen activator inhibitor type 1, and tissue metalloproteinase inhibitor type 1 gene expressions in primary breast cancer.** *Clin Chem* 2002, **48**:1288–1295.

30. Wickert L, Steinkruger S, Abiaka M, Bolkenius U, Purps O, Schnabel C, Gressner AM: **Quantitative monitoring of the mRNA expression pattern of the TGF-beta-isoforms (beta 1, beta 2, beta 3) during transdifferentiation of hepatic stellate cells. using a newly developed real-time SYBR Green PCR.** *Biochem Biophys Res Commun* 2002, **295**:330–335.

31. Yin JL, Shackel NA, Zekry A., McGuinness PH, Richards C, Putten KV, McCaughan GW, Eris JM, Bishop GA: **Real-time reverse transcriptase-polymerase chain reaction (RT-PCR) for measurement of cytokine and growth factor mRNA expression with fluorogenic probes or SYBR Green I.** *Immunol Cell Biol* 2001, **79**:213–221.

32. Wong YW, Sia GM, Too HP: **Quantification of mouse glial cell-line derived neurotrophic factor family receptor alpha 2 alternatively spliced isoforms by real time detection PCR using SYBR Green I.** *Neurosci Lett* 2002, **320**:141–145.

33. Moen EM, Sleboda J, Grinde B: **Real-time PCR methods for independent quantitation of TTV and TLMV.** *J Virol Methods* 2002, **104**:59–67.

34. Aldea C, Alvarez CP, Folgueira L, Delgado R, Otero JR: **Rapid detection of herpes simplex virus DNA in genital ulcers by real-time PCR using SYBR Green I dye as the detection signal.** *J Clin Microbiol* 2002, **40**:1060–1062.

35. Dhar AK, Roux MM, Klimpel KR: **Detection and quantification of infectious hypodermal and hematopoietic necrosis virus and white spot virus in shrimp using real-time quantitative PCR and SYBR Green chemistry.** *J Clin Microbiol* 2001, **39**:2835–2845.

36. Komurian-Pradel F, Paranhos-Baccala G, Sodoyer M, Chevallier P, Mandrand B, Lotteau V, Andre P: **Quantitation of HCV RNA using real-time PCR and fluorimetry.** *J Virol Methods* 2001, **95**:111–119.

37. Manaresi E, Gallinella G, Zuffi E, Bonvicini F, Zerbini M, Musiani M: **Diagnosis and quantitative evaluation of parvovirus B19 infections by real-time PCR in the clinical laboratory.** *J Med Virol* 2002, **67**:275–281.

38. Nozaki A, Kato N: **Quantitative method of intracellular hepatitis C virus RNA using LightCycler PCR.** *Acta Med Okayama* 2002, **56**:107–110.

39. Rohr U, Wulf M, Stahn S, Steidl U, Haas R, Kronenwett R: **Fast and reliable titration of recombinant adeno-associated virus type-2 using quantitative real-time PCR.** *J Virol Methods* 2002, **106**:81.

40. Aarts HJ, Joosten RG, Henkens MH, Stegeman H, van Hoek AH: **Rapid duplex PCR assay for the detection of pathogenic *Yersinia enterocolitica* strains.** *J Microbiol Methods* 2001, **47**:209–217.

41. Collantes-Fernandez E, Zaballos A, Alvarez-Garcia G, Ortega-Mora LM: **Quantitative detection of *Neospora caninum* in bovine aborted fetuses and experimentally infected mice by real-time PCR.** *J Clin Microbiol* 2002, **40**:1194–1198.

42. Jothikumar N, Griffiths MW: **Rapid detection of *Escherichia coli* O157:H7 with multiplex real-time PCR assays.** *Appl Environ Microbiol* 2002, **68**:3169–3171.

43. Knutsson R, Fontanesi M, Grage H, Radstrom P: **Development of a PCR-compatible enrichment medium for *Yersinia enterocolitica*: Amplification precision and dynamic detection range during cultivation.** *Int J Food Microbiol* 2002, **72**:185–201.

44. O'Mahony J, Hill C: **A real time PCR assay for the detection and quantitation of *Mycobacterium avium subsp. paratuberculosis* using SYBR Green and the LightCycler.** *J Microbiol Methods* 2002, **51**:283.

45. Rantakokko-Jalava K, Jalava J: **Development of conventional and real-time PCR assays for detection of *Legionella* DNA in respiratory specimens.** *J Clin Microbiol* 2001, **39**:2904–2910.

46. Ruzsovics A, Molnar B, Unger Z, Tulassay Z, Pronai L: **Determination of *Helicobacter pylori* cagA, vacA genotypes with real-time PCR melting curve analysis.** *J Physiol (Paris)* 2001, **95**:369–377.

47. Lin MH, Tseng CH, Tseng CC, Huang CH, Chong CK, Tseng C P: **Real-time PCR for rapid genotyping of angiotensin-converting enzyme insertion/deletion polymorphism.** *Clin Biochem* 2001, **34**:661–666.

48. Tiemann C, Vogel A, Dufaux B, Zimmer M, Krone JR, Hagedorn HJ: **Rapid DNA typing of HLA-B27 allele by real-time PCR using LightCycler technology.** *Clin Lab* 2001, **47**:131–134.

49. Eckert C, Landt O, Taube T, Seeger K, Beyermann B, Proba J, Henze G : **Potential of LightCycler technology for quantification of minimal residual disease in childhood acute lymphoblastic leukemia.** *Leukemia* 2000, **14**:316–323.

50. Karsai A, Muller S, Platz S, Hauser MT: **Evaluation of a homemade SYBR Green I reaction mixture for real-time PCR quantification of gene expression.** *Biotechniques* 2002, **32**:790–796.

51. Vandesompele J, De Paepe A, Speleman F: **Elimination of primer-dimer artifacts and genomic coamplification using a two-step SYBR Green I real-time RT-PCR.** *Anal Biochem* 2002, **303**:95–98.

52. Al Robaiy S, Rupf S, Eschrich K: **Rapid competitive PCR using melting curve analysis for DNA quantification.** *Biotechniques* 2001, **31**:1382–1386, 1388.

53. Lekanne Deprez RH, Fijnvandraat AC, Ruijter JM, Moorman AF: **Sensitivity and accuracy of quantitative real-time polymerase chain reaction using SYBR Green I depends on cDNA synthesis conditions.** *Anal Biochem* 2002, **307**:63–69.

54. Hiratsuka M, Agatsuma Y, Mizugaki M: **Rapid detection of CYP2C9*3 alleles by real-time fluorescence PCR based on SYBR Green.** *Mol Genet Metab* 1999, **68**:357–362.

55. Pals G., Pindolia K,Worsham MJ: **A rapid and sensitive approach to mutation detection using real-time polymerase chain reaction and melting curve analyses, using BRCA1 as an example.** *Mol Diagn* 1999, **4**:241–246.

56. Teo I, Choi J, Morlese J, Taylor G, Shaunak S: **LightCycler qPCR optimisation for low copy number target DNA.** *J Immunol Methods* 2002, **270**:119.

57. Fiandaca MJ, Hyldig-Nielsen JJ, Gildea BD, Coull JM: **Self-reporting PNA/DNA primers for PCR analysis.** *Genome Res* 2001, **11**:609–613.

58. Nazarenko IA, Bhatnagar SK, Hohman RJ: **A closed tube format for amplification and detection of DNA based on energy transfer.** *Nucleic Acids Res* 1997, **25**:2516–2521.

59. Uehara H, Nardone G, Nazarenko I, Hohman RJ: **Detection of telomerase activity utilizing energy transfer primers: comparison with gel- and ELISA-based detection.** *Biotechniques* 1999, **26**:552–558.

60. Elmore LW, Forsythe HL, Ferreira-Gonzalez A, Garrett CT, Clark GM, Holt SE: **Real-time quantitative analysis of telomerase activity in breast tumor specimens using a highly specific and sensitive fluorescent-based assay.** *Diagn Mol Pathol* 2002, **11**:177–185.

61. Lee MA, Siddle AL, Page RH: **ResonSense®: Simple linear fluorescent probes for quantitative homogeneous rapid polymerase chain reaction.** *Analytica Chimica Acta* 2002, **457**:61–70.

62. French DJ, Archard C L, Brown T, McDowell DG: **HyBeacon probes: a new tool for DNA sequence detection and allele discrimination.** *Mol Cell Probes* 2001, **15**:363–374.

63. French DJ, Archard CL, Anderson MT, McDowell DG: **Ultra-rapid DNA analysis using HyBeacon™ probes anddirect PCR amplification from saliva.** *Molecule Probes* 2002, **16**:319–326.

64. Egholm M, Buchardt O, Christensen L, Behrens C, Freier SM, Driver DA, Berg RH, Kim SK, Norden B, Nielsen PE: **PNA hybridizes to complementary oligonucleotides obeying the Watson-Crick hydrogen-bonding rules.** *Nature* 1993, **365**:566–568.

65. Timcheva II, Maximova VA, Deligeorgiev TG, Gadjev NI, Sabnis RW, Ivanov IG: **Fluorescence spectral characteristics of novel asymmetric monomethine cyanine dyes in nucleic acid solutions.** *FEBS Lett* 1997, **405**:141–144.

66. Nygren J, Svanvik N, Kubista M: **The interactions between the fluorescent dye thiazole orange and DNA.** *Biopolymers* 1998, **46**:39–51.

67. Svanvik N, Nygren J, Westman G, Kubista M: **Free-probe fluorescence of light-up probes.** *J Am Chem Soc* 2001, **123**:803–809.

68. Svanvik N, Westman G, Wang D, Kubista M: **Light-up probes: thiazole orange-conjugated peptide nucleic acid for detection of target nucleic acid in homogeneous solution.** *Anal Biochem* 2000, **281**:26–35.

69. Svanvik N, Stahlberg A, Sehlstedt U, Sjoback R, Kubista M: **Detection of PCR products in real time using light-up probes.** *Anal Biochem* 2000, **287**:179–182.

70. Wolffs P, Knutsson R, Sjoback R, Radstrom P: **PNA-based light-up probes for real-time detection of sequence-specific PCR products.** *Biotechniques* 2001, **31**:766, 769–766, 771.

71. Isacsson J, Cao H, Ohlsson L, Nordgren S, Svanvik N, Westman G, Kubista M, Sjoback R, Sehlstedt U: **Rapid and specific detection of PCR products using light-up probes.** *Mol Cell Probes* 2000, **14**:321–328.

72. Belak S, Thoren P: **Molecular diagnosis of animal diseases: Some experiences over the past decade.** *Expert Rev Mol Diagn* 2001, **1**:434–443.

73. Brunk CF, Li J, Avaniss-Aghajani E: **Analysis of specific bacteria from environmental samples using a quantitative polymerase chain reaction.** *Curr Issues Mol Biol* 2002, **4**:13–18.

74. Dotsch J, Repp R, Rascher W, Christiansen H: **Diagnostic and scientific applications of TaqMan real-time PCR in neuroblastomas.** *Expert Rev Mol Diagn* 2001, **1**:233–238.

75. Giulietti A, Overbergh L, Valckx D, Decallonne B, Bouillon R, Mathieu C: **An overview of real-time quantitative PCR: Applications to quantify cytokine gene expression.** *Methods* 2001, **25**:386–401.

76. Kwok PY: **Approaches to allele frequency determination.** *Pharmacogenomics* 2000, **1**:231–235.

77. Reiss E, Tanaka K, Bruker G, Chazalet V, Coleman D, Debeaupuis JP, Hanazawa R, Latge JP, Lortholary J, Makimura K, Morrison CJ, Murayama SY, Naoe S, Paris S, Sarfati J, Shibuya K, Sullivan D, Uchida K, Yamaguchi H: **Molecular diagnosis and epidemiology of fungal infections.** *Med Mycol* 1998, **36** Suppl 1:249–257.

78. Roth WK, Buhr S, Drosten C, Seifried E: **NAT and viral safety in blood transfusion.** *Vox Sang* 2000, **78** Suppl 2:257–259.

79. Shi MM, Bleavins MR, de la Iglesia FA: **Technologies for detecting genetic polymorphisms in pharmacogenomics.** *Mol Diagn* 1999, **4**:343–351.

80. Shi MM: **Enabling large-scale pharmacogenetic studies by high-throughput mutation detection and genotyping technologies.** *Clin Chem* 2001, **47**:164–172.

81. Takahashi M, Katayama Y, Takada H, Kuwayama H, Terano A: **The effect of NSAIDs and a COX-2 specific inhibitor on *Helicobacter pylori*-induced PGE2 and HGF in human gastric fibroblasts.** *Aliment Pharmacol Ther* 2000, **14 Suppl** 1:44–49.

82. Terry CF, Shanahan DJ, Ballam LD, Harris N, McDowell DG, Parkes HC: **Real-time detection of genetically modified soya using LightCycler and ABI 7700 platforms with taqman, scorpion, and SYBR Green I chemistries.** *J AOAC Int* 2002, **85**:938–944.

83. Livak KJ, Flood SJ, Marmaro J, Giusti W, Deetz K: **Oligonucleotides with fluorescent dyes at opposite ends provide a quenched probe system useful for detecting PCR product and nucleic acid hybridization.** *PCR Methods Appl* 1995, **4**:357–362.

84. Kreuzer KA, Bohn A, Lass U, Peters UR, Schmidt CA: **Influence of DNA polymerases on quantitative PCR results using TaqMan™ probe format in the LightCycler™ instrument.** *Mol Cell Probes* 2000, **14**:57–60.

85. Livak KJ: **Allelic discrimination using fluorogenic probes and the 5' nuclease assay.** *Genet Anal* 1999, **14**:143–149.

86. Nurmi J, Ylikoski A, Soukka T, Karp M, Lovgren T: **A new label technology for the detection of specific polymerase chain reaction products in a closed tube.** *Nucleic Acids Res*, 2000, **28**:E28.

87. Nurmi J, Wikman T, Karp M, Lovgren T: **High-performance real-time quantitative RT-PCR using lanthanide probes and a dual-temperature hybridization assay.** *Anal Chem* 2002, **74**:3525–3532.

88. Pals G, Young C, Mao HS, Worsham MJ: **Detection of a single base substitution in a single cell using the LightCycler.** *J Biochem Biophys Methods* 2001, **47**:121–129.

89. Aslanidis C, Nauck M, Schmitz G: **High-speed prothrombin G->A 20210 and methylenetetrahydrofolate reductase C->T 677 mutation detection using real-time fluorescence PCR and melting curves.** *Biotechniques* 1999, **27**:234–238.

90. Afonina IA, Reed MW, Lusby E, Shishkina IG, Belousov YS: **Minor groove binder-conjugated DNA probes for quantitative DNA detection by hybridization-triggered fluorescence.** *Biotechniques* 2002, **32**:940–949.

91. Li Q, Luan G, Guo Q, Liang J: **A new class of homogeneous nucleic acid probes based on specific displacement hybridization.** *Nucleic Acids Res* 2002, **30**:E5.

92. Shengqi W, Xiaohong W, Suhong C, Wei G: **A new fluorescent quantitative polymerase chain reaction technique.** *Anal Biochem* 2002, **309**:206–211.

93. Bonnet G, Tyagi S, Libchaber A, Kramer FR: **Thermodynamic basis of the enhanced specificity of structured DNA probes.** *Proc Natl Acad Sci USA* 1999, **96**:6171–6176.

94. Broude NE: **Stem-loop oligonucleotides: A robust tool for molecular biology and biotechnology.** *Trends Biotechnol* 2002, **20**:249–256.

95. Kushon SA, Jordan JP, Seifert JL, Nielsen H, Nielsen PE, Armitage BA: **Effect of secondary structure on the thermodynamics and kinetics of PNA hybridization to DNA hairpins.** *J Am Chem Soc* 2001, **123**:10805–10813.

96. Taveau M, Stockholm D, Spencer M, Richard I: **Quantification of splice variants using Molecular Beacon or scorpion primers.** *Anal Biochem* 2002, **305**:227–235.

97. Tyagi S, Kramer FR: **Molecular Beacons: Probes that fluoresce upon hybridization.** *Nat Biotechnol* 1996, **14**:303–308.

98. Antony T, Subramaniam V: **Molecular Beacons: Nucleic acid hybridization and emerging applications.** *J Biomol Struct Dyn* 2001, **19**:497–504.

99. Tan W, Fang X, Li J, Liu X: **Molecular Beacons: A novel DNA probe for nucleic acid and protein studies.** *Chemistry* 2000, **6**:1107–1111.

100. Li JJ, Geyer R, Tan W: **Using Molecular Beacons as a sensitive fluorescence assay for enzymatic cleavage of single-stranded DNA.** *Nucleic Acids Res* 2000, **28**:E52.

101. Sokol DL, Zhang X, Lu P, Gewirtz AM: **Real time detection of DNA.RNA hybridization in living cells.** *Proc Natl Acad Sci USA* 1998, **95**:11538–11543.

102. Perlette J, Tan W: **Real-time monitoring of intracellular mRNA hybridization inside single living cells.** *Anal Chem* 2001, **73**:5544–5550.

103. Dirks RW, Molenaar C, Tanke HJ: **Methods for visualizing RNA processing and transport pathways in living cells.** *Histochem Cell Biol* 2001, **115**:3–11.

104. Liu J, Feldman P, Chung TD: **Real-time monitoring *in vitro* transcription using Molecular Beacons.** *Anal Biochem* 2002, **300**:40–45.

105. Mhlanga MM, Malmberg L: **Using Molecular Beacons to detect single-nucleotide polymorphisms with real-time PCR.** *Methods* 2001, **25**:463–471.

106. Giesendorf BA, Vet JA, Tyagi S, Mensink EJ, Trijbels FJ, Blom HJ: **Molecular Beacons: A new approach for semiautomated mutation analysis.** *Clin Chem* 1998, **44**:482–486.

107. Marras SA, Kramer FR, Tyagi S: **Multiplex detection of single-nucleotide variations using Molecular Beacons.** *Genet Anal* 1999, **14**:151–156.

108. Tapp I, Malmberg L, Rennel E, Wik M, Syvanen AC: **Homogeneous scoring of single-nucleotide polymorphisms: Comparison of the 5'-nuclease TaqMan assay and Molecular Beacon probes.** *Biotechniques* 2000, **28**:732–738.

109. Kuhn H, Demidov VV, Gildea BD, Fiandaca MJ, Coull JC, Frank-Kamenetskii MD: **PNA beacons for duplex DNA.** *Antisense Nucleic Acid Drug Dev* 2001, **11**:265–270.

110. Kuhn H, Demidov VV, Coull JM, Fiandaca MJ, Gildea BD, Frank-Kamenetskii MD: **Hybridization of DNA and PNA Molecular Beacons to single-stranded and double-stranded DNA targets.** *J Am Chem Soc* 2002, **124**:1097–1103.

111. Pierce KE, Rice JE, Sanchez JA, Brenner C, Wangh LJ: **Real-time PCR using Molecular Beacons for accurate detection of the Y chromosome in single human blastomeres.** *Mol Hum Reprod* 2000, **6**:1155–1164.

112. Steuerwald N, Cohen J, Herrera RJ, Brenner CA: **Analysis of gene expression in single oocytes and embryos by real-time rapid cycle fluorescence monitored RT-PCR.** *Mol Hum Reprod* 1999, **5**:1034–1039.

113. Vet JA, Majithia AR, Marras SA, Tyagi S, Dube S, Poiesz BJ, Kramer FR: **Multiplex detection of four pathogenic retroviruses using Molecular Beacons.** *Proc Natl Acad Sci USA* 1999, **96**:6394–6399.

114. Tyagi S, Marras SA, Kramer FR: **Wavelength-shifting Molecular Beacons.** *Nat Biotechnol* 2000, **18**:1191–1196.

115. Stojanovic MN, de Prada P, Landry DW: **Catalytic Molecular Beacons.** *Chembiochem* 2001, **2**:411–415.

116. Todd AV, Fuery CJ, Impey HL, Applegate TL, Haughton MA: **DzyNA-PCR: Use of DNAzymes to detect and quantify nucleic acid sequences in a real-time fluorescent format.** *Clin Chem* 2000, **46**:625–630.

117. Impey HL, Applegate TL, Haughton MA, Fuery CJ, King JE, Todd AV: **Factors that influence deoxyribozyme cleavage during polymerase chain reaction.** *Anal Biochem* 2000, **286**:300–303.

118. Demidov VV: **PD-loop technology: PNA openers at work.** *Expert Rev Mol Diagn* 2001, **1**:343–351.

119. Fang X, Li JJ, Tan W: **Using Molecular Beacons to probe molecular interactions between lactate dehydrogenase and single-stranded DNA.** *Anal Chem* 2000, **72**:3280–3285.

120. Whitcombe D, Theaker J, Guy SP, Brown T, Little S: **Detection of PCR products using self-probing amplicons and fluorescence.** *Nat Biotechnol* 1999, **17**:804–807.

121. Solinas A, Brown LJ, McKeen C, Mellor JM, Nicol J., Thelwell N, Brown T: **Duplex Scorpion primers in SNP analysis and FRET applications.** *Nucleic Acids Res* 2001, **29**:E96.

122. Thelwell N, Millington S, Solinas A, Booth J, Brown T: **Mode of action and application of Scorpion primers to mutation detection.** *Nucleic Acids Res* 2000, **28**:3752–3761.

123. Hart KW, Williams OM, Thelwell N, Fiander AN, Brown, T, Borysiewicz LK, Gelder CM: **Novel method for detection, typing, and quantification of human papillomaviruses in clinical samples.** *J Clin Microbiol* 2001, **39**:3204–3212.

124. Bates JA, Taylor EJA: **Scorpion ARMS primers for SNP real-time PCR detection and quantification of *Pyrenophora teres*.** *Mol Plant Pathol* 2002, **2**:275–280.

125. Shena L, Sims S, Gallitelli D: **Molecular detection of strain L47 of *Aureobasidium pullulans*, a biocontrol agent of postharvest diseases.** *Plant Disease* 2002, **86**:54–60.

126. Jiang Z, Kandimalla ER, Zhao Q, Shen LX, DeLuca A, Normano N, Ruskowski M, Agrawal S: **Pseudo-cyclic oligonucleotides: *in vitro* and *in vivo* properties.** *Bioorg Med Chem* 1999, **7**:2727–2735.

127. Kandimalla ER, Agrawal S: **'Cyclicons' as hybridization-based fluorescent primer-probes: Synthesis, properties and application in real-time PCR.** *Bioorg Med Chem* 2000, **8**:1911–1916.

128. Mirkin CA, Letsinger RL, Mucic RC, Storhoff JJ: **A DNA-based method for rationally assembling nanoparticles into macroscopic materials.** *Nature* 1996, **382**:607–609.

129. Alivisatos AP, Johnsson KP, Peng X, Wilson TE, Loweth CJ, Bruchez MP, Jr, Schultz PG: **Organization of 'nanocrystal molecules' using DNA.** *Nature* 1996, **382**:609–611.

130. Dubertret B, Calame M, Libchaber AJ: **Single-mismatch detection using gold-quenched fluorescent oligonucleotides.** *Nat Biotechnol* 2001, **19**:365–370.

131. Tyagi S, Bratu DP, Kramer FR: **Multicolor Molecular Beacons for allele discrimination.** *Nat Biotechnol* 1998, **16**:49–53.

132. Gaylord BS, Heeger AJ, Bazan GC: **DNA detection using water-soluble conjugated polymers and peptide nucleic acid probes.** *Proc Natl Acad Sci USA* 2002, **99**:10954–10957.

7

Primers and Probes

Stephen A. Bustin and Tania Nolan

7

Primers and Probes

Stephen A. Bustin[*] and Tania Nolan[†]

*Barts and The London, Queen Mary's School of Medicine
and Dentistry, University of London, London, United Kingdom
†Stratagene Europe, Amsterdam, The Netherlands*

7.1. Introduction

It is tempting to start every chapter with the sentence that its content deals with the parameter most critical for successful qPCR. In fact, this simply reinforces the reality that qPCR-based assays are exceedingly complex and success depends on numerous parameters, every one of which has to perform near optimally. Certainly, the design of primers and probes is critical because poor primer/probe design will result in a poor PCR assay and unreliable quantification.

The remarkable technical advances made by high-fidelity nucleoside chemistry have resulted in the easy availability of inexpensive as well as high quality oligonucleotides based not just on DNA but, increasingly on analogues such as Peptide Nucleic Acid (PNA)[1-3] and Locked (or Bridged) Nucleic acid (L(B)NA).[4,5] This, together with the continuous discovery and development of new or modified enzymes[6-8] and developments in the chemistry of DNA probes,[9-12] has driven the tremendous advances seen in real-time PCR applications over the past five years and there is every reason to believe that the pace of innovation is gathering.

There are numerous web-based free and commercial software packages that will assist with primer/probe design. Vector NTI (Informax) is an easy-to-use, albeit expensive, PC-based commercial sequence analysis software that has a very useful primer design module; Beacon Designer (PremierBiosoft) is very powerful and specifically developed for the design of multiplex qPCR assays using either Molecular Beacons or TaqMan probes. This package features folding and BLAST analysis of the amplicon if the www connection is used. An interesting recent development suggests that it may be no longer necessary to spend a long time designing and validating the best primer and primer/probe combinations before starting the actual experimental work. It is now possible to buy a large selection of off-the-shelf assays (e.g., ABI's pre-developed assay-on-demand reagents) whose design has apparently been optimized and whose quality is guaranteed. A second innovation is a bespoke service that is also offered by Applied Biosystems (ABI, Foster City, Calif.) (their assay-by-design) and again promises to design optimal primer/probe combinations and guarantee the quality of the oligonucleotides. Whilst unquestioningly convenient, this approach has several drawbacks: (1) not everyone uses TaqMan chemistry and it is highly unlikely that ABI will design a Scorpion, Beacon, or hybridization probe set; (2) ABI do not reveal the precise sequence of their assay-on-demand primers/probes, only the sequence context. This makes the development of a diagnostic assay difficult and requires the investigator to return to ABI for more reagents. It could also result in additional variability due to batch-to-batch variation; (3) not surprisingly, this is a very expensive option. Furthermore, there may never be predesigned assays for many of the more obscure genes that are found in the numerous species being investigated. Additionally, it is our experience that these assays can also fail to function correctly, and lengthy troubleshooting procedures may still be required. Therefore, while ABI's approach may suit some, another kind of ABI (Applied Brains and Intelligence), i.e., an understanding of what is important and what can or cannot be tolerated, remains important for good primer and probe design. Certainly this is critical for applications such as mutant allele-specific or SNP assays, and a clear *a priori* understanding of the assay requirements will generate results cheaper, faster, and easier than starting with suboptimal primers and probes and having to optimize, redesign, and reoptimize. An intimate initial knowledge of the assay is also desirable to help with the inevitable troubleshooting. Therefore the fundamentals of good primer and probe design are likely to remain a key skill for a little while yet.

7.1.1. Hybridization

Specific annealing of primers and probes is essential for a successful qPCR assay, as any nonspecific annealing will impede accurate quantification. It is a common error to view primer/probe design simply as selecting the Watson-Crick complement of the target sequences and making sure there are no repeats or inverted repeats, especially at the 3' ends. However, there is a lot more to optimal hybridization, as the choice of chemistry, the nucleotide sequence itself and reaction conditions, such as temperature and salt concentration, play an important role.[13,14] Furthermore, oligonucleotides can pair with alternate, nontargeted sites on the genome and target sites may fold into stable structures that must be unfolded to allow an oligonucleotide to bind.[15] Both events will result in suboptimal amplification and may hinder accurate quantification.

7.1.1.1. Temperature of Melting (T_m)

One important parameter characterizing the stability of the interaction between an oligonucleotide and a complementary target is the melting temperature (T_m), which is defined as the temperature at which 50% of a given oligonucleotide is hybridized. It is one of the critical factors that determine the optimal annealing temperature for primers and probes in qPCR reactions and provides a quantitative measure of the stringency of the hybridization reaction. Melting is cooperative, i.e., once the first base pairs have separated, the remaining base pairs are more readily broken and follows first-order kinetics, as it involves only the melting of the nucleic acid. In contrast, renaturation is a second-order reaction and slower, as individual strands have to find their partners before they can anneal. Typically, hybridizations are performed at 5–10°C below the T_m of a duplex. T_m depends on three major parameters:

1. *Sequence:* The specificity of the binding between a nucleic acid target and an oligonucleotide is influenced primarily by the geometry of the bases responsible for the hydrogen bonds between A and T and G and C. The additional hydrogen bond makes G-C-rich sequences more stable than AT-rich ones, hence they require more energy to disassociate the formed hybrid. Therefore, G-C-rich molecules have higher T_ms than AT-rich molecules.

2. *Strand length and concentration:* The rate of renaturation is proportional to the [nucleic acid concentration]^2 and [nucleic acid length]$^{0.5}$ and inversely proportional to the complexity of the nucleic acid. Hence high oligonucleotide concentrations favor hybrid formation, which results in higher T_m.

3. *Salt concentration:* Stability depends on the effects of electrostatic interactions of the phosphate molecules of the nucleic acid backbone. Since salt cations mask the phosphate charges, increasing ionic strength stabilizes double-stranded sequences. Therefore, high ionic strength results in a higher T_m.

Since there are numerous web-based programs that calculate T_m values, it seems unlikely that anyone still needs to determine them manually. Nevertheless, for those that are temporarily disconnected and just have to calculate the T_m of their oligonucleotide, here are two (very) basic methods that give a reasonably accurate result. Bear in mind that even sophisticated T_m calculators will produce different T_ms for the same oligonucleotide and that post-synthesis optimization is the only way to be absolutely certain of a primer's or probe's performance.

1. This method works for oligonucleotides shorter than 20 bases:

$$T_m = 2 \times (A + T) + 4 \times (G + C).$$

2. This method is slightly more sophisticated and takes into account not just the %GC content but also the length of the oligonucleotide (N):

$$T_m = 81.5 + 16.6 \,(\log 10 \,[Na^+]) + 0.41 \,(\%GC) - (625/N).$$

7.1.1.2. Free Energy

Unfortunately, reliance on T_m alone does not produce optimal primers or probes since this parameter does not take into account any folding of the target nucleic acid. Folding results in secondary and tertiary structures that impose kinetic and thermodynamic constraints on the efficient binding of primers and probes. Therefore, the thermodynamics of secondary structure formation are crucial for predicting the structure of the target nucleic acid and identifying optimal hybridization targets for primers and probes. Knowledge of the free-energy change (ΔG) is the most relevant parameter for comparing duplex stabilities. It is used to measure the spontaneity of an annealing reaction; however, it provides no information about the rate of annealing. Unlike T_m, ΔG is independent of the total strand concentration but depends both on the change in internal energy and on the change in entropy of annealing. Spontaneous reactions are characterized by a negative change in free energy ($\Delta G < 0$). Thus, binding reactions with more negative ΔG require progressively more energy to reverse, and therefore reflect stronger bonds. The manner in which specific complementary strands pair up varies according to temperature. But a particular conformation is more stable if the formation of the hydrogen bonds via Watson-Crick pairing results in a more negative ΔG. The conformation resulting in the most negative ΔG is considered optimal and exposes sequences that are available for binding and should be targeted for primer/probe annealing.

Knowledge of the thermodynamic contributions of base pairing, internal and terminal mismatches, dangling ends, and various bulge and loop structures is important for accurate prediction of nucleic acid hybridization. The secondary structure of nucleic acid and its folding energy are determined using nearest-neighbor (NN) parameters that calculate standard enthalpy, entropy, and free-energy changes for base-pair formation during hybridization.[13,16,17] NN parameters include: (1) a helix initiation factor that usually depends on whether the initiation occurs at a C-G or A-T(U) base pair, (2) helix propagation terms that are the sum of the interaction energies required for forming each subsequent base pair, (3) a statistical entropy term for RNA/RNA and DNA/DNA that comes from whether or not the sequence is symmetric, and (4) the contribution of loop regions such as the hairpin, bulge, internal, and multibranched loops. In detail, the main factors affecting the stability of duplex DNA or DNA/RNA are:

1. *Number of correct base pairs.* These provide favorable energy for the base pairing by a combination of Hydrogen-bonds and hydrophobic interactions. The position and nature of any mismatch within an amplicon has significant effects on the stability of the duplex.[18-22]

2. *Type of base pairs.* Thermodynamically, a nucleic duplex structure can be considered to be the sum of its nearest-neighbor interactions,[13] and the stability and the melting behavior of any duplex structure can be calculated from inspection of its primary sequence.[17]

3. *Secondary structure considerations.* The kinetics and the extent of hybridization of a short oligonucleotide are strongly influenced by the existence of secondary structure in the target nucleic acid[23] and rearrangement of this secondary structure so as to expose the target sequence can be rate-limiting. Additionally, only a portion of the target sequence may be hybridized with the remainder involved in intrastrand base-pairing.[15] Therefore, any secondary structure will require the incoming primer or probe to compete with template hairpin structure and is likely to interfere with accurate quantification.

4. *Dangling end effects.* This refers to the interactions between the extreme 5' and 3' ends of a hybridized oligonucleotide and the first neighboring base of the target. Probe (and initially primer) hybridization to a target nucleic acid involves two dangling end contributions and an exhaustive analysis of all possible combinations shows a significant sequence-dependent contribution of dangling ends to duplex stability, with the nature of the closing base pair largely determining the degree of stabilization.[24]

```
GTAGACAATCTCCATCTCCTATCCTGATTAGAG
         * * * * * * * * * * * * * * * * * * * *
         GTTAGAGGTAGAGGATAGGA
```

The above example has two dangling end interactions, with the first one contributing a standard free-energy change (ΔG^0) of -0.96 kcal/mol at 37°C and the second one -0.50 kcal/mol. This compares with Watson-Crick nearest-neighbor increments ranging from -0.58 (TA/AT) to -2.24 (GC/CG) kcal/mol.[17,25] Therefore, dangling ends can contribute more to duplex stability than a Watson-Crick AT-base pair and accounting for these effects is crucial to accurately calculate probe/target binding strength.[24]

5. *Ionic strength.* Mg^{2+} concentration is a crucial factor affecting the performance of the PCR assay. The negative charge of the phosphate backbone of the nucleic acid must be neutralized for duplex DNA to form. This is achieved by pairing a positive ion with the phosphate group. Thus, the stability of the DNA duplex increases with the metal ion concentration and again the T_m is proportional to the metal ion concentration.

6. *Temperature.* As the temperature increases, the ΔG for formation of the duplex DNA becomes less favorable, and eventually, the single-stranded form is favored because of the higher entropy of the single stranded DNA.[14]

The principal conclusion from the above discussion is this: The crucial parameter is not whether primers bind with equal T_m *per se*, but that they bind with **equal efficiency**. Hence primers simply matched for T_m can hybridize to their target with unequal efficiency, whereas primers matched for ΔG^0 at the hybridization temperature will bind with equal efficiency, even if their T_ms are quite different.

Ideally, primers would be designed to be stable at their 5' ends (e.g., with a ΔG^0 of greater than -10 kcal/mol at 37°C) with the slope declining towards the less stable 3' ends (e.g., with a ΔG^0 of -6 kcal/mol at 37°C). This should eliminate false priming due to annealing of 3'-half of primer only.[26] Vector NTI's PCR primer design module allows the user to define the ΔG of the whole oligonucleotide, but also specifically of the 3' end. The program also has a setting that allows the user to rate the importance of primer characteristics such as T_m, T_m difference, GC content, and GC-content difference. Unfortunately this does not extend to specifying the importance of ΔG. Nevertheless, some tweaking can be performed as individual parameters that can be changed include the maximum permitted ΔG of hairpin loops, primer-primer complementarity and 3'-end complementarity. A similar analysis can be performed for hybridization probes.

Note: One problem with designing appropriate primers or probes is that there is considerable variation in the calculated T_ms and ΔG depending upon the method used to determine it. Furthermore, the actual T_m depends on the PCR buffer being used and failure to adjust the reaction conditions to account for these differences can result in failure of qPCR assays.[27]

7.2. Probe Design

Choice of chemistry and probe design are a very personal matter, and there are, as always, numerous options that need to be considered prior to sitting down and designing the probes:[28]

1. Is the aim to quantitate DNA, profile mRNA levels or perform allelic discrimination assays?

2. Which of the ever-expanding real-time chemistries is most appropriate for the experiment?

3. Is the assay designed to detect DNA only, RNA only or potentially both DNA and RNA?[29] This may be particularly difficult if the target is a retrovirus such as HIV-I and the aim is to distinguish HIV DNA from RNA.[30]

4. If the assay is to distinguish between closely related sequences, e.g., be diagnostic for the presence of pathogens, will the primers or probe detect and quantitate any divergent family members?[31-40]

5. Which fluorescent reporter/quencher combinations will be used?

6. Will the probe contain DNA analogues, MGB factors or any other modifications?

7. Will the assay involve multiplexing?

It should really not be necessary to doubt that the probe supplier has labeled the probe with the correct combination of reporter fluorophore and quencher. However, it can happen, as shown in **Fig. 7.1**. The probe was ordered with FAM reporter, and was analyzed using the iCycler (Bio-Rad). In this way it was evident that no fluorescence was detectable with the filter in the FAM position but was detected when the filter was in the HEX position. This probe had not worked well on an ABI 7700, and now we knew why.

Not only may the probe be labeled with the wrong fluorophore, it may also be of inferior quality. **Fig. 7.2** demonstrates the amplification plots obtained using the same templates, primers, and master mixes but separate probes supplied by two major manufacturers. It is our experience that this phenomenon can also occur with different batches of probe from the same manufacturer. Also note that if only a small percentage of probe molecules are missing the quencher group, background fluorescence will be increased significantly.

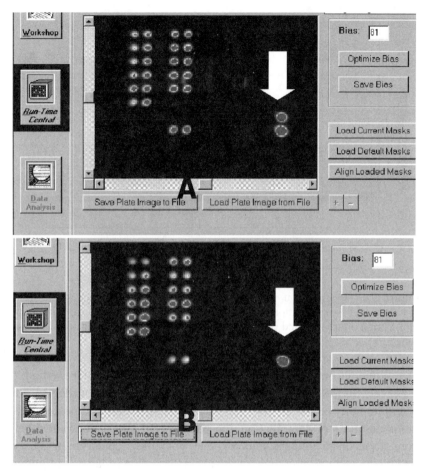

Figure 7.1. Mislabeled reporter probe. (**A**) The fluorescence from two probes supposedly labeled with FAM (arrows) is detected on the Bio-Rad iCycler. Both probes are detected. (**B**) The FAM-specific filter confirms that probe 2 is labeled with FAM, whereas probe 1 is not.

Probe quality is a major issue and in our experience is the major reason why an assay fails to perform according to expectation (see **Chapter 12**). The synthesis of pure dye-labeled, especially dual-labeled, oligonucleotides is challenging because of the more complicated pattern of labeled and unlabeled failure products from synthesis[41] and there is an urgent need for high-performance purification techniques of these special oligonucleotide probes. Currently, reversed-phase high-perform-

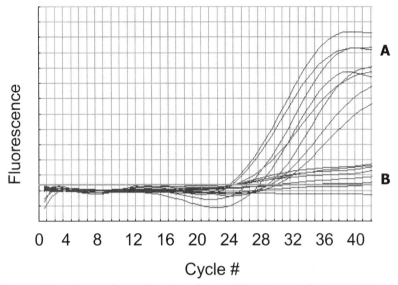

Figure 7.2. Comparison of probes from different manufacturers (Bio-Rad iCycler). (**A**) Amplification plot from a satisfactory probe. (**B**) Amplification plot from a poorly labeled probe that barely rises above back ground fluorescence.

ance liquid chromatography (RP-HPLC) is the most popular method.[42] However, fluorescent dyes affect oligonucleotide retention due to the hydrophobicity of the labels[43] and oligonucleotides require post-purification desalting or deprotection. Ion-pair (IP) RP-HPLC does not suffer from these disadvantages and together with mass spectrometry, may well be the method of choice for the characterization of labeled oligonucleotide impurities.[44]

7.3. Hydrolysis Probes

7.3.1. Gene Expression Analysis

qPCR assays using hydrolysis probes are two-step reactions, with a denaturation step followed by a combined annealing/polymerization step, during which fluorescence is measured. The design of an optimal primer/probe combination, defined as a set that produces the lowest C_t

and highest ΔR (ΔR_n, if ROX or other reference dye is used), involves several steps.

☑ The probe should be designed with the 5' end as close to the 3' end of one of the primers as is possible without them overlapping. This ensures immediate displacement and cleavage by the polymerase.

> **Tip:** It is a good idea to design a complete probe/primer set even when using SYBR Green I chemistry, as it makes it easier to switch to a more specific, probe-based assay.

☑ It should be as short as possible but no longer than 30 nucleotides with a G/C content of around 50%. If the target sequence is AT-rich, analogues such as LNA or PNA, or minor groove binders (MGB) (see **Section 7.14.5**) can be incorporated into the probe design.

☑ Several factors can affect fluorescence quenching: undesired quenching by guanine (G) is avoided by not having a G at the 5' end. Since the fluorescent reporter is attached to the most 5' base, the G would continue to quench the reporter even after cleavage, resulting in reduced fluorescence values (ΔR), which could result in reduced sensitivity. If necessary, the complementary probe with the least number of Gs should be selected. However, this could entail the 5' end of the probe being distant from the 3' end of the primer on the opposite strand. If the amplicon is too long, and the annealing/polymerization step too short, this could reduce the efficiency of hydrolysis by the polymerase. In real-life, this is probably not an issue, unless the amplicon is several hundred bp long and then other concerns are likely to be more important.

☑ Any runs of four or more identical nucleotides, especially G, should be avoided.

> **Tip:** Disruption of a series of Gs by the substitution of an inosine can significantly improve probe performance.[45]

☑ The probe T_m should be 10°C higher than the T_m of the primers, and is usually in the 68–70°C range. This ensures that the probe hybridizes to its complementary target prior to the polymerase extending from the primers.

Tip: The probe should be designed to keep the fluorophore and quencher in the same plane when hybridized to a target. In this way quenching is maximized until the 5'–3' exonuclease activity of the polymerase displaces and cleaves the probe, thereby releasing the fluorophore and physically separating it from its quencher. This is achieved optimally when the fluorophore and quencher are either 22 bases or 33 bases apart.

Synthesis and purification of appropriate double-labeled probes is as critical to the success of a qPCR experiment as the primer/probe design.

7.3.2. SNP/Mutation Analysis

A single mismatch between the probe and target reduces the efficiency of probe hybridization, as the T_m is lower and the ΔG^0 less favorable. Furthermore, according to ABI, the mismatch promotes dissociation rather than cleavage of the mismatched probe following the displacement of its 5' end by the polymerase during the PCR reaction. Consequently, if two probes, one specific for the wild-type sequence, the other specific for the SNP/mutation, are labeled with different reporter dyes, the two sequences can be discriminated by quantitating the increases in the respective dye fluorescence. Since both probes are present in the same reaction tube, the exact-match probe will outcompete the mismatched probe for binding to its target, if the appropriate reaction conditions are applied. Typically the assay is performed as a specific, high-throughput endpoint assay, but it can be done in real-time.

☑ For bi-allelic discrimination, each allele has a specific probe labeled at the 5' end with a fluorescent reporter dye (e.g., FAM or VIC) and a nonfluorescent quencher at the 3' end.

☑ Amplicons should be as short as possible.

☑ Primers are common to each reaction and have complete homology for both alleles.

☑ The ΔG^0 of both probes should be similar.

☑ Use of a MGB, LNA, or PNA increases the T_m and can improve the ΔG and allows the use of a shorter probe (but no shorter than 13 nucleotides), which displays better mismatch discrimination. It also places fluorophore and quencher closer together, thereby reducing background fluorescence.

☑ The polymorphic site should be placed approximately in the central third of the probe sequence, but can be shifted towards the 3' end, as long as it is more than two nucleotides away from it.

Note: If using MGB probes, because of the asymmetric placement of the MGB at the 3' end, complementary probes do not necessarily have the same T_m.

7.4. Hybridization Probes

Assays involving hybridization probes are three-step reactions and fluorescence measurements are taken during the annealing step.

7.4.1. Gene Expression Analysis

☑ Unlike with hydrolysis probes, the dual-probe target site should be as far away as possible from the 5' primer-binding site on the same strand. This allows time for the fluorescence measurements before the probes are displaced by the polymerase.

☑ Optimal binding is achieved by selecting target sequences with approximately 50% G/C content.

☑ Each probe should be 23–35-bases long.

☑ T_ms should be near equal and 5°C to 10°C greater than primer T_ms. Both probes must bind simultaneously to the target DNA during the annealing phase of the PCR. Primers will be elongated immediately by *Taq* polymerase, even at temperatures below 72°C. This may result in early displacement of the probes by the enzyme. The higher T_m ensures that the probes bind during the annealing phase, which generates a signal before probe displacement. On the other hand, at T_m greater than10°C, stable probe binding could interfere with probe displacement and reduce the amplification efficiency.

☑ The 3' end of the upstream probe should be labeled with fluorescein, which serves as the donor in the FRET and blocks the extension of the probe.

☑ The 5' end of the downstream probe should be labeled with Cy5, LightCycler-Red 640 or 705, which serve as the acceptor in the FRET.

☑ The 3' end of the acceptor probe must be phosphorylated to block extension.

☑ The probes should be separated from each other by 1 base (maximum 5 bases) to allow energy transfer between the fluorophores.

7.4.2. SNP/Mutation Analysis

Hybridization probes for SNP/mutation analysis are termed anchor and sensor probes. The anchor probe anneals upstream from the polymorphism/mutation site and has a higher T_m and lower ΔG^0 than the sensor probe. The sensor probe covers the polymorphism site and has a lower T_m and higher ΔG^0. This difference guarantees that the sensor probe melts first. Any mismatch has a strong effect on the hybridization of the sensor probe to the template, with the T_m and ΔG^0 shifts depending on the nature of the mismatch, its neighboring base pairs and any secondary structures around the site of the mismatch.

☑ Select the sensor probe first by analyzing the region surrounding the SNP for probe sequences matching the user defined T_m.

☑ The mismatched base should be in the middle of the sensor probe, not at the 5' end or within the last two 3' bases of the probe.

☑ T_m of anchor probe should be greater than T_m of sensor probe (about 5°C).

7.5. Molecular Beacons™

The binding of Molecular Beacons to their targets is measured at the annealing temperature of a three-step PCR reaction. Appropriate behavior of Molecular Beacons depends on choosing appropriate lengths for the probe and arm sequences, respectively.

7.5.1. Gene Expression Analysis

☑ The T_m of the probe sequence should be 7–10°C higher than the annealing temperature of the PCR so that the probe-target hybrid is stable and the prediction should be made before adding the stem sequences. The probe sequence is usually between 15 and 30 nucleotides long.

Tip: Remember the ΔG^0 contribution to hybridization.

☑ Molecular Beacons should be designed to bind to the center of the amplicon with more than six bases between the 5' ends of the Beacon and the 3' ends of the primers.

☑ Two complementary arm sequences are added on either side of the probe sequence. The T_m of the stem should be 7–10°C higher than the annealing temperature of the PCR. This ensures that the Molecular Beacons remain closed in the absence of targets. This is the crucial step in the design of a successful Molecular Beacon and verification requires the use of a DNA folding program—a good and also free example is found on http://www.bioinfo.rpi.edu/applications/mfold/ or the superb but costly Beacon Designer http://www.premierbiosoft.com/ molecular_beacons/taqman_molecular_beacons.html (you can download a demo)—to calculate the ΔG^0 of formation of the stem hybrid, from which its melting temperature can be predicted. Beacons should be no longer than 39 bases. As the length increases, Beacons can form secondary structures and/or quenching becomes inefficient, resulting in higher background fluorescence. Usually the stems are 5–7 nucleotides and probe-loop sequences are 16–22 nucleotides long. In general, GC-rich stems of 5-base pairs will melt between 55°C and 60°C, GC-rich stems of 6-base pairs will melt between 60°C and 65°C, and GC-rich stems of 7-base pairs will melt between 65°C and 70°C.

☑ It is crucial to check that the free Molecular Beacon cannot form additional hairpin structures that result in the reporter dye and quencher becoming separated. This will result in high background signals due to incomplete quenching. In addition, excessively long stems affect the hybridization kinetics of Beacon and target.

☑ It is advisable to confirm that the Molecular Beacon is not complementary to either of the primers, as this will increase the higher
background signal (BLAST, BLAST, and BLAST again).

Tip: The fluorophore and quencher of Molecular Beacons should
be on different planes when hybridized to the target (e.g.,
2.5 or 3.5 turns of the helix—in practical terms 28 bases or
38–39 bases apart) to reduce the quenching effect and maximize signal detection.

Note: It is vital to perform melting curve analyses before using
the Beacons, as a perfectly designed Beacon may not perform as expected. This will provide an experimental,
rather than a theoretical melting profile. If this is not optimal, it is best to redesign the Beacon.

7.5.2. SNP/Mutation Analysis

Beacons have established a good reputation for large-scale genotyping
of SNPs and mutations[46] and appear to be better at discriminating
between homozygous and heterozygous genotypes of C-to-G transver-
sions.[47]

☑ For maximum discrimination of alleles in SNP/mutation analysis,
minimize the length of the loop sequence, for example by using
DNA analogues.

☑ Amplicons should be no more than 250 bp in length as longer
amplicons cause signals to diminish, possibly due to greater difficulty of the Molecular Beacons in invading the double strands
during the annealing step of PCR.

7.6. Scorpions™

Assays using Scorpions are three-step reactions with fluorescence collected during the annealing step. Originally the Scorpion molecule was
designed as a single hairpin, loop format oligonucleotide. This single

molecule comprised a primer linked to a stem-loop-stem probe. However a simpler, dual molecule, linear version has since been developed. In both cases, the probe is attached to the 5' end of the primer and is complementary to the newly synthesized strand. After elongation of from the primer the probe folds over the primer and hybridizes to the newly formed strand. Therefore probing is an intramolecular event and successful Scorpion probe/primers require correct designing of the folding of probe and primer. The guidelines below are applicable for both Scorpion formats.

> **Tip:** The 5' end of the probe is complementary to the 3' end of the target, i.e., it is the reverse complement of the target and the complement to the other strand than the primer.

7.6.1. Gene Expression Analysis

☑ Probe sequences should be about 17–27 bases. The T_m of the probe sequence should be similar or slightly below that of the primer. There must be no homology with the primer and no inverted repeats within the probe.

☑ The probe target should be 0–20 bases from the 3' end of the primer to which the probe is attached. The farther away the probe target, the lower the probing efficiency, and the advantage of using an intramolecular probe is lost.

☑ Hairpin loop format: A stem sequence of 6 or 7 bases, mostly Cs and Gs, avoiding repetitive motifs is added to either end of the probe so that the two regions of stem can bind to one another and hold the probe in a loop configuration. The 5'-stem sequence should begin with a C, not a G, as G may quench the fluorophore. The ΔG^0 value should be negative and ideally the stem loop should have a T_m of 5–10°C higher than the probe bound to the target.

☑ Use MFold (http://www.bioinfo.rpi.edu/applications/mfold/) to calculate the ΔG^0 of formation of the stem hybrid, from which its melting temperature can be predicted. The ΔG^0 should be at least –2 kcal/mol for the closed form, around –6 kcal/mol for the hybridized form, and any suboptimal folding of the extended amplicon should be no more stable than the unextended form.

☑ Once the sequence has been designed, the fluorophore is placed on the 5' end, and amethyl red quencher and hexaethylene glycol molecule (HEG, a PCR stopper) are placed between the primer and the hairpin loop.

Tip: LightCycler: If Scorpions are being used for detection on channel 2 (640 nm), a specific design is required. As the capillary system will only excite at 470 nm (FAM), it is necessary to incorporate a FAM into Scorpions. This is placed within the stem, attached to a T. Consequently the stem must have an AT-base pair within it. A ROX is placed on the 5' end of the oligonucleotide. During the PCR the FAM is excited and passes its energy on to the ROX. This is quenched in the closed form of the Scorpions™ but once the probe binds to the amplicon, the increase in ROX fluorescence can be observed. The FRET between the ROX and FAM is extremely good and the FAM signal observed in channel 1 remains constant so that a FAM Scorpion™ can be multiplexed with the FRET Scorpion™ without interference from the ROX. However, the FAM signal will show up in channel 2 and it is necessary to remove this crosstalk by using the Roche color compensation kit.

Hybridization (dual probe) format: Design a quencher oligonucleotide that is complementary to the probe sequence. Make it slightly shorter than full-length making probing of the target the more favorable reaction.

☑ Use MFold (http://www.bioinfo.rpi.edu/applications/mfold/) to check the design. Analyze the complete Scorpion, including blocker attached to the amplicon under appropriate salt, Mg^{2+}, and temperature conditions. Anything with a ΔG^0 of less than –4 kcal/mol (i.e., more negative) is a favored form. If alternative folding is highlighted, it should be less favorable by at least 2 kcal/mol. Test the unextended structure without the amplicon. Again any folding should be at least 2 kcal/mol less stable than the properly extended structure.

☑ Place a blocker group in the middle of the Scorpion and the fluorophore of choice (e.g., FAM) at the 5' end. The second probe will have the quencher attached at the 3' end (e.g., Black Hole quencher). Both probes must be HPLC purified.

7.6.2. SNP/Mutation Analysis

When designing a probe for mutation detection, the same principles apply. A design should be found such that, when the probe is bound to the perfectly matched target, it will be unstable or unable to bind to the mismatch. In this case the probe will dissociate from the target with a mismatch. Consider placing the 3' end of the primer on the mismatch rather than the probe region.

7.7. Probe Storage

Probes should be stored frozen both when lyophilized or in solution. It is vital to aliquot the probe in order to minimize potential breakdown due to repeated freezing and thawing. They must be protected from light. Long-term stability is variable, with some probes stable for several years, and others hydrolyzed after six months.

Tip: Store probes at 10× concentration.

7.8. Primer Design

The choice of primers determines amplicon length, melting temperature, amplification efficiency, and yield. The most obvious primer-related problem is the formation of primer-dimers that can compete with and suppress specific product formation. The sequence of a primer, the method of primer synthesis and purification significantly affect the results obtained with any qPCR assay. By always following several quite straightforward steps, it is fairly easy to design primer combinations that bind to unique target sequences **and** amplify the desired amplicon. Again, as with template preparation, it makes sense to design the best possible primers using as much information as possible before starting the actual qPCR assays. Primers targeting mRNA should bind to separate exons to avoid false-positive results due to amplification of contaminating genomic DNA. If the intron/exon boundaries are unknown, or when targeting an intron-less gene, it is necessary to treat the RNA sample with RNase-free DNAse (see Part II, **Chapter 5**).

Tips: Use SYBR Green I and melting curve analyses to identify primers that dimerize. Primers are cheap. Test several primers sets with each probe to identify the optimum primer/probe set. For RT-PCR, try to cross the longest possible intron to minimize any chance of amplification from genomic DNA.

☑ *Use appropriate software.*

Design the primers using one of the many design packages, either commercial or free-to-use on the WWW. ABI instruments come with the Primer Express program; several oligonucleotides manufacturers offer a free online primer-design service; there are numerous sites that will design suitable primers and of course programs such as Vector NTI, DNAStar, Beacon Designer, etc., will do the same on your PC. If you need to design degenerate primers, consult this site first: http://www.dartmouth.edu/artsci/bio/ambros/protocols/other/koelle/degenerate_PCR.html.

Note: There is no replacement for (most) human brains. Use any software intelligently and with some common sense.

☑ *Use the correct sequence.*

Many genes have been sequenced several times, and errors, mutations, or polymorphisms quite often result in the publication of different sequences for the same gene. The presence of a single mismatch at the 3' end of one of the primers will affect priming and polymerization from that primer. A BLAST search (http://www.ncbi.nlm.nih.gov/blast/) using the target sequence as a probe will reveal and align all matched sequences and will reveal any mismatches.

☑ *Consider splice variants.*

Splicing is an important regulatory mechanism for gene expression, with many introns having important regulatory roles. For many genes alternative splicing has clear functional consequences for the protein isoforms produced. Different splice variants may be expressed in the same tissue, or may be tissue- or time-specific. Real-time PCR assays are ideally suited to quantitate these as they can easily distinguish the different splice variants.[48] First identify splice junctions. Choose an amplicon with minimal secondary structure since secondary structures could affect the efficiency of the reaction.

☑ *Choose a small amplicon.*

The length of primers and probe required to generate a specific product defines the minimum practical length of the amplicon. There are several reasons for designing amplicons to be as small as possible: First, as a general rule, the shorter the amplicon, the better the amplification efficiency tends to be. Second, small amplicons are more tolerant of reaction conditions because they are more likely to be denatured during the 92–95°C step of the PCR, allowing the probes and primers to compete more effectively for binding to their complementary targets. Third, since the extension rate of *Taq* polymerase is between 30 and 70 bases/second, shorter polymerization times are required to replicate the amplicon, making amplification of genomic DNA contaminants less likely and reducing the time it takes to complete the assay. Forth, if a synthetic sense-strand oligodeoxyribonucleotide is used to generate amplicon-specific standard curves, it is easier to synthesize a short, rather than a long oligonucleotide. Of course, it may be impossible to find an acceptable short amplicon across a splice junction, and indeed it very often is. In this case, the design parameters relating to amplicon size should be changed bit-by-bit, until the smallest acceptable amplicon is found. In most cases, manual fine-tuning is required to help find a primer combination that was not immediately apparent using the software. It is better to design a suboptimal 70-mer amplicon than an optimal 300-mer. Whenever possible, the amplicon should not have a G/C content in excess of 60% as it may not denature well during thermal cycling, leading to a less efficient reaction. Furthermore, GC-rich sequences are susceptible to nonspecific interactions that result in nonspecific signal in SYBR Green I assays.

☑ *DNA primer characteristics:*

1. The 3'-terminal position is essential for the control of mispriming during the PCR reaction. Primers with one or more G or C residues at that position will have increased binding efficiency due to the stronger hydrogen bonding of G/C residues. It also helps to improve the efficiency of priming by minimizing any "breathing" that might occur.

Tip: If using ABI's Primer Express, set the primer concentrations to 200 nM from default 50 nM and change the G/C clamp from default 0 to 1.

2. Primers with long runs of a single base (i.e., more than three or four, especially G or C) should be avoided. Homopolymeric runs can cause ambiguous binding of oligos to their target site ("slippage effect").

3. Avoid direct repeats. Direct repeats may generate secondary binding sites for primers. Stable hybridization to secondary binding sites result in nonproductive binding of primers to nonspecific regions of the sequence so that efficiency of DNA amplification and detection decreases. A worst-case scenario gives you multiple amplicons from the same template!

4. Primers must have no intraprimer homology beyond 3'-base pairs, as otherwise primers may form secondary structures that can interfere with annealing to the template.

5. DNA primers should be between 15 and 25 bases long to maximize specificity, with a G/C content around the 50%. The longer the oligonucleotide, the less the percentage of full-length product in the crude synthesis. This results in lower yields after purification.

6. T_ms should be in the range of 55°C to 60° and should not differ by more than 1–2°C. Molecular Beacons and hybridization probe-associated primers can have a wider T_m range, but the T_m of any one pair should be similar.

7. Primer-dimers have a negative ΔG value, so primers should be chosen with a value no more than –10 kcal/mol.

8. For primers binding at very AT-rich sequences it is advantageous to substitute one or more of the bases with a LNA analogue (see **Section 7.14.3**).

9. Avoid primers with secondary structure (i.e., inverted repeats) or with sequence complementarity at the 3' ends that could form dimers. Due to competition between intermolecular (primer-template, probe-target) hybridization, and intramolecular hybridization, inverse repeats can cause inefficient priming and probing of the target sequence. PCR reaction and/or probe binding can completely fail because of formation of stable hairpins at the binding region, or inside the amplicon in general.

10. Whenever possible, place modifications at the 5' end. Automated DNA synthesis occurs in the 3' to 5' direction. Each nucleotide addition is 98–99% efficient resulting in 1–2% of the oligonucleotide being truncated and capped at each position. Placing the modification at the 5' end ensures that only the full-length oligonucleotide is modified. Furthermore, because most modifications are more hydrophobic than unmodified oligonucleotide, the full-length modified oligonucleotide binds more tightly to the reverse phase media during HPLC purification. This enhances the separation between the full-length, modified oligonucleotide sequences and the truncated, unmodified oligonucleotide sequences.

7.9. Amplifluor™ Primers

☑ Design several sets of primer candidates as there is always something that will go wrong. Initially, synthesize the primers prepared without the Z sequence, as it is best to test and validate their performance without any possible negative contribution from it.

☑ Target-specific primers should be designed to anneal at 50–60°C. The preferred temperature range for working with UniPrimer is 55–60°C. The calculated T_m (nearest-neighbor method) and ΔG for a given primer pair should be similar.

☑ The size of the target-specific sections of the primers should be 18–25 nucleotides long with 50 to 60% G/C content. However, ensuring matching ΔGs is much more critical than the exact size of the primers.

Note: The UniPrimer itself does not appear to generate homo primer-dimer artifacts with the recommended buffer, enzyme, and primer concentration after 40 cycles.

☑ Validate Target Specific Primers.

Note: All primers should be validated using SYBR Green I and melting curves. The performance of Amplifluor primers is critically dependent on the absence of any primer dimers because any primer dimer will result in a false-positive signal.

☑ Create a tailed primer by adding the Z sequence to one target-specific primer. Resynthesize a target-specific primer and add the Z sequence to the 5' end as follows: 5' `act gaa cct gac cgt aca` *NNNNNNNN* `. . . . . . . .` 3', where *.NNN.* represents the target-specific sequences.

Note: Avoid complementation that leads to homo- and hetero-dimers between the 3' end of the target-specific primer and the UniPrimer. Either the forward or reverse primer can contain the Z sequence.

☒ Validate Tailed Target Specific Primer.

Note: If dimers occur, reduce primer concentration, increase annealing temperature (stay below 60°), and/or reduce the annealing time. If problems persist, shift the position of one or both primers by one or more nucleotides and resynthesize. If problems occur in a primer set only after the Z-tail sequence has been added, put it on the other primer instead.

7.10. LUX Primers

It is easiest to use Invitrogen's LUX Web site at www.invitrogen.com/LUX and follow the link to the LUX Designer Web-based design software. Step-by-step instructions are provided in the software to submit target sequences and generate primer designs. LUX Designer will automatically generate one or more primer designs based on each sequence submitted and the selected design parameters. The design software includes algorithms to minimize primer self-complementarity and interactions between primers. It also assigns rankings to the generated designs based on primer melting temperature, hairpin structure, self-annealing properties, etc. to aid in selection.

Note: In one-step RT-PCR, the reverse primer drives the reverse transcription reaction and labeling of that primer with the LUX fluorophore can inhibit the RT step. Therefore, it is recommended that the forward primer be selected as the labeled primer.

7.11. Oligonucleotide Purification

Removal of blocking groups, which protect bases and backbone during synthesis and cleavage of the oligonucleotide from its CPG support, is usually achieved using concentrated ammonium hydroxide. Benzamide can be present as a result of deprotecting the bases dA and dC. These impurities are usually removed by the oligonucleotide manufacturer. However, in-house produced oligonucleotides are most easily desalted by passing the oligonucleotide through a reverse-phase cartridge (e.g., Sep-Pak Plus C18 Waters, *Cat No. 20515*).

Desalting protocol:

1. Resuspend oligonucleotide in TE to a final concentration of 1–5 mg/ml.

2. Dilute an aliquot of the resuspended oligonucleotides 1:100 in TE; read A_{260}.

3. Secure Sep-Pak cartridge to stand with small clamp.

4. Wash cartridge with 7 ml of 95% MeOH, using 10 ml syringe (flow rate = 1–2 drops/second for all steps).

5. Wash cartridge with Buffer I (5 mM triethylamine in dH_2O titrated with glacial acetic acid to pH 7.0).

6. Load a maximum of 50 O.D. units of resuspended oligonucleotide onto the cartridge.

7. Wash bound oligo with 7 ml Buffer I.

8. Elute desalted oligonucleotide using 3 ml Buffer II (5 mM triethylamine, pH 7.0, 50% MeOH), collect eluant, and monitor A_{260}.

9. Dry peak fractions in a Speed-Vac.

Base-coupling efficiency during oligonucleotides synthesis is less than 100%; hence truncated sequences that lack various portions of the 5' end of the oligonucleotides will accumulate with each coupling. As a rough guide, truncated oligonucleotides accumulate at a rate of about 1% per coupling. Therefore a 20-base oligonucleotide has approximately 20% truncated sequences in the crude product. After de-protection, these molecules are normal DNA with hydroxyls at both ends, which will interfere with qPCR. They can be removed by chromatography or electrophoresis. It is advisable to order HPLC-pure oligonucleotides (see www.idahotec.com/lightcycler_u/lectures/primerpurity.htm). The cost differential is worth the added peace of mind of using the best-quality possible primers. For in-house synthesized oligonucleotides, oligonucleotide purification cartridges are an inexpensive reverse-phase chromatographic method that removes salts as well as truncated sequences. This involves the use of a small plastic cartridge containing a polystyrene copolymer resin as the purification medium. The cartridge packing material is similar to that which is used in reverse phase HPLC columns. However, the yield of oligonucleotides that can be purified by a single cartridge is limited by the amount of resin in the cartridge to the 0.2 micromole or smaller scale. HPLC is needed for the highest product yield, especially for 1.0 micromole and higher. Alternatively, polyacrylamide gel electrophoresis can be used to enrich for full-length sequences as it separates oligonucleotides by size, with the full-length product moving slowest through the medium. However, this is a labor-intensive, time-consuming, and low-yield method.

Gel purification of oligonucleotides:

1. Lyophilize 100 μg of oligonucleotide on a Speed-Vac.
2. Resuspend in 40 μl of TE. Add 20 μl of formamide gel loading dye.
3. Prepare a 12% denaturing polyacrylamide/urea gel (20:1 acrylamide:bis-acrylamide) using 25 × 25 cm plates with 0.75 mm spacers and a comb with larger than 8 mm teeth. Flush the wells thoroughly to prevent a build-up of urea.
4. Prerun gel at 400 V for 15 minutes. Load samples over 3–4 wells and run at 400 V until bromophenol blue is two-thirds down the gel.
5. Remove top plate, cover gel with clingfilm (e.g., Saranwrap), turn over, and lift off remaining glass plate, leaving gel on the clingfilm.
6. Visualize bands using a long-wave (365 nm) handheld UV lamp and cut out the top band with a razor blade and place into a 10-ml tube containing 1 ml of TE. Mash up the gel slice with a sterile scalpel and elute 15 min at room temperature.

Note: Elevated temperature and longer incubation times have been shown to result in the copurification of PCR inhibitors, most likely nonpolymerized acrylamide monomers.[49]

7. Filter the eluate through a prewetted acrodisk (Perkin Elmer, *Cat. No. 02542782*).

8. Collect eluate and add 5 ml of *n*-butanol. Vortex for 30 seconds and spin at 3,500 rpm for 5 minutes. Remove organic (top) phase and place aqueous phase into a microfuge tube. Reextract with 200 μl of TE. Adjust volume to 500 μl, then phenol/chloroform and chloroform extract. Precipitate with EtOH (–70°C) and spin in a refrigerated microfuge for 20 min.

9. Wash pellet in 100 μl of 70% EtOH, dry and resuspend in 25 μl of TE, and quantitate.

Tip: Do not overdry, as partial denaturation of DNA of less than 400 bp can occur,[50] probably due to destabilization of the double helical structure by the removal of water.

Obviously, the quality of the initial synthesis, which varies considerably between manufacturers, will determine what degree of purification is needed. However, remember that the higher the purity, the lower the final yield.

Note: DNA obtained from preparative gel electrophoresis can inhibit the PCR reaction due to damage from the UV-light. Addition of 1 mmol/l guanosine or cytidine to the electrophoresis buffer has a protective effect against UV irradiation.[51]

7.12. Recommended Storage Conditions

☑ *Storage.*

Storage Temperature	Lyophilized	Resuspended
5°C	12 months	3 months
–20°C	24 months+	9 months

Note: Some primers lose their ability to prime the PCR assay after being stored in water or TE buffer at –20°C for several months. There are numerous possible reasons for this, and there is no obvious pattern to which primers can be stored and which can not.[52] For medium-term storage it is probably best to store primers as 10× or even 100× aliquots and make them up fresh every month or so. For truly long-term storage, it is best to lyophilize the primers and store them at –80°C.

☑ *Primer validation.*

It is useful to validate primers using a conventional PCR reaction and by analyzing the results on a nondenaturing polyacrylamide gel. Run the following samples:

Sample	No enzyme	No target	All reagents
Purpose	Visualize native primers	Visualize primer dimers	Visualize specific band, artifacts, and native primers

The criteria for good primer performance are: (1) no primer-dimers in the no target controls and (2) little or no mispriming resulting in aberrant amplicons.

Alternatively, if you do not want to run gels, use SYBR Green I and melting curves to detect any primer dimers (**Fig. 7.3**). Since primer dimers are much shorter than the full amplicon, dimers will melt at a lower T_m than the intended product and are easily distinguished.

Also validate the primers using real-time PCR assays with control template nucleic acid. Choose the primer pair that gives the highest ΔR (or ΔRn) and the lowest C_t.

7.13. Example of Primer Design

If the probe is to distinguish a specific target from several closely related sequences, it is best to align the genes and then to design the probes to recognize the regions of highest sequence diversity.[53] This is illus-

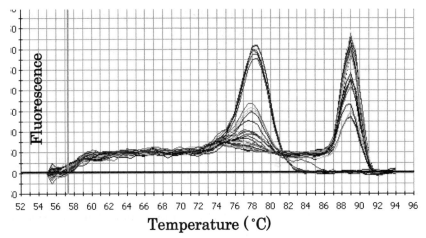

Temperature (°C)

Figure 7.3. Melting curves (Bio-Rad iCycler) showing primer dimers and genuine amplification products.

trated in **Fig. 7.4**, where the alignment of all the sequence variants of the rat angiotensin type II 1b receptor mRNA reveals mismatches in exons 1 and 2. Furthermore, the same gene is often given different names, sometimes similar, sometimes completely different.

Exon 1
```
M90065    AGACCAGACACACACAGCCTTTCCAGCGCCAGCGCTGTGGATGGGGAGCGGCCACCAGGCTTGAAAGAAGCCCAGAGCTGGGCACTGCACAC
S69958    ***************************************************************************************CG********
NM_031009    *******************  **-***********************************************************CG********
U0133     ***************G*******************************************************************CG********
X64052    ************** _***************************************T*******************************  **CG********
M87003    ***************************** _*****************T*****************************************CG********
```

Exon 2
```
M90065    GGTGCATTTTAAATAGTGTCAGAGAGCAATTCACCTCGCCAAGGGAGACATGACCCTTAACTCCTCTACTGAAGATGGAATTAAAA
S69961    *********************** ***********G*********************** ---***********************
NM_031009    ***CG**************************A****A*********T***********************************  *
X64052    *****************************G*********************************************************
M87003    ***************************A****A*********T****************************************
```

Figure 7.4. Rat angiotensin II receptor sequence variation.

First, the nomenclature needs to be sorted: The BLAST search aligned several sequences with the search sequence. They are listed as Angiotensin II receptor, AT1B mRNA for Angiotensin II receptor, Angiotensin receptor 1 (Agtr1), Angiotensin II type I receptor, AT1B=Angiotensin type Ib receptor, and Angiotensin II receptor AT1B gene.

Tip: It is more productive to do a BLAST search with your target sequence and then inspect the retrieved sequences rather than to search with the name of the gene and retrieve hundreds of irrelevant hits.

The second question is: Are these sequencing/reporting errors, or are the mismatches due to genuine alterations or polymorphisms? We had started with M90065 as our reference sequence, so all other sequences are aligned to it either with an asterisk (*), indicating sequence identity, with a dash (–) indicating a deletion, or with an A, C, G, or T indicating a substitution. The following steps result in the selection of a suitable primer/probe set.

1. The GC in sequence M90065 is a CG in all other variants. Hence it is most likely that the correct sequence reads CG.

2. The two As and one of the T mismatches in M87003 are also present in NM_031009. However, that sequence is derived from M87003, so those alterations are unique to that sequence and probably sequencing or reporting mistakes.

3. The deleted triplet in S69958 is derived from a genomic sequence, which could be removed from the final transcript. It could also be a reading/reporting error, as the sequence reads CTCCTC and a momentary lapse in concentration could account for the duplication.

4. Sequences X64052 and M87003 have a T in place of the G found in the other three sequences. Sequences S69961 and X640522 have a G in place of a C. It is impossible to tell what the correct sequence is, or indeed whether these represent polymorphisms.

5. The single G mismatch in U0133 and the deletions in M87003/NM_031009 are most likely sequencing/reporting errors.

6. There are further differences between NM_031009 and the supposed reference sequence it was derived from, M87003, and these are probably also transcription errors.

Note: It is noteworthy that a single, short stretch of sequence can harbor so many ambiguities and strongly underlines the point that any target sequence must be thoroughly checked ***prior*** to selecting primers and probes.

7. The following primer/probe set was designed using ABI's Primer Express and avoids the ambiguous bases:

Forward   5'-CACCAGGCTTGAAAGAAGCC-3'
Reverse   5'-GCGAGGTGAATTGCTCTCTGA-3'
Probe   5'-CACCGTGTGCAGTGCCCAGCTCT-3'

A comparison of the T_m of the primers and ΔG^0 shows that both their T_m values and ΔG values are well balanced (see **Fig. 7.5**). Furthermore, the primers bind to a region of target whose ΔG values are similar, although the T_m values are quite different (**Fig. 7.6**).

7.14. Nucleic Acid Analogues

The development of new protocols and chemistries and the associated phenomenal growth in applications for PCR-based assays, has resulted in DNA oligonucleotides becoming ubiquitous. In the distant past (late 1980s to early 1990s), ABI's PCRMate revolutionized the ability of individual laboratories to synthesize their own oligonucleotides on demand, although at considerable cost.

Note: It is amazing to see a PCRMate exhibited in the Smithsonian Science Museum in Washington, D.C., when we still have a functional instrument sitting in our laboratory, and sad that many have long since been consigned to garbage skips.

It is hard to believe that we have progressed from those days of synthesizing one oligonucleotide at a time, limited by the chemistry to a maximum 40-mer. Today the price of an oligonucleotide has become insignificant; there are numerous companies competing to sell high-quality oligonucleotides of more than 100 bases and one can order 20 or more oligonucleotides one day and expect delivery the next day.

The rapidly expanding field of DNA diagnostics and the development of DNA molecules as therapeutic drug candidates has highlighted some of the limitations of DNA and, not surprisingly, has resulted in the development of analogues that incorporate all of the advantages of native DNA, but are more stable in biological fluids (increased biostability) and have increased affinity for complementary nucleic acid targets (improved hybridization characteristics). These developments have

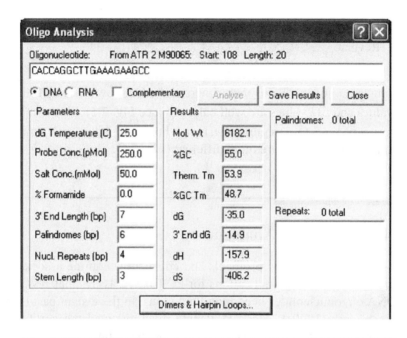

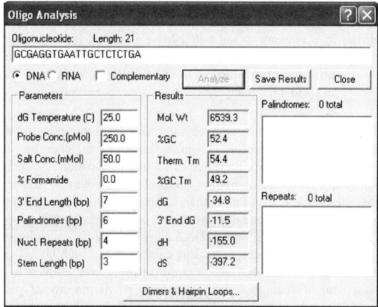

Figure 7.5. Oligonucleotide characteristics as calculated by Vector NTI. While ΔG and T_ms are matched, it was not possible to design the oligonucleotides with lower ΔG values at their 3' ends.

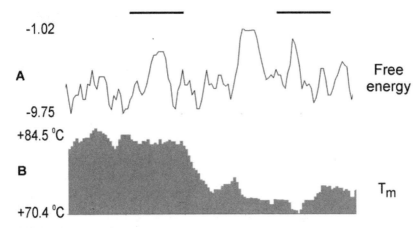

Figure 7.6. Plot of ΔG (**A**) and T_m (**B**) of target region around the splice junction of the Rat angiotensin II receptor mRNA. The horizontal bars indicate the position of the primers.

had direct implications for PCR-based assays and are making some assays possible that were not possible before, or are improving the reliability of those that were limited by the properties of DNA.

Compounds that mimic nucleic acids contain naturally occurring nucleotide bases linked to a chemically modified backbone. The nature of the modified backbone varies considerably but in general must be sufficiently different to the sugar phosphate backbones of DNA and RNA to prevent degradation by intracellular nucleases. However, the basic structure must be similar enough to DNA to enable the linked bases to form H-bonding interactions with cellular DNA. The two most commonly encountered analogues are described in the following three sections.

7.14.1. Peptide Nucleic Acids (PNA)

Peptide or polyamide nucleic acid is a synthetic pseudopeptide DNA/RNA mimic (**Fig. 7.7**), which was functionally designed to be a sequence-specific DNA groove binder. The entire deoxyribose phosphate backbone is replaced by a structurally homomorphous backbone consisting of repeating N-(2-aminoethyl)-glycine units linked by peptide bonds[1] and PNAs recognize complementary sequences by standard Watson-Crick pairing.[2] Unlike DNA, PNAs do not contain pentose sugar moieties or phosphate groups. The N-terminal of PNA oligomers is equivalent to the 5' end of an oligodeoxynucleo-tides. They are very

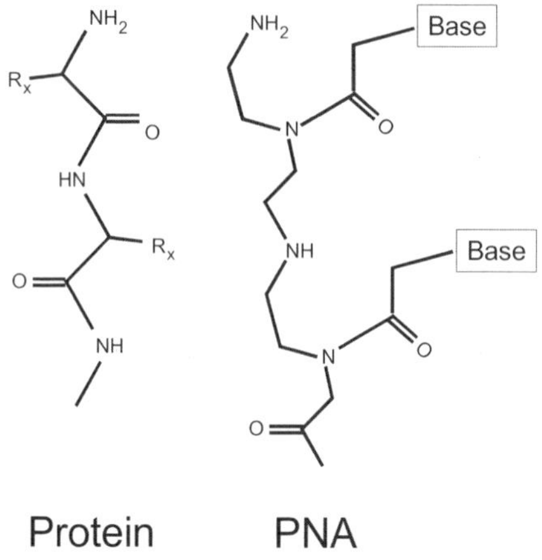

Protein   PNA

Figure 7.7. Comparison of protein and PNA.

potent DNA mimics, but do not appear to be substrates for nucleases or proteases.[54] Since the PNA backbone is not charged, hybridization is not affected by intrastrand repulsion and occurs with enhanced affinity[2] and rates of association.[55] The absence of a repetitive charged backbone also prevents PNAs from binding to proteins that normally recognize polyanions, avoiding a major source of nonspecific interactions. Furthermore, no salt is necessary to facilitate and stabilize the formation of PNA and DNA or RNA duplexes. Therefore, the T_m of a PNA/DNA or PNA/RNA duplex is significantly higher than that of a DNA/DNA duplex and is almost independent of ionic strength. When used at low ionic strength a PNA molecule will bind effectively to a target under low-salt conditions in the presence of a competing DNA or RNA molecule. Since low-salt conditions also destabilize intramolecular interactions of RNA molecules, these conditions favor hybridization of the PNA molecule. On the down side, PNA aggregates and PNA/DNA duplexes precipitate at low pH.

The ΔT_m of a single PNA/DNA mismatch is significantly higher than that of a DNA/DNA mismatch; hence the impact of that mismatch is much greater for the PNA probe. This allows the use of shorter probes, but these will be less specific. While a 15-mer PNA probe will have roughly the same melting temperature as a standard 25-mer DNA probe, it will not have its specificity. It is probably best to aim for a PNA probe length of around 18 bases. Probes longer than that tend to aggregate,[56] a problem also associated with purine-rich PNA probes. Shorter PNA probes are particularly useful for increasing the specificity of a probe for the detection of SNPs or mutations. Stemless PNA Beacons are particularly good at discriminating mismatches.[57]

Although molecules consisting entirely of PNA cannot act as primers to initiate polymerization, PNA–DNA chimeras such as PNA19-TpG-OH, comprised of 19 bases in the form of PNA followed by a dinucleotide (TpG-OH) with a single phosphate and a free 3'OH terminus, can function as efficient primers when annealed with a complementary RNA or DNA template.[58] On the other hand, the inability of PNA probes to serve as primers for DNA polymerases can be a useful feature and has been exploited rather ingeniously. The most prevalent form of Hereditary hemochromatosis (HH), an iron overload disease, is the result of a single base-pair mutation. Fully complementary PNA probes were shown to compete in a PCR reaction with DNA primers hybridizing to the HH mutation site, thereby suppressing amplicon formation. Conversely, PNA probes with a mismatch did not impair the binding of a complementary primer, and resulted in PCR product.[59] This feature has allowed the development of a rapid genetic assay to distinguish HH patients from HH carriers and normal individuals.

Another exciting application for PNA is the combination of PNA-DNA-loop (PD-loop) technology[60] with Molecular Beacons offering the possibility of targeting duplex DNA.[61] Homopyrimidine PNAs are known to invade short homopurine tracts in duplex DNA forming P-loops. If these are formed at two closely located purine tracts in the same DNA strand separated by a mixed purine-pyrimidine sequence, they merge and open the double helix between them. The opposite DNA strand, which is not bound with PNA, exposes and becomes accessible for complexing with an oligonucleotide via Watson-Crick pairing. As a result, the PD-loop emerges which consists of locally open duplex DNA, PNA "openers," and an oligonucleotide. Real-time PCR using stem-loop DNA and stemless PNA beacons can report on cognate targets located within preopened dsDNA sites[57,62] (**Fig. 7.8**). Apart from their use in real-time PCR assays, PNAs are showing great promise as antisense agents for gene therapeutic applications.[63]

7.14.2. PNA Probe Characteristics

PNAs can be readily synthesized by manual or automated methods[64] similar to standard procedures used to make peptides. Alternatively, full-length PNAs can be obtained from ABI.

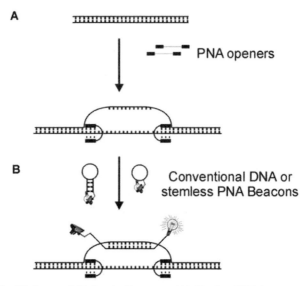

Figure 7.8. The PD-loop and Molecular Beacons. (**A**) Duplex DNA is preopened at an internal site by a pair of PNA openers. This exposes the target sequence located on the displaced DNA strand and allows the DNA/PNA beacon to bind. (**B**) Binding of Molecular Beacons to the exposed dsDNA target sequence yields a fluorescence response due to spatial separation of fluorophore and quencher within unfolded hybridization probes.

☑ Probes with more than three G or four A residues should be avoided. Their A+G content should be less than 60%, as they will otherwise aggregate and have low solubility in aqueous buffers.

☑ Avoid direct repeats. Direct repeats may generate secondary binding sites for primers. Since PNA/PNA duplexes are more stable than PNA/DNA duplexes, this will result in probe aggregation.

☑ A probe length of 12 to 17 units is optimal. Longer PNA probes tend to aggregate and are difficult to purify. The longer the oligonucleotide, the less the percentage of full-length product in the crude synthesis. This results in lower yields after purification.

☑ PNA melting temperatures differ from those of DNA oligonucleotides. Since the PNA strand is uncharged, a PNA/DNA duplex will have a higher T_m than the corresponding DNA/DNA duplex. Typically there will be an increase in T_m of about 1°C per base pair at 100 mM NaCl. At lower salt concentrations the T_m differences will be even more dramatic. A 10-mer PNA will typically have a T_m of about 50°C, and a 15-mer PNA will typically have a T_m of 70°C.

☑ Avoid designing probes with 4-base C or G complements (i.e.,
CCGG), unless they are interrupted by an A or T. Try to avoid
6- and 8-base complements altogether.

☑ PNAs can form duplexes in either orientation, but an antiparallel
orientation is strongly preferred and forms the most regular
duplex. When the orientation of the PNA is antiparallel, the *N*-ter-
minal of the PNA probe is equivalent to the 5' end of the DNA.

7.14.3. Locked Nucleic Acids LNA™

Locked nucleic acids (LNA™),[4,65] also known as Bridged Nucleic
Acids (BNA)[66,67] monomers are bicyclic compounds structurally similar to RNA nucleosides (see **Fig. 7.9**). They are called "locked," or
"bridged," because the furanose ring conformation is restricted in LNA
by a methylene bridge that connects the 2'-oxygen position of ribose to
the 4'-carbon. This bridge results in a locked 3'-*endo* conformation that
reduces the conformational flexibility of the ribose and increases the
local organization of the phosphate backbone. Furthermore, LNA
induces adjacent DNA bases to adopt this conformation, resulting in the
formation of the more thermodynamically stable A form duplex.[5] In
most respects, LNA may be handled like DNA.[68] It is at least as stable
as DNA, is soluble in aqueous buffers and can be ethanol precipitated,
dried, and resuspended. LNA oligonucleotides obey Watson-Crick base
pairing[69,70] and the modification leads to enhanced specificity and
duplex stability with complementary nucleic acid targets.[71] The thermal
stability of a LNA/DNA or LNA/RNA duplex is increased 3°C to 8°C

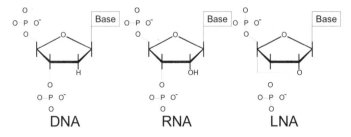

Figure 7.9. Comparison of DNA, RNA, and LNA.

per modified base in the oligonucleotide. This gives LNA oligonucleotides several advantages over PNAs (**Table 7.1**) and makes them very attractive in PCR-based assays and they are beginning to appear in probes for real-time PCR assays. Importantly, the change in T_m caused by a mismatch is significantly greater with a LNA/DNA duplex than with of a DNA/DNA duplex, resulting in enhanced specificity for SNP/mutation analyzes. Indeed, hexamer and heptamer probes consisting entirely of LNA can discriminate between targets that differ by a single base.[72] Design of LNA primers and probes is easy due to a program specifically developed for T_m predictions at www.lna-tm.com.

Table 7.1. Comparison of LNA and PNA.

Parameter	LNA	PNA
T_m increase/monomer against DNA (°C)	2–6	0.5–2.0
T_m increase/monomer against RNA (°C)	3–8	0.5–2.0
Charge	–ve	none
RNaseH	Activates	No activation
Synthesis	Like DNA	Like peptide
ΔT_m at single mismatch against DNA	>>> DNA	>> DNA
Water soluble	Yes	No
Primer function for DNApol	Yes	No

7.14.4. Modified Bases: Super A™, G™, and T™

These bases are designed to overcome some of the problems associated with hybridization. They increase duplex stability, increase mismatch discrimination, reduce self-annealing, and even out the T_ms of A/T vs. G/C-rich sequences. Super A and Super T improve the stability of AT bonds. By incorporating these modified bases into AT-rich sequences, T_ms can be raised for more efficient hybridization. Super G is modified so that G-G self-association through hydrogen bonding in G-rich sequences is eliminated and does not quench adjacent fluorophores attached at the 5' terminus.

7.14.5. Minor Groove Binding Probes

In B-DNA, which makes up the majority of cellular DNA, the antiparallel helix is right handed, the glycosidic bonds are in the anticonformation, and the ribose units are C2'-*endo* puckered. The net effect of this is the creation of two grooves, the major groove (approximately 12Å wide) and the minor groove (near 6Å wide). There are numerous naturally occurring and synthetic sequence selective compounds, which bind in the minor groove of DNA. They tend to bind with relatively little distortion of the phosphate backbone, and in fact stabilize the regular B-DNA structure. Minor groove binding (MGB) ligands have a number of characteristic features that distinguish them from other types of reversible DNA binding agents such as the intercalators. These include an overall annular shape made up of aromatic rings, which matches the curvature of the minor groove of DNA, cationic charges, which provide affinity for the tunnel of negative molecular electrostatic potential in the groove, and in addition many ligands possess H-bond donating or accepting atoms. The vast majority of these compounds selectively bind to AT-rich DNA sequences and such sites possess several unique characteristics. The width of the minor groove is often considerably narrower than mixed sequence DNA so that the planar aromatic rings of AT-selective ligands can slot into the groove and form stabilizing van der Waals contacts. The electrostatic potential of the minor groove varies with base sequence and is most electronegative at AT-rich sequences. Thus positively charged minor groove binding ligands have a higher affinity for this tunnel of electronegativity on the floor of the groove. Additionally, AT-base pairs have two H-bond accepting groups, the O_2 of thymine and the N_3 of adenine, which can further stabilize ligands with appropriately situated H-bond donating groups. In addition, AT-rich sequences contain highly structured networks of coordinated water molecules that add to overall stability, and displacement of these by ligands provides a substantial entropy component to the binding.

Minor groove binders (MGB) such as dihydrocyclopyrroloindole bind to the minor groove of DNA with high affinity. When such MGBs are conjugated with oligodeoxynucleotides, the conjugates form creates very stable hybrids with complementary DNA. TaqMan MGB probes have the MGB at their 3' end, since they are easier to synthesize, whereas the more recently introduced Eclipse probes have the MGB at the 5' end.[9] Fluorescence quenching is more efficient, giving increased sensitivity and specificity[12] and the higher melting temperatures (T_m) allow the design of significantly shorter probes that are also more specific, especially if there is a mismatch in the MGB region of the duplex. MGB probes allow the design of efficient probes for AT-rich regions of the genome and have been used successfully for SNP analysis.[73] One problem with these probes is that the additional restrictions on where the probes can bind may make it even more difficult to find optimal probes around, e.g., splice junction. On the other hand, the shorter length of the probe compensates for this. When designing MGB probes, it is important to remember that because of the asymmetric placement of the minor groove binder at the 3' end, complementary MGB probes do not necessarily have the same T_m.

A recent exciting development from Exiqon (www.probelibrary.com) uses very short LNA probes (8–9 bases) that target highly recurring sequences in humans, mouse, or rat transcriptomes. A set of 90 such probes will cover the entire transcriptome, with each probe detecting approximately 7,000 transcripts. The specificity provided by the primers ensures that only one transcript is detected at any one time. On average, each mRNA contains binding sites for 16 probes and the optimal probe/primer combination is chosen by designing the assay online using Exicon's ProbeFinder™ software. Assays are designed by simply adding a sequence and several assays will be designed automatically. This means that a single probe or small group of probes can be used to assay many transcripts, resulting in a considerable reduction of expense and, perhaps more importantly,increasing the reliability and potential for standardization of the real-time assay.

Useful Websites

Primer Design Background

http://www.uct.ac.za/microbi3ology/pcroptim.htm
http://genxpress.roedlach.at/pdf/PRIM3.pdf

Folding Analyses

http://www.bioinfo.rpi.edu/applications/mfold/

T_m Calculators

http://www.nwfsc.noaa.gov/protocols/oligoTMcalc.html

http://www.microbiology.adelaide.edu.au/learn/oligcalc.htm (alternative site)

http://www.cnr.berkeley.edu/~zimmer/oligoTMcalc.html (alternative site, less pretty)

http://www.pasteur.fr/recherche/unites/neubiomol/meltinghome.html

http://alces.med.umn.edu/rawtm.html

Primer Design

http://www-genome.wi.mit.edu/cgi-bin/primer/primer3_www.cgi

http://bioinformatics.weizmann.ac.il/cgi-bin/primer/primer3.cgi

http://bibiserv.techfak.uni-bielefeld.de/genefisher

http://genome-www2.stanford.edu/cgi-bin/SGD/web-primer

http://eatworms.swmed.edu/~tim/primerfinder

PCR Primers Designed From Protein Multiple Sequence Alignments

http://blocks.fhcrc.org/blocks/codehop.html

Commercial Oligonucleotide Designer

http://www.oligo.net

http://doprimer.interactiva.de

http://www.PremierBiosoft.com/

Tandem Repeats:

http://tandem.biomath.mssm.edu/trf/trf.html (you can either analyze your sequence online or download the software)

Primer and Probe Database

http://medgen31.rug.ac.be/primerdatabase/index.html

http://medgen31.rug.ac.be/primerdatabase/)

PNA

http://www.appliedbiosystems.com/products/productdetail.cfm?prod_id=424

Design of PNA Oligomers

www.appliedbisosystems.com/support/seqguide.clm

http://www.appliedbiosystems.com/support/pnadesigner.cfm

Super-Bases, Eclipse, MGB Probes

www.epochbio.com

Design of LNA^{TM} Oligonucleotides

www.LNA-tm.com

> **Note:** A public real-time primer/probe database has been established
> recently (http://medgen31.rug.ac.be/primerdatabase/index.html
> or http://medgen31.rug.ac.be/primerdatabase/) and the expecta-
> tion is that with time it should hold an extensive catalogue of
> validated primers and probes.

Nearest-Neighbor Parameters

http://www.bioinfo.rpi.edu/~zukerm/seqanal/mfold-3.0-manual.pdf

The following three sites are our favorites:

www.rnature.com

  RNAture is easy to use and generates T_m, free energy, molecular weight, and
  hairpin and dimer formation structures.

http://207.32.43.248/oligocalc.asp

  Oligocalc can incorporate the effects of adding internal modifications, or
  those made at the 5', 3' ends.

http://www.bioinfo.rpi.edu/applications/mfold/

  MFold is a program to test for secondary structures for use in analyzing
  amplicons, linear probes over 30 nucleotides, and Molecular Beacons.

http://www.premierbiosoft.com/netprimer/netprlaunch/netprlaunch.html

  Netprimer is based on SantaLucia's algorithms and provides a vast amount
  of fine tuning. It is available only for Windows and installs an applet on the
  hard disk.

http://www.ncbi.nlm.nih.gov/genome/sts/epcr.cgi

  Electronic PCR is useful for testing a DNA sequence for the presence of
  sequence tagged sites. e-PCR looks for STSs in DNA sequences by search-
  ing for sub-sequences that closely match the PCR primers and have the correct order, orientation, and spacing that they could plausibly prime the
  amplification of a PCR product of the correct molecular weight.

References

1. Nielsen PE, Egholm M, Berg RH, Buchardt O: **Sequence-selective recognition of DNA by strand displacement with a thymine-substituted polyamide.** *Science* 1991, **254**:1497–1500.

2. Egholm M, Buchardt O, Christensen L, Behrens C, Freier SM, Driver DA, Berg RH, Kim SK, Norden B, Nielsen PE: **PNA hybridizes to complementary oligonucleotides obeying the Watson-Crick hydrogen-bonding rules.** *Nature* 1993, **365**:566–568.

3. Orum H, Nielsen PE, Egholm M, Berg RH, Buchardt O, Stanley C: **Single base pair mutation analysis by PNA directed PCR clamping.** *Nucleic Acids Res* 1993, **21**:5332–5336.

4. Kumar R, Singh SK, Koshkin AA, Rajwanshi VK, Meldgaard M, Wengel J: **The first analogues of LNA (locked nucleic acids): Phosphorothioate-LNA and 2'-thio-LNA.** *Bioorg Med Chem Lett* 1998, **8**:2219–2222.

5. Nielsen CB, Singh SK, Wengel J, Jacobsen JP: **The solution structure of a locked nucleic acid (LNA) hybridized to DNA.** *J Biomol Struct Dyn* 1999, **17**:175–191.

6. Hamilton SC, Farchaus JW, Davis MC: **DNA polymerases as engines for biotechnology.** *Biotechniques* 2001, **31**:370–380, 382.

7. Kainz P: **The PCR plateau phase—Towards an understanding of its limitations.** *Biochim Biophys Acta* 2000, **1494**:23–27.

8. Kreuzer KA, Bohn A, Lass U, Peters UR, Schmidt CA: **Influence of DNA polymerases on quantitative PCR results using TaqMan™ probe format in the LightCycler™ instrument.** *Mol Cell Probes* 2000, **14**:57–60.

9. Afonina IA, Reed, MW, Lusby E, Shishkina IG, Belousov YS: **Minor groove binder-conjugated DNA probes for quantitative DNA detection by hybridization-triggered fluorescence.** *Biotechniques* 2002, **32**:940–949.

10. Broude NE: **Stem-loop oligonucleotides: A robust tool for molecular biology and biotechnology.** *Trends Biotechnol* 2002, **20**:249–256.

11. Isacsson J, Cao H, Ohlsson L, Nordgren S, Svanvik N, Westman G., Kubista M, Sjoback R, Sehlstedt U. **Rapid and specific detection of PCR products using light-up probes.** *Mol Cell Probes* 2000, **14**:321–328.

12. Kutyavin IV, Afonina IA, Mills A., Gorn VV, Lukhtanov EA, Belousov ES, Singer MJ, Walburger DK, Lokhov SG, Gall AA, Dempcy R, Reed MW, Meyer RB, Hedgpeth J: **3-minor groove binder-DNA probes increase sequence specificity at PCR extension temperatures.** *Nucleic Acids Res* 2000, **28**:655–661.

13. Breslauer KJ, Frank R, Blocker H, Marky LA: **Predicting DNA duplex stability from the base sequence.** *Proc Natl Acad Sci USA* 1986, **83**:3746–3750.

14. Straus NA, Bonner TI: **Temperature dependence of RNA-DNA hybridization kinetics.** *Biochim Biophys Acta* 1972, **277**:87–95.

15. Gamper HB, Cimino GD, Hearst JE: **Solution hybridization of crosslinkable DNA oligonucleotides to bacteriophage M13 DNA. Effect of secondary structure on hybridization kinetics and equilibria.** *J Mol Biol* 1987, **197**:349–362.

16. SantaLucia J Jr, Allawi HT, Seneviratne PA: **Improved nearest-neighbor parameters for predicting DNA duplex stability.** *Biochemistry* 1996, **35**:3555–3562, .

17. SantaLucia J Jr: **A unified view of polymer, dumbbell, and oligonucleotide DNA nearest-neighbor thermodynamics.** *Proc Natl Acad Sci USA* 1998, **95**:1460–1465.

18. Xia T, SantaLucia J Jr, Burkard ME, Kierzek R, Schroeder SJ, Jiao X, Cox C, Turner DH: **Thermodynamic parameters for an expanded nearest-neighbor model for formation of RNA duplexes with Watson-Crick base pairs.** *Biochemistry* 1998, **37**:14719–14735.

19. Allawi HT, SantaLucia J Jr: **Nearest-neighbor thermodynamics of internal A.C mismatches in DNA: Sequence dependence and pH effects.** *Biochemistry* 1998, **37**:9435–9444.

20. Allawi HT, SantaLucia J Jr: **Thermodynamics of internal C.T mismatches in DNA.** *Nucleic Acids Res* 1998, **26**:2694–2701.

21. Allawi HT, SantaLucia J Jr: **Nearest neighbor thermodynamic parameters for internal G.A mismatches in DNA.** *Biochemistry* 1998, **37**:2170–2179.

22. Peyret N, Seneviratne PA, Allawi HT, SantaLucia J Jr: **Nearest-neighbor thermodynamics and NMR of DNA sequences with internal A.A, C.C, G.G, and T.T mismatches.** *Biochemistry* 1999, **38**:3468–3477.

23. Lvovsky L, Ioshikhes I., Raja MC, Zevin-Sonkin D, Sobolev IA, Liberzon A, Shwartzburd J, Ulanovsky LE: **Interdependence between DNA template secondary structure and priming efficiencies of short primers.** *Nucleic Acids Res* 1998, **26**:5525–5532.

24. Bommarito S, Peyret N, SantaLucia J Jr: **Thermodynamic parameters for DNA sequences with dangling ends.** *Nucleic Acids Res* 2000, **28**:1929–1934.

25. Allawi HT, SantaLucia J Jr: **Thermodynamics and NMR of internal G.T mismatches in DNA.** *Biochemistry* 1997, **36**:10581–10594.

26. Studier FW: **A strategy for high-volume sequencing of cosmid DNAs: Random and directed priming with a library of oligonucleotides.** *Proc Natl Acad Sci USA* 1989, **86**:6917–6921.

27. Teo I, Choi J, Morlese J, Taylor G, Shaunak S: **LightCycler qPCR optimisation for low copy number target DNA.** *J Immunol.Methods* 2002, **270**:119.

28. Didenko VV: **DNA probes using fluorescence resonance energy transfer (FRET): Designs and applications.** Biotechniques 2001, **31**:1106–1111.

29. Moore RE, Shepherd JW, Hoskins J: **Design of PCR primers that detect only mRNA in the presence of DNA.** *Nucleic Acids Res* 1990, **18**:1921.

30. Kollmann TR, Zhuang X, Rubinstein A, Goldstein H. **Design of polymerase chain reaction primers for the selective amplification of HIV-1 RNA in the presence of HIV-1 DNA.** *AIDS* 1992, **6**:547–552.

31. Muralidhar B, Steinman CR: **Design and characterization of PCR primers for detection of pathogenic *Neisseriae*.** *Mol Cell Probes* 1994, **8**:55–61.

32. Antoniw J: **A new method for designing PCR primers specific for groups of sequences and its application to plant viruses.** *Mol Biotechnol* 1995, **4**:111–119.

33. Bagsic RD Fegan M, Li X, Hayward AC: **Construction of species-specific primers for *Pseudomonas andropogonis* based on 16S rDNA sequences.** *Lett Appl Microbiol* 1995, **21**:87–92.

34. Leary TP, Muerhoff AS, Simons JN, Pilot-Matias TJ, Erker JC, Chalmers ML, Schlauder GG, Dawson GJ, Desai SM, Mushahwar IK: **Consensus oligonucleotide primers for the detection of GB virus C in human cryptogenic hepatitis.** *J Virol Methods* 1996, **56:** 119–121.

35. Novati S, Sironi M, Granata S, Bruno A , Gatti S, Scaglia M, Bandi C: **Direct sequencing of the PCR amplified SSU rRNA gene of *Entamoeba dispar* and the design of primers for rapid differentiation from *Entamoeba histolytica*.** *Parasitology* 1996, **112**(Pt 4):363–369.

36. Marchesi JR, Sato T, Weightman AJ, Martin TA, Fry, JC, Hiom, SJ, Dymock D, Wade WG: **Design and evaluation of useful bacterium-specific PCR primers that amplify genes coding for bacterial 16S rRNA.** *Appl Environ Microbiol* 1998, **64**:795–799.

37. Sblattero D, Bradbury A: **A definitive set of oligonucleotide primers for amplifying human V regions.** *Immunotechnology* 1998, **3**:271–278.

38. Kikuchi E, Miyamoto Y, Narushima S, Itoh K: **Design of species-specific primers to identify 13 species of *Clostridium* harbored in human intestinal tracts.** *Microbiol Immunol* 2002, **46**:353–358.

39. Nadkarni MA, Martin FE, Jacques NA, Hunter N: **Determination of bacterial load by real-time PCR using a broad-range (universal) probe and primers set.** *Microbiology* 2002, **148**:257–266.

40. Salazar O, Gonzalez I, Genilloud O:**New genus-specific primers for the PCR identification of novel isolates of the genera *Nocardiopsis* and *Saccharothrix*.** *Int.J Syst Evol Microbiol* 2002, **52**:1411–1421.

41. Gilar M: **Analysis and purification of synthetic oligonucleotides by reversed-phase high-performance liquid chromatography with photodiode array and mass spectrometry detection.** *Anal Biochem* 2001, **298**:196–206.

42. Gilar M, Bouvier ESP: **Purification of crude DNA oligonucleotides by solid-phase extraction and reversed-phase high-performance liquid chromatography.** *J Chromatogr A* 2000, **890**:167–177.

43. Oefner PJ, Huber CG, Umlauft F, Berti GN, Stimpfl E, Bonn GK: **High-resolution liquid chromatography of fluorescent dye-labeled nucleic acids.** *Anal Biochem* 1994, **223**:39–46.

44. Fountain KJ, Gilar M, Budman Y, Gebler JC: **Purification of dye-labeled oligonucleotides by ion-pair reversed-phase high-performance liquid chromatography.** *J Chromatogr B Analyt Technol Biomed Life Sci* 2003, **783**:61–72.

45. Rudert WA, Braun ER, Faas, SJ, Menon R., Jaquins-Gerstl A., Trucco M: **Double-labeled fluorescent probes for 5' nuclease assays: Purification and performance evaluation.** *Biotechniques* 1997, **22**:1140–1145.

46. Mhlanga MM, Malmberg L: **Using molecular beacons to detect single-nucleotide polymorphisms with real-time PCR.** *Methods* 2001, **25**:463–471.

47. Tapp I, Malmberg L, Rennel E, Wik M, Syvanen AC: **Homogeneous scoring of single-nucleotide polymorphisms: Comparison of the 5'-nuclease TaqMan assay and Molecular Beacon probes.** *Biotechniques* 2000, **28**:732–738.

48. Vandenbroucke II, Vandesompele J, Paepe AD, Messiaen L: **Quantification of splice variants using real-time PCR.** *Nucleic Acids Res* 2001, **29**:E68.

49. Etokebe GE, Spurkland A: **Method for avoiding PCR-inhibiting contaminants when eluting DNA from polyacrylamide gels.** *Biotechniques* 2000, **29**:694, 696.

50. Svaren J, Inagami S, Lovegren E, Chalkley R: **DNA denatures upon drying after ethanol precipitation.** *Nucleic Acids Res* 1987, **15**:8739–8754.

51. Grundemann D, Schomig E: **Protection of DNA during preparative agarose gel electrophoresis against damage induced by ultraviolet light.** *Biotechniques* 1996, **21**: 898–903.

52. Hengen PN: Wayward **PCR primers.** *Trends Biochem Sci* 1995, **20**:42–44.

53. Marks JD, Tristem M, Karpas A, Winter G: **Oligonucleotide primers for polymerase chain reaction amplification of human immunoglobulin variable genes and design of family-specific oligonucleotide probes.** *Eur J Immunol* 1991, **21**:985–991, .

54. Demidov VV, Potaman VN, Frank-Kamenetskii MD, Egholm M., Buchard O, Sonnichsen SH, Nielsen PE: **Stability of peptide nucleic acids in human serum and cellular extracts.** *Biochem Pharmacol* 1994, **48**:1310–1313.

55. Smulevitch SV, Simmons CG, Norton JC, Wise TW, Corey DR: **Enhancement of strand invasion by oligonucleotides through manipulation of backbone charge.** *Nat Biotechnol* 1996, **14**:1700–1704

56. Braasch DA, Corey DR: **Synthesis, analysis, purification, and intracellular delivery of peptide nucleic acids.** *Methods* 2001, **23**:97–107.

57. Kuhn H., Demidov VV, Coull JM, Fiandaca MJ, Gildea BD, Frank-Kamenetskii MD: **Hybridization of DNA and PNA molecular beacons to single-stranded and double-stranded DNA targets.** *J Am Chem Soc* 2002, **124**:1097–1103.

58. Misra HS, Pandey PK, Modak MJ, Vinayak R, Pandey VN: **Polyamide nucleic acid-DNA chimera lacking the phosphate backbone are novel primers for polymerase reaction catalyzed by DNA polymerases.** *Biochemistry* 1998, **37**:1917–1925.

59. Kyger EM, Krevolin MD, Powell MJ: **Detection of the hereditary hemochromatosis gene mutation by real-time fluorescence polymerase chain reaction and peptide nucleic acid clamping.** *Anal Biochem* 1998, **260**:142–148.

60. Bukanov NO, Demidov VV, Nielsen PE, Frank-Kamenetskii MD: **PD-loop: A complex of duplex DNA with an oligonucleotide.** *Proc Natl Acad Sci USA* 1998, **95**:5516–5520.

61. Demidov VV: **PD-loop technology: PNA openers at work.** *Expert Rev Mol Diagn* 2001, **1**:343–351.

62. Kuhn H, Demidov VV, Gildea BD, Fiandaca MJ, Coull JC, Frank-Kamenetskii MD: **PNA beacons for duplex DNA.** *Antisense Nucleic Acid Drug Dev* 2001, **11**:265–270.

63. Ray A, Norden B: **Peptide nucleic acid (PNA): Its medical and biotechnical applications and promise for the future.** *FASEB J* 2000, **14**:1041–1060.

64. Mayfield LD, Corey DR: **Automated synthesis of peptide nucleic acids and peptide nucleic acid-peptide conjugates.** *Anal Biochem* 1999, **268**:401–404.

65. Singh SK, Kumar R, Wengel J: **Synthesis of novel bicyclo[2.2.1] ribonucleosides: 2'-amino- and 2'-thio-LNA monomeric nucleosides.** *J Org Chem* 1998, **63**:6078–6079.

66. Imanishi T, Obika S: **BNAs: Novel nucleic acid analogs with a bridged sugar moiety.** *Chem Commun (Camb)* 2002, 1653–1659.

67. Obika S, Hari Y., Sekiguchi M, Imanishi TA: **2',4'-bridged nucleic acid containing 2-pyridone as a nucleobase: Efficient recognition of a C small middle dot G interruption by triplex formation with a pyrimidine motif. Part of this work was supported by a Grant-in-Aid for Scientific Research (B) (No. 12557201) from the Japan Society for the Promotion of Science.** *Angew Chem Int Ed Engl* 2001, **40**:2079–2081.

68. Braasch DA, Corey DR: **Locked nucleic acid (LNA): Fine-tuning the recognition of DNA and RNA.** *Chem Biol* 2001, **8**:1–7.

69. Petersen M, Nielsen CB, Nielsen KE, Jensen GA, Bondensgaard K, Singh SK, Rajwanshi VK, Koshkin AA, Dahl BM, Wengel J, Jacobsen JP: **The conformations of locked nucleic acids (LNA).** *J Mol Recognit* 2000, **13**:44–53.

70. Torigoe H., Hari Y, Sekiguchi M, Obika S, Imanishi T: **2'-O,4'-C-methylene bridged nucleic acid modification promotes pyrimidine motif triplex DNA formation at physiological pH: Thermodynamic and kinetic studies.** *J Biol Chem* 2001, **276**: 2354–2360.

71. Obika S, Uneda T, Sugimoto T, Nanbu D, Minami T, Doi T, Imanishi T: **2'-O,4'-C-methylene bridged nucleic acid (2',4'-BNA): Synthesis and triplex-forming properties.** *Bioorg Med Chem* 2001, **9**:1001–1011.

72. Simeonov A, Nikiforov TT: **Single nucleotide polymorphism genotyping using short, fluorescently labeled locked nucleic acid (LNA) probes and fluorescence polarization detection.** *Nucleic Acids Res* 2002, **30**: E91.

73. Walburger DK, Afonina IA, Wydro R: **An improved real time PCR method for simultaneous detection of C282Y and H63D mutations in the HFE gene associated with hereditary hemochromatosis.** *Mutat Res* 2001, **432**:69–78.

8

Instrumentation

Stephen A. Bustin and Tania Nolan

8

Instrumentation

Stephen A. Bustin[*] and Tania Nolan[†]

*Barts and The London, Queen Mary's School of Medicine and Dentistry, University of London, London, United Kingdom
†Stratagene Europe, Amsterdam, The Netherlands*

8.1. Introduction

We have come a long way since there was the choice of any real-time cycler/detector as long as it was an ABI Prism 7700. Having said that, this instrument initiated the real-time PCR revolution and even though it is (arguably) very ugly, takes up half an average-sized laboratory (not arguably), and the software supplied with the instrument is user-challenging (definitively not arguably), it was the first out and provides the benchmark against which every newly developed instrument continues to be measured. Part of its popularity stems from the ease with which it is possible to obtain quantitative data: although tedious to use, the software was designed to generate normalized amplification plots that managed to hide the ugly reality of poorly labeled probes and barely detectable changes in fluorescence. In contrast, second generation instruments give the user access to raw data plots which makes result appear a lot less pretty, but allows the identification of primer-, probe-, or amplification-related problems and allows the scientist greater control over data analysis.

8.1.1. The Principle

The real-time PCR reaction is performed and fluorescence is detected using combined thermal cyclers/fluorimeters. Fluorimeters are relatively simple optical arrangements that collect light through an optical window in the PCR chamber that allows the passage of visible light in and out of the reaction mixture. The ability to detect extremely low numbers of nucleic acid species using this approach is entirely due to the performance of the PCR, since conventional homogeneous fluorescent assays have relatively low sensitivity compared with other detection technologies. In principle, the real-time approach involves taking one measurement per sample per cycle, usually at the end of extension or annealing. In this manner, the progress of individual reactions can be monitored. The cycle value where fluorescence rises above background noise is termed the "cycle threshold," or C_t value. The number of cycles that an individual assay requires is directly related to the initial target copy number. Control assays, with a known concentration of initial target copy number, can be used to generate a standard curve of cycle threshold number against initial target copy number. The initial target copy number of unknown samples can be determined by interpolation of their cycle threshold using this type of plot (see **Chapter 12**).

Today there are several instruments on the market (see **Section 8.2** for a description of the most popular instruments and some that are very new to the market). These systems all perform the same function in that they monitor changes in fluorescence intensity as the PCR progresses. All systems use an excitation light source, which is typically a halogen lamp, LED, or a laser to generate the wavelengths of light required to excite the fluorophores used in the PCR assay. The intensity of light emitted is measured which is proportional to the concentration of the amplification product being detected. Finally, but definitely not least, is that all systems are supplied with software that allows data analysis to report target quantification, melting curve analyses, and allelic discrimination. The choice of instrument can be difficult, but for research purposes ultimately boils down to two criteria: temperature uniformity for reproducibility, which is better than it used to be[1] but can still vary,[2] and fluorescence sensitivity. Some old hands will still remember using thermocouples to measure the actual temperature of the reaction inside the PCR tube;[3] these days we have to take actual temperatures on trust. For diagnostic applications, licensing arrangements must of course also be taken into account.

A typical fluorescence detection system requires four elements: (1) an excitation source, (2) a suitable fluorophore/quencher detection chemistry combination discussed in the previous chapter, (3) the ability to distinguish emission photons from excitation photons, and (4) a detector that registers emission photons and produces a recordable output (see **Fig. 8.1**).

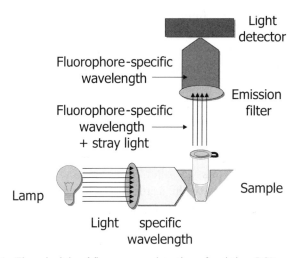

Figure 8.1. The principle of fluorescence detection of real-time PCR amplification.

8.1.2. Excitation Source

The light source provides the energy to excite the reporter fluorophore, and excitation sources include halogen lamps, which emit a broad range of light, lasers and LEDs, which emit more specific wavelengths.

8.1.2.1. Halogen Lamps

Halogen lamps are similar in construction to conventional gas-filled tungsten filament lamps except for a small trace of halogen (normally bromine) in the fill gas. The halogen gas reacts with the tungsten that has evaporated, migrated outward, and been deposited on the lamp wall. As the quartz envelope wall reaches a temperature of approximately 250°C, the halogen reacts with the tungsten to form tungsten halide, which is freed from the wall of the lamp and migrates back to the filament. The halide compound reacts at the filament where temperatures approximating 2,500°C cause the tungsten and halogen to dissociate. The tungsten deposits onto the colder portions of the filament, and the halogen is freed to continue the cycle. Halogen-based lamps emit at all wavelengths in the visible spectrum, producing a continuous spectral output from 350 nm to 2600 nm. Because of this they are often referred to as "white-light" sources. Although halogen lamps are limited by their ability to produce only a limited intensity (watts/cm^2) at any given wavelength, they provide uniform excitation over a much broader range of wavelengths. This allows flexibility to choose dyes at virtually any wavelength in this range. The use of a filter or monochromator allows selection of any given wavelength appropriate to the excitation wavelength range of the compound to be measured. The light passes through an excitation filter, which transmits wavelengths specific to the excitation spectrum of the compound and blocks other wavelengths. This light passes through and excites the sample, and the light emitted by the sample passes through the emission filter, which is at a right angle to the exciting light to minimize light scatter. The emission filter further screens the light, the emitted light is measured by the detector, and the fluorescence value is displayed on the instrument.
Examples: ABI 7300, 7500, Stratagene Mx4000 and Mx3000p, Bio-Rad iCycler.

8.1.2.2. Lasers

A laser generates a light of a specific wavelength, hence no excitation filter is required. The maximum intensity of light is very high, but the wavelength range is very narrow. In laser-driven real-time instruments the software uses a mathematical calculation to subtract the signal from one overlapping dye from the other. The software "decides" what the

probable contribution from one dye is vs. the other based on information given by the user. Therefore the fluorescent signal reported is based on a mathematical "guess." The main disadvantage to using lasers as light sources is the fact that they only emit at certain fixed wavelengths and that the excitation spectra of most dyes fall outside that range. Therefore the use of fluorophores is limited to the ones whose excitation range overlaps the emission range of the laser.
Examples: ABI PRISM 7700 and 7900.

8.1.2.3. Light Emitting Diodes (LEDs)

LEDs are compound semiconductor devices that typically produce light with a narrow bandwidth of 30–40 nm. Therefore, several LEDs are required to cover the wide range of fluorophores in use today. Their main advantage is the relatively low cost compared to lasers. The advantages of LEDs are small size, low power consumption, low self-heating, high reliability; they can be switched on and off quickly, and they are resistant to shock and vibration. The main disadvantages are the limited wavelength selection and that they require a limiting resistor with a voltage drive. The most common LEDs emit at 430, 450, 505, 592, 612, and 637 nm which are the ones suitable for many fluorophores but by no means all. Recently, novel LED materials emitting in the blue and UV range of the spectrum have been described.
Examples: Corbett Rotor-Gene, Roche LightCycler.

8.1.3. Filters

Optical filters are used to select the wavelength of light of interest. They are mainly used in conjunction with white light sources; however, as noted above, LEDs produce a bandwidth of some 30–40 nm and so may also require filtering. They are also used in front of the photodetector to select the wavelength of the fluorescence to be observed. This allows the elimination of scattered light and light from other dyes, which may be present in a given sample. The optical quality of the filter will often determine the performance of an instrument. Equally it is important that the filters are aligned optimally in the light path. For example, placing a filter at a slight incline to the incoming light will alter the optical path for light passing through different parts of the filter. If white light is passed through a filter, certain wavelengths will be attenuated producing an absorption curve. The terms used to designate filters such as wide, narrow, cut-off, short-bandpass, etc., refers to the shape of the curve when light is passed through the filter.

8.1.3.1. Bandpass and Long Pass Filters

Long pass filters allow light above a given wavelength to pass through. They are classified by their "cut-on" wavelength that is defined as the wavelength at 50% of the maximum transmission. Bandpass filters allow a narrow range of wavelengths to pass. These filters are classified according to two criteria, namely, the width of the band at 50% of the maximum transmission and the centre wavelength of the pass wavelengths. Both of these types of filters are typically made from colored and coated glass. The coloring typically acts to absorb the unwanted light. The advantages of ease of manufacture and cost have made this type of filter the most common for many years. However, the filters themselves can sometimes be weakly fluorescent and can thus contribute significantly to background issues. Dichroic filters are used at non-normal angles of incidence, highly reflect one specified wavelength region while optimally transmitting another. Dichroic filters are typically set at 45° to the incident light and are used as beam splitters. They can be considered as long pass or bandpass filters with center of wavelength and pass width change.

8.1.3.2. Monochromators

It is also possible to select the desired wavelength using a totally different principle, namely, either the prism or the diffraction grating. Either of these can be built into devices called monochromators. A diffraction grating is essentially a block of highly reflective metal, usually aluminum, onto which a large number of grooves have been etched. Typically this grating will be 10 to 15,000 lines per mm. When white, or polychromatic, light is shone onto the grating, each groove will act as a point source of light. Thus at the opposite side of the grating interference will take place, some of this will be destructive leading to darkness, others will be constructive. This leads to a series of bright lines of radiation and the wavelength of this constructive interference will depend on the angle of the incident light. Thus by altering this angle it is possible control the wavelength of the light leaving the exit slit. A monochromator will produce a single wavelength or bandpass from its exit slit. The devices can be tuned manually to single wavelength or can be motorized so as to scan across a range of wavelengths. The use of scanning monochromators is particularly useful in producing fluorescence excitation and emission spectra.?

8.1.4. Photodetectors

Detectors convert light energy to an electrical signal and are typically placed after a wavelength separator to detect a selected wavelength of light. The factors that influence the choice of a photodetector include:

1. *Quantum Efficiency*—a measure of how many electrons are produced for every photon absorbed by the light sensitive area of the detector. This is very wavelength dependent and must be measured at a given wavelength.

2. *Sensitivity*—a measure of a how a detector responds to a given photon flux. The sensitivity of the detector can be defined as the ratio of the output current to the incident photon flux. This parameter is closely related to the quantum efficiency, and knowledge of the quantum efficiency at a given wavelength allows the determination of sensitivity.

3. *Spectral Response*—essentially a plot of quantum efficiency against wavelength. The quantum efficiency varies with wavelength thus detectors should be used in the spectral region with the optimal quantum efficiency, and hence sensitivity.

4. *Dynamic Range*—the ability of the detector to produce an accurate output over a range of light flux levels. It usually stated as the ratio of the minimum detectable light to the maximum accurately detectable light level. The minimum light level is usually limited by noise, which in the case of most detectors is background current generated by heat within the detector. The maximum light level is when the detector is saturated with photons and cannot respond.

5. *Response Time*—the time the detector takes to respond to a change in light intensity. This is particularly important in real-time detection where light intensity changes very rapidly.

6. *Noise Equivalent Power*—all detectors produce noise, this is typically referred to as dark current. The noise-equivalent power (NEP) is defined as the power, in watts, which would produce an output from the device if there were no noise.

8.1.4.1. Photomultiplier Tube (PMT)

The two main elements present in a photomultiplier are the photoemissive cathode (photocathode) and a series of electron multiplier electrodes known as dynodes. When a photon of sufficient energy strikes the photocathode, it ejects a photoelectron. The photocathode material is usually a mixture of alkali metals, which make the PMT sensitive to photons throughout the visible region of the electromagnetic spectrum. The photocathode is at a high negative voltage, typically -500 to -1500 volts. The photoelectron is accelerated towards a series of dynodes where additional secondary electrons are generated. This cascading effect creates 10^5 to 10^7 electrons for each photoelectron that is ejected from the photocathode. The amplification depends on the number of dynodes and the accelerating voltage. This amplified electrical signal is collected at an anode at ground potential, which can be measured and whose integrated area is proportional to the number of photons in the flash of light. Because of its sensitivity, it is susceptible to the influences of a number of external parameters, such as electric fields, magnetic fields, and temperature. Furthermore, there can be electronic drift caused by some dark current from the PMT (current present even when no light is on the PMT), and the effects of temperature and age on PMT and lamp.

The drawback of the PMTs is their comparatively small quantum efficiency, i.e., the fraction of photons incident on a device that are actually detected, at 1–10%, compared with up to 80% for a charge-coupled device.

8.1.4.2. Charge-Coupled Device (CCD)

A CCD is a solid-state electronic silicon component that has been micro-manufactured and segmented into an array of individual light-sensitive cells called "photosites." Each photosite is one element of the whole picture that is formed, thus it is called a picture element, or "pixel." The image formed by the optics is projected onto that chip and light striking each of the pixels is converted to electric charge. This charge is greater where there is more light and less where there is less light. As long as light is allowed to impinge on a photosite, electrons will accumulate in that pixel. When the source of light is extinguished simple electronic circuitry and computer are used to unload the CCD array, count the electrons in each pixel, and process the resulting data. Since CCDs are electronic components they are sensitive to heat within the camera as well as light from the object of interest. Furthermore, the individual photosites in the CCD array may vary significantly in their sensitivity to both heat and light. First, this means that the electrons generated by heat rather than by light need to be subtracted from the final tally of electrons in each pixel so that a genuine image can be rendered. This is called "dark subtraction." This is done by subtracting a "dark frame" from the object image (called a "light frame"). The dark frame is created by taking an exposure while the CCD is maintained in complete darkness. This exposure must be the same duration as the light frame and be made with the CCD at the same temperature as during the light frame so that electrons generated during the dark frame replicate the heat-generated electrons present in the light frame.

Second, the variance in electron depth across the CCD array due to inherent differences among the pixels needs to be leveled by dividing each pixel value by the array's average pixel value. This is called "flat fielding." Flat-field images show the inherent variances in pixel value across the CCD array due to differences in photosite sensitivity or to dust specks or vignetting in the optical system. Image processing programs use mathematical algorithms to divide all pixel values in the flat-field image by the average pixel value of the array. The results are then correlated, pixel-by-pixel, against the array values in the light image to produce a better representation of the object of interest. In the final stages of image production, the light frame (object image) is adjusted first by having an appropriate dark frame subtracted and then by having an appropriate flat field divided into the image. This process is called image calibration and results in a more accurate, less noisy image.

8.1.5. Sensitivity

Sensitivity refers to the minimum detectable quantity of a target that can be measured above background signal inherent in the system caused by the electronics of the instrument. Note that merely increasing the instrument's sensitivity will provide a larger signal, but will probably also increase instrument noise. For example, it may detect more of the stray light that has not passed through the sample.

8.1.6. Dynamic Range

Dynamic range refers to the range of concentrations an instrument can read, from the minimum to the maximum detectable. The minimum detectable concentration is determined by the signal-to-noise ratio and the maximum detectable concentration by the chemistry and details of instrument design.

8.1.7. Linearity

Fluorescence intensity is ideally directly proportional (linear) to concentration. However, this linear relationship is affected by several factors that can combine to generate nonreproducible results. When concentration is too high, light cannot pass through the sample to cause excitation; thus very high concentrations can have very low fluorescence. At intermediate concentrations, the surface portion of sample nearest the light absorbs so much light that little is available for the rest of the sample; thus the readings will not be linear, though they will be within the range of a calibration curve.

Because fluorescence quantification is dependent on the instrument, fluorescent reference standards are essential for calibrating measurements made at different times or using different instrument configurations. Linearity is affected by the length of the path that the light must travel; the type, size, and diameter of the sample holder must also be considered. Hence samples must be retested for linearity to incorporate instrument-related factors or if sample holders or wavelength filters are changed. Every unknown sample should always be tested for linearity, and standard curves are ideal for this. If it is linear, the reading will go down by the same factor as the dilution. The accuracy of fluorescence readings depend on light exciting the fluorophore, therefore bubbles in the sample can produce erratic, hence non-reproducible results. A brief spin of the sample holders just prior to setting up the PCR assay is recommended.

8.2. Real-Time Instruments

Real-time PCR instruments constitute a rapidly growing and highly lucrative market with total sales worth $252 million in 2001, and which are predicted to rise to $776 million by 2006 in the US and European markets (http://biotech.frost.com). New instruments are being launched (e.g., ABI 7300, 7500) and prices are falling. There are significant differences between the instruments, in terms of specification and performance as well as in the support available from the manufacturers. It is well worth short listing three instruments prior to purchase, and requesting a two-week "test drive" to discover not just the instruments performance characteristics, but also get to know the software and learn about any idiosyncrasies that may be difficult to live with. When comparing instruments, it is also worth bearing in mind that service contracts, usually at around 10% per annum of the purchase price, add significantly to the purchase cost. It is not surprising that sales representatives will promise that their instrument will do everything you want it to do, but leave out some crucial information that might put their instrument at a disadvantage compared to a competitor's. Therefore, a realistic trial of the system in use with real samples and chemistries will separate the chaff from the wheat, and expose any dissembling from the manufacturers.

The main currently available real-time instruments are listed in **Table 8.1**, with a brief description below of the major ones.

In principle there are two options: to buy an Applied Biosystems' (ABI's) instrument or not. ABI are the leaders in the field, based mainly on the fact that they were the first manufacturer to launch a real-time instrument. ABI have built a vast reagents support network around their real-time instruments, with enzymes, kits, predeveloped primers and probes, and a general air of superiority that comes from having settled on (arguably) the best chemistry and (arguably) the best instruments. The ABI's systems are ideal for anyone interested in getting up and running using standard targets and who is willing to buy into the ABI vision of how real-time assays should be carried out. There is a price to pay, both in monetary as well as in practical terms. ABI's reagents are expensive, and substituting cheaper reagents may or may not result in inferior performance. If anything does go wrong, it is unlikely that ABI will be happy to troubleshoot an assay that used their instrument, but

Table 8.1. Real-Time Quantitative PCR Detection Systems.

Feature	Stratagene, Mx4000	ABI, Prism 7000	ABI, Prism 7700	ABI, 7900 HT	Bio-Rad, iCycler	Roche, Light Cycler	Cepheid, SmartCycler	Corbett Research, Rotor-Gene	MJ Research, DNA Engine Opticon
Excitation source	Quartz-Tungsten Halogen lamp	Tungsten Halogen lamp	Argon laser, 488 nm	Argon laser, 488 nm	Tungsten Halogen lamp	Blue LED	4 LEDs	4 LEDs	96 LEDs
Light Path	4 independent fiber optics w/scanning head, top/top fluorescence	Illuminate whole plate	Fiber Optics cables (96 cables).	Illuminate whole plate.	Illuminate whole plate w/ 2 focusing mirrors. Excites and reads through the top of the plate	Rodenstock optics, capillary tubes excited and read from the bottom	Illuminate whole plate. Excites and reads through the bottom of the tube	Excites and reads through the tube walls near the bottom, rotor system	Excites through bottom of plate and detects from above
Detector	4 photomultiplier tubes (PMT)	CCD	CCD	CCD	CCD	Photo Diode	4 Silicon photodetectors	4 PMTs	PMT
Wavelength separating	Independent filter channels	4-position filter wheel / Spectrograph	Spectrograph	Spectrograph	5-position filter wheel	Filter, Beam splitter	Filters	Filters	none
Sample scan system	Plate and optical system move on opposite axis	One scanning head	Multiplexer	One scanning head	All samples read simultaneously.	Carousel rotates under optical system.	Solid state, no movement	Rotor	All samples read simultaneously
Excitation wavelength	350–750 nm		488 nm (488–514 nm)	488 nm (488–514 nm)	400–700 nm— 5 filter positions available—2 filters provided (485 nm & 580 nm)	470 nm (range 450–670 nm)	< 495–593 nm— 4 channels within this range	470, 530, 585, and 625 nm	450–495 nm
Emission wavelength	350–830 nm		500–650 nm	500–660 nm	400–700 nm— 5 filter positions available—2 provided (535 nm & 620 nm)	530, 640, or 710 nm	505 to > 605 nm, 4 channels within this range	4 detection filters (510, 555, 610, 660 nm and 580, 610 nm high pass)	515–545 nm
Sample container	200 µl 96-well plates, 8 strip tubes, and individual tubes with optically clear caps	96-well format: plates, individual tubes or 8-tube strips with optically clear caps or sealing tape	96 well format: plates, individual tubes or 8-tube strips with optically clear caps or sealing tape	384-well plates with optically clear sealing tape, 96-well unit also available	96-well plates that can be broken down into 4-sampler plates with optical quality sealing tape	capillary tube, 32 samples	16 independently controlled reaction sites (tubes) per module, up to 6 modules can be used, takes specific 25 or 100 µl tubes with optically clear bottoms	36- and 72-well rotors, standard 0.2 ml tubes and 0.1 ml strip tubes	96-well format: plates, individual 200 µl tubes or 8-tube strips with optically clear caps

Continued on next page

Table 8.1—continued

Feature	Stratagene, Mx4000	ABI, Prism 7000	ABI, Prism 7700	ABI, 7900 HT	Bio-Rad, iCycler	Roche, Light Cycler	Cepheid, SmartCycler	Corbett Research, Rotor-Gene	MJ Research, DNA Engine Opticon
Sample volume	10–50 µl	10–50 µl	50 µl (the instrument support volume range (10–50 µl)	5–20 µl	10–50 µl	5–20 µl	25–50 µl	0.1–0.2 ml	10–50 µl
Reading time	96 wells: <7 seconds (30 ms/sample scan—3 reads in 21 s—averaged)	Full plate approximately once every 7 seconds (96 wells)	Full plate approximately once every 7 seconds (96 wells)	Full plate approximately once every 7 seconds (96 wells)	Whole sample plate illuminated and read at one time.	6.4 second for 32 samples (20 ms per capillary)			
Dynamic Range	9 orders of magnitude (5×10^9 copies titrated down to 5 copies)		5 orders of magnitude	5 orders of magnitude	6 orders of magnitude	9 orders of magnitude (10 to 10^{10} copies)		12 orders of magnitude	7 orders of magnitude
Temperature Uniformity	±0.25°C		±0.5°C	±0.5°C	±0.4°C	±0.3°C	±0.5°C	±0.01°C	±0.4°C
Temperature Accuracy	±0.25°C		±0.75°C	±0.25°C	±0.3°C	<±1.0°C		±0.5°C	±0.3°C
Temperature Ramp Rate	40 cycle PCR in less than 1.5 hours. Adjustable ramp rate from 0.1°C/s to 2.2°C/s. Default ramp rate is 2.0°C/s		40 cycle PCR in 2 hours, 1°C/s	In "9600" mode 1°C/s heating and cooling	Heating 3.3°C per second, cooling 2°C per second	~ 30 minutes for average PCR reaction, up to 20°C/s	Heating 10°C/s (max), Cooling 2.5°C/s (max), 40 cycle PCR in 20–42 min (depending on assay)	2.0°C/s	
Interface	RS-232		RS-232	RS485	RS-232 and LPT				
Power	Auto-sensing 100–240 V AC (±10%), 50–60 Hz, 1000 W		220 V	200/208 V, 50/60 Hz, 16 A, Max 3840 W 220/240 V, 50/60 Hz, 16 A, Max 3840 W	100–120 V AC, ±10%; 50–60 Hz, 8.0 A fuse 220–240 V AC, ±10%; 50–60 Hz, 4.0 A fuse Power = 670 W, 910 VA (max); 200 W (typical)	100–120 V or 220–230 V	100–240 V AC, 50–60 Hz, 350 W	100–120 V AC @ 5 A, 200–240 V AC @ 3 A (50/60 HZ)	

Continued on next page

Table 8.1—continued

Feature	Stratagene, Mx4000	ABI, Prism 7000	ABI, Prism 7700	ABI, 7900 HT	Bio-Rad, iCycler	Roche, Light Cycler	Cepheid, SmartCycler	Corbett Research, Rotor-Gene	MJ Research, DNA Engine Opticon
Physical Dimensions	30"(W) × 18"(D) × 20"(H)	15.25"(W) × 19.75"(D) × 20.75"(H)	37"(W) × 27"(D) × 24"(H)	28"(W) × 33"(D) × 25"(H) without automation accessory; 49"(W) × 33"(D) × 25"(H) with automation accessory	12.9" × 14" × 24.5" (thermal cycler w/ optical unit)	17.7"(W) × 15.7"(D) × 11.8"(H)	12"(W) × 10"(L) × 12"(H)—processing block (2.5 linear feet of bench space)	12.5"(W) × 17.3"(D) × 11"(H)	34 cm wide × 46 cm deep × 61 cm high
Weight	110 lb (50 kg)	75 lb (34 kg)	320 lb (146 kg)	70 lb (32 kg) without automation accessory; 250 lb (114 kg) with automation accessory	39 lb (17.6 kg)—thermal cycler w/ optical unit	44 lb (20 kg)	22 lb (10 kg)	33 lbs. (15 kg)	27 kg
Thermal cycler	Peltier w/ resistive heaters (patented process)	Peltier-based technology	Compressor-based technology	Peltier-based technology	Peltier/Joule-based technology	Heating coil and fan	Solid-state heater with forced air cooling	Centrifugal system	Peltier-based technology
Multiplexing	Yes—4 dyes	Yes	Yes	Yes	Yes—4 dyes	Two dyes—need color compensation kit	Yes—4 dyes	Yes—4 dyes	No
Real-Time monitoring	Yes	Yes	No	Yes	Yes	Yes	Yes	Yes	Yes
Support SYBR Green dye	Yes	Yes	Yes	Yes	Yes	Yes	Yes	Yes	Yes
Sensitivity	Supports two fold discrimination in starting copy number; < 1.49 ng FAM labeled beta-actin molecular beacon with 2 molar excess target (V = 50 l) above NTC background	Supports two-fold discrimination in starting copy number; can distinguish between 5,000 and 10,000 genomic equivalents with 99.7% confidence level	Supports two-fold discrimination in starting copy number; can distinguish between 5,000 and 10,000 genomic equivalents with 99.7% confidence level	Supports two-fold discrimination in starting copy number	Differentiate between 1,000 & 2,000 genomic equivalents		< 10 nm for FAM/TET/TAM/ROX		Detect down to one starting copy, < 5 nM Flourescein

reagents from several different sources. More frustratingly, ABI will only support TaqMan and SYBR Green chemistries and the detection software is designed for that purpose. Nevertheless, there can be no doubt that any ABI's instrument will be high on anyone's comparison list and, if the need is for a really high throughput system, only ABI supply a suitable machine.

There are several alternatives to ABI. The field is actually quite crowded, with instruments at every price point with many more sets to be launched in the near future.

8.2.1. ABI Prism® Systems

8.2.1.1. ABI 7300 and 7500 Real-Time PCR Systems

The laser-based ABI PRISM® 7700 has now been retired and ABI have launched two new models to replace the halogen-based 7000. One of the known, but not necessarily acknowledged problems with the 7000 was that the lamp's manufacturer, Gilway Technical Lamp, Woburn, Mass., quoted a life expectancy of only 200 h for its halogen lamp (*Cat. No. L6409 EKE 21V-150W*), and this has now been presumably remedied. Another inconvenience was that the software was designed for TaqMan or SYBR Green chemistries only and had be tweaked to permit three-step PCR protocols with data collection during the annealing step. The four-color detection 7300 is an updated 7000 instrument with a slightly smaller footprint (34 × 45 × 49 cm—W × D × H) and weight (29 kg) and significant enhancements to the software. This takes advantage of the Windows XP operating system, is now wizard-driven, and features an auto-baseline and threshold. It is still a 0.2-ml tube/96-well system with a tungsten-halogen lamp illuminating the samples through a single excitation filter. Fluorescence emission is detected through four emission filters recording fluorescence on to a CCD camera. The 7500 is a much more advanced system, passing light from a tungsten-halogen lamp through five excitation filters through the sample wells. This improves the ability to excite dyes at longer wavelengths, and is claimed to result in greater sensitivity and precision for dyes on the red side of the spectrum. Fluorescence emission is passed through five emission filters and detected by a CCD camera. The 7500's key selling point is an upgrade path (at additional cost, no doubt) to a high-speed thermal cycling block, which in combination with ABI's new master mix formulations promises significantly shorter real-time PCR runs. Both instruments promise to be workhorses in the mould of the ABI PRISM® 7700 and the 7000, with the immense advantage of using more user-friendly software.

8.2.1.2. ABI Prism® 7900

This is the ultimate, no-expense-spared high-throughput real-time PCR amplification and detection system with 384-well plate capability that in real-time mode can process more than 5,000 sample wells per day. This is more than ten times the throughput of any other instrument currently available. It can automate the process of loading plates and up to 84 (!) can be stacked up waiting to be processed. A 488 nm laser scans and excites the fluorescent dyes in each of the 384 wells with continuous wavelength detection from 500–660 nm. Fluorescence detection is via a spectrograph and cooled CCD camera.

8.2.2. Bio-Rad Instruments

8.2.2.1. iQCycler

The iQCycler real-time detection system is extremely compact (it has a footprint of $33 \times 62 \times 36$ cm (W × D × H)). The iCycler incorporates a Peltier-driven heating and cooling thermal cycler to which an independent optical module is attached. The optical unit consists of a fan-cooled halogen-based light source with optical filters that allow selection of specific wavelengths for excitation of fluorophores and emission of fluorescence. Light originates at the lamp, passes through an infrared absorbing glass heat filter and a five position interchangeable excitation filter and is reflected onto the 96-well plate in the thermal cycler by a complex set of mirrors, exciting the fluorophores in the wells. The detection system includes an emission filter wheel identical to the excitation filter and an image intensifier that uses technology developed for night vision. Fluorescence is detected using a 350,000-pixel array on a CCD, which allows simultaneous imaging of all 96 wells. There are several interesting features to this instrument:

1. Well factors are used to compensate automatically for optical system disuniformity or pipetting nonuniformity. They are calculated after cycling the filter wheels through all monitored positions while collecting light from a plate, which must be uniform. Sources can be either the experimental plate itself or they may be collected, less satisfactorily, indirectly from an external source plate. When collecting directly from the experimental plate the software inserts a 90-second step at the initial 95°C-step, during which each filter pair to be used in the experiment is briefly moved into position, and optical data are collected from the plate. Well factors are calculated and written to a separate file. Each monitored well must contain the same composition of fluorophores and within each dye layer the fluorophore must be present at the same concentration. However, the concentration between dye layers need not be the same.

   Note: A major disadvantage of this approach is that it is extremely cumbersome to optimize multiplex experiments accurately since this requires that all reactions are run as simplex and multiplex tests simultaneously.

   Note: With SYBR Green I, the fluorescence of the intercalator is not sufficiently high during the denaturation step to calculate statistically significant well factors. Use of SYBR Green Supermix (Bio-Rad, *Cat. No. 170-8880*) includes fluorescein, which results in sufficient fluorescence at 95°C to allow the calculation of dynamic well factors.

2. A thermal gradient (1–25°C) can be programmed across the thermal block, with the coolest temperature in row H and the hottest temperature in row A. All wells in each respective row are at the same temperature, so that there are eight different temperatures across the block with 12 wells at each temperature. This is very useful for optimizing PCR reaction conditions, though of little practical use for qPCR reactions, especially if they are to be multiplexed.

3. The simultaneous imaging of the iQCycler can be used to capture an image of an experimental plate to check the response of a probe or to assess the completion of a reaction. This is useful for checking that a probe has the correct fluorophore attached. However, although the experiment can be viewed in real time it is not possible to analyze the data until completion of the experiment.

The supplied software permits all the usual analyses, such as melting curves and allelic discrimination. Its multiplexing abilities are demonstrated in **Chapter 18**. As an overall package, the iQCycler is an attractive system and with Bio-Rad's image analysis pedigree results in a powerful instrument that has the advantage of being compact.

8.2.3. Stratagene's Instruments

8.2.3.1. Mx4000

The Mx4000 is a little less compact than the ABI 7000 or Bio-Rad iQCycler but makes up for this by incorporating its own computer within the instrument. All data are written to its integrated hard disk first and then downloaded to an external PC. This ensures that any problems with communication between the thermal cycler and an external computer are avoided and data from the current experiment is preserved. The system uses a quartz tungsten halogen lamp (life expectancy 2,000 h) to excite fluorescence in the 350 to 750 nm and four photomultiplier tubes for detection in the 350 nm to 830 nm range allowing the use of all dyes from Alexa 350 to Cy7. This instrument has been designed very much with multiplexing in mind, and each of the four scanning fiberoptic heads independently excites and detects dyes, reading up to four dyes in a single tube. Its excitation and emission filters are slightly offset from the peak excitation and emission wavelengths of the matched fluorophore. This offset aids in limiting leakage of fluorescence from adjacent dyes, thereby minimizing background and crosstalk while enhancing dye discrimination. Since these filters are easily changed by the user and can even be mismatched when used this provides the ultimate in flexibility of fluorescence detection.

The scanning approach results in good uniformity of the optical system thus obviating the requirement for any optical correction approaches. The result of this is that it is not necessary to use preassay plate calibration factors, or reference dye (ROX) incorporation for any assays. The format of the software provides a welcome emphasis on displaying raw, uncorrected machine collected data, i.e., not beautified, algorithm-modified data. This allows powerful troubleshooting and increases the flexibility of the instrument. The absolute linearity of detection and filter flexibility also allows the system to be used for all fluorimeter applications including Enzyme activity studies measured by monitoring the release of ANC after cleavage of the enzyme specific substrate. Using the Mx4000 with Alexa 350 filters fitted the release of ANC is detected by excitation at 350 nm and detection of free cleavage product at 460 nm. These assays can be assessed either as end-point reading (as in a fluorimeter) or in real-time to ensure that only data from the linear phase of enzyme activity is used. Similarly, GFP protein and RNA or DNA nucleic acid templates stained with Ribogreen™ or Picogreen™ can be detected and quantified.

The thermal cycler itself is a hybrid consisting of Peltier, resistive and convective technologies that result in improved temperature uniformity across the whole plate and reduced over- or undershooting of set temperatures.

The software has some powerful features that make it user friendly for the beginner and yet flexible and fully informative for the connoisseur. Thermal profiles are not restricted to default settings, data can be selected at any stage and all selected data choices can be viewed in real time. In addition, all data can also be fully analyzed at any stage of the experiment, a particularly useful feature for impatient scientists. Quantitative data can be analyzed either with respect to standard curves or by using comparative quantification. All the usual analysis options are available including allelic discrimination/SNPs, melting curve, or even access to raw data as amplification plots or even as every data point collected from each well for each dye. As a complete system the software enables post analysis exports of all data charts directly into PowerPoint or as image files. This means that the process of experiment set up to manuscript or slides for presentation can be as little as 3 hours! As with Corbett, the software is designed and written in-house by Stratagene Inc. and so regular upgrades are provided which incorporate user requests.

8.2.3.2 Mx3000P

The Mx3000P differs from the Mx4000 in that it is a much smaller (19kg, 13" (33 cm) W × 18" (46cm) D × 17" (43 cm) H) and has a simpler instrument design. This system has a filter wheel arrangement with four filters matched for excitation and emission. Scanning of each dye is sequential and data is detected by a single PMT. However, in other respects the instruments are similar, including an independent internal PC to run the machine and prevent data loss due to computer failures. Both machines use identical operating software allowing files from either system to be analysed using a common program. Although a tremendously low-cost system, the data are remarkable, detecting around 9 logs dynamic range with excellent reproducibility across the block. Overall, this is a carefully designed, fully featured qPCR system.

8.2.4. Corbett Research Rotor-Gene RG-3000

The Rotor-Gene RG-3000 is another instrument designed for multiplexing and can detect all current real-time chemistries. The instrument unit uses a 72-well rotor that can run special 0.1 ml strip tubes in strips of four. During the run the rotor spins at approximately 500 rpm as the tubes are thermally cycled in a low-mass air oven. This removes the need for temperature equilibrium time and results in shorter hold times, with temperature uniformity claimed to be better than with conventional systems.

As the sample tubes spin past the detector modules, a high powered LED strobes the sample and a Hamamatsu photomultiplier (PMT) collects the fluorescent energy. These data are sent to a Laptop or Desktop PC that averages the energy of each sample over a number of revolutions. These data are displayed in real-time on the screen as fluorescence versus cycle number or temperature plot.

The Rotor-Gene uses LEDs that can excite fluorophores at 470, 530, 585, and 625 nm. This allows for multiplexed samples to be run. The LEDs irradiate the tube from the sidewall and the photomultiplier detects the energy from the base of the chamber. The detection filter wheel has six detection filters between 510 and 660 nm placed on a filter wheel. High-pass filters transmit light at and above the specified filter designation, allowing for an increase in sensitivity during certain applications. The Rotor-Gene is calibrated for sample volumes of 20 to 25 µl, though lower volumes are possible with a recommended denaturation time during cycling of 15 seconds. The instrument is compact ($32 \times 44 \times 28$ cm (W $\times$ D $\times$ H)) and light (15 kg) and the software supplied makes extensive use of Microsoft Wizards, although its user-friendliness is not quite on a par with Stratagene's. Corbett Research take great care to incorporate customer's suggestions and requirements into their upgrades, and software upgrades are freely available from their website.

There are several interesting features of their analysis software:

1. *The quenched FRET analysis.* FRET analysis normally measures the energy transferred from one probe to another after excitation (e.g., LightCycler LC640 and LC705 dyes). Quenched FRET looks at the decrease in energy of only one donor probe, hence uses less spectral bandwidth per probe set. This is useful for mutation analysis, as four different alleles can be multiplexed without crosstalk.

2. *Another useful feature is the Dynamic Tube option.* This is used to determine the average background of each individual sample just before amplification commences. Standard Normalization simply takes the first 5–12 cycles and uses this as an indicator for the "background" level of each sample. All data points for the sample are then divided by this value to normalize the data. This process is then repeated for all samples. This can be inaccurate as for some samples the background level over the first five cycles may not be indicative of the background level just prior to amplification. Dynamic Tube Normalization uses the second derivative of each sample trace to determine a starting point for each sample. The background level is then averaged from cycle 1 up to this starting cycle number for each sample. The first couple of cycles in a quantification run are not usually representative of the rest of the experiment. For this reason, better results can be obtained if the first few cycles are ignored (up to 10 cycles can be ignored). On the other hand, if the first cycles look similar to the subsequent ones, more accurate results will be obtained by disabling this function, as the normalization algorithm will have more data to work with. All analyses can be performed while the Rotor-Gene is running.

One ground-breaking development is the introduction of the CAS-1200 robotic liquid handling system, a compact ($32 \times 44 \times 28$ cm (W × D × H)) and fairly light (20 kg) instrument, to provide a precise and labor saving means for setting up PCR reactions. The instrument is highly configurable and can be programmed to set up a variety of reactions at the same time. It is capable of preparing multiple Master Mixes, standard dilutions, and using separate groups of samples. The reproducibility of pipetting is at least twice as good as compared to manual pipetting (**Fig. 8.2**).

For maximum precision CAS-1200 uses graphite-impregnated tips, which enable liquid level sensing. The tip moves to just below the surface of the liquid rather than the bottom of the tube preventing carry over of material on the outside of the tip. CAS-1200 software provides a user

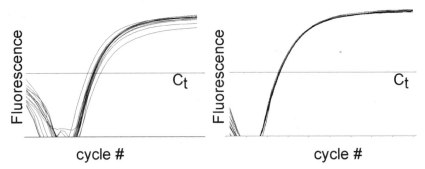

Figure 8.2. Amplification plots demonstrating the superior reproducibility of robotic vs. manual pipetting.

friendly, easy to follow user interface. The screen layout corresponds to the hardware setup of the robot. The status of any component can be examined by clicking it on the screen. Hovering the cursor above a well gives a description and highlights the destination of its contents. Likewise, any alterations are executed by simply pointing to the corresponding aspect of the hardware on the screen and changing the desired parameters.

The progress of a run can be followed in real time. The software highlights the position of the pipette head on the screen as it moves. A progress bar and an update table also follow the course of a run. Reports are generated before and after a run and are automatically saved for future reference. Laborious calculations are unnecessary as the software calculates the amount of Master Mix necessary for the run. CAS-1200 software can also be run in virtual mode. Runs can be set up, that progress followed and templates were stored even if the robot is switched off or not connected. It is possible therefore, to configure runs at a remote location. Virtual mode is also a useful tutorial tool. It is extremely good value for money, especially when bought in conjunction with the Rotor-Gene.

New developments for the Rotor-Gene RG-3000:

1. The RG-3000 has the ability to acquire data in just one revolution of the rotor, 150 ms for 72 samples; this feature enables it to capture melt data during the cycling process at high speed. Corbett Research have also developed a new cycling method for which they have coined the phrase "optical denaturation." An amplified sample containing SYBR Green I is used as a denaturation refer-

ence. Following the initial hold at 95°C for 3–10 minutes, the annealing step at 60°C is reduced to 40 seconds; after the first annealing step an optodenaturation command is issued, which applies full heater power and monitors the reference sample at high speed. As soon as the sample is seen to denature, the power is turned off and the system is cooled back to the annealing temperature. This approach is only possible on the Rotor-Gene as all samples have an identical dynamic temperature profile; therefore when the reference denatures, all samples also denature. This process has the advantage that different amplicons do not necessarily require denaturation at 94–95°C for 15 seconds as is standard for most block style cyclers. Instead the temperature is now dependent on the length of amplicon, the sequence, and the volume, so the denaturation conditions are automatically determined by the optical feedback of the system and not the user. This allows for faster run times and minimizes the thermal stress placed upon the enzyme.

2. Optical Temperature Calibration Rotor. The RG-3000 can be used in conjunction with a new optical calibration rotor that uses special thermally sensitive samples that result in a melt peak at defined temperatures 50°C, 70°C, and 95°C. These peaks are sharp and accurate to ±0.2°C and allow for the RG-3000 to be calibrated remotely without the need for a service technician. This is a major advantage in diagnostic laboratories where temperature performance must be validated on a regular basis. If the RG-3000 were to have drifted in temperature specification, then the software can automatically correct for the variation, recalibrate the machine and issue a temperature calibration report.

3. Corbett Research have developed a 72-well disposable rotor that can be loaded automatically by the CAS-1200 robot; it is then sealed with caps or heat sealed, placed directly into the Rotor-Gene and run.

8.2.5. Roche Applied Science

8.2.5.1. LightCycler™

The LightCycler instrument combines a microvolume fluorimeter with one of the fastest thermal cycler available.[4] There are two reasons for its speed: (1) Heating and cooling are controlled by alternating heated and ambient air as the medium for temperature transfer. Due to its low mass, very rapid temperature exchange rates can be achieved within the thermal chamber. (2) This instrument uses glass capillaries as reaction vessels. Because of the high ratio of surface area to volume of these capillaries, they are highly efficient at transferring heat, permitting rapid cycling conditions.[5] In addition, the glass capillary serves as an optical element for signal collection, piping the light, and concentrating the signal at the tip of the capillary. The effect is efficient illumination and fluorescent monitoring of microvolume samples containing as little as 5 µl of reaction mixture that are centrifuged into the tips of the composite glass/plastic reaction vessel.[6] Performance of the LightCycler is not sacrificed for speed: its sensitivity and specificity are equal to that of the ABI 7700.[7] However, there may be some problems in the real world with this arrangement.[8]

The instrument can handle 32 samples placed in a carousel at any one time. The carousel is rotated past a blue LED, and the emitted light is filtered and focused onto the capillary tip. Fluorescent light emitted from the sample is then passed through a dichroic mirror and is read by three photodetection diodes with three bandpass filters (530 nm, 640 nm, and 710 nm) that allow the use of spectrally distinct fluorescent probes.[9] Signals are obtained as the machine positions the capillaries sequentially over the optical unit (fluorescence acquisition time is 10–100 ms) and data can be collected once per cycle, continuously or stepwise after defined temperature intervals.

8.2.5.2. LightCycler® 2

The LightCycler 2 is the most recent qPCR system from Roche and has been developed as a progression of the original LightCycler concept. This system has 6 detection channels to monitor emission at 530, 560, 610, 640, 670, and 710 nm and is compatible with all detection chemistries. Two capillary sizes are available 100 µl and 20 µl to allow alternative reaction volumes to be used. As with the LightCycler, PCR can be performed rapidly and with good homogeneity in the air heated and cooled environment. New software has also been developed for this system, incorporating a relative quantification option, grouping of melting curves and automatic calling of melting temperatures. It is marketed as greatly improved over previous version in that it is more user-friendly and has simplified data management.

8.2.6. Techne Quantica

This attractively styled compact instrument (Footprint 50 × 45cm—Weight 25 kg) uses a standard 96-well plate format with optical heat sealed film together with a solid-state white light source for fluorophore excitation (range 470 nm to 650 nm) and detection by PMT (range 500 nm to 710 nm). The block uniformity at 50°C is ±0.3°C and the manufacturers claim very high sample-to-sample uniformity and experimental reproducibility, with a coefficient of variation of 5–8%. A thermal gradient can be programmed across the block, with a maximum gradient of 30°C (between 20 and 70°C). It is capable of very rapid cycling, with ramp rates of up to 3°C/s. It can perform all current chemistries, and the application software is based on Microsoft "Wizards," similar to the Rotor-Gene. There are two models available—one a single channel, the other a dual channel instrument with enhanced read time capability. Multiplexing is possible using up to four paired excitation and emission filters.

8.2.7. Cepheid Smart Cycler®

The Smart Cycler is based on the company's I-CORE® (Intelligent Cooling/Heating Optical Reaction) technology, which uses sixteen individual modules that incorporate a state-of-the-art microfluidics and microelectronic design based. The individual temperature control, together with proprietary sealable reaction tubes, permits each sample to be subjected to different experimental conditions. This offers "random access" capability that can speed up assay optimization by allowing researchers to operate each reaction site independently of the others. This allows up to sixteen different cycling protocols to be performed at the same time, and multiple experiments can be started at different time, allowing several operators to use the instrument concurrently. Each I-CORE unit has its own optical subsystem, which is capable of four-channel detection and can quantitate up to four targets in one reaction tube. The Smart Cycler software enables single or multiple operators to define and simultaneously carry out any number of separate experiments, each with a unique set of cycling protocols, threshold criteria, and data analysis.

Several other instruments are available, with more detailed information on the web, including a portable, battery-powered device.[10]

8.3. Outlook

It seems likely that the instrument market will follow two paths: One
will result in ever-higher throughput instruments, linked to robots, that
are housed in core facilities and run standard assays 24 hours long.
A second path will result in personal real-time instruments that will be
miniaturized and sit on the researcher's bench, allowing to tweak reaction conditions, use a variety of chemistries, and carry out real-time
analyses at researcher's convenience.

Relevant Websites

http://www.roche-applied-science.com/no_cache/lightcycler.cfm
http://www.lightcycler-online.com/
http://www.techneusa.com/Molecular/quantica.htm
http://www.smartcycler.com/
http://www.mjr.com/html/instruments/opticon/
http://www.corbettresearch.com/index2.php
http://home.appliedbiosystems.com/
http://www.stratagene.com

Survey of real-time thermal cyclers:

http://www.the-scientist.com/yr2001/dec/profile_011210.html

Filters:

http://www.jyhoriba.co.uk/indexfilters.htm
http://www.omegafilters.com/products/fluorescence/

PMT:

http://www.hamamatsu.com/

References

1. Linz U: **Thermocycler temperature variation invalidates PCR results.**
   Biotechniques 1990, **9**:286, 288, 290–293.

2. Wilhelm J, Hahn M, Pingoud A: **Influence of DNA target melting behavior on real-time PCR quantification.** *Clin Chem* 2000, **46**:1738–1743.

3. Stamm S, Gillo B, Brosius J: **Temperature recording from thermocyclers used for PCR.** *Biotechniques* 1991, **10**:430–435.

4. Wittwer CT, Fillmore GC, Hillyard DR: **Automated polymerase chain reaction in capillary tubes with hot air.** *Nucleic Acids Res* 1989, **17**:4353–4357.

5. Wittwer CT, Garling DJ: **Rapid cycle DNA amplification: Time and temperature optimization.** *Biotechniques* 1991, **10**:76–83.

6. Wittwer CT, Fillmore GC, Garling DJ: **Minimizing the time required for DNA amplification by efficient heat transfer to small samples.** *Anal Biochem* 1990, **186**:328–331.

7. Nitsche A, Steuer N, Schmidt CA, Landt O, Siegert W: **Different real-time PCR formats compared for the quantitative detection of human cytomegalovirus DNA.** *Clin Chem* 1999, **45**:1932–1937.

8. Zuna J, Muzikova K, Madzo J, Krejci O, Trka J: **Temperature non-homogeneity in rapid airflow-based cycler significantly affects real-time PCR.** *Biotechniques* 2002, **33**:508, 510, 512.

9. Wittwer CT, Ririe KM, Andrew RV, David DA, Gundry RA, Balis UJ: **The LightCycler: A microvolume multisample fluorimeter with rapid temperature control.** *Biotechniques* 1997, **22**:176–181.

10. Belgrader P, Young S, Yuan B, Primeau M, Christel LA, Pourahmadi F, Northrup MA: **A battery-powered notebook thermal cycler for rapid multiplex real-time PCR analysis.** *Anal Chem* 2001, **73**:286–289.

9

Basic RT-PCR Considerations

Stephen A. Bustin and Tania Nolan

9

Basic RT-PCR Considerations

Stephen A. Bustin[*] and Tania Nolan[†]

*Barts and The London, Queen Mary's School of Medicine
and Dentistry, University of London, London, United Kingdom
†Stratagene Europe, Amsterdam, The Netherlands*

9.1. Introduction

It is quite remarkable that the seemingly minor step of converting an mRNA template into cDNA prior to the PCR reaction transforms the RT-PCR assay into a byword for lack of reproducibility and precision (**Fig. 9.1**). However, the difficulties inherent in conventional RT-PCR assays have been pointed out from the very beginning,[1] with numerous studies highlighting more than a few problems, such as sample processing,[2] suitability of internal controls,[3] standardization of the technique, and quality control management.[4,5] These often combine to make the

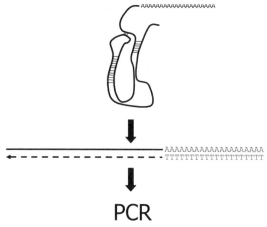

PCR

Figure 9.1. The principle of reverse transcription.

resulting data unreliable[6-8] and have hindered the technique's translation from research use into a practical diagnostic tool.[9-11] These problems are not confined to conventional RT-PCR assays and indeed they persist in real-time RT-PCR studies and since the expectations have become that much greater, have become particularly challenging.

Conventional RT-PCR can be used to demonstrate beyond doubt the presence or absence of target mRNA in the tissue or cells under investigation. However, problems started to appear when quantification reared its head only four years after the invention of the PCR[12] and qualitative answers were no longer deemed sufficient.[13,14] Numerous variations on the theme of competitive PCR were invented, with the claim that it was possible to quantitate mRNA levels not just accurately, but also reproducibly.[15] All these methods had one thing in common: they were exceedingly tedious to perform, requiring endless optimizations, comparisons, and resyntheses of primers and/or amplicons until some condition believed to indicate quantitative amplification could be achieved. In practice, these methods were applied to quantification of steady-state mRNA levels and, not surprisingly resulted in the publication of numerous papers often reporting contradictory results. Far from being due to slapdash technique, this was caused by inherent problems with reproducibility of conventional RT-PCR assays. This subject has been dealt with in great detail, and anyone interested to know why they should be cautious when interpreting conventional quantitative RT-PCR data, should read one of the several reviews that deal with this subject.[15-17]

The introduction of real-time chemistries was supposed to solve all problems associated with conventional PCR. Use of a probe would increase the specificity making Southern blot analyses and DNA sequencing of amplicons unnecessary. Use of fluorescent dyes would allow the amplification and analysis step to be combined in a homogeneous assay, thus making the assay rapid (no more post-PCR processing), precise (the instrument and software would calculate accurate copy numbers), and truly quantitative (use of internal or external standards). In real-life, this has not happened. This is not to deny that real-time RT-PCR is a revolutionary advance on conventional RT-PCR. Quite the opposite! However, it is crucial not to lose sight of the real, severe, and numerous complications that remain associated with the reverse transcription step and that make biologically meaningful quantification of steady-state mRNA copy numbers at best difficult and at worst pointless. Just as an example, the resolving power of RT-PCR is limited by the efficiency of RNA-to-cDNA conversion, which depends on the enzyme used. However, the conversion efficiency is significantly (more than 3-fold) lower when target templates are rare and it is negatively affected by nonspecific or background RNA present in the RT reaction.[18]

In this chapter the events of the RT step are dissected into the various critical components that must be considered if the RT-PCR assay is ever to become a reliable molecular technique.

9.2. Total RNA versus mRNA

The first decision to be made is whether to use mRNA or total RNA as the target for the RT-PCR assay. The perception is that if maximum sensitivity is required, then mRNA is the preferred choice,[2] and a recent report shows that the effects of background RNA are noticeable when only very small numbers of RNA template are available for conversion to cDNA. On the other hand, this inhibitory effect is absent when larger amounts of RNA template are available.[18] Since the conversion efficiency of RT enzymes is very low (in the region of 6%) with low copy number targets, one could argue that quantification of such low copy numbers is not reliable anyway and that the presence or absence of total RNA will not make much difference to the end result.

Most RT-PCR protocols use total RNA and there are several reasons for this:

- Purification of mRNA involves an additional step and the increased sensitivity could be balanced by the possible loss of material.

- Not all mRNA molecules have polyA tails.

- Normalization against total or rRNA is not possible when using mRNA.

- The concentration of mRNA may be insufficient to allow quality assessment using the RNAChip and the Agilent 2100.

On balance, in most instances it is advisable to use total RNA, as the sensitivity of the qRT-PCR assay is likely to be determined by several factors in addition to whether mRNA or total RNA was used in the first place.

Note: Sometimes there is so little material to start off with, that a preamplification step needs to be carried out. The use of "Switch Mechanism at the 5' end of Reverse Transcript" (SMART™) amplification has recently been validated by real-time RT-PCR and shown to maintain the expression profile of mRNA.[19]

9.3. Priming

The second decision in the RT experimental design concerns the priming of the cDNA reaction from the RNA. This can be done using random primers, oligo-dT, or target sequence specific primers. Each of the three methods differ significantly with respect to cDNA yield and variety as well as specificity and, since the choice of primer can cause marked variation in calculated mRNA copy numbers,[20] the implications of using any particular method should be considered carefully.[21] It is worth pointing out that the T_m of both random primers and oligo-dT is well below the optimum temperature of thermostable RTs, hence neither can be used with thermostable RT enzymes without some low temperature preincubation step.

Ambion have shown that unintended endogenous priming can occur regardless of which primers are used to prime the RT reaction. They performed ^{32}P-labeled standard AMV, MMLV, and RNaseH⁻ MMLV reverse transcription reactions with or without added primers. The product of these paired reactions appears identical regardless of whether or not primers were present. This demonstrates that virtually all the cDNA in these reactions was synthesized by endogenous random priming. The result is typical for reactions performed with any

AMV or MMLV reverse transcriptase under standard reaction conditions (http://www.ambion.com/catalog/CatNum.php?1740). Such nonspecific priming can lead to lowered and/or variable signal in the subsequent PCR assay, although how much of a problem this is in real-life remains unclear. Not surprisingly, Ambion's EndoFree RT kit (*Cat. No. 1740*) addresses this problem.

9.3.1. Random Primers

Random primers prime reverse transcription at multiple points along the transcript, therefore produce more than one cDNA transcript per original target. Hence this method is by definition, nonspecific, but yields the most cDNA and is most useful for transcripts with significant secondary structure. First-strand cDNA synthesis with random primers should be conducted at room temperature. However, the majority of cDNA synthesized from total RNA will be ribosomal RNA-derived. This could create real problems if the target of interest is present at low levels, as it may not be primed effectively by random primers and its amplification may not be quantitative. Indeed, it has been demonstrated that random hexamers can overestimate mRNA copy numbers by up to 19-fold compared with a sequence-specific primer.[20]

9.3.2. Oligo-dT

cDNA synthesis using oligo-dT is more specific to mRNA than random priming, as it will not transcribe rRNA. It is the best method to use when the aim is to obtain a faithful cDNA representation of the mRNA pool, although obviously it will not prime any RNA molecule that lacks a polyA tail, e.g., those specifying histones or viral RNAs. However, oligo-dT priming requires very high-quality RNA that is full length, hence is not a good choice for transcribing RNA that is likely to be fragmented, such as that typically obtained from LCM tissue or from archival material. Furthermore, the RT may fail to reach the primer probe binding site if secondary structures exist that impede its processivity or if the primer/probe binding site is at the extreme 5' end of a long mRNA. This may be the case if the mRNAs contains a very long untranslated 3' region (UTR) or if splice variants differs at the 5' end of the mRNA (e.g., the MHC class II transactivator isoforms I, III, and IV).

9.3.3. Target-Specific Primers

Target-specific primers synthesize the most specific cDNA and are the recommended and most sensitive option for quantification.[21] The main disadvantage of this method is that it requires separate priming reactions for each target; hence is not possible to return to the same preparation and amplify other targets at a later stage. It is also wasteful if only limited amounts of RNA are available.

9.4. Choice of Enzyme

Since RNA cannot serve as a template for PCR, the first step in an RT-PCR assay is the reverse transcription of the RNA template into cDNA. Although there is a large selection of reverse transcriptases to choose from (see **Table 9.1**), there are several problems associated with these enzymes: All have a relatively high error rate, and some have low thermal stability and/or a strong tendency to produce truncated cDNA products because of pausing. Thermal stability is a particular problem as the significant secondary structure of RNA transcripts[22] requires their denaturation for efficient reverse transcription.[23-25] In one experiment, the secondary structure of human tumor necrosis factor receptor I (TNFR-I) mRNA was predicted based on its lowest folding energy and three combinations of primers selected from open regions and four combinations of primers from closed regions were used for single-step RT-PCR.[26] The different primers generated distinct quantities of RT-PCR products from the same concentration of TNFR-I mRNA, implying that the determination of gene expression by RT-PCR was affected by the mRNA secondary structure. In addition, the sensitivity of the open-region RT-PCR was approximately one hundred-fold higher than that in the closed regions of TNFR-I mRNA. The low efficiency of the closed-region RT-PCR was not correlated with the G/C content of the TNFR-I mRNA structure. These results suggest that consideration of the influence of intrinsic mRNA structure of a gene is essential prior to the determination of mRNA expression by quantitative RT-PCR. This has resulted in extensive research to improve these enzymes and find new ones and, consequently, there are many enzymes to choose from. It is also worth bear-

Table 9.1. RT Enzymes.

Enzyme	Supplier	T_{opt} (°C)	RNaseH	Features
AMV-RT	Various	37	+++	
MMLV-RT	Various	45	+	
Omniscript	Qiagen	37	+	Not AMV- or MMLV-derived
Sensiscript	Qiagen	37	+	Not AMV- or MMLV-derived
Powerscript	Clontech	42	−	
Superscript II	Invitrogen	42–50	−	
StrataScript	Stratagene	42	−	Point mutation in RNaseH domain of MMLV-RT
ImProm-II	Promega	55	−	
MMLV PM	Promega	42–55	−	Point mutation in RNaseH domain of MMLV-RT
Tfl pol	Promega	60–72	−	one tube/one enzyme RT-PCR
Tth pol	Various	60–72	−	one tube/one enzyme RT-PCR
Expand RT	Roche	42	−	Point mutation in RNaseH domain of MMLV-RT
RevertAid	Fermentas	42–45	−	Point mutation in RNaseH domain of MMLV-RT
Thermoscript	Invitrogen	50–65	−	

ing in mind that the RT step can display sequence-specific inefficiency with particular amplicons and if the C_ts are consistently low, it may be necessary to check the efficiency of the RT step and change enzymes.

9.4.1. RT Properties

- Processivity

  This is not a problem for the small amplicons that are typical of real-time RT-PCR assays, especially when using random or specific primers.

- Fidelity

  Retroviral RTs are error-prone as they do not contain a 3'–5' proof-reading activity, their affinities for paired or mispaired primer termini are similar[27] but the extension of mispaired termini proceeding 20–700-fold faster than the rate of dissociation from the primer-template.[28] Fidelity is not necessarily a problem with qRT-PCR assays, since the amplicons are short and the product is discarded after the assay. However, there is a direct relationship between fidelity and processivity.[29] Templates can contain termination[30] or pausing[31] sites where the RT is likely to terminate or at least pause its processive synthesis.[32] Some termination sites are associated with secondary structure, but it is interesting, and from the point of view of a qPCR assay relevant, that many are sequence-related, with template A the strongest terminator residue.[33] Problems with the RT reaction may be caused by the primer inadvertently being located at or near a sequence-specific termination/pause site and could be solved by choosing a different first strand primer. The Mn^{2+} ions required for the RT activity of DNA-dependent DNA polymerases such as *Tth* are known to reduce enzyme fidelity.[34,35]

- Sensitivity and specificity

  RTs have differing abilities to copy small amounts of template (sensitivity). RNA transcripts often exhibit significant secondary structure, which slows or stops the ability of the RT to generate transcripts.[23,36,37] RTs also differ in their ability to transcribe RNA secondary structures accurately (specificity).

- Thermal stability

  Increasing the reaction temperature to $50°C$[38] or $55°C$,[39] depending on the RT, greatly enhances both the accuracy and the processivity of retroviral RTs. This concept can be taken a stage further by carrying out the RT step using a thermostable RT at as high a temperature as is possible without denaturing the RNA. RNA secondary structure is less of a problem, as the intra- and intermolecular base pairing is reduced and false priming is minimized, resulting in improved specificity. On the other hand, oligo-dT or random hexamers will not hybridize and initiate priming from the RNA. Secondary structures in mRNA can have at least two effects: (1) they can cause early termination during the synthesis of cDNA and (2) they can cause the RT to skip over the secondary structure and continue RNA synthesis without termination.[40] Both are more likely to occur at $42°C$ than at $60°C$. Since secondary structures in RNA differentially affect the abilities of different RTs to transcribe different transcripts,[22] this will affect the reliability of qPCR s. Early termination of cDNA may result in underestimation of target mRNA levels and skipping may delete a primer or probe hybridization site from the target mRNA. In either case, quantification would be unreliable and inaccurate. Therefore, G/C-rich templates are best reverse transcribed using thermostable RTs.

- RNase H activity

  RNase H activity degrades RNA in an RNA:cDNA hybrid and can be a problem if the RNA hydrolysis competes with cDNA synthesis. Even reduced RNase H activity can interfere with the synthesis of cDNA.[41] However, as always things are not quite as simple. RNase H[-ve] RT can limit the sensitivity of qRT-PCR detection since the undegraded RNA template can bind to the newly synthesized cDNA and restrict its accessibility to primers during subsequent PCR amplification. This effect may be gene-specific, as it is apparent only for some genes and can be relieved to a certain degree by extensive denaturation conditions (97°C and longer denaturation times).[42] For such templates, RNase H-mediated destruction of the template can prevent this problem and improve the sensitivity of qRT-PCR analysis.

- Divalent ion requirement

  Most reverse transcriptases require a divalent ion for activity. Enzymes that use Mg^{2+} are likely to produce more accurate cDNA copies than those that use Mn^{2+}, since Mn^{2+} adversely affects the fidelity of DNA synthesis.

- Additives

  The use of additives such as betaine or trehalose is designed to optimize the efficiency of the RT step by increasing the specificity and thermostability of the enzyme and/or by resolving the secondary structure of the RNA template. Their real effect remains unclear, though, because these additives behave differently with different enzymes, templates and reaction conditions. Therefore, their use cannot be recommended globally; instead, it is recommended to use them to enhance the RT step only as a last resort since their varied effects are likely to result in poorly reproducible quantification:

  1. *Trehalose:* Following the discovery that *in vitro* trehalose protects some enzymes against heat inactivation,[43] this non-reducing disaccharide used at 0.6 M in the presence of 15% glycerol was shown to not just maintain but actually increase the enzy-

matic activity of MMLV-RT at 60°C.[44] Total yield of a 10 kb transcript was significantly increased and early termination was significantly reduced. The relevance of this for qPCR, which typically amplifies a 60–100 bp amplicon, is unclear, although if the amplicon were to contain a termination site it is conceivable that the trehalose might have a beneficial effect. Another effect of trehalose is its apparent ability to increase the specificity of oligonucleotide-dT priming by Superscript II.[45] Extrapolation of this result suggests that addition of trehalose to mutant–allele-specific qPCR assays should improve the specificity of the assay, since trehalose should suppress extension from the mismatched primer. However, the validity of this extrapolation remains unproven.

2. ***Betaine (trimethylglycerine)*** is a naturally occurring methyl group donor and its natural function is as an osmoprotectant.[46] It can bind and stabilize A/T-base pairs and may decrease the melting temperature of DNA by reducing the thermal stability of G/C-base pairs.[47] It has been used successfully to improve the efficiency of conventional PCR assays and to increase the tolerance of the assay to inhibition by heparin[48] and reduce recombination events during PCR assays using internal standards.[49,50] Recently, a combination of 2 M betaine and 0.6 M trehalose has been reported as optimal for increasing the average size of cDNA synthesized using MMLV-RT and for reducing the number of stop sites in the transcript.[51] One problem with these additives is that the various reports recommend different optimal concentrations. This probably suggests that the effects are template and amplicon dependent and that careful titration and optimization of their concentration prior to any assay is required for these additives to have any positive effects. This is especially so because adding too much has an inhibitory effect.[51]

9.4.2. AMV-RT

Avian myeloblastosis virus (AMV) RT can polymerize DNA from either RNA or DNA templates[52,53] using DNA primers, with octamers and above more effective than hexamers. It is made up of subunits,[54,55] with the alpha subunit the most active in the single-strand cDNA-directed synthesis of double-strand DNA.[56] Sodium pyrophosphate and spermidine help drive the DNA polymerase activity forward and denature RNA secondary structure, respectively.[57] AMV-RT is noncompetitively inhibited by tRNAs that bind reversibly and randomly and do not alter the affinity of RNA for the polymerase. In contrast, rRNA binding to AMV-RT decreases the affinity of the RNA for the enzyme.[58] It is more robust, exhibits greater processivity than Moloney murine leukemia virus (MMLV) RT,[22] and retains significant polymerization activity up to 55°C,[38] although it is usually used at 42°C in two-step RT-PCR. Its error rate is 4.9×10^{-4} based on misincorporation studies.[59] Life Technologies offers the ThermoScript™ RT, a recombinant, genetically engineered AMV RNase H^{-ve} RT with increased thermal stability compared with standard AMV-RT. This allows reactions to be run at temperatures up to 65°C to generate long cDNA transcripts. Numerous other suppliers also offer modified AMV-RT variants for generating long cDNAs.

9.4.3. MMLV-RT

Native MMLV-RT has significantly less RNase H activity than native AMV-RT,[60] but is less thermostable and is typically used at 37°C. RNA can act as a primer, but DNA primers of 9–15 bases are optimal for priming polymerization of DNA from DNA or RNA templates.[61] The error rate is slightly higher than that of AMV-RT.[59] Following the separation of the polymerization and RNase H domains,[24,60,62] several modified MMLV-RT-derived enzymes have been introduced that offer higher efficiency and improved synthesis of cDNA. PowerScript™ RT (Clontech) and SuperScript™ II (Invitrogen) are derived from MMLV-RT and lack any RNaseH activity, Promega Corp. (Madison, Wis.), New England Biolabs (Beverly, Mass.), Stratagene (La Jolla, Calif.), and Epicentre (Madison, Wis.) also offer RNase H-Minus variants of MMLV-RT. THERMO-RT™ (Display Systems Biotech, Inc.) is another RNase H^{-ve} MMLV-RT variant but in addition, as the name implies, it is highly thermostable. Polymerization of long cDNA copies requires an increase of the $MgCl_2$ concentration to 8 mM.[63] Further to the increased sensitivity observed with RNase H^{+ve} RTs, Ambion have launched a new kit for high sensitivity one step RT-PCR reactions (MessageSensor™, *Cat. No. 1745*).

9.4.4. DNA-Dependent DNA Polymerases

Tth from *Thermus thermophilus*,[64] *Tfl* from *Thermus flavus*,[65] and *Bca*BEST™ from *Bacillus caldotenax* are DNA polymerases that exhibit both RNA- and DNA-dependent polymerization activities in the presence of Mn^{2+}. Since they are thermostable enzymes, they can be used to synthesize first-strand cDNA at significantly higher temperatures than either AMV or MMLV RTs. This increases the efficiency of reverse transcription by melting RNA secondary structure and decreases nonspecific primer binding. Although there are reports of significantly reduced sensitivity of *Tth* polymerase,[66] this may well be template or condition dependent. The sensitivity of target detection using *Tth* polymerase can be extremely high, and the detection of low abundant mRNA from single cells has been reported.[67]These polymerases do not have 3'–5' exonuclease activities, hence their error rates are comparatively high. To solve this problem, Roche have launched *C. therm.* polymerase, the Klenow fragment of the DNA polymerase from the thermophilic eubacterium *Carboxydothermus hydrogenoformus*. *C. therm.* polymerase exhibits high thermal stability and offers high-fidelity first-strand cDNA synthesis, with a transcriptional error rate half that of *Tth*.

9.4.5. Omniscript/Sensiscript

These enzymes are not derived from MMLV or AMV-RT and are supposed to have a higher affinity for RNA than either. Omniscript RT is designed for reverse transcription of 50 ng–2 µg of RNA and is recommended for use with difficult-to-transcribe templates. The Sensiscript RT is designed for reverse transcription of less than 50 ng of RNA; it is not recommended for use with viral RNA when carrier RNA is present.

9.5. RT-PCR

There are numerous options for carrying out RT-PCR assays, and the choice boils down to personal preference (or prejudice) as well as the underlying purpose of the experiment. First, the RT-PCR can be performed as a one enzyme, one tube procedure (sometimes described as one-step) or a two-enzyme procedure, either as a one-tube or a two-tube reaction assay. Single-tube RT-PCR procedures, whether one- or two-enzyme-based, are the techniques of choice in most clinical and high-throughput laboratories because they are simple to use and offer a reduced risk of cross-contamination since there are no steps between cDNA synthesis and PCR amplification.[68-71] In two-tube RT-PCR, first-strand synthesis is performed in a small reaction volume, and an aliquot is then added to a PCR reaction for amplification of a specific target. However, it is also worth bearing in mind that the RT enzyme itself[72] and certain RNase inhibitors[73] will be carried forward from the RT step and can inhibit the PCR reaction (**Table 9.2**).

Table 9.2. Comparison of one tube and two tube assays.

One tube-one/two enzymes			Two tube-two enzyme		
Feature	Advantages	Disadvantages	Feature	Advantages	Disadvantages
Reduced hands-on time	More rapid Fewer errors Higher throughput		Dedicated enzymes	Separate optimisation enhanced sensitivity	More pipetting errors
Less pipetting	Fewer errors		Multiple priming options	Separate cDNA pool Multiple targets	
Reagents added at start	Less contamination	No separate optimization	cDNA synthesis	Safer long-term storage	
Higher temperature	Higher specificity	Target-specific priming only			

9.5.1. Two-Enzyme Procedures: Separate RT and PCR Enzymes

Dedicated RNA- and DNA-dependent DNA polymerases can be used either in separate (e.g., Stratagene's "Brilliant Two-Step qRT-PCR kit," *Cat. No. 600544*) or in single reactions (e.g., Stratagene's "Brilliant One-Step qRT-PCR kit," *Cat. No. 600542*; Promega's "Access RT-PCR system," *Cat. No. TB220*; Finnzymes RobusT RT-PCR, *Cat. No. F-580S*; ABI's TaqMan One-step RT-PCR kit, *Cat. No. 4310299*). In "uncoupled" two-tube, two-enzyme procedures first-strand cDNA synthesis is performed in the first tube, under optimal conditions, using random, oligo-dT or sequence-specific primers. An aliquot of the RT reaction is then transferred to another tube (containing the thermostable DNA polymerase, DNA polymerase buffer, and PCR primers and probe) for qPCR carried out under optimal conditions for the DNA polymerase. In "continuous" one-tube, two-enzyme procedures the reverse transcriptase produces first-strand cDNA in the presence of Mg^{2+}, high concentrations of dNTPs, and either target-specific or oligo-dT primers. Following the RT reaction, an optimized PCR buffer (without Mg^{2+}), a thermostable DNA polymerase, and target-specific primers are added to the tube and PCR is performed. Alternatively, a single buffer can be used for both steps, obviating the need to open the tubes between the two steps. As the entire RT reaction is used in the subsequent PCR, this approach may be useful when template amounts are limited. Inter-assay variation of two-step RT-PCR assays can be very small, when carried out properly, with correlation coefficients ranging between 0.974 and 0.988.[74]

9.5.2. Single RT and PCR Enzyme

Alternatively, a single enzyme able to function both as an RNA- and DNA-dependent DNA polymerase can be used (ABI "EZ kit," *Cat. No. 402877*; Promega AccessQuick, *Cat. No. 9PIA170)* in one-tube/one-enzyme procedures that are performed in a single tube without secondary additions to the reaction mix. However, there are several disadvantages to this approach:

1. Since all reagents are added to the reaction tube at the beginning of the reaction, it is not possible to separately optimize the two reactions.

2. The one-tube/one-enzyme assay is about 10-fold less sensitive than an uncoupled assay, due possibly to the less efficient RT-activity of *Tth* polymerase,[66,75] although the sensitivity of *Tth*-based assays can be extremely high.[67]

3. A direct comparison of one-enzyme- and two-enzyme continuous assays has revealed more consistent sample-to-sample results with the latter.

4. The assay uses significantly more units of DNA polymerase which can drive up the cost of the single enzyme assay.

5. The most thorough study comparing one-step and two-step reaction conditions using SYBR Green chemistry found that the one-

step reaction was characterized by extensive accumulation of primer dimers, which obscured the true results in quantitative assays.[74]

6. A recent report suggests that under certain circumstances a template switching activity of viral RTs can generate artifacts during transcription.[76] This does not occur with bacterial polymerases.

Note: Promega claim their one-enzyme continuous assay is more sensitive than an uncoupled assay.

An interesting concept is the "Ready-To-Go™ RT-PCR Beads" from Amersham Biosciences. The kit contains room-temperature stable reactions designed for performing single-tube RT-PCR. Each bead contains recombinant MMLV-RT, *Taq* DNA polymerase, RNase inhibitor, buffer, and dNTPs in a proprietary "glass" matrix. In addition to the RT-PCR Beads, the kits also contain positive control reaction beads and separate pd(T)12–18 and pd(N)6 primers. Gene-specific PCR primers can be added at the same time as the cDNA synthesis primer to perform one-step RT-PCR, or PCR primers can be added after first-strand synthesis for two-step reactions.

9.5.3. Problems with RT

9.5.3.1. Secondary Structure

Use of *Tth* or AMV-RT at elevated temperatures reduces the secondary structure of the RNA template and helps read-through of the polymerase. Other strategies for dealing with RNA structure include supplementing the reverse transcription reaction with 2–5% dimethyl sulphate (DMSO), which disrupts base pairing. In addition, DMSO can increase the yield during amplification. Sodium pyrophosphate (less than 4 mM) may also be included in the RT step of two-step assays that use AMV RT to overcome RNA secondary structure and increasing the yield of first-strand cDNA. The pyrophosphate slows the DNA polymerization rate of the enzyme and is presumed to make it less susceptible to falling off the template at strong secondary structures. However, this is not a recommended approach if using MMLV-RT since this enzyme has an increased sensitivity to pyrophosphate.

9.6. One-Enzyme/One-Tube RT-PCR Protocol

9.6.1. Preparations

- Maintain a dedicated set of micropipettes and use filter barrier tips for all qRT-PCR reactions.

> **Tip:** Only use pre-sterilized branded tips. Try Axygen's "MAXYmum"-type ones.

- Dilute the template so that 5 μl are added to each qRT-PCR reaction. This reduces inaccuracies due to attempting to pipette very low volumes.

- Use RNase-free water (Ambion, *Cat. Nos. 9922/9924* or *9932/9934*), aliquot (20 ml) and store at –20°C.

- Always aliquot all reaction components and use fresh aliquots if product is detected in NTC or contamination is suspected.

- Defrost all reagents on ice prior to making up reaction mixes. Avoid exposing fluorescent probes and SYBR Green I to light (wrap in tin foil).

- Perform the qRT-PCR as soon as possible.

- Two minus-template control reactions, one prepared at the beginning of the assay before any DNA is dispensed, and the other at the end should always be performed, to confirm the absence of contamination.

- A lot of heartache can be prevented and contamination avoided by using dedicated sets of micropipettes for RT-PCR only, with one micropipette reserved for dispensing RNA. They must be calibrated regularly, especially pipettes dispensing 10, 2, or 1 μl.

- Use the pipette appropriate for the volume being dispensed and ban overwinding of volume settings above the maximum volume of the pipette design!

9.6.2. Primers and Probes

Forward and reverse primers (10 μM each) can be mixed together and should be stored alongside the probes (5 μM) in aliquots at –70°C.

9.6.3. RT-PCR Enzyme

Tth DNA Polymerase 2.5 U/μl.

> **Note:** Enzymes must be mixed gently and slowly using a micro-pipette tip without generating bubbles. Rapid pipetting of the viscous enzyme solution (it is in 50% glycerol) will result in volume errors.

9.6.4. RT-PCR Solutions

- 5× *Tth* RT-PCR buffer (250 mM Bicine, 575 mM potassium acetate, 0.05 mM EDTA, 300 nM Passive Reference ROX,* 40% (w/v) glycerol, pH 8.2),
- 10 mM dATP, 10 mM dCTP, 10 mM dGTP, 20 mM dUTP,
- 25 mM $Mn(OAc)_2$.

> **Note:** Hold the micropipette at a 90° angle to the microfuge tube and try not to touch the side of the tube with the side of the pipette tip.

9.6.5. Preparation of Master Mix

Mix buffer, dNTPs, $Mn(OAc)_2$, primer, and probes by briefly vortexing, followed by centrifugation to collect residual liquid from the top and sides of the tubes. Mix enzyme by inverting the tube several times, followed by brief centrifugation. Make the master mix by combining the reagents in the order shown on **Table 9.3**, mix gently by repeatedly pipetting up and down (making sure there are no bubbles), and finally add *Tth* polymerase and mix gently again.

> **Note:** This is the order in which reagents should be added to the master mix. Proper mixing of reagents is essential. Tubes should be kept cold at all times (the Stratacooler from Stratagene is ideal).

> **Note:** The required ROX* or reference dye concentration will vary depending upon the instrument used and is not necessary for some systems, e.g. Stratagene or Bio-Rad.

---

* ROX is an inert dye that is conventionally added to qPCR reactions to normalize for differences in mastermix volume added and also for optical differences in the detection systems of the qPCR instruments.

Table 9.3. Single-enzyme RT-PCR.

Reagent	Volume/25 μl reaction (μl)	Final concentration
5× RT-PCR buffer	5.0	1×
25 mM Mn(OAc)$_2$	3.0	3 mM
10 mM dATP	0.75	300 μM
10 mM dCTP	0.75	300 μM
10 mM dGTP	0.75	300 μM
20 mM dUTP	0.75	600 μM
10 μM Forward Primer	0.5	200 nM
10 μM Reverse Primer	0.5	200 nM
5 μM Probe	0.5	100 nM
Tth DNA Pol (2.5 U/μl)	1.0	0.1 U/μl
RNase-free water	to 20	

Perform a qRT-PCR protocol of:

1 cycle:	RT step	3 min	60°C	
40 cycles:	Denaturation	15 s	92°C	
	Annealing/extension	45 s	62°C	Collect data

9.6.6. Preparation of Standard Curve

The first time an assay is run, a full standard curve experiment must be carried out. Subsequently, only five dilution points need to be included with every run.

1. Prepare duplicate 10-fold serial dilutions of the DNA or RNA to be used to generate the standard curve.

2. The dilutions should cover the range 1×10^1–1×10^8 starting copy numbers. C_ts for each dilution point will be determined in triplicate; hence each standard curve will be made up of a total of six C_ts per dilution point.

3. Aliquot 60 μl of the master mixes into adjacent wells of a 96-well reaction plate. Twelve wells should be reserved for no-template controls (**Fig. 9.2A**).

   Tip: The quality of the plastic consumables obviously plays an important role in obtaining reproducible results. They must be uniform, optically clear, and not interfere with the fluorescence readings. A comparison between ABI's and

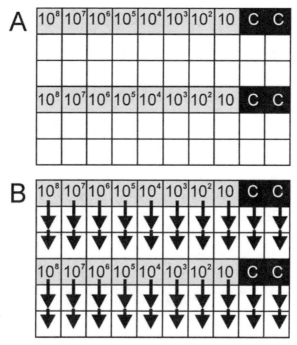

Figure 9.2. Microtiter plate setup for standard curve. Standard curves are prepared in duplicate and each duplicate is assayed in triplicate.

ABgene's plasticware suggests that it is worth shopping around for cheaper consumables without compromising the quality of data (www.abgene.com/technical.html).

4. Add 15 µl from each of the dilution points to individual sample wells and aspirate using the micropipette tip.

5. To each of the three no-template-control wells add 15 µl of water.

6. Transfer 25 µl of master mix/template and master mix/water from each well to the empty wells in the two rows below to generate triplicate samples (**Fig. 9.2B**).

7. Cap the wells and ensure that they are properly sealed.

Tip: It is crucial to ensure that the lids are tightly sealed as the small volumes in which the assays are carried out mean that product is easily lost to evaporation. Quite apart from ruining the experiment itself, it could result in the contamination of the thermal cycler.

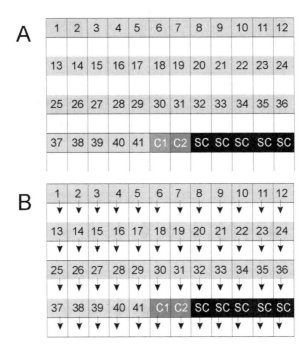

Figure 9.3. Microtitre plate setup for template quantification. Two no-template controls and a minimum of five standard curve dilutions should always be run. The range of standard curve dilutions should encompass all the values of all unknown samples.

8. Transfer the plate to the qPCR system thermal cycler, e.g., ABI PRISM 7700, and perform the RT-PCR reaction as detailed in **Table 9.3**.

9.6.7. Template Reaction

1. Aliquot 40 µl of the master mix into the adjacent wells of every other row of a 96-well reaction plate. Four wells should be reserved for no-template controls and ten wells for the standard curve (**Fig. 9.3A**).

2. Add 10 µl of RNA template to individual unknown sample wells and aspirate using the micropipette tip.

Tip: Use between 5 and 250 ng of total RNA. Perform rapid DNase I treatment if the RNA was not DNase-treated at the time of preparation: Combine 1 μg total RNA, 1 μl 10× DNAse I buffer (200 mM *Tris*-HCl pH 8.4, 0.5 mM KCl, 0.02 mM $MgCl_2$), 1 unit/μl DNase I, and ddH_2O to 10 μl. Incubate for 15 min at 30°C. Inactivate by adding 1 μl of 0.025 mM EDTA and heat for 10 min at 65°C.

3. Add 10 μl of water to each of the two no-template control wells.

4. Transfer 25 μl of master mix/template and master mix/water from each well to the empty well in the row below to generate duplicate samples (**Fig. 9.3B**).

5. Cap the wells firmly.

6. Take the 10-fold serial dilutions of the standard 10^2–10^6 copies of amplicon and add 10 μl to each of the five wells containing the master mix.

7. Aspirate using the micropipette tip and transfer 25 μl to each adjacent empty well.

8. Cap the tubes and ensure that they are properly closed.

9. Transfer the plate to the thermal cycler and perform the RT-PCR reaction as detailed in **Table 9.3**.

9.6.8. Troubleshooting

The main problem with using a one-enzyme/one-tube reaction is that it is more difficult to establish whether the problem lies with the RT or the PCR reactions.

1. If there is no signal, try a DNA template to make sure the PCR component is performing satisfactorily. Then mix that DNA template with increasing amounts of the RNA sample and repeat the PCR step. This will reveal whether there are any inhibitors of the PCR step in the RNA template. EtOH precipitation and extensive washing in 70% EtOH may remove any inhibitors from the RNA template. If problems with the PCR step have been excluded, the problem must lie with the RT step.

2. Check the RNA concentration and quality. Increase, or decrease, the amount of template RNA.

3. Try another set of primers targeting an unrelated gene to see whether the problem is amplicon specific.

4. Change the enzyme, increase the length of the RT step, or try using larger amount of enzyme.

5. Try using a two-enzyme protocol, as this may be more sensitive.

9.7. Two-Enzyme/Two-Tube RT-PCR Protocol

9.7.1. RT-PCR Enzymes

- MMLV-RT 50 U/μl;
- AmpliTaq Gold 5 U/μl.

9.7.2. RT-PCR Solutions

The two-step RT-PCR reaction requires two reaction mixes:
- RT Reaction Mix;
- PCR Reaction Mix.

1. RT step:
- 2.5 mM dATP, 2.5 mM dCTP, 2.5 mM dGTP, 2.5 mM TTP;
- 50 μM oligo $d(T)_{16}$ or 10 μM sequence-specific reverse primer;
- 10× RT buffer: 500 mM KCl, 100 mM *Tris*-HCl, pH 8.3;
- 25 mM $MgCl_2$.

2. PCR step:
- 10× TaqMan® Buffer 500 mM KCl, 0.1 mM EDTA, 100 mM *Tris*-HCl, pH 8.3, and 600 nM Passive Reference;
- 10 mM dATP, 10 mM dCTP, 10 mM dGTP, 20 mM dUTP;
- 25 mM $MgCl_2$.

9.7.3. Preparation of Master Mix

Mix the individual ingredients (*except for enzymes*) for the separate RT and PCR steps by briefly vortexing, followed by centrifugation to collect residual liquid from the top and sides of the tubes. Mix enzymes by inverting the tubes several times, followed by brief centrifugation. Make the master mix by combining the reagents in the order shown on **Table 9.4**, mix gently by repeatedly pipetting up and down (making sure there are no bubbles), and finally add enzymes and mix gently again.

Note: For SYBR-Green-I assays optimization for specificity is essential. Therefore, $MgCl_2$ (3 mM instead of 5 mM) and primer (20–50 nM instead of 200 nM) concentrations are lower than in standard assays.

9.7.4. Preparation of Standard Curve

The first time an assay is run, a full standard curve experiment must be carried out. Subsequently, only five dilution points need to be included with every run.

1. Prepare duplicate 10-fold serial dilutions of the DNA or RNA to be used to generate the standard curve.
2. The dilutions should cover the range 1×10^1–1×10^8 starting copy numbers. C_ts for each dilution point will be determined in triplicate, hence each standard curve will be made up of a total of six C_ts per dilution point.

RT Step

3. Prepare the RT reaction mix as described in **Table 9.4**. Each assay requires 10 µl of RT-mix and 2.5 µl of RNA. Hence RTs carried out on eight duplicate dilution series will require $10 \times 8 \times 2 = 160$ µl of RT mix. Two NTC require an additional 20 µl. Therefore, to be on the safe side, 200 µl should be prepared.
4. Aliquot 10 µl of the master mixes into a microfuge tube.
5. Add 2.5 µl from each of the dilution points to individual tubes and aspirate using the micropipette tip.
6. To each of the two NTC tubes add 2.5 µl of water.
7. Cap the tubes and ensure that they are properly sealed.
8. Transfer the plate to a thermal cycler and perform the RT-step reaction as detailed in **Table 9.4**.

Table 9.4. Two-enzyme RT-PCR.

RT-Step

Reagent	Volume/12.5 µl reaction (µl)	Final concentration
10× RT buffer	1.25	1×
25 mM MgCl$_2$	2.75	5.5 mM
2.5 mM dNTP mix	2.50	500 µM each
10 µM specific primer*	0.25	200 nM
50 U/µl MMLV-RT	0.3	1.25 U/µl
RNase-free water	2.95	

* If using oligo -dT$_{16}$ primer, the final concentration should be 2.5 µM, i.e., use 0.63 µl. Place at 48ºC for 30 min. If using oligo -dT$_{16}$ primer, a 10 min step at 25 ºC is required to maximize primer/template annealing.

To quantitate the efficiency of the first strand reaction, see:
http://www.ambion.com/techlib/misc/cDNA_quant.html

PCR-Step

Reagent	Volume/25 µl reaction (µl)	Final concentration
10× PCR buffer	2.50	1×
25 mM MgCl$_2$	5.5	5.5 mM
10 mM dATP	0.5	200 µM
10 mM dCTP	0.5	200 µM
10 mM dGTP	0.5	200 µM
20 mM dUTP	0.5	400 µM
10 µM Forward Primer	0.5	200 nM
10 µM Reverse Primer	0.5	200 nM
5 µM Probe	0.5	100 nM
AmpliTaq Gold (5 U/ µl)	0.125	0.025 U/µl
RNase free water	18.88	
cDNA template	2.5	

Perform a PCR protocol of:

1 cycle:	Activation	10 min	95ºC	
40 cycles:	Denaturation	15 s	95ºC	
	Annealing/extension	45 s	62ºC	Collect data

PCR Step

9. Prepare the PCR Reaction Mix as described in **Table 9.4**. Each assay requires 22.5 µl of PCR mix and 2.5 µl of cDNA. Hence

PCR assays carried out on eight duplicate dilution series in triplicate will require 22.5 µl × 8 × 2 × 3 = 1080 µl of PCR mix. Six NTC require an additional 135 µl. Therefore, to be on the safe side, 1.3 ml should be prepared.

Note: No more than 10% of the final PCR volume should derive from the finished RT reaction.

10. Aliquot 60 µl of the master mixes into the adjacent wells of every other row of a 96-well reaction plate.

11. Add 15 µl from each of the dilution points to individual wells and aspirate using the micropipette tip.

12. To each of the two NTC wells add 15 µl of water.

13. Transfer 25 µl of master mix/template and master mix/water from each well to the empty wells in the two rows below to generate triplicate samples.

14. Cap the wells and ensure that they are properly sealed. It is crucial to ensure that the lids are tightly sealed as the small volumes in which the assays are carried out mean that product is easily lost to evaporation.

15. Transfer the plate to a real-time thermal cycler and perform the PCR step as detailed in **Table 9.4**.

9.7.5. Unknown Template Reaction

RT Step

1. Prepare the RT master mix as described in **Table 9.4**. Each assay requires 10 µl of RT master mix and 2.5 µl of RNA. The exact amount of RT master mix required will depend on the number of assays.

2. Aliquot 10 µl of the RT master mixes into microfuge tubes.

3. Add 2.5 µl of RNA template (5–250 ng) to each RT master mix.

4. To each of two NTC tubes add 2.5 µl of H_2O.

5. Cap the tubes and ensure that they are properly sealed.

6. Transfer the plate to a thermal cycler and perform the RT-step reaction as detailed in **Table 9.4**.

PCR Step

7. Prepare the PCR master mix as described in **Table 9.4**. Each assay requires 22.5 μl of PCR master mix and 2.5 μl of cDNA. The exact amount of PCR master mix required will depend on the number of assays. Allow for four NTC tubes

   Note: No more than 10% of the final PCR volume should derive from the finished RT reaction.

8. Aliquot 45 μl of the PCR master mixes into the adjacent wells of every other row of a 96-well reaction plate.

9. Add 5 μl from each cDNA preparation to individual wells and aspirate using the micropipette tip.

10. To each of two NTC wells add 5 μl of sham cDNA, two a further two NTC wells add 5 μl H_2O.

11. Transfer 25 μl of master mix/template and master mix/water from each well to the empty wells in the row below to generate duplicate samples.

12. Cap the tubes and ensure that they are properly sealed.

13. Transfer the plate to a real-time thermal cycler and perform the PCR step as detailed in **Table 9.4**.

9.7.6. Troubleshooting

Two positive controls should always be included, one for the RT step and one for the PCR step. The controls should be RNA or DNA that undergo RT-PCR or PCR, respectively. If no fluorescence is detected with the RT control, but the PCR control is normal, then there was a problem with the RT step. If neither result in fluorescence, then the problem was with the PCR.

RT step:

• Check that all reagents were mixed properly and have been added at the correct concentration.

• If using oligo-dT, was a 10 min at 25°C step included?

• If using specific primers, was the reverse primer used?

• Was the temperature of the RT reaction too high? If using 37°C or 42°C, the temperature could be increased to overcome secondary structure problems. However, this will reduce the activity of the RT.

- If the target is very GC-rich or is known to form extensive secondary structures, denature RNA/primer mix (*without enzyme*) for 5 min at 75°C.

- For such templates it may also be useful to increase the RT-reaction time.

- If possible, check the integrity of the RNA using an RNAChip on the Agilent 2100. Try carrying out an RT-PCR reaction using a different target, e.g., a reference gene.

- Reduce/increase the amount of RNA.

- Use fresh aliquots of dNTP.

- Use a new lot of RT.

- Use new aliquot of reverse primer.

- Use 5–20 U of an RNase inhibitor, especially if the assay contains low amounts of RNA (less than 10 ng).

PCR step:

Observation: No increase in fluorescence with cycling.

Possible causes:

- **SYBR Green I:** SYBR-Green I is supplied in DMSO and can take a long time to thaw out. Therefore, use of stock solutions that are incompletely thawed can easily result in changes to the SYBR Green I concentration. When the stock solution is thawed, dye is more concentrated in the first volumes of liquid DMSO. Subsequent rounds of incomplete thawing will further lower the concentration of the remaining stock. Therefore, it is essential that the whole volume be allowed to thaw and then mixed thoroughly before any portions are removed. Ensure the correct dilution of SYBR Green was used. Is SYBR Green I concentration too high? Reduce concentration. Once SYBR Green I has been diluted it goes off very quickly and should be kept in the dark at 5°C for no more than one week. Dilution into a solution of DMSO may stabilize SYBR Green, but may affect the PCR assay. One major consideration when storing working solutions of SYBR stains is that there is a significant increase in the pH of *Tris* buffers when stored at 4°C versus room temperature. If your buffers were prepared at pH 8.0 at room temperature, then the pH will increase to

8.5 at 4°C. This increased pH is beyond the range at which SYBR stains are most stable.

- **TaqMan:** The probe is not binding to the target efficiently because the annealing temperature is too high. Verify the calculated T_m using appropriate software. Note that Primer Express T_ms can be significantly different than T_ms calculated using other software packages.

- **Molecular Beacon/Scorpion:** The probe is not binding to the target efficiently because the loop portion (MB) or the probe (S) is not completely complementary to the target. Perform a melting curve analysis to determine if the probe binds to a perfectly complementary target. Make sure the Scorpion probe sequence is complementary to the newly synthesized strand. The assay medium may contain insufficient salt for MB stems to form.

- A reagent is missing from the PCR reaction, repeat the PCR.

- The $MgCl_2$ concentration is not optimal. Change in 0.5 mM increments.

- Hot-start DNA polymerase was not activated. Ensure that the 10-minute incubation at 95°C was performed as part of the cycling parameters.

- Ensure the annealing and extension times are sufficient. Check the length of the amplicon and increase the extension time if necessary.

- The probe is not binding to the target efficiently because the PCR product is too long. Design the primers so that the PCR product is less than 150 bp in length.

- The probe is not binding to the target efficiently because the Mg^{2+} concentration is too low. Perform a Mg^{2+} titration to optimize the concentration.

- The probe has a nonfunctioning fluorophore. Verify that the fluorophore functions by detecting an increase in fluorescence in the denaturation step of thermal cycling or at high temperatures in a melting curve analysis. If there is no increase in fluorescence, resynthesize probe.

- Resynthesize the probe using a different fluorophore.

- The probe may have been photobleached if it has been exposed to light for too long. Resynthesize the probe.
- Redesign the probe.
- The reaction is not optimized and no or insufficient product is formed. Verify formation of sufficient amount of specific product by gel electrophoresis.
- Ensure that the correct amount of cDNA template was used (**not more than 10%**). Reduce the amount of cDNA template to 5% before repeating PCR. It is also possible to check for PCR inhibitors by adding the cDNA template into an assay that is known to work.

There is an increase in fluorescence in control reactions without template:

- The reaction has been contaminated. Use fresh aliquots of everything, including template C_t reported for the no-target control sample (NTC) in experimental report is less than the total number of cycles but the curve on the amplification plot is horizontal.

Relevant Websites

Basics of RT-PCR

http://www.ambion.com/basics/rtpcr/index.html
http://www.promega.com/guides/pcr_guide/070_12/promega.html
http://www.qiagen.com/literature/pcrlit.asp

Polymerase

http://www.promega.com/techserv/enzymes/

Suppliers of kits

Amersham Biosciences: www.apbiotech.com
BD Biosciences-CLONTECH: www.bdbiosciences.com
Epicentre: www.epicentre.com
Invitrogen: www.invitrogen.com
Maxim Biotech Inc.: www.maximbio.com
Novagen: www.novagen.com

Promega: www.promega.com
Qiagen: www.qiagen.com
Roche Molecular Biochemicals: biochem.roche.com
Stratagene: www.stratagene.com
Takara: www.takara-bio.co.jp/english/index.htm

References

1. Kwok S, Higuchi R: **Avoiding false positives with PCR.** *Nature* 1989, **339**:237–238.

2. Burchill SA, Lewis IJ, Selby P: **Improved methods using the reverse transcriptase polymerase chain reaction to detect tumour cells.** *Br J Cancer* 1999, **79**:971–977.

3. Willhauck M, Vogel S, Keilholz U: **Internal control for quality assurance of diagnostic RT-PCR.** *Biotechniques* 1998, **25**:656–659.

4. Lambrechts AC, 't Veer LJ, Rodenhuis S: **The detection of minimal numbers of contaminating epithelial tumor cells in blood or bone marrow: Use, limitations and future of RNA-based methods.** *Ann Oncol* 1998, **9**:1269–1276.

5. Raj GV, Moreno JG, Gomella LG: **Utilization of polymerase chain reaction technology in the detection of solid tumors.** *Cancer* 1998, **82**:1419–1442.

6. Hughes T, Janssen JW, Morgan G, Martiat P, Saglio G, Pignon JM, Pignatti FP, Mills K, Keating A, Gluckman E: **False-positive results with PCR to detect leukaemia-specific transcript.** *Lancet* 1990, **335**:1037–1038.

7. Bauer P, Rolfs A, Regitz-Zagrosek V, Hildebrandt A, Fleck E: **Use of manganese in RT-PCR eliminates PCR artifacts resulting from DNase I digestion.** *Biotechniques* 1997, **22**:1128–1132.

8. Henke W, Jung M, Jung K, Lein M, Schlechte H, Berndt C, Rudolph B, Schnorr D, Loening SA. **Increased analytical sensitivity of RT-PCR of PSA mRNA decreases diagnostic specificity of detection of prostatic cells in blood.** *Int J Cancer* 1997, **70**:52–56.

9. Keilholz U, Willhauck M, Rimoldi D, Brasseur F, Dummer W, Rass K, de Vries T, Blaheta J, Voit C, Lethe B, Burchill S: **Reliability of reverse transcription-polymerase chain reaction (RT-PCR)-based assays for the detection of circulating tumour cells: A quality-assurance initiative of the EORTC Melanoma Cooperative Group.** *Eur J Cancer* 1998, **34**:750–753.

10. Schittek B, Blaheta HJ, Urchinger G, Sauer B, Garbe C: **Increased sensitivity for the detection of malignant melanoma cells in peripheral blood using an improved**

protocol for reverse transcription-polymerase chain reaction. *Br J Dermatol* 1999, **141**:37–43.

11. Lion T: **Current recommendations for positive controls in RT-PCR assays.** *Leukemia* 2001, **15**:1033–1037.

12. Wang AM, Doyle MV, Mark DF: **Quantitation of mRNA by the polymerase chain reaction.** *Proc Natl Acad Sci USA* 1989, **86**:9717–9721.

13. Foley KP, Leonard MW, Engel JD: **Quantitation of RNA using the polymerase chain reaction.** *Trends Genet* 1993, **9**:380–385.

14. Clementi M, Menzo S, Bagnarelli P, Manzin A, Valenza A, Varaldo PE: **Quantitative PCR and RT-PCR in virology.** *PCR Methods Appl* 1993, **2**:191–196.

15. Freeman WM, Walker,SJ, Vrana KE: **Quantitative RT-PCR: Pitfalls and potential.** *Biotechniques* 1999, **26**:112–115.

16. Jung R, Soondrum K, Kruger W, Neumaier M: **Detection of micrometastasis through tissue-specific gene expression: Its promise and problems.** *Recent Results Cancer Res* 2001, **158**:32–39.

17. Fryer RM, Randall J, Yoshida T, Hsiao LL, Blumenstock J, Jensen KE, Dimofte T, Jensen RV, Gullans SR: **Global analysis of gene expression: Methods, interpretation, and pitfalls.** *Exp Nephrol* 2002, **10**:64–74.

18. Curry J, McHale C, Smith MT: **Low efficiency of the Moloney murine leukemia virus reverse transcriptase during reverse transcription of rare t(8;21) fusion gene transcripts.** *Biotechniques* 2002, **32**:755, 768, 770, 772, 754–768, 770, 772.

19. Seth D, Gorrell MD, McGuinness PH, Leo MA, Lieber CS, McCaughan GW, Haber PS: **SMART amplification maintains representation of relative gene expression: Quantitative validation by real time PCR and application to studies of alcoholic liver disease in primates.** *J Biochem Biophys Methods* 2003, **55**:53–66.

20. Zhang J, Byrne CD: **Differential priming of RNA templates during cDNA synthesis markedly affects both accuracy and reproducibility of quantitative competitive reverse-transcriptase PCR.** *Biochem J* 1999, **337**:231–241.

21. Lekanne Deprez RH, Fijnvandraat AC, Ruijter JM, Moorman AF: **Sensitivity and accuracy of quantitative real-time polymerase chain reaction using SYBR Green I depends on cDNA synthesis conditions.** *Anal.Biochem* 307: 63–69.

22. Brooks EM, Sheflin LG, Spaulding SW: **Secondary structure in the 3' UTR of EGF and the choice of reverse transcriptases affect the detection of message diversity by RT-PCR.** *Biotechniques* 1995, **19**:806–815.

23. Buell GN, Wickens MP, Payvar F, Schimke RT: **Synthesis of full length cDNAs from four partially purified oviduct mRNAs.** *J Biol Chem* 1978, **253**:2471–2482.

24. Kotewicz ML, Sampson CM, D'Alessio JM, Gerard GF: **Isolation of cloned Moloney murine leukemia virus reverse transcriptase lacking ribonuclease H activity.** *Nucleic Acids Res* 1988, **16**:265–277.

25. Shimomaye E, Salvato M: **Use of avian myeloblastosis virus reverse transcriptase at high temperature for sequence analysis of highly structured RNA.** *Gene Anal Tech* 1989, **6**:25–28.

26. Kuo KW, Leung MF, Leung WC: **Intrinsic secondary structure of human TNFR-I mRNA influences the determination of gene expression by RT-PCR.** *Mol Cell Biochem* 1997, **177**:1–6.

27. Creighton S, Huang MM, Cai H, Arnheim N, Goodman MF: **Base mispair extension kinetics. Binding of avian myeloblastosis reverse transcriptase to matched and mismatched base pair termini.** J Biol Chem **267**:2633–2639.

28. Zinnen S, Hsieh JC, Modrich P: **Misincorporation and mispaired primer extension by human immunodeficiency virus reverse transcriptase.** *J Biol Chem* 1994 **269**:24195–24202.

29. Bebenek K, Abbotts J, Wilson SH, Kunkel TA: **Error-prone polymerization by HIV-1 reverse transcriptase. Contribution of template-primer misalignment, miscoding, and termination probability to mutational hot spots.** *J Biol Chem* 1993, **268**:10324–10334.

30. DeStefano JJ, Buiser RG, Mallaber LM, Fay PJ, Bambara RA: **Parameters that influence processive synthesis and site-specific termination by human immunodeficiency virus reverse transcriptase on RNA and DNA templates.** *Biochim Biophys Acta* 1992, **1131**:270–280.

31. Klarmann GJ, Schauber CA, Preston BD: **Template-directed pausing of DNA synthesis by HIV-1 reverse transcriptase during polymerization of HIV-1 sequences in vitro.** *J Biol Chem* 1993, **268**:9793–9802.

32. Bebenek K, Abbotts J, Roberts JD, Wilson SH, Kunkel TA: **Specificity and mechanism of error-prone replication by human immunodeficiency virus-1 reverse transcriptase.** *J Biol Chem* 1989, **264**:16948–16956.

33. Abbotts J, Bebenek K, Kunkel TA, Wilson SH: **Mechanism of HIV-1 reverse transcriptase. Termination of processive synthesis on a natural DNA template is influenced by the sequence of the template-primer stem.** *J Biol Chem* 1993, **268**:10312–10323.

34. Beckman RA, Mildvan AS, Loeb LA: **On the fidelity of DNA replication: Manganese mutagenesis *in vitro*.** *Biochemistry* 1985, **24**:5810–5817.

35. Fromant M, Blanquet S, Plateau P. **Direct random mutagenesis of gene-sized DNA fragments using polymerase chain reaction.** *Anal.Biochem* 1995, **224**:347–353.

36. Bassel-Duby R, Spriggs DR, Tyler KL, Fields BN: **Identification of attenuating mutations on the reovirus type 3 S1 double-stranded RNA segment with a rapid sequencing technique.** *J Virol* 1986, **60**:64–67.

37. Huibregtse JM, Engelke DR: **Direct identification of small sequence changes in chromosomal DNA.** *Gene* 1986, **44**:151–158.

38. Freeman WM, Vrana SL, Vrana KE: **Use of elevated reverse transcription reaction temperatures in RT-PCR.** *Biotechniques* 1996, **20**:782–783.

39. Malboeuf CM, Isaacs SJ, Tran NH, Kim B: **Thermal effects on reverse transcription: Improvement of accuracy and processivity in cDNA synthesis.** *Biotechniques* 2001, **30**:1074.

40. Zhang YJ, Pan HY, Gao SJ: **Reverse transcription slippage over the mRNA secondary structure of the LIP1 gene.** *Biotechniques* 2001, **31**:1286, 1288, 1290.

41. DeStefano JJ, Buiser RG, Mallaber LM, Myers TW, Bambara RA, Fay PJ: **Polymerization and RNase H activities of the reverse transcriptases from avian myeloblastosis, human immunodeficiency, and Moloney murine leukemia viruses are functionally uncoupled.** *J Biol Chem* 1991, **266**:7423–7431.

42. Polumuri SK, Ruknudin A, Schulze DH: **RNase H and its effects on PCR.** *Biotechniques* 2002, **32**:1224–1225.

43. Hottiger T, De Virgilio C, Hall MN, Boller T, Wiemken A: **The role of trehalose synthesis for the acquisition of thermotolerance in yeast. II. Physiological concentrations of trehalose increase the thermal stability of proteins *in vitro*.** *Eur J Biochem* 1994, **219**:187–193.

44. Carninci P, Nishiyama Y, Westover A, Itoh M, Nagaoka S., Sasaki N., Okazaki Y., Muramatsu M, Hayashizaki Y. **Thermostabilization and thermoactivation of thermolabile enzymes by trehalose and its application for the synthesis of full length cDNA.** *Proc Natl Acad Sci USA* 1998, **95**:520–524.

45. Mizuno Y, Carninci P, Okazaki Y, Tateno M, Kawai J, Amanuma H, Muramatsu M, Hayashizaki Y. **Increased specificity of reverse transcription priming by trehalose and oligo-blockers allows high-efficiency window separation of mRNA display.** *Nucleic Acids Res* 1999, **27**:1345–1349.

46. Lucht JM, Bremer E: **Adaptation of Escherichia coli to high osmolarity environments: osmoregulation of the high-affinity glycine betaine transport system proU.** *FEMS Microbiol Rev* 1994, **14**:3–20.

47. Rees WA. Yager TD, Korte J, Von Hippel PH: **Betaine can eliminate the base pair composition dependence of DNA melting.** *Biochemistry* 1993, **32**:137–144.

48. Weissensteiner T, Lanchbury JS: **Strategy for controlling preferential amplification and avoiding false negatives in PCR typing.** *Biotechniques* 1996, **21**:1102–1108.

49. Shammas FV, Heikkila R, Osland A: **Fluorescence-based method for measuring and determining the mechanisms of recombination in quantitative PCR.** *Clin Chim Acta* 2001, **304**:19–28.

50. Shammas FV, Heikkila R, Osland A: **Improvement of quantitative PCR reproducibility by betaine as determined by fluorescence-based method.** *Biotechniques* 2001, **30**:950–952, 954.

51. Spiess AN, Ivell R: **A highly efficient method for long-chain cDNA synthesis using trehalose and betaine.** *Anal Biochem* 2002, **301**:168–174.

52. Myers JC, Spiegelman S, Kacian DL: **Synthesis of full-length DNA copies of avian myeloblastosis virus RNA in high yields.** *Proc Natl Acad Sci USA* 1977, **74**:2840–2843.

53. Houts GE, Miyagi M, Ellis C, Beard D, Beard JW: **Reverse transcriptase from avian myeloblastosis virus.** *J Virol* 1979, **29**:517–522.

54. Ueno A, Ishihama A: **Reverse transcriptase associated with avian sarcoma-leukosis viruses. II. Comparison of subunit structure and catalytic properties.** *J Biochem (Tokyo)* 1982, **91**:323–330.

55. Ueno A, Ishihama A, Toyoshima K: **Reverse transcriptase associated with avian sarcoma-leukosis viruses. I. Comparison of intra-virion content of multiple enzyme forms.** *J Biochem (Tokyo)* 1982, **91**:311–322.

56. Kato A, Ishihama A, Noda A, Ueda S: **Improved purification and enzymatic properties of three forms of reverse transcriptase from avian myeloblastosis virus.** *J Virol Methods* 1984, **9**:325–339.

57. Oyama F, Kikuchi R, Omori A, Uchida T: **Avian myeloblastosis virus reverse transcriptase is easier to use than the Klenow fragment of DNA polymerase I for labeling the 3'-end of a DNA fragment.** *Anal Biochem* 1988, **172**:444–450.

58. Yamaura I, Cavalieri LF: **Inhibition of reverse transcription of 70S and 35S avian myeloblastosis RNAs by nonprimer tRNA's.** *J Virol* 1978, **27**:300–306.

59. Ricchetti M, Buc H: **Reverse transcriptases and genomic variability: The accuracy of DNA replication is enzyme specific and sequence dependent.** *EMBO J* 1990, **9**:1583–1593.

60. Gerard GF, Fox DK, Nathan M, D'Alessio JM: **Reverse transcriptase. The use of cloned Moloney murine leukemia virus reverse transcriptase to synthesize DNA from RNA.** *Mol Biotechnol* 1997, **8**:61–77.

61. Verma IM, Baltimore D: **Purification of the RNA-directed DNA polymerase from avian myeloblastosis virus and its assay with polynucleotide templates.** *Methods Enzymol* 1974 **29**:125–130

62. Tanese N, Goff SP: **Domain structure of the Moloney murine leukemia virus reverse transcriptase: Mutational analysis and separate expression of the DNA polymerase and RNase H activities.** *Proc Natl Acad Sci USA* 1988, **85**:1777–1781.

63. Roth MJ, Tanese N, Goff SP: **Purification and characterization of murine retroviral reverse transcriptase expressed in *Escherichia coli*.** *J Biol Chem* 1985, **260**:9326–9335.

64. Myers TW, Gelfand DH: **Reverse transcription and DNA amplification by a *Thermus thermophilus* DNA polymerase.** *Biochemistry* 1991, **30**:7661–7666.

65. Harrell RA, Hart RP: **Rapid preparation of *Thermus flavus* DNA polymerase.** *PCR Methods Appl* 1994, **3**:372–375.

66. Cusi MG, Valassina M, Valensin PE: **Comparison of M-MLV reverse transcriptase and *Tth* polymerase activity in RT-PCR of samples with low virus burden.** *Biotechniques* 1994, **17**:1034–1036.

67. Chiocchia G, Smith KA: **Highly sensitive method to detect mRNAs in individual cells by direct RT-PCR using *Tth* DNA polymerase.** *Biotechniques* 1997, **22**:312–318.

68. Aatsinki JT, Lakkakorpi JT, Pietila EM, Rajaniemi HJ: **A coupled one-step reverse transcription PCR procedure for generation of full-length open reading frames.** *Biotechniques* 1994, **16**:282–288.

69. Wang RF, Cao WW, Johnson MG: **A simplified, single tube, single buffer system for RNA-PCR.** *Biotechniques* 1992, **12**:702, 704.

70. Goblet C, Prost E, Whalen RG: **One-step amplification of transcripts in total RNA using the polymerase chain reaction.** *Nucleic Acids Res* 1989, **17**:2144.

71. Mallet F, Oriol G, Mary C, Verrier B, Mandrand B: **Continuous RT-PCR using AMV-RT and *Taq* DNA polymerase: Characterization and comparison to uncoupled procedures.** *Biotechniques* 1995, **18**:678–687.

72. Fehlmann C, Krapf R, Solioz M: **Reverse transcriptase can block polymerase chain reaction.** *Clin Chem* 1993, **39**:368–369.

73. Lau JY, Qian KP, Wu PC, Davis GL: **Ribonucleotide vanadyl complexes inhibit polymerase chain reaction.** *Nucleic Acids Res* 1993, **21**:2777.

74. Vandesompele J, De Paepe A, Speleman F. **Elimination of primer-dimer artifacts and genomic coamplification using a two-step SYBR Green I real-time RT-PCR.** *Anal Biochem* 2002, **303**:95–98.

75. Easton LA, Vilcek S, Nettleton PF: **Evaluation of a 'one tube' reverse transcription-polymerase chain reaction for the detection of ruminant pestiviruses.** *J Virol Methods* 1994, **50**:343–348.

76. Mader RM, Schmidt WM, Sedivy R, Rizovski B, Braun J, Kalipciyan M., Exner M, Steger GG, Mueller MW: **Reverse transcriptase template switching during reverse transcriptase-polymerase chain reaction: Artificial generation of deletions in ribonucleotide reductase mRNA.** *J Lab Clin Med* 2001, **137**:422–428.

10

The PCR Step

Stephen A. Bustin and Tania Nolan

10

The PCR Step

Stephen A. Bustin[*] and Tania Nolan[†]

*Barts and The London, Queen Mary's School of Medicine
and Dentistry, University of London, London, United Kingdom
†Stratagene Europe, Amsterdam, The Netherlands*

10.1. Introduction

In theory, the PCR reaction should be a cinch for anyone who has ever struggled to set up RT-PCR assays. It targets DNA, which is easy to prepare, everyone seems to use *Taq* polymerase and the only worry is associated with contaminating the laboratory with amplified material from the previous PCR assay. Well, of course it is nowhere near as simple as that and the need to generate reproducible quantitative data makes careful consideration of the assay conditions paramount.

Maximizing PCR efficiency is an ever-present aim;[1] unfortunately, the copurification of inhibitors of the PCR reaction can present a serious problem.[2] Common inhibitors include various components of body fluids and reagents encountered in clinical and forensic science (e.g., hemoglobin, urea, and heparin), food constituents (e.g., organic and phenolic compounds, glycogen, fats, and Ca^{2+}), and environmental compounds (e.g., phenolic compounds, humic acids, and heavy metals).[3] Clearly, this has important implications for clinical and public health investigations, as so many of the investigations involve samples that are likely to contain these compounds. In addition, factors like DNA fragmentation[4,5] and the presence of residual anticoagulant heparin[6] or proteinase K-digested heme compounds like hemoglobin[7] or myoglobin[8] will negatively affect PCR efficiency. The problem with this type of inhibitor is that it makes the comparison of qPCR results from different patients, or different samples from the same patient impossible as it results in different amplification efficiencies and hence C_ts of the same target from different patients. Worryingly, laboratory plasticware has been identified as one potential source of PCR inhibitors.[9] On a positive note, at least it might be expected that the same batch of plasticware will have broadly similar inhibitory effects on all the samples. Incidentally, it is also important to remember that reagents can have a significant effect on assay reproducibility, with lot-to-lot variation an essential consideration.[10] Finally, contamination of the PCR assay is an ever-present danger.[11]

10.2. Choice of Enzyme

The question of which enzyme to use is not quite as simple as one might assume:

☑ The choice of chemistry influences the choice of enzyme: for anyone using TaqMan probes, there is an absolute requirement for an enzyme with a $5' \rightarrow 3'$ exonuclease activity, as otherwise the probe will not be hydrolyzed. Selecting an appropriate enzyme is not as straightforward as it should be, as three out of seven polymerases, which were declared by the manufacturer to posses $5' \rightarrow 3'$ exonuclease activity did not, and the remaining had significantly different reaction efficiencies.[12] One solution is to purchase *Taq* polymerase only from Applied Biosciences, Inc. (ABI), since at least this should guarantee that the assay will work. Alternatively, one could compare different *Taq* polymerase samples from several manufacturers and then go with the less expensive. Conversely, hybridization probes or Molecular Beacons must not be hydrolyzed since they are reused in each PCR cycle. Indeed, the use of enzymes with no 5'→3' exonuclease activity results in better signal yield, quality of amplification curves, and accuracy of quantification.[13]

☑ Although at first sight it might appear that fidelity is not important when amplifying the very small amplicons characteristic of qPCR, think again! True, qPCR is concerned with quantitating, not cloning DNA or cDNA amplicons. However, error rates in polymerases lacking proofreading activity can result in 20–40% of the amplification products of a 200 bp amplicon having mutations after 20 cycles.[14,15] This can affect the sensitivity of the PCR assay in two ways: a mutation at or near the 3' end of the primer-binding site will result in no or reduced extension of that mismatched template strand. If that happened at an early stage of the reaction, it would result in significantly fewer templates being amplified. Furthermore, since incorporation of mismatches is a random event, variation in C_ts between replicates would be expected. Second, a mutation within the probe target area would reduce the efficiency of hybridization or, indeed, abolish it completely. After all, allelic discrimination assays work on the basis of single-base mismatches. This problem would be exacerbated by the use of nucleic acid analogues such as LNA, which enhance the effects of a mismatch on a probe or primer's T_m.

☑ Additional factors that need to be considered are manufacturing batch-to-batch variability, thermostability, processivity, and cost, not necessarily in that order.

10.3. Thermostable DNA Polymerases

Every major molecular biology reagent manufacturer sells thermostable enzymes suitable for real-time PCR, and every manufacturer makes wholly plausible claims as to why their enzyme is better than any other one. From the basic and original *Taq* polymerase to engineered versions and new super thermostable and processive enzymes, the choice is bewildering (**Table 10.1**). Is it too cynical to think that there is no real difference in everyday use and that the best advice might be to choose an enzyme suitable for the chemistry from a reliable manufacturer, haggle for the best possible price and then stick with that enzyme until the new improved version becomes available?

Table 10.1. Properties of some of the more commonly used enzymes. It is apparent that only a few can be used for hydrolysis probes, so in fact the huge choice is somewhat restricted.

Enzyme	Half life 95°C (h)	Elongation rate (nt/s)	Processivity (nt)	Fidelity	RT activity	5'-3' exo	3'-5' exo
KOD HiFi	12	100–130	> 300	+++++	Y	N	Y
Pfu	6–18	25	10–20	++++	N	N	Y
Tth	0.3	25–33	30–40	+	Y	Y	N
Pwo	?	40–50	40	+++	N	N	Y
Tgo	2	?	?	+++++	N	N	Y
Vent	6.7	67	10	++	N	N	Y
Deep Vent	23	23	< 20	+++	N	N	Y
9°N$_m$	7.7	?	?	?		N	5%
Taq	1.6	60	150	+	Y	Y	N
Tfl	0.6	40	50–60	+	Y	Y	N

Of course manufacturers know this, and make it as difficult as possible to compare prices and enzyme properties. Unit definitions and recommended amounts to be used per assay differ between manufacturers so that an apparently less expensive enzyme might require more units per reaction than its rival. It is certainly worth experimenting with the amount of polymerase that is added to the PCR reaction. Very often using smaller amounts of enzyme results in identical C_ts, and not only reduces cost but can even improve the specificity of the assay.

Most DNA polymerases have functions other than that of 5'→3' polymerization. The polymerase may have an associated 3'→5' exonuclease activity, 5'→3' exonuclease activity, the ability to use RNA rather than DNA as substrate and may be capable of non-template-dependent addition of nucleotides.

The 3'→5' exonuclease activity is associated with a proofreading role[16] where it removes an incorrectly inserted (noncomplementary) base and thereby allows the polymerase reaction to continue. The proof-reading and polymerization reactions are in competition. A DNA polymerase with $3' \rightarrow 5'$ exonuclease activity will demonstrate higher fidelity than one without, which may affect enzyme choice for some applications. The so-called $5' \rightarrow 3'$ exonuclease activity is involved with excision repair within a cell. This activity is actually that of a single-strand dependent endonuclease, so the conventional name is inaccurate.[17] Additionally, some DNA polymerases have a reverse transcriptase activity (replication of DNA from RNA templates), which is usually enhanced by altering the cation in the reaction (e.g., Mn^{2+} instead of Mg^{2+}).

Individual thermophilic polymerases have unique requirements, e.g., pH and salt optima, as well as characteristics that affect the efficacy of the PCR reaction. For example, the presence of short double-stranded DNA fragments inhibits the activity of some DNA polymerases, as they bind to such fragments without sequence specificity.[18,19]

Several optimized polymerase mixtures have been developed which combine a standard polymerase, such as *Taq*, with a small amount of a high-fidelity polymerases, such as *Pfu*, Vent, and Deep Vent. Several of the enzymes are sold as inactive enzymes requiring heat activation to regenerate polymerase activity for "Hot Start."[20]

Note: AmpliTaq Gold has been reported to be contaminated with *Escherichia coli* DNA[21] and it is not unreasonable to assume that other recombinant enzymes are also contaminated with DNA from their host bacterium.

Taq—*Thermus aquaticus* (numerous suppliers). The first and best known,[22] perhaps the most robust and certainly the cheapest of all thermophilic polymerases, *Taq* polymerase can use a variety of substrates quite efficiently. These include, but are not limited to: dUTP, biotinylated-dNTPs, 7-deaza-dGTP, fluorescent-dNTPs, digoxigenin-dUTP, radiolabeled dNTPs, and dITP. The optimal ratio of normal dNTP to modified dNTPs needs to be empirically determined. *Taq* polymerase has no $3' \rightarrow 5'$ activity. It has a half-life of 40 min at 95°C and at 72°C, its extension rate is 50–60 nucleotides per second.[23] It is usually used at 0.25–1.0 U per 25 µl of reaction volume. The fidelity of *Taq* polymerase is optimal at pH 5–6 at 70°C.[24] However, DNA yield and pH are directly proportional; as pH increases the yield of amplified DNA increases. Hence *Taq* polymerase is used at a higher pH range to give sufficient yield of product.

Note: It is not widely appreciated that *Taq* DNA Polymerase has some RT activity at 68–78°C, with an elongation rate of 2–6 nucleotides per second.[25] Furthermore, this activity is sufficient to allow its use in single-enzyme RT-PCR assays.[26]

KlenTaq—*Thermus aquaticus* (various). Also is known as Stoffel fragment. KlenTaq is an *N*-terminal 289 amino acids deletion generating a more thermostable, 5'-exonuclease-free version of *Taq*. When used with hybridization probes it is superior to *Taq* polymerase in terms of signal yield, quality of amplification curves, and accuracy of quantitative measurements.[13] In addition, it retains its activity with broad range of Mg^{2+} concentrations.

Tth—*Thermus thermophilus* (various). The DNA-dependent DNA polymerase activity of *Tth* is broadly similar to that of *Taq* polymerase, with a similarly high error rate, but lower processivity and elongation rate.[27] Hence significantly larger amount of enzyme per reaction must be used. However, it can amplify target DNA in the presence of phenol-saturated buffer,[28] and is less inhibited by blood components[29] and other inhibitors.[30] Its Mg^{2+} range is narrow, it is slightly less thermostable than *Taq* polymerase (half-life at 95°C is 20 min) and there is no real advantage in using it for standard PCR assays. Its main claim to fame is that it has efficient RNA-dependent DNA polymerase (RT) activity at high temperature in the presence of Mn^{2+} ion[31] and is widely used for one-enzyme/one-tube RT-PCR assays.

Tfl—*Thermus flavus* (Promega). Its properties are very similar to those of *Tth* polymerase, although it may be slightly more thermostable (half-life 30–40 min at 94°C.)[32] It has a 5'→3' nuclease activity, can act as an RT at high temperature in the presence of Mn^{2+}, and has a narrow Mg^{2+} range.

Pfu—*Pyrococcus furiosus* (Stratagene). This is a very stable (half live is more than 18 h at 95°C), very high-fidelity enzyme, but has relatively slow elongation rates. It does not have a 5'→3' exonuclease activity.[33] To ensure high fidelity, free Mg^{2+} should be about 1.2 mM (i.e., for reactions containing 200 μM each of 4 dNTPs, use 2 mM Mg^{2+}). *Pfu* does not like dUTP.

 Note: The lower error rate is achieved only at pH 8.6 (at 25°C) whereas at pH 8.0, its fidelity is not much better than that of *Taq* DNA Polymerase.

Vent—*Thermococcus litoralis* (NEB). Vent is a high-fidelity enzyme that will not extend templates containing dUTP.

Deep Vent—*Pyrococcus species GB-D* (NEB). Super stable and tolerates a wide range of co-solvents such as formamide and DMSO. Deep Vent has four times more $3' \rightarrow 5'$ exonuclease activity than Vent DNA polymerase and 5–15 times more activity than *Taq*. It will also not extend templates containing dUTP.

> **Note:** High dNTP levels (up to 400 μM) are important to ensure that its strong $3' \rightarrow 5'$ exonuclease activity will not start to degrade DNA product.

Tgo—*Thermococcus gorgonarius* (Roche). This enzyme combines high fidelity with high thermal stability.

Pwo—*Pyrococcus woesei* (Roche). This enzyme has even higher thermal stability (its half-life is greater than 2 hours at 100°C) with slightly lower fidelity than *Tgo*. It has a $3' \rightarrow 5'$, but no detectable $5' \rightarrow 3'$ exonuclease activity. It prefers MgSO$_4$ to MgCl$_2$ and does not like dUTP.

KOD HiFi (Novagen) is a recombinant form of *Thermococcus kodakaraensis*. KOD1 DNA Polymerase and possesses a very strong $3' \rightarrow 5'$ exonuclease activity. It is characterized by its extremely low error rate, an extension rate that is twice as fast as *Taq* polymerase and 5 times faster than *Pfu* polymerase and a processivity that is 10–15 times higher than *Pfu* polymerase.[34] The enzyme has very little $5' \rightarrow 3'$ exonuclease activity. To improve its specificity, the enzyme is also available as a hot start preparation complexed with two monoclonal antibodies that inhibit the DNA polymerase and $3' \rightarrow 5'$ exonuclease activites during PCR reaction assembly at ambient temperatures.[35]

> **Note:** For non-TaqMan applications with difficult templates this is the enzyme of choice. Here is one enzyme where the manufacturer's claims are not exaggerated.

Pyra exo(-) (Qbiogene) was originally isolated from *Pyrococcus abyssi* and is a highly processive enzyme with no $3' \rightarrow 5'$ exonuclease activity. It is very thermostable: 90% of polymerase activity remains after 5 hours incubation at 92°C, 70% after 5 hours at 95°C, and 60% after 5 hours at 100°C.

Tfu (Qbiogene) was originally isolated from *Thermococcus fumicolans* and has a $3' \rightarrow 5'$ exonuclease activity. 60% of the DNA polymerase activity remains after 5 hours incubation at 92°C, 40% after 5 hours at 95°C, and 10% after 5 hours at 100°C.

10.3.1. Fidelity

Fidelity is the enzyme's ability to replicate faithfully a DNA molecule. Error rates are commonly expressed as the mutation rate per base pair duplicated, and accuracy as the inverse of error rate. In other words, accuracy is the average number of nucleotides the polymerase incorporates before making an error and thermostable DNA polymerases have error rates between 1.0×10^{-4} to 1.6×10^{-6} errors per nucleotide per extension. However, while every manufacturer boasts of at least one enzyme in his portfolio that has a lower error rate than everyone else's, it is well known (even to the manufacturers) that fidelity is influenced by numerous factors other than the polymerase, including physical damage to DNA, temperature, ion effects, and dNTP concentration. Fidelity is a function of the rates of the 5'→3' polymerase and 3'→5' exonuclease activities and the relationship between the two depends on various factors, including the binding of the correct dNTP by polymerase, the rate of phosphodiester bond formation, the rate of pyrophosphate release, and the continuation of extension after a misincorporation. Furthermore, it is not valid to compare error rates compiled from different sources as the methods used to obtain those data differ significantly.

10.3.2. Processivity and Elongation Rates

Polymerization is either distributive or processive. A distributive polymerase dissociates from the template after the addition of each nucleotide, whereas a processive polymerase maintains its association with the template for a succession of nucleotide additions.[36] The elongation rate is the maximum number of nucleotides polymerized per minute per molecule of DNA polymerase. It should not be confused with processivity; the turnover rate does not consider whether a polymerase is processive or distributive. The polymerases used for PCR assays are repair-type, rather than truly replicative polymerases.[37] This explains their poor elongation rates of tens of nucleotides per second, rather than the hundreds of nucleotides per second being polymerized by genuine replicases[38] and why they are significantly more error prone. However, the small amplicons used for qPCR mean that this is not really a problem, indeed for nuclease assays it is possible that an overprocessive enzyme might displace, rather than cleave the TaqMan probe. Therefore, the choice of enzyme should not be determined by its processivity or elongation rates alone.

10.3.3. Thermostability

Every manufacturer claims some record thermal stability for his enzymes but, in truth, it probably does not matter all that much. All thermostable enzymes in common use are sufficiently stable for the limited requirements imposed by qPCR. Reaction conditions influence thermal stability: a novel approach to raising the salt tolerance, processivity, and thermostability of current *Taq*-like DNA polymerases has been applied recently.[39] The helix-hairpin-helix (HhH) motif is a widespread motif involved in nonspecific DNA binding of proteins such as DNA topoisomerases. Fusing HhH cassettes with either NH_2 terminus or COOH terminus of *Taq* polymerase or its Stoffel fragment broadens the salt concentration range of the polymerase activity significantly and increases their thermal stability. Some common inhibitors of *Taq* polymerase are listed in **Table 10.2**.

10.3.4. Robustness

There are two categories of inhibition: (1) soluble inhibitors of *Taq* DNA polymerase may co-purify with the DNA (see **Chapter 6**) and (2) modifiers bound to a DNA template may make it unrecognizable as a substrate for PCR. Use of a unique reporter template and primer combination can distinguish between these two types of inhibition.[40] Diffusible factors that inhibit *Taq* polymerase are indicated by the lack of or reduced amplification of the reporter template product. However, inhibitors bound to the DNA will prevent its efficient denaturation, interfere with primer annealing or prevent *Taq* DNA polymerase from extending along that DNA. Since this type of inhibition is not diffusible, the addition of such extracts will have no effect on the reporter template product.

Table 10.2. *Taq* polymerase inhibitors.

Chemical Name	Final Concentration
BSA	No inhibition
NH$_4$	No inhibition
NP-40	No inhibition
Propidium Iodide	No inhibition
Spermidine	No inhibition
Ca^{2+}	> 3.5 mM
Chloroform	> 50 mM
Dimethylformamide	>50 mM
DMSO	> 10%
DTT	> 1 mM
EDTA	> 50 mM
Ferric ion	> 10 μM
Formamide	> 50 mM
Hemoglobin/heme	heme will interfere with PCR
NaCl	> 50 mM
Phenol	> 50 mM
KCl	> 50 mM
SDS	> 50 mM
Siliconized tubes	inhibition
Triton X-100	inhibition

An excessive amount of DNA template added to a PCR reaction can inhibit amplification. That amount is variable and is probably associated with inhibitors of the reaction copurified during the DNA preparation. Another source of variability is common with cDNA transferred from an RT reaction, since high concentrations of RT can inhibit the PCR assay. Different polymerases will react differently to such inhibitors and it is worthwhile checking each DNA preparation for inhibition and testing several polymerases for their efficiency at amplifying the template. In addition, the plateau phase in PCR assays is caused by the DNA amplification products inhibiting the polymerase.[18] This effect can be used to increase the specificity of the *Taq* polymerase by adding oligonucleotides that bind with high affinity to the enzyme.[41] These oligonucleotide inhibitors bind *Taq* polymerase with dissociation constants in the low picomolar range and efficiently inhibit polymerase activity at 25°C but not at temperatures above 40°C.

PCR amplification bias of one allele relative to another in a heterozygous sample has been observed and results in incorrect or ambiguous genetic typing of that sample.[42] Preferential amplification can result from significant GC percentage differences between alleles and conditions of the reaction that allow the denaturation of one allele but not the other.[43] If the PCR products from different alleles differ in length, or if the target DNA is sufficiently degraded,[44] preferential amplification can also occur. Finally, less efficient priming of DNA synthesis of one allele versus another can occur because of mismatches between the primer and the specific allelic template, resulting in preferential amplification of the other allele.[45]

There are some interesting differences in the susceptibility of various thermostable polymerases to inhibitors of the PCR reaction. AmpliTaq Gold and the *Taq* polymerases are totally inhibited in the presence of 0.004% (v/v) blood, whereas HotTub (*Tfl*) from *Thermus flavus*, *Pwo*, r*Tth*, and *Tfl* DNA polymerases are able to amplify DNA in the presence of 20% (v/v) blood without reduced amplification sensitivity; the DNA polymerase from *Thermotoga maritima* (Ultma) appears to be the most susceptible to a wide range of PCR inhibitors. HotTub and *Tth* are the most resistant to the inhibitory effect of K^+ and Na^+ ions[46] and biological samples.[30,47] (See **Table 10.2.**)

Thus, the PCR-inhibiting effect of various components in biological samples can, to some extent, be eliminated by the use of the appropriate thermostable DNA polymerase. Since a change of enzymes entails reoptimization of the qPCR assay, it is best to choose an enzyme from a reputable manufacturer, stick with it, and hope he does not bring out a new and improved version too soon since that will entail reoptimization. One thing to bear in mind is that some enzymes are in fact enzyme mixes that combine a highly processive enzyme with a proofreading enzyme to balance fidelity and yield.[48]

It is worth noting, slightly tongue-in-cheek, that sometimes inhibition of the PCR reaction is a desired outcome. The polymerase inhibition assay designed to detect DNA-damaging agent is one such time.[49] Nevertheless, that report details the kind of DNA damage that inhibits DNA polymerases and confirms the sensitivity of PCR assays to template problems.

10.4. To UNG or not to UNG

If the PCR assay is contaminated with PCR products from a previous assay, quantification becomes meaningless. Sadly, this is one of the major problems in the use of PCR as an analytical tool.[50] Sometimes the reagents used to prepare the PCR become contaminated. After the amplification a positive sample may contain 250 ng PCR product in 50 µl. This gives a total of 4×10^{11} copies of a 600 bp double-stranded product, i.e., 1 µl contains approximately 8×10^9 copies. Therefore, if the PCR tube is opened, the resulting aerosol will contain a very large number of amplified products. The microscopic droplets will float in the air for a long time, and can be carried a long way. Since a single template copy is sufficient to create a false-positive reaction, it is obvious that great care must be taken to avoid this carry-over contamination.

If the reagents used for PCR mix become contaminated, there is only one good way to eliminate this contamination: All reagents and stock buffers must be replaced with new chemicals and new water, which have never been in contact with the areas of sample preparation and PCR analysis. There is no point in looking for the one reagent, which is contaminated. Contamination may occur in more than one solution, or it can be in a stock solution where it may be difficult to find the source. The time wasted in this search exceeds the costs of exchanging all the reagents.

Direct UV irradiation can effectively remove contaminating DNA,[50-52] but the irradiation of the PCR reagents must take place before addition of polymerase, primers, and template DNA. The subsequent addition of these substances to the Strip can cause a new contamination.[53] Furthermore, this approach may be inefficient because the large numbers of mononucleotides present in the reaction will absorb much of the UV light.[54] Also note the discussion in *Chapter 6*.

The use of Uracil-N-Glycosylase (UNG) is a common way of reducing contamination by amplicons[55] (**Fig. 10.1**). UNG catalyzes the removal of uracil from single- and double-stranded DNA that has been synthesized in the presence of dUTP. The apyriminic sites formed by UNG are susceptible to cleavage by heat under alkaline conditions. Conveniently, a thermolabile version of the enzyme has become available, with a half-life at 45°C of about half a minute.[56] Incorporation of dUTP into the amplified fragments will alter the composition of the

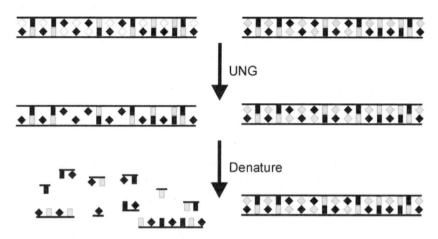

Figure 10.1. The use of UNG to hydrolyze DNA templates amplified using dUTP.

product so that it is different from the template DNA composition.[57] UNG is added together with the normal PCR enzyme to the reaction mix. The UNG enzyme will cleave the uracil base from DNA strands before amplification, and leave all the old amplified products unable to act as templates for new amplification, but will not react on unincorporated dUTP or new template. This will efficiently remove contaminating PCR products from the reaction after the PCR vessel has been closed, and thus no new contamination is possible. However, the efficiency of removal is sequence and amplicon-length dependent, with UNG not effective at inactivating amplicon sizes typical of real-time PCR assays (greater than 100 bp).[58]

10.5. Hot Start PCR

Sample preparation at room temperature may result in nonspecific priming from the template or even result in primer dimerization, all of which can significantly affect the sensitivity of the PCR reaction.[59] The idea behind hot start is to withhold the key component, polymerase activity, from the reaction mixture, until the sample has reached a temperature where all DNA is denatured. This should result in more specific priming, amplification, and more accurate quantification. Whether this is actually the case is debatable, but since it is very often the perception that matters, most manufacturers have jumped on the bandwagon and offer at least one enzyme that requires heat activation prior to the PCR reaction. Practically, a pre-PCR denaturation hold step is added, usually 95°C for 10 min. Alternatively, it is possible to omit the heat-activation step and add additional cycles. This results in slow activation of the enzyme (time-release) during the first ten or so cycles, which may improve specificity.[60] Despite numerous advertisements trying to convince us that there are significant differences between the various hot-start enzymes, there is probably little difference in the real-life performance of these enzymes qPCR, except for the exceptional performance of Novagen's KOD.

Several companies offer hot-start reagents that rely on antibody-mediated inactivation of the polymerase. For instance, Clontech's TITANIUM™ *Taq* DNA polymerase includes TaqStart™ antibody for a built-in hot-start, as does the company's Advantage™ line of PCR kits. Invitrogen's Platinum® *Taq* DNA Polymerase is another antibody-based hot-start enzyme. A thermolabile inhibitor containing monoclonal antibodies to *Taq* is bound to this enzyme and is denatured during the initial PCR denaturation step, releasing active *Taq* polymerase. Stratagene offers hotstart variants of their PfuTurbo®, Herculase™, and YieldAce™ DNA polymerases.

Still other companies offer mutant or modified hot-start polymerases. Applied Biosystems' AmpliTaq Gold® DNA Polymerase is a chemically modified form of AmpliTaq® polymerase that is inactive until incubation at 95°C for 1–10 minutes. The company also sells this enzyme in its GeneAmp™ Gold PCR Reagent Kit, which includes a multiplex control. Qiagen's HotStarTaq™ DNA Polymerase is a modified form of *Taq* that is inactive at ambient temperatures and is activated by a 15-minute incubation at 95°C. The company's HotStarTaq Master Mix Kit is a mixture of the enzyme, QIAGEN PCR Buffer, and dNTPs for quick room-temperature setup of reactions. Recently, QIAGEN introduced ProofStart™, a hot-start proof-reading enzyme that is chemically modified to inactivate polymerase and exonuclease activities, thus preventing degradation of primers. Qiagen supply Q-Solution as well as a specially formulated buffer with the enzyme. Stratagene's SureStart™ *Taq* DNA polymerase, a chemically inactivated version of Stratagene's Taq2000™ DNA polymerase, can be activated by incubation for 12 minutes at 92–95°C or during the denaturation steps of thermal cycling; a similar product, FastStart *Taq* DNA Polymerase, is offered by Roche Molecular Biochemicals.

10.6. PCR Assay Components

In general, probe-based qPCR assay conditions require very little optimization, since amplicons are short and the instrument detects C_ts well before the reaction reaches the plateau phase. Nevertheless, some tinkering can be required to tweak the assay, especially if the aim is to target low copy number targets. The use of glass capillaries in the LightCycler necessitates particular care, since *Taq* polymerase, $MgCl_2$, and target DNA can stick to the glass and significantly affect the efficiency of amplification. The inclusion of bovine serum albumin (BSA) in the PCR mixture helps, but its lack of stability during repeated cycles at 95°C can result in its precipitation and failure of the PCR assay.[61] Nevertheless, if primers and probes have been designed carefully and the template has been prepared meticulously, then the assay will work and work well. Intercalating dye-based qPCR assays are another story. Because the dyes will bind nonspecifically to any double-stranded template, optimization procedures need to be somewhat more rigorous.

10.6.1. Enzyme Concentration

There is no point in adding more than the recommended number of units of DNA polymerase to the assay as at best it will have no effect and at worst it can result in artifacts.[22] However, recent evidence suggests that doubling the enzyme concentration for multiplex assays can result in a 100-fold increase in assay sensitivity.[62]

> **Tip:** Pipetting errors are the most frequent cause of excessive enzyme levels. Accurate dispensing of submicroliter volumes of enzyme solutions in 50% glycerol is nearly impossible. Use of master mixes will increase the initial pipetting volume of reactants and reduce pipetting errors.

10.6.2. Mg^{2+} Concentration

The appropriate concentration of free Mg^{2+} is an key parameter affecting PCR optimization.[63] One the one hand it is essential for the activity of DNA polymerases, on the other hand excess amounts reduce enzyme fidelity[24,64] and increase the level of nonspecific amplification.[65] Recently, PCR analysis of several variable number of tandem repeat polymorphisms (VNTR) gave reproducibly wrong results in truly heterozygous subjects due to selective, Mg^{2+}-dependent, amplification of only one of the alleles.[66] Mg^{2+} concentration also affects the T_m of the various hybrids that form during cycling, including primer-template, template-template, and primer-primer ones. The concentration of free Mg^{2+} is dependent on the final concentration of dNTPs, primers, chelating agents, and template. Although 1.5 mM $MgCl_2$ concentration is suitable for most PCR applications, higher concentrations are often used with other probe-based chemistries and so titration of the Mg^{2+} concentration for each experimental target/primer combination can significantly improve the sensitivity and specificity. For these reasons, it is important to empirically determine the optimal Mg^{2+} concentration for each reaction.

 Tip: It is essential to thaw the $MgCl_2$ solution and vortex it prior to pipetting as it forms a concentration gradient when frozen and the vortexing will result in a uniform solution. These two steps, though seemingly simple, eliminate the source of many failed experiments.

 Note: It is probably best to add the $MgCl_2$ separately to a core reagent as reaction buffer solutions already containing $MgCl_2$ can vary in their performance,[67] possibly because $MgCl_2$ precipitates as a result of multiple freeze/thaw cycles. Heating the buffer at 90°C for 10 minutes restores the homogeneity of the solution.

10.6.3. Primers

The first problem with primers is that some protocols require the addition of primers in μM concentration, e.g., 0.5 μM, whereas others call for the addition of picomoles. The second problem is that the recommended primer range stretches from 0.05 to 1 µM, depending on manufacturer, enzyme or kit, with the rather unhelpful suggestion that extensive optimization of the precise primer concentration is required. However, despite the cost, some optimization is well worth doing as the aim should be to use as little primer as possible to achieve a certain C_t. Lower primer concentrations also increase the specificity of the assay by making primer dimers less likely. Of course, it is important to balance the specificity requirement with the need to maintain the efficiency of the assay, but since the C_t is likely to appear long before the primers run out, this should not be difficult. Reducing product by primer limiting is a technique commonly used in multiplex assays. This prevents the early reduction of reaction components due to the production of a high concentration of amplicon from a first target that is present at a significantly higher concentration than a second target.

10.6.4. dNTPs

As long as the concentration of dNTPs is well above the K_m of each dNTP (approximately 10 µM), all should be well. Low dNTP concentration may enhance enzyme fidelity, but then again this may encourage the 3'→5' exonuclease activity and can result in nibbling of primer or newly synthesized DNA. The standard range of 100–200 µM is good for 99% of assays, and it is more important to keep the concentrations of the four dNTPs the same, as a large imbalance can result in misincorporation. Any changes in dNTP concentration must be mirrored by an equimolar change in Mg^{2+} concentration, since dNTPs chelate Mg^{2+} and any change in the dNTP concentration also changes the effective Mg^{2+} concentration. This will affect product specificity, primer annealing, probe hybridization, the formation of primer dimers, and melting temperature. In addition, DNA polymerase activity requires free magnesium; hence a small increase in the dNTP concentration can rapidly inhibit the PCR reaction. Too low Mg^{2+} concentration—and the reaction becomes nonspecific and yields are reduced, too high—and the reaction is more efficient, but less specific. Again, if the primers and probes have been designed to function at a specific Mg^{2+} concentration, it is best to stick with that.

Note: dNTPs should be diluted in 10 mM *Tris* pH 8.0, since dNTPs are hydrolyzed into di- and monophosphates by acid pH. dNTP solutions are also sensitive to repeated cycles of thawing and freezing. They are stable at 4°C for several weeks, so a week's supply can safely be kept at 4°C, with further aliquots stored at –80°C. Note that during long-term freezing small amounts of water evaporating on the walls of the storage tube will effectively change the concentration of the dNTP solution. Therefore a brief spin in a microfuge is recommended.

10.6.5. Template

The amount of template required for successful amplification depends on the complexity of the DNA sample. For example, the 200-bp target in a 2-kb plasmid represents 10% of the input DNA. Conversely, a 200-bp target in the human genome (3.3×10^9 bp) represents approximately 0.000006% of the input DNA. Approximately 1,000,000-fold more human genomic DNA is required to maintain the same number of target copies per reaction (see box below). Two common mistakes are the use of too much plasmid DNA, or too little genomic DNA. Of course, if the number of target sequences in a sample were known, there would be no need to carry out a qPCR assay. Nevertheless, the optimum amount of starting template should be more than 10^4 copies, generating a C_t of approximately 25–30 cycles, with a final DNA concentration of no more than 10 ng/μl.

Box. Approximate numbers of molecules in nucleic acid preparations.

1 μg of 1kb RNA = 1.77×10^{12} molecules
1 μg of 1kb dsDNA = 9.12×10^{11} molecules
1 μg of lambda DNA = 1.9×10^{10} molecules
1 μg of *E. coli* genomic DNA = 2×10^8 molecules
1 μg of human genomic DNA = 3.04×10^5 molecules

10.6.6. Inhibition of PCR by RT Components

Components of the cDNA reaction, in particular the reverse transcriptase itself, can significantly inhibit subsequent qPCR amplification.[68] Using undiluted single-cell cDNA reaction mix directly as template for qPCR, alters he amplification kinetics of qPCRs dramatically in a nonsystematic fashion. A simple and robust precipitation protocol has been described that is suitable for purification of single-cell cDNA that completely removes inhibitory RT components without detectable loss of cDNA.[69]

10.6.7. Water

It is all too easy to contaminate a PCR assay by reusing an old bottle of water. In fact, of all the reagents added to the PCR, water is by far the cheapest, so it is not worth the risk. The best tactic is to buy RNase-free water (e.g., Ambion DEPC-treated water, *Cat. No. 9922*), aliquot it into 10-ml test tubes, and then use one test tube per assay. If preparing more than one master mix at a time, the 10 ml can be subdivided into microfuge tubes, which are then discarded after each master mix has been completed.

10.7. Reaction Conditions

For once, these are fairly standardized, depending on the chemistry being used and on the instrument. Some, such as the LightCycler, have extremely fast ramp times and can minimize the time spent at each step. On the other hand, hydrolysis probes need to be hydrolyzed, so a certain minimum polymerization time is required to ensure that all hybridized probes are indeed denatured. Since most amplicons are small, denaturation times can be kept to a minimum, and the strict guidelines for good primer/probe design allow standard annealing temperatures to be used. So, in this respect at least, most laboratories use very similar protocols. Of course, each thermal cycler has its idiosyncrasies and these will affect amplification results. Lack of uniformity across the thermal block is one obvious source of variability and should be checked for the system being used, this usually becomes obvious over time and with each reaction being run in duplicate and triplicate.

10.7.1. Denaturation Temperature

It is critical that complete strand separation occurs during the denaturing step. A temperature of 94 to 96°C is usually sufficient, although the half-life of *Tth* polymerase can be extended by denaturing at 92°C. However, the use of a lower denaturation temperature risks that the strands may not separate adequately. For G/C-rich sequences, denaturation temperatures may need to be increased to 97°C or even 98°C, although it may be necessary to use an enzyme that is more thermostable than *Taq* polymerase.

10.7.2. Annealing Temperature

Successful priming can depend on a surprisingly narrow window of annealing temperature. However it is unlikely that one or two degrees above or below the calculated T_m will make much of a difference to the observed C_t. However, for reliable quantification it is necessary to use the optimal annealing temperature, as too low a temperature can result in false priming from partially matched sequences and too high a temperature will result in inefficient priming, both of which will result in increased C_ts. Due to the high molar excess of primer to template, the optimal annealing temperature is dependent on the rate of cooling from the denaturing temperature. It is thus usually several degrees higher than the calculated T_m for the primer template. Oligonucleotides can bind and rebind to their target numerous times, a process driven by the high concentration of primers. Once bound, the primer may be extended by the polymerase, thus extending the DNA strand and stabilizing the interaction. This is why good priming of PCR reactions is observed with DNA primers even when there is a considerable mismatch, as long as the 3' base is matched, and at rather higher temperatures than might be expected.

10.7.3. Polymerization Temperature

Taq polymerase is optimally active at about 70°C, although it works reasonably well at temperatures between 30°C and up to 80°C. For 5'-nuclease assays, the polymerase is used at 60–62°C, for everything else a temperature of 70–72°C is used.

10.7.4. Reaction Times

Reaction times depend largely on the instrument being used, with the proviso that denaturation times are kept to below 1 min. Most suggested extension times err on the side of extreme caution: For the typical real-time PCR amplicon of 70–120 bp, a combined annealing/extension time of 30–40 seconds is more than adequate. If a separate annealing step is used, it need be no longer than 30 s. When you calculate these times, do not take into consideration the time needed for the instrument to reach the programmed temperature (ramping time).

10.7.5. Multiplexing

Multiplexing is great, but requires careful optimization of protocol.[70] If there is a decline in real-time PCR efficiency in multiplex real-time PCR assays, the following steps are recommended to optimize the reaction.

Note: Perform one optimization step at a time and then repeat the reaction to test for efficiency before moving on to the next step. Always run single reaction in the same experiment, in parallel with the multiplex reactions.

1. Increase all the dNTP concentrations to 400 μM each.
2. Double the amount of polymerase enzyme.
3. Increase the buffer concentration to 1.5 times
4. Increase the $MgCl_2$ in the reaction.
5. Consider reducing the primer concentration of the gene with the highest abundance to 1/4 of the concentration used in a single reaction.

10.7.6. Additives

When all else fails and the qPCR reaction is producing inconsistent results, or even none at all, it may be worth considering adding a chemical additive to the reaction buffer.[71] Alternatively, it might be as well to review primers and probes and/or choose alternative amplicons or enzymes. High G/C content is one of the most frequent reasons for poor amplification,[72] but often high G/C-content regions are localized,[73] and choice of an alternative region on the target under investigation might provide an easier solution to the problem than laboriously trying to find an additive that will improve the PCR assay. This is especially true for qPCR, as there must be significant doubts about the reliability of any quantitative data thus obtained. However, pausing can also be caused by specific primary sequences that do not form into secondary structures,[74] making it difficult to pinpoint the source of the problem. Some of the primary sequences responsible for extension arrest may result from stretches of alternating purine and pyrimidine residues.[75] Such sequences have been shown to favor a left-handed helix,[76] forcing the polymerase to pause until equilibrium results in the formation of a right-handed helix. Ten such residues have been shown to be a strong arrest site.[75] Pausing of *Taq* polymerase appears to be followed by a template-independent polymerase activity,[77,78] thus exacerbating the problem. The resultant mismatched 3' base is not extendible by the polymerase since it has no 3'→5' exonuclease activity. Pause sites may turn into termination sites with the partial extension products being effectively permanently removed from the amplification process. This leads to a reduction in amplification efficiency and makes any accurate quantification impossible.

Because there are a million-and-one things that can cause problems with the PCR assay, there are a million-and-one reagents and all have some claim to address a million-and-one functions. Magic ingredients include nonionic detergents such as Tween 20,[79] additives such as glycerol and gelatin, formamide,[80] bacteriophage T4 Gene 32 protein, and bovine serum albumin,[81] tetramethylammonium chloride (TMAC),[82] sucrose and trehalose,[83] and even EtBr.[84] These are claimed to stabilize the polymerase, enhance its processivity, disrupt template secondary structure, and decrease melting temperature, all the way to commercial preparations that claim to solve all pCR-related problems, but not reveal quite how. The list of commercial additive mixtures includes, among the others, the Stratagene's Taq Extender™ PCR Additive (*Cat. No. 600148*) and PerfectMatch® PCR Enhancer (Cat. No. 600129), CLONTECH's GC-Melt™ (part of the Advantage-GC kit, *Cat. No. K1907-1*), and Novagen's NovaTaq™ PCR Master mix (*Cat. No. 71007-3*). One rather serious drawback of these additives is that it is impossible to predict which one might be useful for any particular assay. Three factors are important if an additive is to be useful: high potency, high specificity, and a wide effective range.[85] Potency of an additive is defined as the maximum amount of amplification observed at any concentration of that additive. The specificity is defined as the ratio of the correct amplification product to all other, nonspecific amplification products. A wide effective range makes it more likely that an additive will yield positive results for many different amplicons. There are reports of PCR amplifications in which specificity was improved by formamide, but not DMSO,[86] and reactions in which DMSO was more effective than formamide at increasing yield and specificity.[72]

The most common additive is dimethyl sulfoxide (DMSO),[87] which is added at a concentration of 2–10%.[88,89] Recently, a number of other sulfoxides have been identified as novel enhancers of high G/C-target amplification.[90] Propyl sulphate and methyl sec-butyl sulfoxide were most effective with moderately high G/C content targets. However, propyl sulphate was completely ineffective with a very high G/C content (73%) template and only marginally effective with a high-content (64%) template. Both appeared to have some effect with lower G/C content (58%) templates. Only tetramethylene sulfoxide was consistently effective. What is clear from these studies is that different additives have significantly different effects on different targets, and while *a priori* the target's G/C content might make one additive appear more favorable than another, it requires experimental evidence to choose the most appropriate one. Overall, sulfoxides are more potent enhancers than corresponding sulfones, a conclusion, which is probably made more reliable by the comparison having been carried out by the same group.[91] On the plus side, DMSO decreases secondary structure, lowers the melting temperature of the primers, can suppress recombinant molecules forming during the PCR,[92] and works with *Tth* polymerase.[93] On the down side, it inhibits *Taq* polymerase activity at concentrations higher than 10%.

Another stabilizing agent is betaine (*N,N,N*-trimethylglycine),[43,94] which is sometimes used in combination with DMSO[95] and is present in a number of commercially available PCR enhancement kits. Betaine increases the thermal stability of proteins,[96] which may prevent nonspecific interaction of polymerase and template and reduce or even eliminate the base pair composition dependence of DNA thermal melting transitions by equalizing the contributions of GC- and AT-base pairs.[97] A comparison of the amplification efficiencies of G/C-rich templates in the presence of betaine with those using DMSO, glycerol, trehalose, or TMAC showed that only betaine had any appreciable effect.[73]

10.8. PCR Protocols for Popular Assays

Not only is the number of possible fluorescence-based chemistries bewildering, with each one requiring subtly differences in reaction conditions and thermal profiles, but the choice of reagents can be equally confusing. Commercial kits are now available from numerous suppliers, and they are designed to address the huge variety of templates, conditions, chemistries, and personal preferences that make up every PCR assay. There are two basic varieties of commercial kit:

1. **Master mix kits:** These are the easiest to use since everything is preformatted and the PCR assay simply requires the addition of template, primers and probe (or SYBR Green I), and water to volume. They are ideal for standard assay conditions that are already optimized, e.g., for those carried out in diagnostic or forensic laboratories. Some master mix kits are (there are many more):

   - SYBR Green I: ABI (*Cat. No. 4309155*), Stratagene (*Cat. No. 600548*), Qiagen (*Cat. No. 204143*), and Roche (*Cat. No. 2239264*);

   - Hybridisation probes: Roche (*Cat. No. 2239272*);

   - TaqMan: ABI (*Cat. No. N808-0228*);

   - General: Stratagene (*Cat. No. 600549*), Qiagen (*Cat. No. 204343*).

2. **Core reagent kits:** These kits are available with separate supplies of enzyme, Mg^{2+} or Mn^{2+}, dNTPs, and often separate reference dye; they are most appropriate when the assay requires optimization. Their flexibility makes them more useful for the general research laboratory that is interested in quantitating many different targets, rather than repeatedly quantitating few targets. Some core reagent kits are:

   - SYBR Green I: ABI (*Cat. No. 4304886*), Stratagene (*Cat. No. 600546*);

- TaqMan: ABI (*Cat. No. 4304437*);
- General: Stratagene (*Cat. No. 600530*).

"Home brew" kits are significantly cheaper and, provided the separate reagents are bought from reputable suppliers, will be as reliable as commercial ones. Indeed, there may be less variability, since it will be possible to purchase larger stocks of enzyme, the most likely source of lot-to-lot variation with commercial kits.

10.8.1. Preparations

- Maintain a dedicated set of micropipettes and use filter barrier tips for all qPCR reactions.

  Tip: Only use pre-sterilized branded tips. Try Axygen's "maxymum"-type ones.

- Dilute the template so that 5 µl or 10 µl are added to each qPCR reaction. This reduced inaccuracies due to attempting to pipette very low volumes.
- Use DNase/RNase-free water (Ambion, *Cat. No. 9922/9924* or *9932/9934*), aliquot (20 ml), and store at –20°C.
- Always aliquot all reaction components and use fresh aliquots if product is detected in NTC or contamination is suspected.
- Defrost all reagents on ice prior to making up reaction mixes. Avoid fluorescent probes and SYBR Green I being exposed to light (wrap in tin foil).
- Perform the qPCR as soon as possible. Some assays are stable for 12 h if stored at 4°C overnight; however others are more sensitive to storage. Reactions containing glycerol and DMSO or made from commercial master mixes can be stored at –20°C.

The qPCR protocols are applicable for commercial or home brew reagents. **Do check stock concentrations** since these can vary between suppliers. The reactions are quoted for 25 µl reactions since this is the most popular reaction volume, despite most manufacturers recommending 50 µl reactions. In some cases, especially with very low target copy numbers, the higher volume may give better reproducibility between samples; however for most reactions it makes no difference and reaction volumes as low as 1 µl–5 µl have been reported. If in doubt perform a comparison experiment to establish if there are differences for a particular assay.

10.8.2. Double-Stranded DNA-Binding Dye Assays

The most popular of the dsDNA-binding dyes is SYBR Green I. These dyes are remarkably inexpensive and so are widely used for primer and assay optimization as well as large screening projects. Their main disadvantage in qPCR is that they bind to all dsDNA, including nonspecific products and primer dimers. This requires the additional step of post-PCR melting curves to provide a qualitative assessment of the final PCR product. Numerous manufacturers supply suitable core reagent kits: Applied Biosystems (*Cat. No. 430488*), Stratagene (*Cat. No. 600546*).

To perform the SYBR Green I assay:

1. Make the master mix by adding the reagents in the order shown on **Table 10.3**, mix gently by repeatedly pipetting up and down (making sure there are no bubbles), and finally add *Taq* polymerase and mix gently again.

2. Add the template to the reaction tubes or wells.

    Note: Make sure you know which sample has gone into which tube/well.

3. Add the appropriate volume of reaction mix to each tube or well containing template. Cap carefully, spin briefly to ensure there are no bubbles, and place the tubes, strips, or 96/384-well plate into the PCR block.

4. Perform a PCR reaction according to the thermal profile given in **Table 10.3**.

10.8.2.1. Troubleshooting

No increase in fluorescence with cycling:

- A reagent is missing from the PCR reaction, repeat the PCR;
- The MgCl$_2$ concentration is not optimal. Increase up to 5.0 mM in 0.5 mM increments;

Table 10.3. General SYBR Green I protocol.

Using Stratagene Brilliant SYBR Green I Core reagent kit (*Cat. No. 600546*):

Master mix	1× reaction (µl)
dH$_2$O	TBD
10× buffer	2.5
50 mM MgCl$_2$ (2.5 mM final)	1.25
20 mM dNTP (0.8 mM final)	1
10 µM Primers	TBD
Rox diluted 1:200	0.375
SYBR Green I diluted 1:5000	0.25
5 U/µl Taq	0.25
Template	5–10

* *TBD volumes to be determined depending upon the volumes of primers added (recommended final concentration is 50–150 nM).*

Perform a qPCR protocol of:

1 cycle:	Activation:	95°C	10 min	
40 cycles:	Denaturation	95°C	30 s	
	Annealing:	50–60°C	1 min	**Collect data**
	Extension:	72°C	30 s	**Collect data**

Followed by a melting profile:

1 cycle:	95°C	1 min	
41 cycles:	55°C	30 s	**Collect data**
	repeat and increase T by 1°C per cycle		**Collect data**

- Hot-start DNA polymerase was not activated. Ensure that the 10-minute incubation at 95°C was performed as part of the cycling parameters;
- Ensure the correct dilution of SYBR Green I was used;
- Optimize the primer concentration;
- Too high a template concentration was used, frequently occurs when a plasmid template is used (dilute 1 in 10^5 and repeat PCR);
- Ensure that the template sample is of good quality. If unsure, make new serial dilutions of template before repeating PCR. It may also be possible to check for PCR inhibitors by adding this target into an assay that is known to work;
- Ensure the annealing and extension times are sufficient. Check the length of the amplicon and increase the extension time if necessary;

- Use a sufficient number of cycles in the PCR reaction;
- Ensure the annealing temperature is appropriate for the primers used;
- Gel analyze PCR product to determine if there was successful amplification;
- Is SYBR Green I concentration too high? Reduce concentration.

If there is a large abundance of primer-dimer and nonspecific PCR products:

- For products larger than 300 bp, increase extension temp above the T_m of the primer-dimer and/or nonspecific products. Ensure the instrument is set to collect data during extension;
- Reduce the $MgCl_2$ concentration;
- Increase the annealing temperature;
- Design more optimal primers.

10.8.3. Hydrolysis (TaqMan) Probe Reaction

The hydrolysis or TaqMan probe assay is currently the most widely applied qPCR detection assay. This approach has a wide range of applications and is relatively simple to design and to multiplex. It is best used for relatively straightforward quantification assays where detection of very low copy numbers is not essential. Although some assays can be optimized to detect low copy number targets, this is not the most suitable chemistry for highly sensitive assays and Molecular Beacons or Scorpions may be preferable.

1. Make the master mix by adding the reagents in the order shown on **Table 10.4**, mix gently by repeatedly pipetting up and down (making sure there are no bubbles), and finally add *Taq* polymerase and mix gently again.

2. Add the template to the reaction tubes or wells.

   Note: Make sure you know which sample has gone into which tube/well.

3. Add the appropriate volume of reaction mix to each tube or well containing template. Cap carefully, spin briefly to ensure there are no bubbles, and place the tubes, strips, or 96/384-well plate into

the PCR block. Reactions containing hydrolysis probes are usually performed using a two-step PCR profile. During this reaction the double-stranded template is melted at 95°C and the annealing and extension steps both occur during a single incubation at 60°C. Although this is suboptimal for amplification by *Taq* polymerase it is believed to encourage more efficient cleavage of the internal probe, resulting in maximum fluorescent signal per cycle. The thermal profile for a hydrolysis probe reaction is given in **Table 10.4**.

4. Perform a PCR reaction according to the thermal profile given in **Table 10.4**.

Table 10.4. General hydrolysis probe protocol.
Using the Stratagene Brilliant Core reagent kit
(*Cat. No. 600530*):

Master mix	1× reaction (µl)
dH$_2$O	TBD
10× buffer	2.5
50 mM MgCl$_2$ (2.5 mM final)	2.5
20 mM dNTP (0.8 mM final)	1
10 µM Primers	TBD
Rox diluted 1:200	0.375
5 µM Probe	1
5 U/µl Taq	0.25
Template	5–10

* *TBD volumes to be determined depending upon optimization data.).*

Perform a qPCR protocol of:

1 cycle:	Activation	95°C	10 min	
40 cycles:	Denaturation	95°C	30 s	
	Annealing/extension	60°C	1 min	**Collect data**

10.8.3.1. Troubleshooting

No increase in fluorescence with cycling:

- The probe is not binding to the target efficiently because the annealing temperature is too high. Verify the calculated T_m, using appropriate software. Note that Primer Express T_ms can be significantly different than T_ms calculated using other software packages;

- The probe is not binding to the target efficiently because the annealing temperature is too low and the primers have bound and elongated, blocking the probe-binding site. Verify the calculated T_m using appropriate software. Note that Primer Express T_ms can be significantly different than T_ms calculated using other software packages;

- The probe is not binding to the target efficiently because the PCR product is too long and is folding in solution. Design the primers so that the PCR product is smaller than 150 bp in length;

- The probe is not binding to the target efficiently or being cleaved effectively because the Mg^{2+} concentration is too low. Perform a Mg^{2+} titration to optimize the concentration;

- The probe has a nonfunctioning fluorophore. Verify that the fluorophore functions by detecting an increase in fluorescence in the denaturation step of thermal cycling or at high temperatures in a melting curve analysis. If there is no increase in fluorescence, resynthesize probe;

   Tip: Check all new probes are correctly labeled. Same probes ordered with HEX labels are produced with FAM by mistake. Perform a DNase I digest to verify probe labeling.

- Resynthesize the probe using a different fluorophore;

- Redesign the probe;

- The reaction is not optimized and no or insufficient product is formed. Verify formation of enough specific product by gel electrophoresis.

There is an increase in fluorescence in control reactions without template:

- The reaction has been contaminated. Use fresh aliquots of everything, including template.

C_t reported for the no-target control sample (NTC) in experimental report is less than the total number of cycles but the curve on the amplification plot is horizontal:

- Variation in fluorescence intensity. Review the amplification plot and set baseline cycles appropriately and if appropriate, adjust the threshold accordingly.

10.8.4. Molecular Beacon Melting Curve to Test Beacon and Scorpion Assays

Reactions including Molecular Beacons and Scorpions rely upon the correct structure being maintained at the correct temperatures and in the presence and absence of specific template. This can usually be predicted using software analysis but when the assay is required to distinguish between similar sequences, e.g., for allelic discrimination, it is useful to establish the thermal characteristics of the matched and mismatched oligonucleotide and target. With this information the thermal properties of the qPCR reaction can be optimized for maximum discrimination between sequences. For best results perform the melting curve analysis under the appropriate PCR reaction conditions for a Molecular Beacon or Scorpion (**Table 10.5**), though an enzyme other than *Taq* polymerase should be used to minimize the risk of probe hydrolysis. The thermal conditions are defined such that the reaction is incubated at decreasing temperatures and fluorescent data collected at each step. The thermal profile for a melting curve is shown on **Table 10.6**.

Table 10.5. General Molecular Beacon/Scorpion protocol.

Using the Stratagene Brilliant Core reagent kit (*Cat. No. 600530*):

Master mix	1× reaction (µl)
dH$_2$O	TBD
10× buffer	2.5
EITHER Scorpion: 50 mM MgCl$_2$ (2.5 mM final)	1.25
OR MB: 50 mM MgCl$_2$ (3.5 mM final)	1.75
20 mM dNTP (0.8 mM final)	1
10 µM Primers	TBD
Rox diluted 1:200	0.375
5 µM Probe	TBD
5 U/µl *Taq*	0.25
Template	10

* *TBD volumes to be determined depending upon optimization data.).*

Tip: Check the concentrations of kit components.

Perform a qPCR protocol of:

1 cycle:	Activation:	95°C	10 min	
40 cycles:	Denaturation	95°C	15 s	
	Annealing:	TBD*	1 min	**Collect data**
	Extension:	72°C	30 s	

Table 10.6. Molecular Beacon melting curve thermal profile.

1 cycle:	95°C	3 min	
56 cycles:	80°C	1 min	**Collect data**
		repeat and increase T by 1°C per cycle	**Collect data**

10.8.5. Molecular Beacon/Scorpion Reaction

1. Make the master mix by adding the reagents in the order shown on **Table 10.5**, mix gently by repeatedly pipetting up and down (making sure there are no bubbles), and finally add the polymerase (e.g., Novagen KOD, *Cat. No. 71086*) and mix gently again.

2. Add the template to the reaction tubes or wells.

   Note: Make sure you know which sample has gone into which tube/well.

3. Add the appropriate volume of reaction mix to each tube or well containing template. Cap carefully, spin briefly to ensure there are no bubbles, and place the tubes, strips, or 96/384-well plate into the PCR block. The thermal profile is given in **Table 10.5**. If a melting curve analysis has been performed use this information to define the annealing temperature.

4. Perform the melting curve according to the profile given in **Table 10.6.**

10.8.5.1. Troubleshooting

No increase in fluorescence with cycling:

- The oligonucleotide is not binding to the target efficiently because the loop portion (Molecular Beacon) or the probe portion (Scorpion) is not completely complementary. Perform a melting curve analysis to determine if the probe binds to a perfectly complementary target. Make sure the Scorpion probe sequence is complementary to the newly synthesized strand;

- The Molecular Beacon/Scorpion is not binding to the target efficiently because the annealing temperature is too high. Perform a melting curve analysis to determine the optimal annealing temperature;

- The Molecular Beacon/Scorpion is not binding to the target efficiently because the PCR product is too long. Design the primers so that the PCR product is smaller than 150 bp in length;
- The Molecular Beacon/Scorpion is not binding to the target efficiently because the Mg^{2+} concentration is too low. Perform a Mg^{2+} titration to optimize the concentration;
- The Molecular Beacon/Scorpion has a nonfunctioning fluorophore. Verify that the fluorophore functions by detecting an increase in fluorescence in the denaturation step of thermal cycling or at high temperatures in a melting curve analysis. If there is no increase in fluorescence, resynthesize the Molecular Beacon/Scorpion;
- Resynthesize the Molecular Beacon/Scorpion using a different fluorophore;
- Redesign the Molecular Beacon/Scorpion;
- The reaction is not optimized and no or insufficient product is formed. Verify formation of sufficient amount of specific product by gel electrophoresis.

There is an increase in fluorescence in control reactions without template:

- The reaction has been contaminated. Use fresh aliquots of everything, including template.

C_t reported for the no-target control sample (NTC) in experimental report is less than the total number of cycles but the curve on the amplification plot is horizontal:

- Variation in fluorescence intensity. Review the amplification plot and, if appropriate, adjust the threshold accordingly.

10.9. General Troubleshooting

Promega has a very useful Amplification Assistant[SM] PCR Troubleshooting Program, an interactive help session that can be accessed via the web (http://www.promega.com/amplificationasst/). The program is designed to help researchers after a failed PCR attempt and requires the user to input reaction conditions, results, and component information. It is a little tedious, but does take the user through the relevant steps that could have caused the failed PCR. Unfortunately, if you have modified your conditions, e.g., if your RT step is only 3 minutes, it pipes up and comments that an RT step of less than 15 minutes is not recommended. The Amplification Assistant provides custom advice based on the information supplied by the user and saves all the parameters entered during a particular session so that users can easily review or modify previous entries. Other online PCR resources can be found on the Web sites of most of the suppliers of PCR reagents or instruments.

Relevant Websites

http://www.promega.com/guides/pcr_guide/070_02/promega.html

References

1. Furrer B, Candrian U, Wieland P, Luthy J: **Improving PCR efficiency.** *Nature* 1990, **346**:324.

2. Cone RW, Hobson AC, Huang ML: **Coamplified positive control detects inhibition of polymerase chain reactions.** *J Clin Microbiol* 1992, **30**:3185–3189.

3. Wilson IG: **Inhibition and facilitation of nucleic acid amplification.** *Appl Environ Microbiol* 1997, **63**:3741–3751.

4. Golenberg EM, Bickel A, Weihs P: **Effect of highly fragmented DNA on PCR.** *Nucleic Acids Res* 1996 **24**:5026–5033.

5. Pikaart MJ. Villeponteau B: **Suppression of PCR amplification by high levels of RNA.** *Biotechniques* 1993, **14**:24–25.

6. Beutler E, Gelbart T, Kuhl W: **Interference of heparin with the polymerase chain reaction.** *Biotechniques* 1990, **9**:166.

7. Akane A, Matsubara K, Nakamura H, Takahashi S, Kimura K: **Identification of the heme compound copurified with deoxyribonucleic acid (DNA) from bloodstains, a major inhibitor of polymerase chain reaction (PCR) amplification.** *J Forensic Sc*i 1994, **39**:362–372.

8. Belec L, Authier J, Eliezer-Vanerot MC, Piedouillet C, Mohamed AS, Gherardi, RK: **Myoglobin as a polymerase chain reaction (PCR) inhibitor: A limitation for**

PCR from skeletal muscle tissue avoided by the use of Thermus thermophilus polymerase. *Muscle Nerve* 1998, **21**:1064–1067.

9. Chen Z, Swisshelm K, Sager R: **A cautionary note on reaction tubes for differential display and cDNA amplification in thermal cycling.** *Biotechniques* 1994, **16**:1002–1004, 1006.

10. Burgos J, Ramirez C, Tenorio R, Sastre I, Bullido M: **Influence of reagents formulation on real-time PCR parameters.** *Mol Cell Probes* 2002, **16**:257.

11. Kwok S, Higuchi R: **Avoiding false positives with PCR.** *Nature* 1989, **339**:237–238.

12. Kreuzer KA, Bohn A, Lass U, Peters UR, Schmidt CA: **Influence of DNA polymerases on quantitative PCR results using TaqMan™ probe format in the LightCycler™ instrument.** *Mol Cell Probes* 2000, **14**:57–60.

13. Wilhelm J, Pingoud A, Hahn M: **Comparison between Taq DNA polymerase and its Stoffel fragment for quantitative real-time PCR with hybridization probes.** *Biotechniques* 2001, **30**:1052–1056, 1058, 1060

14. Cha RS, Thilly WG: **Specificity, efficiency, and fidelity of PCR.** *PCR Methods Appl* 1993, **3**:S18–S29.

15. Ling LL, Keohavong P, Dias C, Thilly WG: **Optimization of the polymerase chain reaction with regard to fidelity: modified T7, Taq, and vent DNA polymerases.** *PCR Methods Appl* 1991, **1**:63–69

16. Shevelev IV, Hubscher U: **The 3'->5' exonucleases.** *Nat Rev Mol Cell Biol* 2002, **3**:364–376

17. Lyamichev V, Brow MA, Dahlberg JE. **Structure-specific endonucleolytic cleavage of nucleic acids by eubacterial DNA polymerases.** *Science* 1993, **260**:778–783

18. Kainz P: **The PCR plateau phase—Towards an understanding of its limitations.** *Biochim Biophys Acta* 2000, **1494**:23–27

19. Kainz P, Schmiedlechner A, Strack HB: **Specificity-enhanced hot-start PCR: Addition of double-stranded DNA fragments adapted to the annealing temperature.** *Biotechniques* 2000 **28**:278–282.

20. Moretti T, Koons B, Budowle B: **Enhancement of PCR amplification yield and specificity using AmpliTaq Gold DNA polymerase.** *Biotechniques* 1998, **25**:716–722.

21. Koponen JK, Turunen AM, Yla-Herttuala S: **Escherichia coli DNA contamination in AmpliTaq Gold polymerase interferes with TaqMan analysis of lacZ.** *Mol Ther* 2002, **5**:220–222.

22. Longley MJ, Bennett SE, Mosbaugh DW: **Characterization of the 5' to 3' exonuclease associated with *Thermus aquaticus* DNA polymerase.** *Nucleic Acids Re*s 1990 **18**: 7317–7322.

23. Lawyer FC, Stoffel S, Saiki RK, Chang SY, Landre PA, Abramson RD, Gelfand DH: **High-level expression, purification, and enzymatic characterization of full-length *Thermus aquaticus* DNA polymerase and a truncated form deficient in 5' to 3' exonuclease activity.** *PCR Methods Appl* 1993, **2**:275–287.

24. Eckert KA, Kunkel TA: **High fidelity DNA synthesis by the *Thermus aquaticus* DNA polymerase.** *Nucleic Acids Res* 1990, **18**:3739–3744.

25. Jones MD, Foulkes NS: **Reverse transcription of mRNA by *Thermus aquaticus* DNA polymerase.** *Nucleic Acids Res* 1989, **17**:8387–8388.

26. Shaffer AL, Wojnar W, Nelson W: **Amplification, detection, and automated sequencing of gibbon interleukin-2 mRNA by *Thermus aquaticus* DNA polymerase reverse transcription and polymerase chain reaction.** *Anal Biochem* 1990, **190**:292–296.

27. Carballeira N, Nazabal M, Brito J, Garcia O: **Purification of a thermostable DNA polymerase from *Thermus thermophilus* HB8, useful in the polymerase chain reaction.** *Biotechniques* 1990 **9**:276–281.

28. Katcher HL, Schwartz I: **A distinctive property of *Tth* DNA polymerase: Enzymatic amplification in the presence of phenol.** *Biotechniques* 1994, **16**:84–92.

29. Bej AK, Mahbubani MH: **Applications of the polymerase chain reaction in environmental microbiology.** *PCR Methods Appl* 1992, **1**:151–159.

30. Wiedbrauk DL, Werner JC, Drevon AM: **Inhibition of PCR by aqueous and vitreous fluids.** *J Clin Microbiol* 1995, **33**:2643–2646.

31. Myers TW, Gelfand DH: **Reverse transcription and DNA amplification by a *Thermus thermophilus* DNA polymerase.** *Biochemistry* 1991, **30**:7661–7666.

32. Harrell RA, Hart RP: **Rapid preparation of *Thermus flavus* DNA polymerase.** *PCR Methods Appl* 1994, **3**:372–375.

33. Cline J, Braman JC, Hogrefe HH: **PCR fidelity of pfu DNA polymerase and other thermostable DNA polymerases.** *Nucleic Acids Res* 1996, **24**:3546–3551.

34. Takagi M, Nishioka M, Kakihara H, Kitabayashi M, Inoue H, Kawakami B, Oka M, Imanaka T: **Characterization of DNA polymerase from *Pyrococcus sp.* strain KOD1 and its application to PCR.** *Appl Environ Microbiol* 1997, **63**:4504–4510.

35. Mizuguchi H, Nakatsuji M, Fujiwara S, Takagi M, Imanaka T: **Characterization and application to hot start PCR of neutralizing monoclonal antibodies against KOD DNA polymerase.** *J Biochem (Tokyo)* 1999, **126**:762–768.

36. Von Hippel PH, Fairfield FR, Dolejsi MK. **On the processivity of polymerases.** *Ann NY Acad Sci* 1994, **726**:118–131.

37. Hamilton SC, Farchaus JW, Davis MC: **DNA polymerases as engines for biotechnology.** *Biotechniques* 2001, **31**:370–380, 382.

Color Plates

Table 13.6. Primer optimization matrix set up tube table
(see page 534 for explanations)

R= Reverse (primer final concentration) **F**= Forward (primer final concentration)

NOTE: All 50 nm of final concentration primers use 1 µM of primer stocks, all other concentrations use 5 µM of primer stocks.

	µl		µl		µl		µl		µl
F(50 nM) 1 µM stock R (50 nM) 1 µM stock	3 3	F(50 nM) 1 µM stock R (100 nM) 5 µM stock	3 1.2	F(50 nM) 1 µM stock R (300 nM) 5 µM stock	3 3.6	F(50 nM) 1 µM stock R (600 nM) 5 µM stock	3 7.2	F(50 nM) 1 µM stock R (900 nM) 5 µM stock	3 10.8
ddH₂O	15.6	ddH₂O	21.4	ddH₂O	15	ddH₂O	11.4	ddH₂O	7.8
F(100 nM) 5 µM stock R (50 nM) 1 µM stock	1.2 3	F(100 nM) 5 µM stock R (100 nM) 5 µM stock	1.2 1.2	F(100 nM) 5 µM stock R (300 nM) 5 µM stock	1.2 3.6	F(10 0nM) 5 µM stock R (600 nM) 5 µM stock	1.2 7.2	F(100 nM) 5 µM stock R (900 nM) 5 µM stock	1.2 10.8
ddH₂O	17.4	ddH₂O	19.2	ddH₂O	16.8	ddH₂O	13.2	ddH₂O	9.6
F(300 nM) 5 µM stock R (50 nM) 1 µM stock	3.6 3	F(300 nM) 5 µM stock R (100 nM) 5 µM stock	3.6 1.2	F(300 nM) 5 µM stock R (300 nM) 5 µM stock	3.6 3.6	F(300 nM) 5 µM stock R (600 nM) 5 µM stock	3.6 7.2	F(300 nM) 5 µM stock R (900 nM) 5 µM stock	3.6 10.8
ddH₂O	15	ddH₂O	16.8	ddH₂O	14.4	ddH₂O	10.8	ddH₂O	7.2
F(600 nM) 5 µM stock R (50 nM) 1 µM stock	7.2 3	F(600 nM) 5 µM stock R (100 nM) 5 µM stock	7.2 1.2	F(600 nM) 5 µM stock R (300 nM) 5 µM stock	7.2 3.6	F(600 nM) 5 µM stock R (600 nM) 5 µM stock	7.2 7.2	F(600 nM) 5 µM stock R (900 nM) 5 µM stock	7.2 10.8
ddH₂O	11.4	ddH₂O	13.2	ddH₂O	10.8	ddH₂O	7.2	ddH₂O	3.6
F(900 nM) 5 µM stock R (50 nM) 1 µM stock	10.8 3	F(900 nM) 5 µM stock R (100 nM) 5 µM stock	10.8 1.2	F(900 nM) 5 µM stock R (300 nM) 5 µM stock	10.8 3.6	F(900 nM) 5 µM stock R (600 nM) 5 µM stock	10.8 7.2	F(900 nM) 5 µM stock R (900 nM) 5 µM stock	10.8 10.8
ddH₂O	7.8	ddH₂O	9.6	ddH₂O	7.2	ddH₂O	3.6	ddH₂O	0
NTC 1 F(50 nM) 1 µM stock R (50 nM) 1 µM stock	3 3							NTC 2 F(900 nM) 5 µM stock R (900 nM) 5 µM stock	10.8 10.8
ddH₂O	15.6							ddH₂O	0

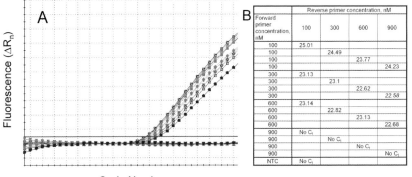

A — Fluorescence (ΔRₙ) vs Cycle Number

B

Forward primer concentration, nM	Reverse primer concentration, nM			
	100	300	600	900
100	25.01			
100		24.49		
100			23.77	
100				24.23
300	23.13			
300		23.1		
300			22.62	
300				22.58
600	23.14			
600		22.82		
600			23.13	
600				22.68
900	No Ct			
900		No Ct		
900			No Ct	
900				No Ct
NTC	No Ct			

Plate 13.1. A, B, and C. (*Continued on next page.*)

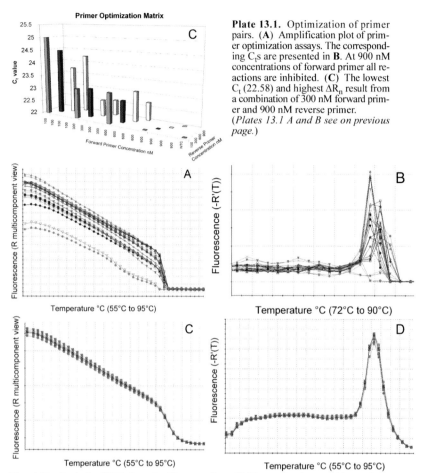

Plate 13.1. Optimization of primer pairs. (**A**) Amplification plot of primer optimization assays. The corresponding C_ts are presented in **B**. At 900 nM concentrations of forward primer all reactions are inhibited. (**C**) The lowest C_t (22.58) and highest ΔR_n result from a combination of 300 nM forward primer and 900 nM reverse primer.
(*Plates 13.1 A and B see on previous page.*)

Plate 13.2. Analyzing SYBR Green I melting curve data. (**A**) The raw data from a melting profile are presented as a plot of fluorescence units against temperature. (**B**) The first derivative view, with respect to temperature (–R'(T)) provides a clear view of the rate of SYBR Green I loss and the temperature range over which this occurs. For this example a view of that data between 72°C and 90°C will be used. The small peak at 74.5°C is more than likely due to primer dimer product formation since this is the only peak to occur in the NTC sample. The main peaks occur around 85.55°C though there are some with a distinctly different profile and a peak at 86.55°C. These distinct profiles represent different products in the final PCR product. **C** and **D** show optimized dissociation curves.

Plate 13.3. Optimization of probe concentration. In this optimization reducing the probe concentration below 200 nM does not alter the C_t but does result in reduced R_n. Increasing the probe concentration from 200 nM to 300 nM does not influence the data, and so 200 nM is the optimum probe concentration for this reaction.

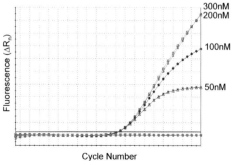

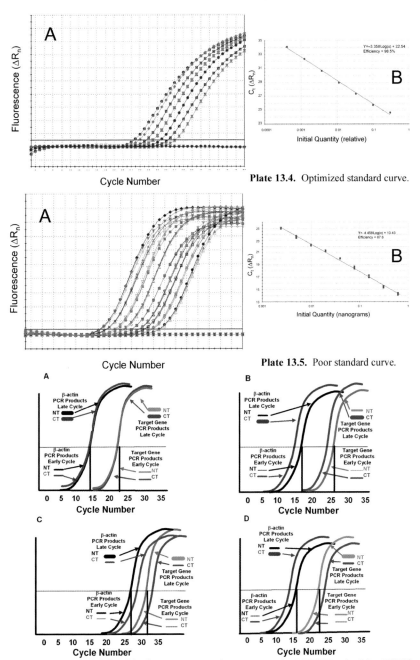

Plate 13.4. Optimized standard curve.

Plate 13.5. Poor standard curve.

Plate 14.1. Schematic depiction of simultaneous gene expression measurement by StaRT-PCR and real-time RT-PCR in two different samples. Shown is PCR amplification of a native template (NT) and respective internal standard competitive template (CT) for a target gene and reference gene (β-actin). (*See explanations on pages 554–559.*)

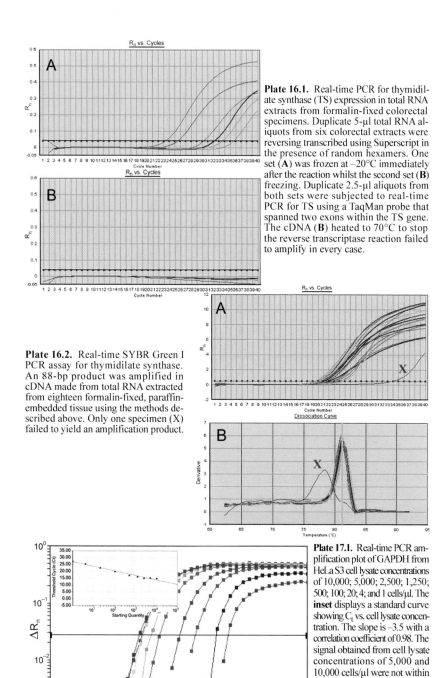

Plate 16.1. Real-time PCR for thymidilate synthase (TS) expression in total RNA extracts from formalin-fixed colorectal specimens. Duplicate 5-µl total RNA aliquots from six colorectal extracts were reversing transcribed using Superscript in the presence of random hexamers. One set (**A**) was frozen at –20°C immediately after the reaction whilst the second set (**B**) freezing. Duplicate 2.5-µl aliquots from both sets were subjected to real-time PCR for TS using a TaqMan probe that spanned two exons within the TS gene. The cDNA (**B**) heated to 70°C to stop the reverse transcriptase reaction failed to amplify in every case.

Plate 16.2. Real-time SYBR Green I PCR assay for thymidilate synthase. An 88-bp product was amplified in cDNA made from total RNA extracted from eighteen formalin-fixed, paraffin-embedded tissue using the methods described above. Only one specimen (X) failed to yield an amplification product.

Plate 17.1. Real-time PCR amplification plot of GAPDH from HeLa S3 cell lysate concentrations of 10,000; 5,000; 2,500; 1,250; 500; 100; 20; 4; and 1 cells/µl. The **inset** displays a standard curve showing C_t vs. cell lysate concentration. The slope is –3.5 with a correlation coefficient of 0.98. The signal obtained from cell lysate concentrations of 5,000 and 10,000 cells/µl were not within the linear range indicating that there was inhibition of the RT-PCR at these higher cell lysate concentrations.

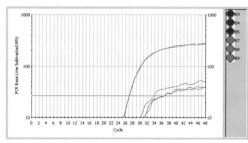

Plate 18.1. Two HEX-labeled linear probes were designed to hybridize to the lectin gene. Both probes were the identical DNA sequences, purchased from the same vendor and only differed in the 3' quencher (BH2 or TAMRA). Genomic DNA (100 ng) was extracted from soybean powder (Fluka) and amplified (denature: 95°C × 3 min; anneal/extend 50 cycles of 95°C ×10 s, 60°C × 45 s) with 200 nM of each primer and 100 nM of probe. The traces on the right represent the reactions using the TAMRA-quenched probe, the traces to the left—the reactions using the BH2-quenched probe.

Plate 18.2 (Right). Two VIC-TAMRA labeled TaqMan probes with identical DNA sequences were purchased on different dates from the same vendor. 100 nM of each probe was diluted in 1× PCR buffer (3 replicate wells) and exposed in Imaging Services (iCycler iQ detection

system) at 320, 80, and 40 ms. Pixel saturation, due to high levels of background fluorescence, was detected at every exposure except 40 ms.

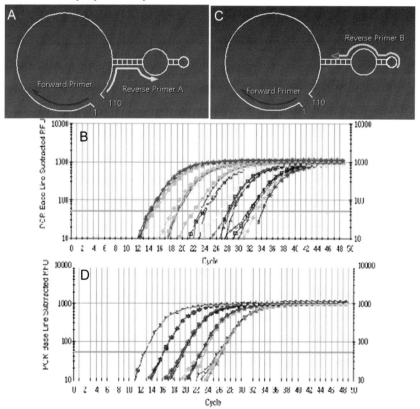

Plate 18.3. Panels **B** and **D** show amplification traces of a ten-fold dilution series of the cyclophilin target with primer set A (**A**) and primer set B (**C**), respectively. Both experiments were performed on the same plate using the same plasmid dilution series.

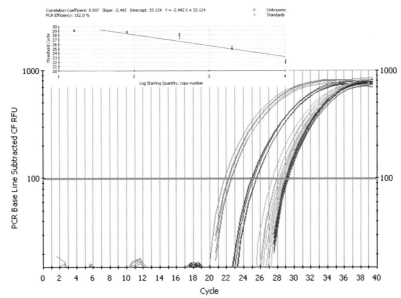

Plate 18.4. A five-fold dilution series (10,000–16 copies) of IL1-beta plasmid was amplified with 300 nM of forward and reverse primers, designed to amplify IL1-beta and to produce primer-dimers due to a GGG/CCC overlap at their 3' ends. The fluorescent data were collected at the annealing temperature of 60°C.

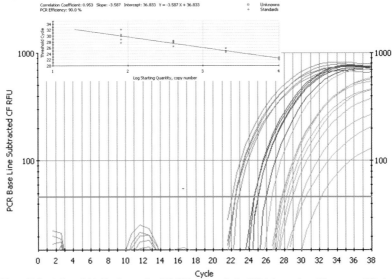

Plate 18.5. A five-fold dilution series (10,000–16 copies) of IL1-beta plasmid was amplified with 300 nM of forward and reverse primers, designed to amplify IL1-beta and to produce primer-dimers due to a GGG/CCC overlap at their 3' ends. The amplification was performed at an annealing temperature of 60°C; however, the fluorescent data was collected at 82°C after the primer dimers had melted. The formation of primer dimers resulted in a poor correlation coefficient (R = 0.953) and a PCR efficiency of 90% as displayed in the standard curve (**inset**).

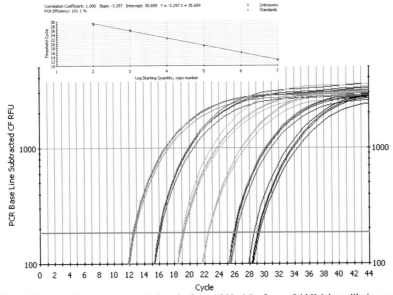

Plate 18.6. Amplification using redesigned primers (300 nM) of a ten-fold IL1-beta dilution series from 10^7–10^2 copies of DNA. Data were collected at the annealing temperature (60°C), using SYBR Green I. The standard curve resulted in a correlation coefficient of 1.000 and a PCR efficiency of 101.1% (**inset**).

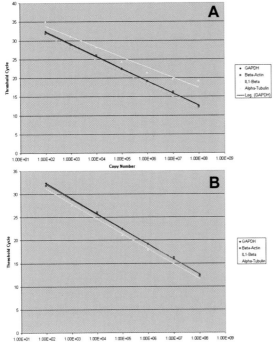

Plate 18.7. Standard curves for a non-optimized (panel **A**) and optimized (panel **B**) four-target multiplex real-time PCR assay. In panel **A**, the slope of the upper curve is different from the three other curves, representing unequal efficiencies. In Panel **B** the slopes of the curves are all parallel, representing equalized efficiencies.

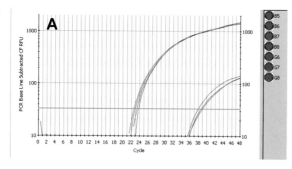

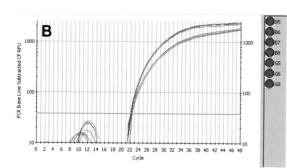

Plate 18.8. Panel **A** shows amplification traces of a single reaction amplified alone (green traces) or in a four-target multiplex (blue traces). This is a non-optimized multiplex reaction, as there is a large shift in the observed C_t values. Panel **B** shows the same targets, this time with the optimized conditions, as demonstrated by no shift in the observed C_t values between the single and multiplex reactions.

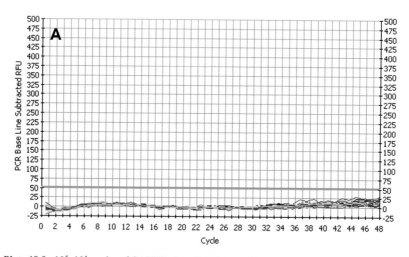

Plate 18.9. 10^5–10^1 copies of GAPDH plasmid DNA (ten-fold dilution series) were co-amplified with 10^9 copies of α-tubulin plasmid DNA using different concentrations of DNA polymerase, dNTPs, and Mg^{2+}. Amplified products were detected by FAM-GAPDH-BH1 and HEX-α-tubulin-BH2 linear probes. Primer concentrations for both GAPDH and α-tubulin remained constant at 300nM. (**A**) 1× commercially available supermix, (**B** and **C**) 1× commercially available supermix supplemented with additional reagents. (*See Panels B and C on next page.*)

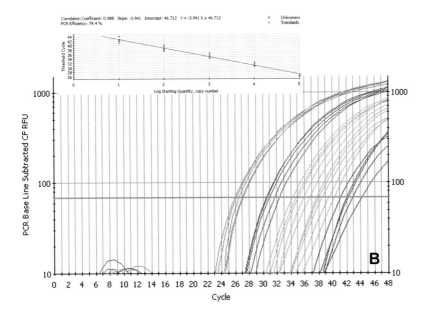

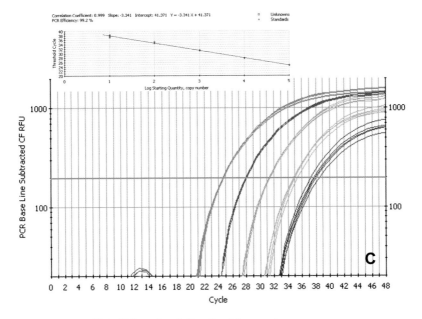

Plate 18.9 *continued. See Panel A on previous page.*

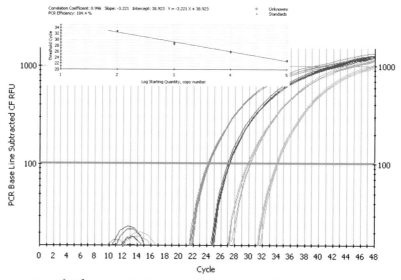

Plate 18.10. 10^5–10^2 copies of GAPDH plasmid DNA (ten-fold dilution series) were coamplified with 10^9 copies of α-tubulin plasmid DNA using a 1× commercially available supermix. Amplified products were detected by FAM-GAPDH-BH1 and HEX-α-tubulin-BH2 linear probes. The primers designed to amplify the α-tubulin gene were reduced to 25 nM while the primer for GAPDH was 250 nM.

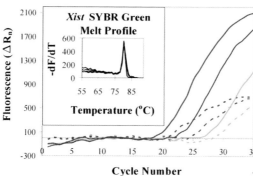

Plate 21.2 (Bottom). Theoretical folding (http://bioinfo.math.rpi.edu/~mfold/dna/form1.cgi) of the chosen *Xist* template at annealing temperature (53°C). The sequences corresponding to primers and Molecular Beacons binding sites are indicated. Although the G-B1 probe includes some nucleotides likely to be engaged in secondary structure, it gives an improved signal over B-1, probably through a more stable interaction with the target.

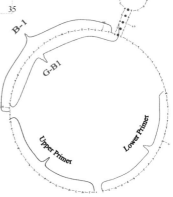

Plate 21.1 (Top). Comparison of the fluorescent signals generated by Molecular Beacons B-1 and G-B1 during real-time PCR of the same *Xist* template. Green—10 male mouse genomes; red—100 genomes; blue—1000 genomes. Solid lines—TET-G-B1 probe; broken lines—FAM-B1 probe. Probes were synthesized in-house and were used at equal concentration (0.6 μM) and under the same conditions. Probes' binding sites (loops) were different as shown in **Plate 21.2**, stems were identical. **Inset:** The same PCR assay was performed using SYBR Green as a probe instead of Molecular Beacons. Melting profile analysis of the amplification product reveals a single peak.

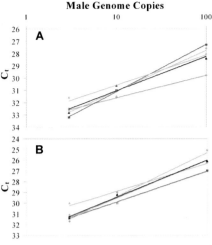

Male Genome Copies

Plate 21.3. Primer concentration effects on multiplex *Xist/Sry* amplification of 3, 10, and 100 male mouse genomes. PCR conditions were kept constant in all experiments, primers concentrations were varied as follows:
Green—0.1 µM *Xist*/0.1 µM *Sry* (concentration refers to each of the two primers in a pair);
red—0.1 µM *Xist*/0.3 µM *Sry*;
black—0.3 µM *Xist*/0.3 µM *Sry*;
light purple—0.3 µM *Xist*/0.5 µM *Sry*;
blue—0.5 µM *Xist*/0.5 µM *Sry*.
(A) *Sry* C_t values; (B) *Xist* C_t values. (C_t values were averages of three determinations. Molecular Beacons *Xist* TET-G-B1 and *Sry* FAM-2NEG used in this experiment onwards were synthesized by Research Genetics, Inc., and were added at 0.3 µM final concentration. Linear regression trendlines are shown for each concentration of the primers.

Plate 21.4 (Right). Multiplex amplification of *Xist* and *Sry* templates in male and female mouse genomes. Solid lines—*Xist*; broken lines—*Sry* (0.3 µM each *Xist* TET-G-B1 and *Sry* FAM-2NEG probes). (A) Male genomes; (B) Female genomes. Yellow—3 genomes; green—10 genomes; red—100 genomes; blue—1,000 genomes. **Inset**: *Xist* (red) and *Sry* (blue) genomic standards obtained from the male genomes C_t values (linear regression trendlines).

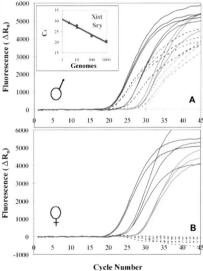

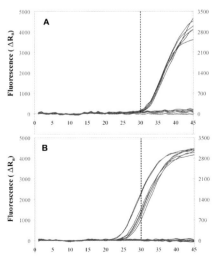

Plate 21.5 (Left). Real-time PCR *Xist* and *Sry* plots from single mouse blastomeres. Data in each panel derive from every cell individually recovered from the same 8-cell stage embryo. Blastomeres were isolated following laser zona-drilling (see pp. 690–691 and **Fig. 21.4** for details. (A) Male embryo; (B) Female embryo. Red—*Xist* (fluorescence intensity scale on the left); blue—*Sry* (fluorescence intensity scale on the right).
Molecular Beacons were the same as in the experiments of **Figs. 21.2** and **21.3** and **Plates 21.3** and **21.4** and were used at 0.3 µM concentration.

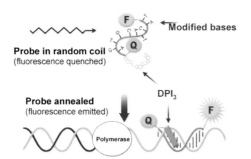

Plate 23.1. The MGB Eclipse probe. The MGB Eclipse Probe rests in a random coil quenched form and fluoresces when it hybridizes to a target. Q is the Eclipse Quencher and F is a fluorophore.

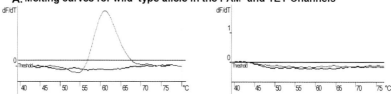

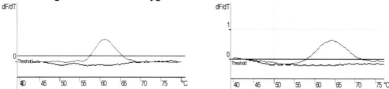

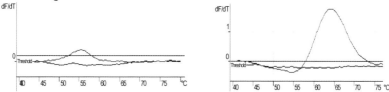

Plate 23.2. The detection of IL-13-02 alleles in a wild-type, a heterozygous, and a mutant sample. The first derivative melting curve profiles in the FAM and TET channels for (**A**) wild-type, (**B**) heterozygous, and (**C**) mutant samples.

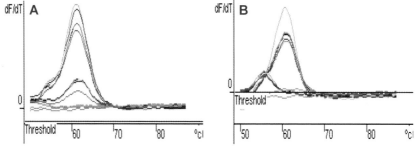

Plate 23.3 Melting curve analysis of IL5 alleles in 15 genomic DNA samples. (**A**) Melting curve profiles in the FAM channel. (**B**) Melting curve profiles in the TET channel.

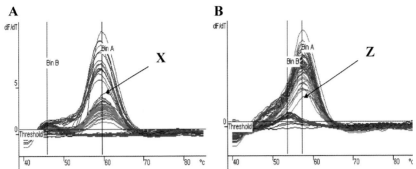

A

B

Plate 23.4. The analysis of 71 human genomic DNA samples for DIO2-02 alleles. (**A**) FAM channel and (**B**) TET channel. Wild-type, heterozygous, and mutant samples are shown in blue, green, and red, respectively. Samples X and Z are wild-type and mutant samples, respectively.

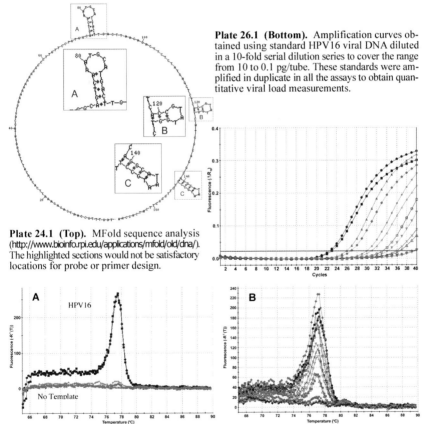

Plate 26.1 (Bottom). Amplification curves obtained using standard HPV16 viral DNA diluted in a 10-fold serial dilution series to cover the range from 10 to 0.1 pg/tube. These standards were amplified in duplicate in all the assays to obtain quantitative viral load measurements.

Plate 24.1 (Top). MFold sequence analysis (http://www.bioinfo.rpi.edu/applications/mfold/old/dna/). The highlighted sections would not be satisfactory locations for probe or primer design.

Plate 26.2 SYBR Green I dissociation profile. Melting curve analysis was performed on the standard curve sample products of PCR in order to identify nonspecific PCR products. (**A**) No product is evident in the no-template control (NTC) sample; hence these primers do not interact significantly. (**B**) The products formed from the template of the standard curve are homologous indicating that the primers produce a single product.

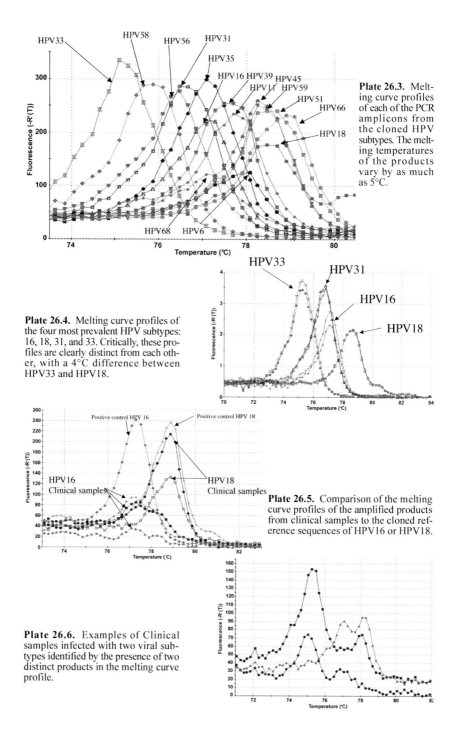

Plate 26.3. Melting curve profiles of each of the PCR amplicons from the cloned HPV subtypes. The melting temperatures of the products vary by as much as 5°C.

Plate 26.4. Melting curve profiles of the four most prevalent HPV subtypes: 16, 18, 31, and 33. Critically, these profiles are clearly distinct from each other, with a 4°C difference between HPV33 and HPV18.

Plate 26.5. Comparison of the melting curve profiles of the amplified products from clinical samples to the cloned reference sequences of HPV16 or HPV18.

Plate 26.6. Examples of Clinical samples infected with two viral subtypes identified by the presence of two distinct products in the melting curve profile.

38. Kelman Z, Hurwitz J, O'Donnell M: **Processivity of DNA polymerases: Two mechanisms, one goal.** *Structure* 1998, **6**:121–125.

39. Pavlov AR, Belova GI, Kozyavkin SA, Slesarev AI: **Helix-hairpin-helix motifs confer salt resistance and processivity on chimeric DNA polymerases.** *Proc Natl Acad Sci USA* 2002, **99**:13510–13515.

40. Reiss RA, Rutz B: **Quality control PCR: A method for detecting inhibitors of *Taq* DNA polymerase.** *Biotechniques* 1999, **27**:920–926.

41. Dang C, Jayasena SD: **Oligonucleotide inhibitors of *Taq* DNA polymerase facilitate detection of low copy number targets by PCR.** *J Mol Biol* 1996, **264**:268–278.

42. Shanmugam V, Sell KW, Saha BK: **Mistyping ACE heterozygotes.** *PCR Methods Appl* 1993, **3**:120–121.

43. Weissensteiner T, Lanchbury JS: **Strategy for controlling preferential amplification and avoiding false negatives in PCR typing.** *Biotechniques* 1996, **21**:1102–1108.

44. Mutter GL, Boynton KA: **PCR bias in amplification of androgen receptor alleles, a trinucleotide repeat marker used in clonality studies.** *Nucleic Acids Res* 1995, **23**:1411–1418.

45. Walsh PS, Erlich HA, Higuchi R: **Preferential PCR amplification of alleles: Mechanisms and solutions.** *PCR Methods Appl* 1992, **1**:241–250.

46. Al Soud WA, Radstrom P: **Capacity of nine thermostable DNA polymerases to mediate DNA amplification in the presence of PCR-inhibiting samples.** *Appl Environ Microbiol:* 1998 **64**: 3748–3753.

47. Poddar SK, Sawyer MH, Connor JD: **Effect of inhibitors in clinical specimens on *Taq* and *Tth* DNA polymerase-based PCR amplification of influenza A virus.** *J Med Microbiol* 1998, **47**:1131–1135.

48. Barnes WM: **PCR amplification of up to 35-kb DNA with high fidelity and high yield from lambda bacteriophage templates.** *Proc Natl Acad Sci USA* 1994, **91**:2216–2220.

49. Jenkins GJ, Burlinson B, Parry JM: **The polymerase inhibition assay: A methodology for the identification of DNA-damaging agents.** *Mol Carcinog* 2000, **27**:289–297.

50. Rys PN, Persing DH: **Preventing false positives: Quantitative evaluation of three protocols for inactivation of polymerase chain reaction amplification products.** *J Clin Microbiol* 1993, **31**:2356–2360.

51. Sarkar G, Sommer SS: **Shedding light on PCR contamination .** *Nature* 1990, **343**:27.

52. Sarkar G, Sommer S: **More light on PCR contamination.** *Nature* 1990, **347**:340–341.

53. Erlich HA, Gelfand D, Sninsky JJ: **Recent advances in the polymerase chain reaction.** *Science* 1991, **252**:1643–1651.

54. Frothingham R, Blitchington RB, Lee DH, Greene RC, Wilson KH: **UV absorption complicates PCR decontamination.** *Biotechniques* 1992, **13**:208–210.

55. Victor T, Jordaan A, du TR,Van Helden PD: **Laboratory experience and guidelines for avoiding false positive polymerase chain reaction results.** *Eur J Clin Chem Clin Biochem* 1993, **31**:531–535.

56. Taggart E, Carroll K, Byington C, Crist G, Hillyard D: **Use of heat labile UNG in an RT-PCR assay for enterovirus detection.** *J Virol Methods* 2002, **105**:57.

57. Longo MC, Berninger MS, Hartley JL: **Use of uracil DNA glycosylase to control carry-over contamination in polymerase chain reactions.** *Gene* 1990, **93**:125–128.

58. Espy MJ, Smith TF, Persing DH: **Dependence of polymerase chain reaction product inactivation protocols on amplicon length and sequence composition.** *J Clin Microbiol* 1993, **31**:2361–2365.

59. Chou Q, Russell M, Birch DE, Raymond J, Bloch W: **Prevention of pre-PCR mispriming and primer dimerization improves low-copy-number amplifications.** *Nucleic Acids Res* 1992, **20**:1717–1723.

60. Kebelmann-Betzing C, Seeger K, Dragon S, Schmitt G, Moricke A., Schild TA, Henze G, Beyermann B: **Advantages of a new Taq DNA polymerase in multiplex PCR and time-release PCR.** *Biotechniques* 1998, **24**:154–158.

61. Teo I, Choi J, Morlese J, Taylor G, Shaunak S: **LightCycler qPCR optimisation for low copy number target DNA.** *J Immunol Methods* 2002, **270**:119.

62. Exner MM, Lewinski MA: **Sensitivity of multiplex real-time PCR reactions, using the LightCycler and the ABI PRISM 7700 Sequence Detection System, is dependent on the concentration of the DNA polymerase.** *Mol Cell Probes* 2002, **16**:351–357.

63. Williams JF: **Optimization strategies for the polymerase chain reaction.** *Biotechniques* 1989, **7**:762–769.

64. Eckert KA, Kunkel TA: **DNA polymerase fidelity and the polymerase chain reaction.** *PCR Methods Appl* 1991, **1**:17–24.

65. Saiki RK, Scharf S, Faloona F, Mullis KB, Horn GT, Erlich HA, Arnheim N: **Enzymatic amplification of beta-globin genomic sequences and restriction site analysis for diagnosis of sickle cell anemia.** *Science* 1985, **230**:1350–1354.

66. Kaiser R, Tremblay PB, Roots I, Brockmoller J: **Validity of PCR with emphasis on variable number of tandem repeat analysis.** *Clin Biochem* 2002, **35**:49–56.

67. Hu CY, Allen M, Gyllensten U: **Effect of freezing of the PCR buffer on the amplification specificity: allelic exclusion and preferential amplification of contaminating molecules.** *PCR Methods Appl* 1992, **2**:182–183.

68. Chandler DP, Wagnon CA, Bolton,H Jr: **Reverse transcriptase (RT) inhibition of PCR at low concentrations of template and its implications for quantitative RT-PCR.** *Appl Environ Microbiol* 1998, **64**:669–677.

69. Liss B: **Improved quantitative real-time RT-PCR for expression profiling of individual cells.** *Nucleic Acids Res* 2002, **30**:E89.

70. Wittwer CT, Herrmann MG, Gundry CN: **Elenitoba-Johnson KS: Real-time multiplex PCR assays.** *Methods* 2001, **25**: 430–442.

71. Pomp D, Medrano JF: **Organic solvents as facilitators of polymerase chain reaction.** *Biotechniques* 1991, **10**:58–59.

72. Varadaraj K, Skinner DM: **Denaturants or cosolvents improve the specificity of PCR amplification of a G + C-rich DNA using genetically engineered DNA polymerases.** *Gene* 1994, **140**:1–5.

73. McDowell DG, Burns NA, Parkes HC: **Localised sequence regions possessing high melting temperatures prevent the amplification of a DNA mimic in competitive PCR.** *Nucleic Acids Res* 1998, **26**:3340–3347.

74. Weaver DT, DePamphilis ML: **Specific sequences in native DNA that arrest synthesis by DNA polymerase alpha.** *J Biol Chem* 1982, **257**:2075–2086.

75. Weaver DT, DePamphilis ML: **The role of palindromic and non-palindromic sequences in arresting DNA synthesis *in vitro* and *in vivo*.** *J Mol Biol* 1984, **180**:961–986.

76. Zacharias W, Larson JE, Klysik J, Stirdivant SM, Wells RD: **Conditions which cause the right-handed to left-handed DNA conformational transitions. Evidence for several types of left-handed DNA structures in solution.** *J Biol Chem* 1982, **257**:2775–2782.

77. Clark JM: **Novel non-templated nucleotide addition reactions catalyzed by procaryotic and eucaryotic DNA polymerases.** *Nucleic Acids Res* 1988, **16**:9677–9686.

78. Hu G: **DNA polymerase-catalyzed addition of nontemplated extra nucleotides to the 3' end of a DNA fragment.** *DNA Cell Biol* 1993, **12**:763–770.

79. Demeke T, Adams RP: **The effects of plant polysaccharides and buffer additives on PCR.** *Biotechniques* 1992, **12**:332–334.

80. Comey CT, Jung JM, Budowle B: **Use of formamide to improve amplification of HLA DQ alpha sequences.** *Biotechniques* 1991, **10**: 60–61.

81. Kreader CA: **Relief of amplification inhibition in PCR with bovine serum albumin or T4 gene 32 protein.** *Appl.Environ.Microbiol* 1996, **62**: 1102–1106.

82. Chevet E, Lemaitre G, Katinka MD: **Low concentrations of tetramethylammonium chloride increase yield and specificity of PCR.** *Nucleic Acids Res* 1995, **23**:3343–3344.

83. Louwrier A, van der Valk A: **Can sucrose affect polymerase chain reaction product formation?** *Biotechnology Letters* 2001, **23**:175–178.

84. Hall LM, Slee E, Jones DS: **Overcoming polymerase chain reaction inhibition in old animal tissue samples using ethidium bromide.** *Anal Biochem* 1995, **225**:169–172.

85. Chakrabarti R, Schutt CE: **The enhancement of PCR amplification by low molecular weight amides.** *Nucleic Acids Res* 2001, **29**:2377–2381.

86. Sarkar G, Kapelner S, Sommer SS: **Formamide can dramatically improve the specificity of PCR.** *Nucleic Acids Res* 1990, **18**:7465.

87. Winship PR: **An improved method for directly sequencing PCR amplified material using dimethyl sulphoxide.** *Nucleic Acids Res* 1989, **17**:1266.

88. Rasmussen HN, Rasmussen OF, Andersen JK, Olsen JE: **Specific detection of pathogenic *Yersinia enterocolitica* by two-step PCR using hot-start and DMSO.** *Mol Cell Probes* 1994, **8**:99–108.

89. Sun Y, Hegamyer G, Colburn NH: **PCR-direct sequencing of a GC-rich region by inclusion of 10% DMSO: Application to mouse c-jun.** *Biotechniques* 1993, **15**:372–374.

90. Chakrabarti R, Schutt CE: **Novel sulfoxides facilitate GC-rich template amplification.** *Biotechniques* 2002, **32**:866, 868, 870–722, 874.

91. Chakrabarti R, Schutt CE: **The enhancement of PCR amplification by low molecular-weight sulfones.** *Gene* 2001, **274**:293–298.

92. Shammas FV, Heikkila R, Osland A: **Fluorescence-based method for measuring and determining the mechanisms of recombination in quantitative PCR.** *Clin Chim Acta* 2001, **304**:19–28.

93. Sidhu MK, Liao MJ, Rashidbaigi A: **Dimethyl sulfoxide improves RNA amplification.** *Biotechniques* 1996, **21**:44–47.

94. Henke W, Herdel K, Jung K, Schnorr D, Loening SA: **Betaine improves the PCR amplification of GC-rich DNA sequences.** *Nucleic Acids Res* 1997, **25**:3957–3958.

95. Baskaran N, Kandpal RP, Bhargava AK, Glynn MW, Bale A, Weissman SM: **Uniform amplification of a mixture of deoxyribonucleic acids with varying GC content.** *Genome Res* 1996, **6**:633–638.

96. Santoro MM, Liu Y, Khan SM, Hou LX, Bolen DW: **Increased thermal stability of proteins in the presence of naturally occurring osmolytes.** *Biochemistry* 1992, **31**:5278–5283.

97. Rees WA, Yager TD, Korte J, Von Hippel PH: **Betaine can eliminate the base pair composition dependence of DNA melting.** *Biochemistry* 1993, **32**:137–144.

11

Data Analysis and Interpretation

Stephen A. Bustin and Tania Nolan

11

Data Analysis and Interpretation

Stephen A. Bustin* and Tania Nolan†

**Barts and The London, Queen Mary's School of Medicine
and Dentistry, University of London, London, United Kingdom
†Stratagene Europe, Amsterdam, The Netherlands*

11.1. Introduction

In the previous chapters the fundamental technical aspects of real-time qPCR assays have been dissected and discussed. In this chapter the focus turns to the conversion of those accurate numerical data into relevant information that can be compared and validated between laboratories and address biological questions in a meaningful way.

In principle, quantification by real-time assays is easy; the more copies of nucleic acid there are at the beginning of the assay, the fewer cycles of amplification are required to generate a specific number of products. Therefore, the number of cycles required for the fluorescence to reach the specific threshold level of detection, C_t, is inversely correlated to the amount of nucleic acid in the original sample. Conversion of the C_t to the quantity of nucleic acid in the sample is achieved by interpolation of the C_t value versus a linear standard curve of C_t values obtained from a serially diluted standard. Such curves are linear over at least six to eight orders of magnitude, a dynamic range that is unsurpassed by other methods for quantitative DNA analysis. However, in practice, a C_t value on its own means nothing.

11.2. Precision, Accuracy, and Relevance

Since the precision of real-time assays is not in question, what is the problem? It is important to realize that (1) a result can be precise, but at the same time precisely wrong, (2) precise quantification is not the same as accurate quantification, and (3) that high accuracy is difficult to achieve. What is the difference between precise and accurate? Precision relates to the reproducibility and repeatability of results, i.e., how similar are values that have been obtained in exactly the same way? Repeatability and reproducibility are not the same: we will use the term **reproducibility** when the same person carries out a repeat assay, whereas **repeatability** is when a different individual carries out the same assay, not necessarily in the same laboratory. Reproducibility is best measured by the coefficient of variation (CV) of an assay, obtained by dividing the standard deviation (SD) by the arithmetic mean of the measured values. For any given assay, reproducibility determines the minimum difference in initial target concentration that the assay can distinguish. It says nothing about the relevance of the data that may be highly reproducible, but remain reproducibly meaningless. The reason for this is that one is not attempting to generate precise data *per se*, but biologically relevant ones. Accuracy, on the other hand, is a measure of the agreement between experimental mean and true value, which is probably not known. **Fig. 11.1** illustrates the difference graphically. Hence it is the degree of accuracy, not the precision, of quantitative data that is likely to be biologically meaningful. An interesting study looked at both intra- and inter-assay variability and concluded that the minimum difference that can be differentiated between sets of replicate samples is 23% and that the minimum difference between groups of paired treated and control samples is 52%.[1]

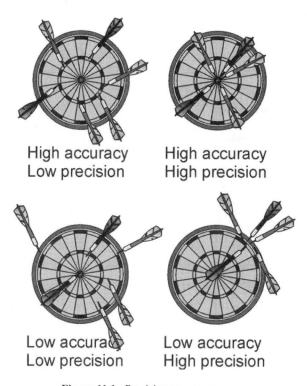

High accuracy
Low precision

High accuracy
High precision

Low accuracy
Low precision

Low accuracy
High precision

Figure 11.1. Precision vs. accuracy.

Quantitative data, by definition, are numerical results that lend themselves to statistical analysis. However, there are significant problems regarding the efficient evaluation and the mathematical and statistical analysis of the enormous amount of data acquired by this technology, as these functions are not included in the software provided by the manufacturers of the detection systems.[2]

It will soon become clear that preparing the template, selecting primers and probes and carrying out the qPCR assay was the easy bit! They are as nothing compared to the problems facing the investigator when it comes to interpreting those C_ts.[3] Not surprisingly, this is one area where everyone has their own opinion and it is way beyond the scope of this book (or any book) to discuss or even describe them. However, two issues stand out and if they are addressed in a satisfactory way, then one might disagree with the way the result was interpreted, but it should have some validity. These two issues are interlinked and concern the question of what is being quantitated, simplified as relative or absolute quantification.

11.3. Quantitative Principles

PCR is an exponential amplification of a DNA target molecule population of initial quantity, N_0. Assuming an amplification efficiency of 100%, every molecule would be duplicated at each cycle and the population size at cycle n, N_n, would be double the size of the population at cycle $n-1$ (N_{n-1}). With a reaction yield of 100%, there is a nonambiguous relation between the initial copy number (N_0) and the number of molecules after n cycles of amplification (N_n) and it is possible to extrapolate to the number of molecules that were present at the start of the reaction. This is described in the formula $N_n = N_0 \times 2^n$. However, in real life the yield of the amplification reaction is not 100% and hence the amplification rate is less than 2; in fact, it can be anywhere between 1 and 2. If a single initial molecule undergoes one cycle of amplification, the reaction dynamics are stochastic and the number of molecules can be either 2 or remain 1. As the reaction proceeds, the number of molecules after cycle n will be randomly distributed between 1 and 2^n. This has two consequences: (1) initial copy numbers cannot be determined, they can only be statistically estimated and (2) because of the variability surrounding every PCR assay, a **consistent** relationship between the amount of input target and absolute amount of amplified product is difficult to obtain.

A more appropriate mathematical model would take amplification efficiency into consideration[4] and might be based on equation $N_n = N_0(1 + E)n$, where E is the amplification efficiency. From this equation, a second one can be derived, $LogN_n = [Log(1 + E)] \times n + LogN_0$, which describes a linear relationship in the format, $y = mx + b$, whose slope (m) has the value of $Log(1+E)$ and whose y-intercept (b) is $LogN_0$. Using linear regression analysis one can determine both the initial number of template and the efficiency of the amplification. This equation is used to determine the properties of a standard curve (see **Sections 11.8** and **11.9**. The slope of the line is the negative reciprocal of the log of the efficiency. The y-axis intercept is the log of the amount of PCR product at threshold (in fluorescence units) divided by the log of efficiency. However, this equation makes some assumptions:

1. Growth of real time PCR product is an unlimited process and assumes that the amplification efficiency is equal as well as constant.

2. Since there is only one "E," the efficiency must be constant within each reaction from cycle one up to the C_t.

3. The C_t values of the unknowns will be converted to concentrations using the equation derived from the standards. Therefore, the amplification efficiency of the standards and of the unknowns must be the same.

Unfortunately, in real-life amplification experiments, the efficiency changes from cycle to cycle and the kinetics can be different even for the same gene from the same tissue sample.[5] Hence a lower C_t does not necessarily mean that the specific target was present initially at a higher copy number. Quite apart from any variation due to sample loading, amplification of template by PCR is a process involving multiple components, including amount of templates, primers, ions, and nucleotides, enzyme activity, and reaction temperature. Except for the reaction temperature, which is well controlled in modern thermal cyclers, all of these components change dynamically as the reaction progresses and subsequently affect amplification efficiency. Since the reaction eventually saturates, amplification efficiency must eventually fall to zero.[5] The fine detail and possible solutions to this problem are discussed within the context of numerous different mathematical models,[4,6-14] all of which attempt to provide more accurate quantification of real-time PCR assays.

Note: There is a typographical error in equation 3 of one of the models,[13] with the correct equation available from http://www.wzw.tum.de/gene-quantification/.

11.4. Effect of Initial Copy Numbers

Estimates of initial copy numbers greater than 1,000 are quite accurate, and errors have been calculated to be as little as 1%, depending on the amplification rate. However, for initial copy numbers less than 1,000, the precision of the estimate may become limiting. The reason for this is that when the number of target molecules is small, the magnitude of the influence of statistical variations on the outcome of the qPCR assay can no longer be ignored. As discussed above, if a single initial molecule undergoes one cycle of amplification, the number of molecules can be either 2 or remain 1. In fact, if the amplification efficiency is 0.8, there is a 20% probability that after one cycle of amplification there is still one copy. Mathematical descriptions of PCR reactions in these conditions have been published[15] and expected outcomes of the PCR in different conditions, together with confidence intervals, have been calculated. These calculations show that relative uncertainties (ratio of uncertainty over true value) range from 100% for a few copies to 10–20% for initial copy numbers close to 100.[16] Uncertainty is inversely correlated with amplification efficiency: for an initial 100 copy number target the relative uncertainty is 10% if the amplification efficiency is 0.9, but 25% if it is 0.5. For a single copy target, an amplification efficiency of 0.9 results in a relative uncertainty of 99%, but this increases to 225% if the amplification efficiency is 0.5. The high variance implies that any differences brought about by experimental treatment need to be relatively large in size before they can be detected reliably. Furthermore, the detection limit of a significant difference in a given experimental setting must be assessed prior to the experiment to work out the sample sizes required to achieve a statistically and biologically meaningful result.

There are reports of successful qPCR from very low target copy numbers. Reliable quantification of as few as 10 genomic hepatitic C virus RNA copies in chimpanzee plasma has been reported.[17] The authors' intra-assay CV at 10 copies is low at 3.1%, with the inter-assay CV a remarkable 4.4% at 10 copies and 4.15% for 100,000 copies. Another report describes the detection of single copies of the Herpes simplex virus thymidine kinase gene in a high background of genomic DNA using a hydrolysis probe and the ABI Prism 7700 and clearly demonstrates the stochastic sampling effects in the quantification of small numbers of molecules.[18] The target was detected in 23 out of 30 replicate samples containing an average of one copy of target. This percentage (76.7%) is in accordance with the Poisson probability distribution, which predicts that 63.2% of the samples would contain at least one or more targets, and 36.8% would contain no target. Closer analysis of the data reveals another interesting observation, not commented upon by the authors. C_ts for the one-copy replicates ranged from 43.3–48.8, whereas the C_ts for ten-copy replicates ranged from 43.3–43.9. Therefore, in addition to the Poisson probability distribution (some samples do not contain any template), there appears to be an added influence affecting the amplification of such low copy number targets, since a C_t difference of 5 within the single copy samples corresponds to an apparent 32-fold-difference in copy number terms.

11.5. Monte Carlo Effect

An apparent 32-fold difference in copy number when measuring low target numbers at high C_t may well be an example of the "Monte Carlo" effect, an inherent limitation of PCR amplification from small amounts of any complex template due to differences in amplification efficiency between individual templates in an amplifying cDNA population.[19] Any PCR template diluted past a certain threshold copy number will display large variations in amplification. The same is true for a cDNA molecule within a cDNA library: each cDNA template has a certain probability of being amplified or being lost. The Monte Carlo effect is dependent upon template concentration: the lower the abundance of any template, the less likely its true abundance will be reflected in the amplified product. One model for this phenomenon considers primer annealing to any individual template molecule during each PCR cycle as a random event. Under conditions of primer excess, the probability of primer annealing is dependent upon annealing temperature, annealing time, and the number of available templates. If the number of molecules of a particular template is limiting, then that template within a complex mixture will have slight and random differences in amplification efficiencies depending upon whether the primers were able to anneal. If these differences occur early in the PCR assay, large variations in final product concentration can be produced during the exponential phase of the amplification reaction. cDNAs of lower abundance will be more likely to experience the Monte Carlo effect, since their probability of primer annealing is lower.

11.6. Amplification Efficiency

Clearly, knowledge of cycle-by-cycle amplification efficiency is an important parameter for judging the reliability of the copy number estimation. The estimation of the amplification rate of a reaction must be based on the data collected from that reaction only. It cannot be based on a set of related reactions since there are variations of the amplification rate from one reaction to another. The estimation must also be able to detect the end of the "exponential phase." Incidentally, one of the key (and unique) features of the Corbett Rotor-Gene is that it provides cycle-by-cycle amplification efficiency calculations. This can provide very interesting information: 12 identical samples containing a nominal 100,000 copies of DNA were amplified and fluorescence was detected using a TaqMan probe labeled with FAM and TAMRA. The average amplification efficiency for all samples was 1.78 with 95% confidence intervals of 1.75–1.80 and a coefficient of variation of 6.7%. Twelve replicates of another amplicon containing a nominal 100,000 copies of DNA were amplified, resulting in a similar average amplification efficiency of 1.75. However, in this experiment the 95% confidence intervals were 1.6–1.89 and the coefficient of variation was 12.9%. Since the experiments were carried out by the same investigator using the same instrument, micropipettes, and master mixes, the differences in amplification efficiency must be due to the different amplicons. Differences in amplification efficiency can have profound effects as shown in **Table 11.1**.

In other words, a 10% reduction in efficiency (from 2 fold to 1.9 fold per cycle) will result in an 80% drop in the amount of product. A 20% decrease in efficiency per cycle (1.8 fold amplification per cycle) will result in a 95% reduction, and a 30% decrease will result in a 99% reduction in yield compared to 2 fold per cycle.

Table 11.1. Relationship between amplification efficiency and expected target copy number.

Amplification rate per cycle	Expected copy number after 30 cycles	% of expected copy number
2	$2^{30} = 1 \times 10^9$	100
1.9	$1.9^{30} = 0.2 \times 10^9$	20
1.8	$1.8^{30} = 0.05 \times 10^9$	5
1.7	$1.7^{30} = 0.008 \times 10^9$	1

11.7. Relative, Comparative or Absolute Quantification

The question of how to express quantitative RT-qPCR data has still not been answered to universal satisfaction. It is usually simplified around the terms relative, comparative, and absolute, and numerous papers have been published, arguing the merits of one over the other, with several discussion groups providing a wide range of opinion among the individuals carrying out real-time PCR experiments. It is important to remember that the term "absolute" is misleading if it is not properly qualified. It implies some number without any units, i.e., 2×10^6 copies of a particular mRNA. In biological samples, this is of course quite meaningless. Instead, the mRNA copy number must be related to some biological parameter, e.g., cell number, mg tissue, μg DNA, μg total RNA, reference gene copy number, rRNA copy number, or the age at which the investigator obtained his/her PhD. In this sense, all quantification is relative. Since "absolute" quantification is obtained using standard curves, the term "standard curve quantification" has been proposed.[20] However, as often happen, as "absolute" sounds better and is snappier, this term has become widely accepted and is probably here to stay. There is no reason why it should not be used as long as its limitations are clearly understood. For the purposes of this discussion, absolute and relative (sometimes referred to as comparative) are defined as shown in **Fig. 11.2**. It is worth remembering that any quantitative data represent a snapshot of a specific time point, at a particular time (it could be day or night) on a particular day (it could be summer or winter) and that the data could be (and probably would be) significantly different if the sample were taken at another time and day. Therefore, it is important to record as many parameters as possible *vis-à-vis* one's samples so that they can be properly stratified and compared.

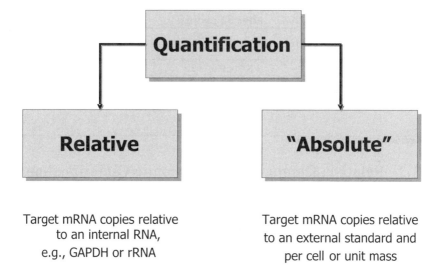

Figure 11.2. Relative vs. absolute quantification.

11.8. Absolute Quantification

Any meaningful comparison of DNA or mRNA levels requires either that the amplification efficiencies of the amplicons being targeted are the same or that a standard is used that compensates for any differences. Absolute quantification refers to an analysis where the comparison of unknown samples to an external standard provides an accurate and reliable method for the quantification of nucleic acids.[21] In theory, the most accurate way of achieving this is to construct standard curves. The principle of using a standard curve in qPCR is the same as in any other laboratory analysis: C_ts obtained from an unknown sample are compared to C_ts generated from a series of samples of known concentration or copy number. Results can be expressed as copy number per unit mass of something. Admittedly, there is a major problem with that "something." The expression of a target nucleic acid is usually compared across many samples, often from different individuals, and sometimes from different tissues. In theory, the amount of product from each reaction is proportional to the initial amount of target in each sample. However, since small differences in nucleic acid input or reaction conditions can lead to large differences in PCR product yield, the amount of starting material must be quantitated with rigorous accuracy to normalize sample data and correct for tube-to-tube differences. Therefore, if absolute quantification is to be accurate, it needs to take that variability into account.

11.9. Standard Curves

The steps involved in constructing a standard curve are very straight-forward:

1. A series of five to six serial dilutions (2,5,10-fold) of known concentration or copy numbers is prepared using amplicon-specific sense-strand oligonucleotides, T7-transcribed RNA, linear plasmid DNA, universal reference RNA, genomic DNA or whatever standard is being used. Their concentration range should match the expected concentration range of the sample.

   Note: The accuracy of the absolute quantification assay is entirely dependent on the accuracy of the standards. An optimum standard curve should be amplicon-specific to ensure that the amplification efficiency of the standards and the target are as similar as possible.

2. Serial dilutions are analyzed by q(RT)PCR in separate sample wells but within the same run and the resulting C_ts are recorded.

   Note: The unknown result should lie within the testing interval known to be linear.

3. A plot of C_t vs. the logarithm of the copy number corresponding to that C_t results in a straight line, the standard curve, which is the linear regression line through the data points. The number of target gene copies can then be extrapolated from the standard curve

equation (**Fig. 11.3**). A standard curve provides several vital pieces of information:

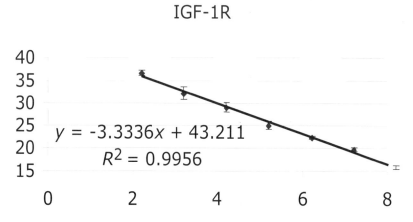

Figure 11.3. Standard curve of IGF-IR demonstrating near 100% amplification efficiency.

- ☑ **R_2-value:** The square of the coefficient of regression will indicate how good the line fits the data. Linear regression analysis of the standard curves should show a high correlation (R_2 coefficient > 0.98). In the above example, there is near perfect correlation between C_t and copy number, with 99.78% of the total variance in the C_t explained by variation in the copy number. Such R_2 values are common for most good, carefully constructed standard curves.

- ☑ **Efficiency of amplification:** Optimal standard curves are based on amplification efficiencies of as close to 100% as possible. At this efficiency the template doubles after each cycle during exponential amplification. Efficiency depends on numerous factors, including length of the amplicon, its G/C content, and any secondary structure. The slope of the standard curve can be used to determine the efficiency of the PCR reaction by the following equation: *Efficiency* = $[10^{(-1/\text{slope})}] - 1$. In the above example, the efficiency of amplification is 99.5%.

- ☑ **y-intercept:** The y-intercept is less reproducible than the slope, but gives some indication of how sensitive the assay is. In the example above, sensitivity is apparently not optimal, since the y-intercept suggests that it will require 43.3 cycles to be certain that there is no target present in the RT-PCR assay.

The cycle where fluorescence first rises above background is dependent on the amount of target present at the beginning of the reaction. With most real-time qPCR machines it takes about 10^{10} copies of PCR product to produce a signal above background. The equation $N_n = N_0(1 + E)^n$ predicts that if there are 1,000,000 copies at the beginning of the PCR reaction, and an efficiency of 1.9, the instrument will detect a signal around cycle 14. If the starting copy number is 1,000, the first signal will appear around cycle 25. A single copy target will be detected around cycle 36. This is the basis of real-time quantitative PCR with external standards.

To construct a standard curve a single number is needed that defines the position of the curve. Most thermal cycler software chooses the place where the fluorescence signal first exceeded that level of background fluorescence. The maximal sensitivity of the real-time instrument thus becomes the benchmark for quantification. Current real-time instruments have a maximal sensitivity of about 10^{10} copies of PCR product, so the threshold is the number of cycles it takes to go from the starting copy number to 10^{10} copies.

The instrument software performs all calculation steps required to generate a standard curve. The threshold method assumes that all samples have the same concentration of DNA at the point were the fluorescence signal significantly increases over the background fluorescence. Measuring "the level" of background fluorescence can be a challenge. It is no problem with reactions that are behaving nicely, but often the investigator has to deal with background drift over the course of the reaction. In real reactions the baseline can drift up, drift down, or drift for some number of cycles and then level out. Averaging over a drifting background will give an overestimate of variance and thus increase the threshold level. In practice it probably does not matter very much where the threshold is set, as long as it is within the logarithmic phase of amplification and the same for all the reactions that are being compared.

The LightCycler uses an alternative algorithm for calculating the standard curve, the "Second Derivative Maximum Method." It differs in the way the threshold cycle is determined and performs its calculations automatically without user intervention.

4. The unknown sample should be tested in duplicate or, preferably, in triplicate. The equation defining the linear standard curve can be used to determine the concentration or copy number of the nucleic acid target: *Copy number* = ((C_t) – (*intercept*)) / (*slope*). The replicate readings should be sufficiently close (less than 0.5 C_ts) to indicate a valid analysis. The limits depend on the concentration of the template in the sample. If the readings are too far apart then the sample should be retested.

The main disadvantage of using an external standard is that it cannot provide a control for detecting inhibitors of the PCR reaction. This requires the addition of an internal control template that could be amplified and any variation from the expected C_t would suggest the presence of inhibitors. Inclusion of such an internal control generates more confidence in negative results where no template is detectable. In our opinion, this control template should be a synthetic oligonucleotide with primer and probe sequences that do not occur in nature. This would make such an internal control universal. Other opinion favors naturally occurring templates, e.g., a virus, as it can be added prior to nucleic acid extraction and will mimic the extraction of a whole virus more closely than a synthetic recombinant DNA construct.[22]

So, the principle of a standard curve is not in question. But, in practice, what is to be used as the standard to generate the standard curve? There are many ongoing discussions of what kind of standard can be used to make up a standard curve.[23,24] The ideal would be a DNA sample, which behaves in the same way as the unknown sample. One problem with "natural" DNA is that the extraction procedure used to isolate the nucleic acid can affect the accuracy of a standard curve.[25]

11.9.1. Recombinant DNA

Typically, constructing a recombinanat DNA standard curve would involve using a cloned target gene, such as a double stranded plasmid, a pure fragment of the insert or alternatively a PCR fragment. These can be quantified in solution using A_{260}, Picogreen or a DNAChip in conjuntction with the Agilent 2100 Bioanalyzer. The molecular mass of the dsDNA can be used to calculate the copy numbers present in 10-fold dilutions, which constitute accurate calibration points over several orders of magnitude. The main advantages of this approach are that:

☑ DNA standards are easy to prepare;

☑ They are stable and dilutions can be stored over extended time periods.

The main disadvantages are that:

☒ DNA must be cloned;

☒ Plasmid DNA must be linearized;

☒ Insert or PCR fragments must be gel-purified;

☒ No mimicking of RT step.

11.9.2. Genomic DNA

A genomic DNA preparation can be used to generate a standard curve. Any high-quality DNA preparation will do, which can then be subjected to physical shearing to generate fragments in the 1–5,000 bp range. This can be verified and the DNA quantitated on the DNAChip on the Agilent 2100. Again, the molecular mass of the DNA can be used to calculate the copy numbers of the target amplicon present in serial dilutions, which can be used to generate standard curves.

The main advantages are:

☑ Genomic DNA standards are easy to prepare;

☑ They are very stable and dilutions can be stored over extended time periods;

☑ The target constitutes a tiny percentage of all sequences present; hence PCR conditions are more like the real-life situation.

The main disadvantages are that

☒ Dynamic range is more restricted;

☒ No mimicking of RT step;

☒ Cannot be used for RT-PCR reactions if the amplicons are designed over intron-exon boundaries.

11.9.3. SP6 or T7-Transcribed RNA

SP6 or T7 transcripts can be obtained by cloning the target amplicon behind a suitable promoter, transcribing the RNA to generate genuine "mRNA," gel purify and/or DNAse treat the sample, and quantitate it, using A_{260}, Ribogreen or the RNAChip, and the Agilent 2100. Alternatively, the cloning step can be avoided by using SP6/T7-containing forward primers, and then using SP6/T7 polymerase to transcribe directly from the PCR fragments. Again, the RNA must be purified, quality assessed, and quantitated. The molecular mass of the ssRNA can be used to calculate the copy numbers present in 10-fold dilutions, which constitute accurate calibration points over several orders of magnitude. The main advantages of this approach are that:

   ☑ RNA standards should mimic the RT step most faithfully.

The main disadvantages are that:

   ☒ The procedure is very tedious, even if PCR fragments are used;

   ☒ RNA is unstable which can cause problems during the dilution process as well as for longer-term storage;

   ☒ New standards have to be transcribed regularly, causing problems with the reproducibility of the standard curve.

11.9.4. Universal RNA

Universal RNA samples are most like the samples undergoing RT-PCR analysis in that they contain mostly rRNA and a full complement of mRNA, mimicking most accurately the *in vivo* situation. The additional RNA can interfere with the efficiency of the RT step which leads to incorrect standard curves.[26] This RNA can be purchased commercially (Stratagene) and since it is produced in vast batches, could form the basis of a universally acceptable standardization system for RT-PCR. The main advantages:

   ☑ Commercial source should ensure reproducibility;

   ☑ Most accurate mimicking of *in vivo* situation.

On the other hand, there are significant disadvantages associated with their use:

   ☒ Not all target mRNAs may be represented in the universal RNA;

☒ Trust in manufacturer's reliability and sample quality required;

☒ Dynamic range is more restricted.

11.9.5. Sense-Strand Oligonucleotides

The reasoning behind using amplicon-specific sense-strand DNA oligonucleotides is that they mimic the RNA strand during the RT step. There are several advantages to using these to generate a standard curve:

☑ They are easily synthesized and purified and the concentration of the stock solution is determined accurately by the manufacturer;

☑ Vast amounts are synthesized and this permits their distribution to other laboratories, resulting in a potentially "universal" standard for that particular amplicon;

☑ A comparison of the regression curves generated by using T7-generated transcripts versus sense-strand oligonucleotides suggests that they are very similar.

On the other hand, there are significant disadvantages associated with their use:

☒ Unless handled with extreme care, highly concentrated DNA identical to the amplicon being amplified invites contamination into the laboratory;

☒ Oligonucleotides, especially when diluted, "go off" easily. This requires constant redilution of concentrated stocks, with the associated contamination risks, but also making inaccurate results due to pipetting and general operator error more likely;

☒ It is difficult to dilute accurately low concentrations of oligonucleotides;

☒ The size of the amplicon is limited to the maximum length of the oligonucleotides that can be synthesized and purified. The longer the oligonucleotides, the more truncated failure sequences are present in the crude mixture. With coupling efficiencies of 99%, nearly 40% of a 50-mer, 60% of a 90-mer, and 80% of a 160-mer may be failed sequences. On the other hand, if the coupling efficiency is 98%, those same lengths would generate 63%, 83%, and

96% failure sequences, respectively. Incomplete deprotection can lead to the accumulation of side reactions, such as base insertions, caused by small amounts of detritylated amidite present during coupling, and deletions, caused by failure sequences that are not capped and subsequently extended. Hence the sense oligonucleotides used to generate standard curves must be purified by polyacrylamide gel electrophoresis. In practice, this limits the size of amplicon to a maximum of about 150. However, with improving coupling efficiencies this is likely to change and, in general, real-time amplicons are much shorter than that.

 Note: Up to 30 A_{260} units of crude oligonucleotides can be loaded in a single lane on a preparative polyacrylamide gel. This will yield sufficient full-length oligonucleotide for generation of the standard curve.

11.10. Relative Quantification

Relative quantification is used to compare the changes in steady-state mRNA levels two or more genes to each other, with one of them acting as an endogenous reference, the normalizer (hence the term comparative).[27] In order to compare experiments, these fold differences are then expressed relative to a calibrator sample. This calibrator sample is included with each assay and is considered to have a constant difference in mRNA levels for the gene of interest and the normalizer gene. Thus, the number of target gene copies is normalized to the reference gene, for example, a suitable reference gene and then all samples are expressed as an n-fold difference relative to that mRNA. In theory, this should be superior to and far more convenient than absolute quantification. This is because the result is a ratio; hence RNA concentration is irrelevant. The underlying justification for the comparative C_t method of relative quantification is as follows:

1. Based on the exponential amplification of target gene, as well as normalizer, the amount of amplified molecules at the threshold cycle is given by:

$$X_T = T_0(1 + E_T)^{C_{t,t}} = K_T \quad ,$$

where X_T is the number of target copies at the threshold cycle, T_0 is the initial number of target copies, E_T is the efficiency of target amplification, $C_{t,t}$ is the threshold cycle for target amplification, and K_T is a constant.

2. A similar equation can be written for the endogenous reference reaction:

$$X_R = R_0(1 + E_R)^{C_{t,r}} = K_R \quad ,$$

where X_R is the number of normalizer copies at the threshold cycle, R_0 is the initial number of calibrator copies, E_R is the efficiency of normalizer amplification, $C_{t,r}$ is the threshold cycle for calibrator amplification, and K_R is a constant.

3. Dividing X_T by X_R gives the ratio of target gene copies (T) to standard gene copies (R, calibrator reference) at the threshold cycle and normalizes the expression of the target gene:

$$T_0/R_0 \times (1 + E)^{(C_{t,t}-C_{t,r})} = K \quad ,$$

where $C_{t,t}-C_{t,r}$ is the difference in threshold cycles for target and reference (normalizer). T_0/R_0 is the normalized amount of target and the equation can be rearranged to

$$T_0/R_0 = K(1 + E)^{C_{t,r}-C_{t,t}} \text{ or } T_0/R_0 = K(1 + E)^{-\Delta C_t} \quad .$$

This equation is based on the precondition that the efficiencies of target and reference amplification are approximately equal. Comparing serial dilutions of target and reference gene simultaneously, the plot of log input amount versus ΔC_t (C_t target gene – C_t reference gene) has a slope of approximately 0. In practice, anything less than 0.1 is deemed to be acceptable.

K is dependent on (1) the reporter dye used with the probe, (2) sequence context effects on the fluorescence properties of the probe, (3) purity of the probe, and (4) efficiency of the probe cleavage; the exact value of K need not be equal to 1. However, affecting factors are assumed to vary only negligibly among single samples so that K is assumed to be equal and thus does not influence the comparison of calculated relative ratios.

For comparison of different runs the run efficiencies have to be calculated. The efficiency of PCR provides information about the amplification rate and varies from 0 to 1. The rate equal 1 (= 100%) means that in each cycle the number of copies is doubled. The efficiency can be calculated from the slope of a standard curve:

$$E = 10^{-1/s} - 1 \quad ,$$

where E is the run efficiency and s is the slope of generated standard curve.

There are two main problem with quantification relative to an internal control, be that rRNA or a reference gene approach:

1. This approach tends to introduce a significant statistical bias that results in misleading biological interpretation.[28] This is particularly true when there are vast differences in the expression levels of target and normalizer or when the target gene is expressed at very low levels. In this case the relationship between target and reference levels may not regress to a zero intercept. This is crucial, because the relationship between the two may not be linear at very low target copy numbers. Interestingly, this problem with the ratio method has been described before, albeit in another context,[29] but seems to have been forgotten.

2. It is difficult to find a reference mRNA whose expression is constant and against which the target gene copy numbers can be normalized during the experimental conditions. This is particularly so for *in vivo* biopsies.

Nevertheless, under certain circumstances, if it can be shown that experimental treatment does not affect the reference gene chosen as the normalizer, relative quantification can be useful. There are several mathematical models that calculate relative expression ratios, some of which correcting for differences in amplification efficiency [5,11-14,16,30] and some not.[31,32]

11.11. Normalization

Data normalization, while a vital aspect of experimental design,[33] remains a real problem for absolute quantification[34] and it is impossible to give general advice about the most appropriate procedure. This is because different experimental setups, targets, and samples sources are so divergent, that no single set of rules or even recommendations can be correct for every one. This is especially relevant when in vivo biopsies have been obtained from different individuals, and can easily result in the misinterpretation of the target genes' expression profiles. RT-PCR-specific errors in the quantification of mRNA transcripts are easily compounded by any variation in the amount of starting material between samples. The ideal internal standard should be expressed at a constant level among different tissues of an organism, at all stages of development, and should be unaffected by the experimental treatment. In addition, an endogenous control should also be expressed at roughly the same level as the RNA under study. In the absence of any one single RNA with a constant expression level in all of these situations,[35] various reference genes, rRNA, and total RNA are most commonly used to normalize gene expression patterns.

11.11.1. Tissue Culture

The situation is easiest for experiments involving tissue culture cells that are being subjected to certain treatments, with mRNA levels measured before and after treatment. One approach is to normalize against cell numbers and express mRNA levels as copy numbers per cell. Assuming that cells are counted accurately and that mRNA extraction is equally efficient from each sample, this will generate precise, accurate, and meaningful results. Since experiments are easily repeated, this approach will also generate sufficient numbers of replicates to perform validating statistical analyses.

Working with tissue culture cells has another advantage: it is likely that one of the many genes proposed as internal standards will be suitable as a normalizer for relative quantification. Indeed, this is one of the few experimental designs where relative quantification may be acceptable. However, note that cellular subpopulations of the same pathological origin can be highly heterogeneous[36] and that careful consideration of the appropriate reference genes is crucial. The first step is to screen a selection of reference genes using, e.g., ABI's endogenous control plate (*Cat. No. 4308134*), and to choose two or three whose mRNA levels do not change over the course of the experiment. The mRNA levels of the target can then be reported as a value relative to the average mRNA levels of the selection of reference genes.

11.11.2. Nucleated Blood Cells (NBC)

In theory, it should be possible to prepare DNA or RNA from a specific number of NBC and report the results of the q(RT)PCR assay as copies per cell. This may be sufficient for reporting the presence or absence of chromosomal translocations or pathogens, but is not as appropriate for reporting analyses of mRNA levels. In practice, blood is made up of numerous, variable subpopulations of cells of different lineage at different stages of differentiation, and differences in mRNA expression patterns are likely to be masked by this variability, a problem exacerbated when attempting to compare mRNA levels between different individuals. One approach is to use flow cytometry[37] or antibody-coated beads[38] to sort cells and enrich for specific populations. Nucleic acids can be prepared from these cells in the conventional manner or cells can be collected in a combined (RT)PCR lysis buffer with (RT)PCR assays carried out immediately.[37] Quantification relative to a lineage-specific marker may also be appropriate: Primers and fluorescent probes have been reported for numerous subtypes of NBC, e.g., CD45 (pan-NBC), CD3 (T-lymphocyte), CD19 (B-lymphocyte), CD14 (monocyte), and CD66 (granulocyte), and the specificity of quantification by real-time RT-PCR compares well with flow cytometric analysis of enriched cell populations.[39] Reporting of target mRNA quantities relative to any one of these markers should result in biologically valid data. In the absence of enrichment or linage-specific normalizers, expressing mRNA levels per cell is the least bad option. Normalization against total RNA is also possible, as there is relatively little variation in the amount of total RNA per NBC.[40] However, normalization against total RNA does not overcome the problem of variable subpopulations leading to inappropriate quantification and conclusions.

11.11.3. Solid Tissue Biopsies

Biopsies contain numerous cell types in variable proportions and there is no easy way of sorting or counting them without affecting the expression profile of the sample. Cancers in particular contain not just normal and cancer cells, but there may be several subclones of cancer cells together with stromal, immune, and vascular cells.[41] This variability means that while it is acceptable to generate qualitative results, there must be a question mark over quantitative data. In our opinion, there must be a question mark over the use of relative quantification because (1) nothing at all is known about the mRNA levels of any potential normalizer in a particular biopsy, (2) even if universally expressed, its levels may be altered locally by tissue-specific factors, and (3) it may be expressed by some cells and not others. It is our opinion, that relative quantification is not an option for quantitating mRNA levels from **whole** *in vivo* biopsies, although there are circumstances where it may be valid. If "absolute" quantification is the only valid option, what should be used for data normalization?

11.11.4. Cell Number

Normalization against cell number establishes a direct quantitative relationship between a target mRNA copy number and the cells from which the RNA is derived. It is a useful option for cells obtained from Laser Capture Microdissection (LCM), where defined numbers of cells can be used for RNA extraction. Assuming that the method of extracting RNA is reliable and generates reproducible amounts of RNA from a given number of cells, copy numbers can be expressed as absolute numbers per cell. A second option is quantification relative to a normalizer, as long as it is clear that its mRNA levels are constant between cells and samples. Nevertheless, unlike with tissue culture cells where under appropriate circumstances the case for relative quantification is clear, it is already known that reference gene copy numbers vary considerably between individuals, and extensive validation would need to be carried out before this would be acceptable for LCM-derived cells.

11.11.5. Total RNA

Normalization to total cellular RNA[40] has been shown to produce quantitative results that are biologically meaningful.[42] This approach is crucially dependent on accurate quantification of the RNA using

RiboGreen RNA quantification or absorbance measurement at OD_{260} in a spectrophotometer as well as quality assessment using the RNA 6000 LabChip with the Agilent 2100 Bioanalyzer.

An important consideration when using total RNA for normalization is the lack of internal control for RT or PCR inhibitors. All quantitative methods assume that the RNA targets are reverse transcribed and subsequently amplified with similar efficiency. The risk with normalization against external standards is that a proportion of the samples might contain some inhibitor that significantly reduces the efficiency of the RT-PCR reaction, resulting in inaccurate quantification. Therefore, it is necessary to develop universal internal standards that can be added to the RNA preparation to monitor the efficiency of reverse transcription reaction.

There are obvious limitations to this approach. Total RNA levels may be elevated in highly proliferating cells and this will affect the accuracy of any comparison of absolute copy numbers between normal and tumor cells. In addition, the accuracy of the quantification will be critically dependent on the accuracy of RNA measurement. It is not always possible to quantify total RNA, especially when dealing with very limited amounts of clinical samples, or when mRNA has been extracted.

11.11.6. DNA

The use of Trizol makes it possible to isolate total DNA at the same time as the RNA is being extracted. Hence there is the potential to normalize mRNA levels to that DNA. This can be done either to the quantity of that DNA with copy numbers expressed as absolute numbers per unit DNA, or against one or several markers amplified from that DNA and expressed relative to those markers.

11.11.7. rRNA

Ribosomal RNA (rRNA), which constitutes 85–90% of total cellular RNA, has been proposed as an alternative normalizer,[43,44] despite reservations concerning its expression levels, transcription by a different RNA polymerase,[45] and possible imbalances in rRNA and mRNA fractions between different samples.[46] rRNA levels vary less under conditions that affect the expression of mRNAs,[36,47,48] and the use of rRNA has been shown to be more reliable than that of the HrK genes in rat livers,[49] human skin fibroblasts,[50] and malignant human[44] and mouse[43] cell lines.

However, rRNA levels can be affected by biological factors and drugs[51] and they vary significantly in hemopoietic subpopulations[37] and in both normal and cancer biopsies taken from different individuals.[42] Furthermore, from the discussion above it is clear that the vast difference in expression levels between rRNA and any target gene can result in misleading quantification data. There is also no agreement on whether 28S or 18S rRNA is the more appropriate target. Finally, another drawback is that rRNA cannot be used for normalization when quantitating targets from polyA-enriched samples.

11.12. Reference Genes (Houskeeping Genes)

Historically, so-called reference genes, believed to be constitutively expressed and minimally regulated, have been used widely as internal RNA references for Northern blotting, RNase protection, and qualitative RT-PCR analyses. Commonly used reference genes are GAPDH, β-actin,[52] histone H3,[53] ribosomal highly basic 23-kDa protein,[54] cyclophilin,[55] β-2-microglobulin,[56] porphobilinogen deaminase,[27] and others. GAPDH was a curious choice, since its gene product was well known to have a number of diverse activities unrelated to its glycolytic function that include a role in membrane fusion, microtubule bundling, phosphotransferase activity, nuclear RNA export, DNA replication, DNA repair, apoptosis, age-related neurodegenerative disease, prostate cancer, and viral pathogenesis.[57] Its role as a regulated gene has been known for a long time (**Table 11.2**) and for most experimental conditions its use appears to be inappropriate. However, under certain defined conditions GAPDH mRNA levels seem to remain invariant and as long as that has been verified, GAPDH can be used as a normalizer.[31,37,58,59]

β-actin was one of the first RNAs to be used as an internal standard, and it is still advocated as a quantitative reference for RT-PCR assays. This is despite widespread evidence that its mRNA levels can vary widely in response to experimental manipulation in human breast epithelial cells[51] and blastomeres,[60] as well as in various porcine tissues[61] and canine myocardium.[62] Matrigel™, which is widely used for

Table 11.2. Published instances of GADH behaving as a regulated gene.

Conditions	Tissue	Extracellular factors	Diseases
Age[71] Apoptosis[72-74] Cell cycle[75] Developmental stage[76,77] Food deprivation[78] Hypoxia[79-81] Oxidative stress[82,83] Pregnancy[84] Serum[85]	Blood cells[86] Breast biopsies[87] Colon biopsies[88] Endothelial cells[89] Skin[90] T-cells[91] Testicular cells[92] Thyrocytes[93]	Fudenine[94] UV[95] IL2[96] NO[97] 12-O-tetradecanoyl-phorbol-13-acetate[98] Dexamethasone[99] Carbon tetrachloride[100] Cholinergic agonist[101] Creatine[102] Tri-iodothyronine (T(3)) and Norepinephrine[103] Insulin[103-107] Retinoic acid[103] Calcium ionophore A23187[108] Growth hormone[109] Vitamin D[110] Manganese[111] TP53[112]	Breast cancer[113] Cervical cancer[114] Colorectal cancer[115] Lung cancer[116] Liver cancer[117] Hepatomas[118] Malignant murine cell Lines[119] Neurodegenerative Diseases[120] Pancreatitis/pancreatic Cancer[121] Prostate cancer[122-124] Renal cancer[125]

cell attachment and to induce cell differentiation, adversely affects β-actin mRNA levels.[63] In addition, the presence of pseudogenes interferes with the interpretation of results[64-66] and primers commonly used for detecting β-actin mRNA amplify DNA as well.[67] There are numerous other reports that suggest β-actin should not be used to normalize qRT-PCR data.[68]

A recent systematic analysis and comparison of their usefulness on *in vivo* tissue biopsies has concluded that a single reference gene should not be used for normalization.[42] The recent demonstration of the effectiveness of normalization against the geometric mean of multiple carefully selected HKG is interesting.[69] However, this method requires extensive practical validation to identify a combination of reference genes appropriate for every individual experiment, something that is not at all trivial. In addition, as the choice of reference gene panel is tissue- or cell-dependent, this is not a universal method. Most importantly, it seems reasonable to assume that most genes are regulated and that this will cause significant unpredictable differences in their expression patterns between and even within the same individual. If reference genes are to be used, they must be validated for the specific experimental setup and it is probably necessary to choose more than one, as was done for example for expression profiling of *T* Helper cell differentiation.[70]

11.13. Basic Statistics

Statistics is a fundamental aid to help with the investigation and interpretation of qPCR assays. As such, any serious investigator must have a grasp of the basic principles and while he does not need to be familiar with the technical details of statistical calculations, he should understand when such calculations are valid, when they are not and how they should be meaningfully interpreted. A detailed discussion of the most appropriate statistical tests to be applied to quantitative PCR data is way beyond the scope of this book. Fortunately there are several good websites that make a superb job of explaining the background even to a biologist. The following pages are designed to give basic recommendations on statistics and data presentation appropriate to analyzing and reporting qPCR data.

The genetic backgrounds of human beings vary tremendously and biochemical measurements on human subjects rarely give exactly the same result from one experiment to the next and this variability is also inherent in any effect recorded in response to environmental effects. Therefore, it is very unlikely that quantitative measurements of, say mRNA copy numbers, or changes in mRNA levels in response to extracellular stimuli will produce exactly the same result time after time. Hence the use of qPCR to quantitate comparisons between biological materials is almost certain to result variations in absolute data depending upon the experimental design. These differences may be due to real effects, random variation or both. It is the job of the investigator to decide how much variation is due to chance, so that any remaining variation can be assumed to be due to a real effect. Also, it is of little use to conduct a poorly designed study and hope that any flaws can be redeemed by sophisticated statistical jiggery pokery. Therefore it becomes important to consider how data are collected and what statistical tests are to be performed at the outset of any study, before data have even been collected in order to ensure that the results are comparable and generalisable.

Statistical tests always examine a null hypothesis, which states that there is no difference between two (or more) populations and that any observed differences between samples from these populations are due to chance alone. One might want to compare paired normal and cancer biopsies to determine whether mRNA specifying a particular oncogene is upregulated in the tumor. The aim of any qRT-PCR experiments would be to reject the null hypothesis and show that tumor biopsies do indeed express significantly higher levels of oncogene mRNA than the paired normal samples. The statistical analysis of a well-designed experiment should consider several factors:

The first question concerns sample size and power considerations. If, for example, the aim of the experiment is to compare mRNA levels between paired adjacent normal and cancer tissue, the probability of obtaining effects of a certain size can be calculated for a given number of samples. The quantitative results obtained with qPCR require some knowledge of the expected size of the difference between the two sample groups, and the variability of the measurement.

The question of whether the qPCR assay is being carried out on a representative sample is another typical problem. Quantification of mRNA levels from in vivo biopsies may or may not be comparable between individuals. Some individuals may have been suffering from a viral infection; hence interleukin-2 levels may be raised. There may be significant age differences between the individuals from whom the tissue was obtained, resulting in different insulin-like growth factor-I mRNA levels. A tissue biopsy taken near a colorectal cancer may contain mainly stromal and muscle cells, whereas the paired tumor may be mainly epithelial cell-derived.

Randomization is an important part of any clinical trial. It may be impractical to randomize tissue samples used for qPCR assays, but experiments should be carried out without the investigator knowing what samples they are dealing with until the experiments are ready to be analyzed.

Data display is an underrated, but important part of result analysis. The choice of group intervals when plotting histograms can affect the shape of the plotted distribution: too wide an interval may obscure important features of the data, too narrow an interval may result in random variation that could distract attention from the shape of the underlying distribution.

The summary statistics used and the analysis undertaken must reflect the design of the study and the nature of the data. One characteristic of many data obtained using qPCR is the huge range of mRNA levels observed when comparing tissue samples from individual human subjects. Therefore, the use of the median, rather than the mean, may be more reliable and informative.

11.13.1. Data Presentation

qPCR generates very large amounts of numerical continuous data and it is impractical and probably meaningless to communicate the results in raw data form. Hence it is necessary to condense the data into a small set of numbers, together with the appropriate statistics and present them as a visual image with the principal objective to convey the essential features of the data. The usual features that are of interest are some measure of location that describes the level of the data values and some measure of variability, i.e., a description of how data values change from sample to sample.

11.13.2. Mean and Median

Measures of location are the mean and the lower, median and upper quartiles. The mean of n observations is the sum of the observations divided by their number. The main disadvantage of using the mean is that it is vulnerable to outliers. Outliers are single observations, which if excluded from the calculation have a noticeable influence on the result. It can never be concluded that they should be excluded from the final data summary or that they result from an erroneous measurement. The lower, median, and upper quartiles are values, which divide the distribution into four parts of equal area. They are estimated from the data by first ordering the data from the smallest to the largest and then counting upwards the appropriate number of observations. The median quartile is either the observation at the center of the ordering (odd number of observations) or the simple average of the middle two observations (even number of observations). The quartiles are calculated in a similar way. The median has the advantage that it is not affected by outliers. On the down side, it is not statistically efficient, as it does not make use of all the individual data values.

11.13.3. Standard Deviation

Measures of variability are the range and interquartile range as well as the standard deviation (SD). The range is calculated as the largest minus the smallest observation, hence is vulnerable to outliers. The interquartile range is the difference between the upper and lower quartiles and is not vulnerable to outliers. SD is the best measure of spread of an approximately normal distribution, with about 95% of the data within 2 SD of the mean. This is not the case when there are extreme values in a distribution or when the distribution is skewed, when interquartile range is the preferred measure of spread.

Note: When adding or subtracting average values reported with their SD, one does not simply add the SD to produce the final SD. Instead, the SD are squared, added, and then the square root of the sum is taken: $SD_{tot} = (S1^2 + S2^2 + ...)^{1/2}$. Note that the squares of the errors are added even if the actual values are subtracted. This is because simply adding errors would overstate the probable error since this would be assume that all the errors were maximum and in the same direction. This not likely, and chances are that an error in one set of data may help cancel an error in another set.

Similarly, when multiplying or dividing average values reported with their SD one does not add the standard deviations to produce the final SD. Instead, the fractional SDs are squared, added, and the square root of the sum is taken to get the fractional total deviation. If the values are $A \pm \delta A$, $B \pm \delta B$, ..., and these are used to compute $X = A \times B \times ...$, the total error δX is then $\delta X/X = ((\delta A/A)^2 + (\delta B/B)^2 + ...)^{1/2}$. Note that the squares of the errors are added even if the actual values are divided.

11.13.4. Plots

Data can be plotted in many ways, with dot plots, histograms, box-and-whisker, and scatter plots-the most appropriate ones for qPCR data. Dot plots retain the individual subject values and clearly demonstrate differences between groups in a readily appreciated way. Furthermore, any outliers are immediately obvious (**Fig. 11.4**). However, if there are too many data points, dot plots become unwieldy and impractical. A particularly useful variation joins the dots of associated, or paired samples if, for example, they represent mRNA copy numbers of a cancer marker before and after treatment (**Fig. 11.5**). Histograms reveal patterns in large data sets. They are obtained by first dividing up the range of the numerically continuous variable (e.g., mRNA copy number) into several nonoverlapping and equal intervals, then counting the number of observations in each interval. The area of each histogram is proportional to the number of samples in the particular mRNA level group. One reason for producing histograms is to get some idea of the shape of the distribution of the data. Box-and-whisker is a useful way to present data, as it is easier to convey the central location and spread of values pictorially than by quoting a list of descriptive statistics. In nonparametric terms, the central "box" represents the distance between the first and third quartiles with the median between them marked with a line, and the minimum as the origin of the leading "whisker" and with the maximum as the limit of the trailing "whisker." In parametric terms, the arithmetic mean is bounded by one standard deviation or by its confidence interval. The association between quantitative variables can be investigated by means of a scatter plot, which in this example (**Fig. 11.6**) shows good association between the mRNA levels of two genes. If one variable, x, clearly causes the other, y, then it is usual to plot the x variable on to the horizontal axis and the y variable on to the vertical axis. Thus, since the induction of c-*myc* mRNA causes the expression of VEGF mRNA, c-*myc* mRNA levels are plotted along the x-axis and VEGF mRNA levels along the y-axis.

11.13.5. Relative (Receiver) Operating Characteristics

The detection of occult disease in the blood, bone marrow, or lymph nodes of cancer patients that have undergone supposedly curative surgery is a potentially useful diagnostic application for qPCR.[126] Tumor- or tissue-specific markers such as prostate-specific antigen (PSA),[127] guanylyl cyclase C (GCC)[128] or tyrosinase[129] are just three markers used to detect prostate cancer, colorectal, or melanoma cells. The problem is that the quantitative assays produce a continuous measurement of

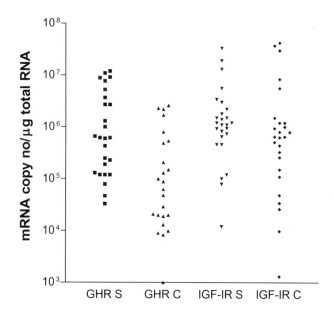

Figure 11.4. A dot plot comparing GHR and IGF-IR mRNA levels in the colon. The wide range as well as the presence of outliers is clearly revealed.

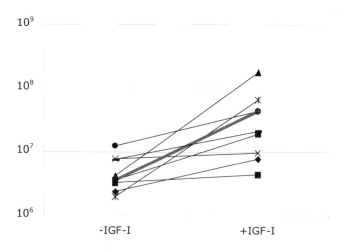

Figure 11.5. Dot plot showing changes in mRNA levels after treatment.

mRNA copy numbers that requires a diagnostic cutoff to calculate the sensitivity and specificity of the test. Unfortunately, it is not known what cutoff point is biologically and clinically relevant.

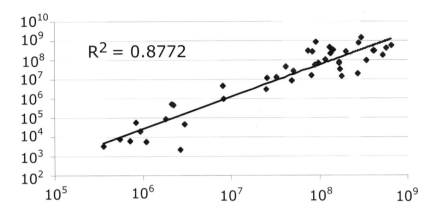

Figure 11.6. Scatter plot showing association between two mRNAs.

One way of displaying the ability of a test to discriminate between patients at risk of treatment failure and not without having to specify a particular cutoff level is to graph the sensitivity on the y-axis against the false-positive rate for all possible cut-off values of the diagnostic test on the x-axis. The resulting curve is known as the relative (or receiver) operating characteristic curve (ROC) and is shown in **Fig. 11.7**. The history of ROC plots is fascinating: they were first used to define detection cutoff points for radar equipment with different operators. These plots can be used in a similar way to define cutoff points for diagnostic tests. A perfect diagnostic test would be one with no false-positive or false-negative results and would be represented by a line that started at the origin and went up the y-axis to a sensitivity of 1, and then horizontally across to a false-positive rate of 1. A test that produces a false-positive result at the same rate as true-positive results would produce an ROC on the diagonal line $y = x$. A reasonably good diagnostic test will display an ROC curve in the upper left triangle. However, bear in mind that defining cutoff levels for diagnostic tests is a difficult process, which must combine a number of ethical and practical considerations.

11.13.6. Probability

Nothing is ever certain, but obviously we would like to know how likely it is that any differences between samples are due to chance alone. Unfortunately, all statistical tests can reveal is the probability that we

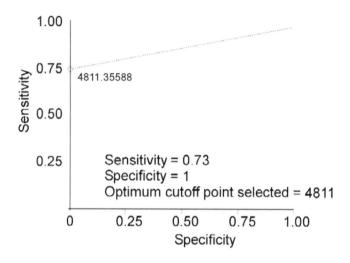

Figure 11.7. Receiver operating characteristic curve plot.

would observe at least as large a difference between samples as we do, given that the null hypothesis is true. This probability is the *p* value so beloved of clinicians. The value of the *p-level* represents a decreasing index of the reliability of a result. The higher the *p-level*, the less likely it is that the observed relation between variables in the sample is a reliable indicator of the relation between the respective variables in the population.

A *p-level* of 0.05 indicates that there is a 5% probability that the relation between the variables found in our sample is a "fluke." In many areas of research, the *p-level* of 0.05 is customarily treated as a "borderline acceptable" error level.

If $p = 0.50$, there is a 50% chance of getting a difference between samples at least as large as we did, if the sampled populations really were the same. This obviously is as close to certainty as we are likely to get, hence we would accept the null hypothesis, and conclude that there is no difference between the two populations we sampled. The accepted standard is that we should reject the null hypothesis if $p < 0.05$, i.e., there is a 5% chance (or less) of getting at least as large a difference between samples as we did, if the populations sampled were really the same. In other words, if we were to repeat our experiment 20 times, we could expect that there would be one experiment in which the relation between the variables in question would be equal or stronger than in ours. The value of p, below which we will reject the null hypothesis is called the p value; p is usually chosen as 0.05. It is important to remember that if $p = 0.05$, there is a 5% chance that we will reject the null hypothesis when it is actually true! This is called a Type I error. You might think we could avoid this error by only rejecting the null hypothesis if the p value is even smaller; say, 0.01 or 0.001. However, if we do this, we are likely to accept the null hypothesis when it is false! This is called a Type II error. Setting $p = 0.05$ is a standard that is generally accepted as a good compromise between Type I and Type II errors.

In practice, once a statistical test has been chosen, the value of a statistic is calculated from the sample data using a formula. This value is then compared to a critical value to decide whether to accept or reject the null hypothesis. The critical value is determined by the appropriate p value (usually, $p = 0.05$) and the degrees of freedom (df) of the data, which vary depending on the test being performed. If the statistic is greater than the critical value, the null hypothesis is rejected.

Critical values can have one-tailed or two-tailed levels of significance. Two-tailed tests are more conservative and are less likely to reject the null hypothesis and are usually appropriate in a biological context. They do not assume any direction of difference between populations, e.g., although the mRNA levels of a particular gene might be altered in a tumor sample, it could be either up- or downregulated. However, this cannot be predicted at the beginning, hence a two-tailed test is appropriate.

11.13.7. Parametric and Nonparametric Tests

11.13.7.1. Parametric Methods

There are so many different statistical tests, most with weird and wonderful names and highly specialized, that it is near impossible for the mere biologist to decide which one might be the most appropriate one to apply. However, there are a few basic pointers that allow the use of general tests that will be appropriate and generate statistical information that is relevant and meaningful. On the other hand, the dictum that there are lies, damned lies and statistics is very much applicable and one must take care not to over interpret a p value, especially as there is no black and white delineation of biological data.

Arguably the most important distinction is between parametric and nonparametric tests and the first thing that needs to be done is to examine the data characteristics. Parametric tests, e.g., the t-test, assume that the sampled data follow a normal statistical (Gaussian) distribution. Some qPCR measurements will result in data that are normally distributed, but many will be skewed. Taking the logarithm of the mRNA copy numbers can often transform the skew distribution and a histogram on the transformed scale appears to have a normal distribution.

In addition, many parametric tests require that the variability of all the samples is the same. Although biological data rarely display a strict Gaussian distribution, they can follow a bell-shaped distribution that is approximately Gaussian. If sample sizes are large, analyses such as ANOVA work well even if the distribution is only approximately Gaussian. Hence parametric tests are used routinely in many fields of biology. The mean and the amount of variability (variance, standard deviation) of a population are typical statistical parameters used with parametric tests. Since these parameters are calculated by sampling a subset of the whole population, the larger the sample size, the closer the sample statistics are to the true population parameters. Two parameters usually plotted with average data, and often confused and misused are the standard error of the mean (SEM) and the standard deviation (SD). The SEM compares two sample means and determines whether or not they are statistically different. Therefore, it measures the precision with which a population mean is estimated and is calculated by dividing the SD by the square root of the number of samples. It is often plotted as errors bars around the mean on a graph. However, if a number of different samples of size n are taken from the same population, their means will be slightly different and a plot of these means will be far less variable than the data of the original samples. Therefore, it is important to bear in mind that the SEM provides no information about the variability of the original data and even highly variable data can give a small SEM if the sample size is large enough. The standard deviation is by far the most important information provided with the mean. It describes the average deviation from the mean and its magnitude indicates how much variability there is in the data. A normal distribution is completely described by two parameters, the mean and the standard deviation. Populations with small values of the SD have a distribution concentrated close to the mean; those with a large SD have a distribution spread widely along the measurement axis. In normally distributed data 68% of the data should fall within 1 standard deviation of the mean (1.0 × SD), 95% of the distribution lies within 1.96 × SD and 99% within 2.58 × SD. Confidence intervals define a range of values within which a sample mean is likely to lie with a given level of certainty. A simple statement such as mean A = 2.5×10^6, mean B = 6.9×10^7, $p < 0.05$ does not describe the results of a study well. It creates an artificial dichotomy between significant and nonsignificant results, since the p-value depends to a large extent on the size of the study. Thus a large study may find small, unimportant differences that are highly significant and a small study may fail to find real, important differences. The confidence interval gives an estimate of the precision with which a statistic estimates a value such as the mean and any quantitative data reporting means or medians should also report confidence intervals. So, for example, when reporting the detection of tissue-specific markers in the blood of cancer patients, it allows the reader to judge whether clinical and statistical significance has been confused.

11.13.7.2. Nonparametric Methods

Nonparametric methods were developed to be used in cases when the researcher does not know the parameters of the distribution of the variable of interest in the population (hence the name nonparametric). In more technical terms, *nonparametric* methods do not rely on the estimation of parameters (such as the mean or the standard deviation) describing the distribution of the variable of interest in the population. Therefore, these methods are also sometimes (and more appropriately) called *parameter-free* methods or *distribution-free* methods. Basically, there is at least one nonparametric equivalent for each parametric general type of test. In general, these tests fall into the following categories:

- **Tests of differences between groups (independent samples):** Usually, when there are two samples that are to be compared concerning their mean value for some variable of interest, one would use the t-test for or one of its nonparametric alternatives, the Wald-Wolfowitz runs test, the Mann-Whitney U test, and the Kolmogorov-Smirnov two-sample test. If there were multiple groups, one would use analysis of variance or its nonparametric equivalent, the Kruskal-Wallis analysis of ranks and the Median test.

- **Tests of differences between dependent groups:** If the objective is to compare two variables measured in the same sample one would use the t-test for dependent samples or its nonparametric alternative, Wilcoxon's matched pairs test. If the variables of interest are dichotomous in nature (i.e., "mRNA present" vs. "mRNA absent") then McNemar's Chi-square test is appropriate. If there were more than two variables that were measured in the same sample, then one would use repeated measures ANOVA. Nonparametric alternatives to this method are Friedman's two-way analysis of variance and Cochran Q test.

- **Tests of relationships between variables:** The Chi-squared test (or Fisher's exact test if the total number of observations is less than twenty or any of the expected frequencies are less than five) is the appropriate statistic for examining associations between discrete variables. Regression and correlation are techniques for dealing with the relationship between two or more continuous variables. Regression describes one variable as a function of one or more other variables. The dependent variable (y) is plotted on the vertical axis, the predictor variable (x) on the horizontal axis of a graph. The assumption is that a change in x will lead directly to a change in y, and that essentially x causes y. The regression equation $y = \alpha + \beta x$, where α is the intercept and β is the regression coefficient, describes the relationship between y and x. On a graph, a is the value of the equation when $x = 0$, and β is the slope of the line. When x increases by one unit, y is expected to change by β units. The obvious example is the standard curve obtained when plotting the logarithm of copy number against the C_t. Here the slope represents the amplification efficiency and the intercept gives an approximate idea of the sensitivity.

Multiple regression looks at the simultaneous relationship between one dependent and a number of independent variables. It differs from correlation, which refers to the interdependence or corelationship of variables and reflects the closeness of the linear relationship between X and Y. It is a measure of the degree of dependency between two variables and says nothing about the cause of the dependency, which could be some third factor entirely. The strength of the association is summarized by the correlation coefficient (r), a dimensionless quantity ranging from -1 (perfect inverse correlation) through 0 (no correlation) to 1 (perfect correlation). Note that $r = 1$ does NOT mean that there is a good causal relationship between X and Y, it shows only that the sample data are close to a straight line. Spurious correlations can arise due to the influences of one or more "other" variables and are one of the most common reasons for applying healthy skepticism to any interpretation of biological data that implies a causal relationship between two variables, e.g., the levels of two mRNAs. There may be (and often is) a third variable that influences both and if one controls for that variable the correlation will disappear. The main problem with spurious correlations is that typically the "hidden" agent is unknown. A correlation coefficient based on the original data that follow a Gaussian distribution is known as the Pearson correlation coefficient, when it is calculated from the ranks of the data it is known as the (nonparametric) Spearman rank correlation coefficient. Perhaps the best way to interpret the value of r is to square it (r^2). r^2 has a value that ranges from zero to one, and gives the proportion of the variation of one variable explained by the other. For example, a correlation coefficient of 0.9 means that $0.9^2 = 0.81$, or 80% of the variance in X can be explained by variation in Y. Likewise, 80% of the variance in Y can be explained by variation in X. Calculation of the r^2 value is appropriate only from the Pearson correlation coefficient. Note that if there are outliers, the correlation should be used with caution. They could be derived from a different population than the others, the nucleic acid may have been extracted by a different investigator and contain inhibitors, different reagent or enzyme lots might have been used for part of the experiment or the data could be simply wrong. Excluding outliers from the data set may change a positive or negative correlation to zero. It is always best to reextract the nucleic acid from another tissue sample or, if that is not possible, to repurify and reassay it.

11.13.7.2.1. *When to Use Which Method*

It is not easy to give simple advice concerning the use of nonparametric procedures. Each nonparametric procedure has its peculiar sensitivities and blind spots. For example, the Kolmogorov-Smirnov two-sample test is not only sensitive to differences in the location of distributions (for example, differences in means) but is also greatly affected by differences in their shapes. The Wilcoxon matched pairs test assumes that one can rank order the magnitude of differences in matched observations in a meaningful manner. If this is not the case, one should rather use the Sign test. In general, if the result of a study is important (e.g., is the detection of a specific cancer-associated marker in the blood of prognostic significance), then it is always advisable to run different nonparametric tests. If there are discrepancies in the results using these different tests, one should always be suspicious and try to understand why some tests give different results.

11.13.7.2.2. *When to Use Nonparametric Tests*

Because nonparametric tests make fewer assumptions about the distribution of the data they are less likely to commit a Type I error (rejecting a null hypothesis when it is true). However, they are less powerful than the parametric tests that assume Gaussian distributions and p-values tend to be higher, making it harder to detect real differences as being statistically significant. Furthermore, if a nonparametric test is used when the data follow a normal distribution, then the calculated p-value will always exceed that of the Student's t-test and the nonparametric confidence intervals will be wider. Thus one is less likely to declare a result significant using a nonparametric test than using a parametric one with the same data, i.e., one is more likely to commit a Type II error. This problem is overcome by choosing larger data sets of at least 20–25 data points per group where the difference in power is minor. With very small groups, nonparametric tests have zero power. Nonparametric tests are especially useful for RT-PCR assays, since the data generated are spread over a huge range, usually several orders of magnitude, with gene expression not detected in some samples. Since nonparametric tests only consider the relative ranks of the values, this does not matter for the purpose of analysis. It is important to try and obtain as many sample points as possible to have as much power as possible. Small samples simply do not contain enough information to allow accurate statistical analyses.

When a data set is large (e.g., $n > 100$), the sample means will follow the normal distribution even if the respective variable is not normally distributed in the population or is not measured very well. Thus, parametric methods, which are usually much more sensitive are in most cases appropriate for large samples.

11.13.7.2.3. *Mann-Whitney U Test*

This nonparametric equivalent to the t-test makes no assumptions about whether the data are normally distributed. It compares the order, or rank, of the data rather than their numerical value. For example, after quantitating the mRNA copy numbers from two cancer samples, the entire data set is ranked, treating all data from both samples as a single list. The largest data point has a rank of 1, the next largest has a rank of 2 and so on. The ranks for each individual data set are then summed. If the two samples have similar values, the ranks would tend to go back and forth between samples. For example, the highest-ranking value might be in sample 2, the next one in sample 1, the next two in sample 2, the next three in sample 1, and so on. Summing the ranks from each sample will result in two sums that are about equal. On the other hand, if mRNA levels in sample 1 were higher than those in sample 2, the ranks of sample 1 would all be larger numbers, and the sum of the ranks of sample 1 would be much larger than that of sample 2. The Mann-Whitney test tells us how different the rank sums must be to indicate a significant difference between the two samples. It makes three assumptions:

1. Only two samples are being compared.
2. Subjects in samples were chosen independently.
3. The two samples were not paired in any way (e.g. matched cases and controls). If samples were paired, the Wilcoxon Signed Rank test should be used.

11.14. Conclusion

It has probably become clear that data analysis is far from simple. Conversion of C_ts into copy numbers is one thing, placing copy numbers into the proper context is another and interpreting them correctly is another thing again. "God does not play dice," Albert Einstein once said, expressing his contempt for the notion that the universe is governed by probability. It is sometimes re-interpreted to mean that if something is real, it is obvious and does not require statistics to prove it. Unfortunately, real-time PCR results are not like quantum theory; they are not black and white and they are open to interpretation. Therefore, having obtained C_t values, the first important step is to convert them to copy numbers and to interpret these within a biologically meaningful context. The next step is to apply the most appropriate statistical analyses in order to obtain a degree of confidence that the data are meaningful in the real world. Finally, the application of common sense will result in real-time data that are not precise but meaningless, but are truly relevant to the scientific study.

References

1. Gentle A, Anastasopoulos F, McBrien NA: **High-resolution semi-quantitative real-time PCR without the use of a standard curve.** *Biotechniques* 2001, **31**:502, 504–506, 508.

2. Muller PY, Janovjak H, Miserez AR, Dobbie Z: **Processing of gene expression data generated by quantitative real-time RT-PCR.** *Biotechniques* 2002, **32**:1372–1379.

3. Klein, D: **Quantification using real-time PCR technology: Applications and limitations.** *Trends Mol Med* 2002, **8**:257–260.

4. Raeymaekers L: **Basic principles of quantitative PCR.** *Mol Biotechnol* 2000, **15**:115–122.

5. Liu W, Saint DA: **Validation of a quantitative method for real time PCR kinetics.** *Biochem Biophys Res Commun* 2002, **294**:347–353.

6. Raeymaekers L: **General principles of quantitative PCR.** In: *Quantitative PCR Protocols.* B. Kochanowski and U. Reischl, eds. Totowa, NJ: Humana Press, 1999, pp. 31–41.

7. Raeymaekers L: **Quantitative PCR: Theoretical considerations with practical implications.** *Anal Biochem* 1993, **214**:582–585.

8. Raeymaekers L: **Quantitative PCR.** In: *Clinical Applications of PCR.* Lo YMD, ed. Totowa, NJ: Humana Press, 1998, pp. 27–38.

9. Hayward AL, Oefner PJ, Sabatini S, Kainer DB, Hinojos CA, Doris PA: **Modeling and analysis of competitive RT-PCR.** *Nucleic Acids Res* 1998, **26**:2511–2518.

10. Vu HL, Troubetzkoy S, Nguyen HH, Russell MW, Mestecky J: **A method for quantification of absolute amounts of nucleic acids by (RT)-PCR and a new mathematical model for data analysis.** *Nucleic Acids Res* 2000, **28**:E18.

11. Meijerink J, Mandigers C, van de Locht L, Tonnissen E, Goodsaid F, Raemaekers J: **A novel method to compensate for different amplification efficiencies between patient DNA samples in quantitative real-time PCR.** *J Mol Diagn* 2001, 3:55–61.

12. Pfaffl MW: **A new mathematical model for relative quantification in real-time RT-PCR.** *Nucleic Acids Res* 2001, **29**:E45

13. Liu W, Saint DA: **A new quantitative method of real time reverse transcription polymerase chain reaction assay based on simulation of polymerase chain reaction kinetics.** *Anal Biochem* 2002, **302**:52–59.

14. Pfaffl MW, Horgan GW, Dempfle L: **Relative expression software tool (REST) for group-wise comparison and statistical analysis of relative expression results in real-time PCR.** *Nucleic Acids Res* 2002, **30**:E36.

15. Nedelman J, Heagerty P, Lawrence C: **Quantitative PCR with internal controls.** *Comput Appl Biosci* 1992, **8**:65–70.

16. Peccoud J, Jacob C: **Theoretical uncertainty of measurements using quantitative polymerase chain reaction.** *Biophys J* 1996, **71**:101–108.

17. Puig M, Mihalik K, Yu M, Feinstone S, Major M: **Sensitivity and reproducibility of HCV quantitation in chimpanzee sera using TaqMan real-time PCR assay.** *J Virol Methods* 2002, **105**:253.

18. Lockey C, Otto E, Long Z: **Real-time fluorescence detection of a single DNA molecule.** *Biotechniques* 1998, **24**:744–746.

19. Karrer EE, Lincoln JE, Hogenhout S, Bennett AB, Bostock RM, Martineau B, Lucas WJ, Gilchrist DG, Alexander D: ***In situ* isolation of mRNA from individual plant cells: Creation of cell-specific cDNA libraries.** *Proc Natl Acad Sci USA* 1995, **92**:3814–3818.

20. Ginzinger DG: **Gene quantification using real-time quantitative PCR: An emerging technology hits the mainstream.** *Exp Hematol* 2002, **30**:503–512.

21. Ke LD, Chen Z, Yung WK: **A reliability test of standard-based quantitative PCR: exogenous vs endogenous standards.** *Mol Cell Probes* 2000, **14**:127–135.

22. Niesters HG: **Quantitation of viral load using real-time amplification techniques.** *Methods*, 2001, **25**:419–429.

23. Pfaffl MW, Hageleit M: **Validities of mRNA quantification using recombinant RNA and recombinant DNA external calibration curves in real-time RT-PCR.** *Biotechnology Letters* 2001, **23**:275–282.

24. Fronhoffs S, Totzke G, Stier S, Wernert N, Rothe M, Bruning T, Koch B, Sachinidis A, Vetter H, Ko Y: **A method for the rapid construction of cRNA standard curves in quantitative real-time reverse transcription polymerase chain reaction.** *Mol Cell Probes* 2002, **16**:99–110.

25. Niesters HG, van Esser J, Fries E, Wolthers KC, Cornelissen J, Osterhaus AD: **Development of a real-time quantitative assay for detection of Epstein-Barr virus.** *J Clin Microbiol* 2000, **38**:712–715.

26. Freeman WM, Walker SJ, Vrana KE: **Quantitative RT-PCR: Pitfalls and potential.** *Biotechniques* 1999, **26**:112–115.

27. Fink L, Seeger W, Ermert L, Hanze J, Stahl U, Grimminger F, Kummer W, Bohle RM: **Real-time quantitative RT-PCR after laser-assisted cell picking.** *Nat .Med* 1998, **4**: 1329–1333.

28. Hocquette JF, Brandstetter AM: **Common practice in molecular biology may introduce statistical bias and misleading biological interpretation.** *J Nutr Biochem* 2002, **13**:370–377.

29. Poehlman ET, Toth MJ: **Mathematical ratios lead to spurious conclusions regarding age- and sex-related differences in resting metabolic rate.** *Am J Clin Nutr* 1995, **61**:482–485.

30. Soong R, Beyser K, Basten O, Kalbe A, Rueschoff J, Tabiti K: **Quantitative reverse transcription-polymerase chain reaction detection of cytokeratin 20 in noncolorectal lymph nodes.** *Clin Cancer Res* 2001, **7**:3423–3429.

31. Winer J, Jung CK, Shackel I, Williams PM: **Development and validation of real-time quantitative reverse transcriptase-polymerase chain reaction for monitoring gene expression in cardiac myocytes** *in vitro*. *Anal Biochem* 1999, **270**:41–49.

32. Livak KJ, Schmittgen TD: **Analysis of relative gene expression data using real-time quantitative PCR and the 2(-delta delta C(T)) method.** *Methods* 2001, **25**:402–408,.

33. Karge WH, Schaefer EJ, Ordovas JM: **Quantification of mRNA by polymerase chain reaction (PCR) using an internal standard and a nonradioactive detection method.** *Methods Mol Biol* 1998, **110**:43–61.

34. Thellin O, Zorzi W, Lakaye B, De Borman B, Coumans B, Hennen G, Grisar T, Igout A, Heinen E: **Housekeeping genes as internal standards: Use and limits.** *J Biotechnol* 1999, **75**:291–295.

35. Haberhausen G, Pinsl J, Kuhn CC, Markert-Hahn C: **Comparative study of different standardization concepts in quantitative competitive reverse transcription-PCR assays.** *J Clin Microbiol* 1998, **36**:628–633.

36. Goidin D, Mamessier A, Staquet MJ, Schmitt D, Berthier-Vergnes O: **Ribosomal 18S RNA Prevails over glyceraldehyde-3-phosphate dehydrogenase and beta-actin genes as internal standard for quantitative comparison of mRNA levels in invasive and noninvasive human melanoma cell subpopulations.** *Anal Biochem* 2001, **295**:17–21.

37. Raaijmakers MH, van Emst L, De Witte T, Mensink E, Raymakers RA: **Quantitative assessment of gene expression in highly purified hematopoietic cells using real-time reverse transcriptase polymerase chain reaction.** *Exp Hematol* 2002, **30**:481–487.

38. Deggerdal A, Larsen F: **Rapid isolation of PCR-ready DNA from blood, bone marrow and cultured cells, based on paramagnetic beads.** *Biotechniques* 1997, **22**:554–557.

39. Pennington J, Garner SF, Sutherland J, Williamson LM: **Residual subset population analysis in WBC-reduced blood components using real-time PCR quantitation of specific mRNA.** *Transfusion* 2001, **41**:1591–1600.

40. Bustin SA: **Absolute quantification of mRNA using real-time reverse transcription polymerase chain reaction assays.** *J Mol Endocrinol* 2000, **25**:169–193.

41. Baisse B, Bouzourene H, Saraga EP, Bosman FT, Benhattar J: **Intratumor genetic heterogeneity in advanced human colorectal adenocarcinoma.** *Int J Cancer* 2001, **93**:346–352.

42. Tricarico C, Pinzani P, Bianchi S, Paglierani M, Distante V, Pazzagli M, Bustin SA, Orlando C: **Quantitative real-time reverse transcription polymerase chain reaction: Normalization to rRNA or single housekeeping genes is inappropriate for human tissue biopsies.** *Anal Biochem* 2002, **309**:293–300.

43. Bhatia P, Taylor WR, Greenberg AH, Wright JA: **Comparison of glyceraldehyde-3-phosphate dehydrogenase and 28S-ribosomal RNA gene expression as RNA loading controls for Northern blot analysis of cell lines of varying malignant potential.** *Anal Biochem* 1994, **216**:223–226.

44. Zhong H, Simons JW: **Direct comparison of GAPDH, beta-actin, cyclophilin, and 28S rRNA as internal standards for quantifying RNA levels under hypoxia.** *Biochem Biophys Res Commun* 1999, **259**:523–526.

45. Paule MR, White RJ: **Transcription by RNA polymerases I and III.** *Nucleic Acids Res* 2000, **28**:1283–1298.

46. Solanas M, Moral R, Escrich E: **Unsuitability of using ribosomal RNA as loading control for Northern blot analyses related to the imbalance between messenger and ribosomal RNA content in rat mammary tumors.** *Anal Biochem* 2001, **288**:99–102.

47. Barbu V, Dautry F: **Northern blot normalization with a 28S rRNA oligonucleotide probe.** *Nucleic Acids Res* 1989, **17**:7115.

48. Schmittgen TD, Zakrajsek BA: **Effect of experimental treatment on housekeeping gene expression: Validation by real-time, quantitative RT-PCR.** *J Biochem Biophys Methods* 2000, **46**:69–81.

49. de Leeuw WJ, Slagboom PE, Vijg J: **Quantitative comparison of mRNA levels in mammalian tissues: 28S ribosomal RNA level as an accurate internal control.** *Nucleic Acids Res* 1989, **17**:10137–10138.

50. Mansur NR, Meyer-Siegler K, Wurzer JC, Sirover MAL: **Cell cycle regulation of the glyceraldehyde-3-phosphate dehydrogenase/uracil DNA glycosylase gene in normal human cells.** *Nucleic Acids Res* 1993, **21**:993–998.

51. Spanakis E: **Problems related to the interpretation of autoradiographic data on gene expression using common constitutive transcripts as controls.** *Nucleic Acids Res* 1993, **21**:3809–3819.

52. Kreuzer KA, Lass U, Landt O, Nitsche A, Laser J, Ellerbrok H, Pauli G, Huhn D, Schmidt CA: **Highly sensitive and specific fluorescence reverse transcription-PCR assay for the pseudogene-free detection of beta-actin transcripts as quantitative reference.** *Clin Chem* 1999, **45**:297–300.

53. Kelley MR, Jurgens JK, Tentler J, Emanuele NV, Blutt SE, Emanuele MA: **Coupled reverse transcription-polymerase chain reaction (RT-PCR) technique is comparative, quantitative, and rapid: Uses in alcohol research involving low abundance mRNA species such as hypothalamic LHRH and GRF.** *Alcohol* 1993, **10**:185–189.

54. Jesnowski R, Backhaus C, Ringel J, Lohr M: **Ribosomal highly basic 23-kDa protein as a reliable standard for gene expression analysis.** *Pancreatology* 2002 **2**:421–424.

55. Haendler B, Hofer-Warbinek R, Hofer E: **Complementary DNA for human T-cell cyclophilin.** *EMBO J* 1987, **6**:947–950.

56. Lupberger J, Kreuzer KA, Baskaynak G, Peters UR, le Coutre P, Schmidt CA: **Quantitative analysis of beta-actin, beta-2-microglobulin and porphobilinogen deaminase mRNA and their comparison as control transcripts for RT-PCR.** *Mol Cell Probes* 2002, **16**:25–30.

57. Sirover MA: **New insights into an old protein: The functional diversity of mammalian glyceraldehyde-3-phosphate dehydrogenase.** *Biochim Biophys Acta* 1999, **1432**:159–184.

58. Edwards DR, Denhardt DT: **A study of mitochondrial and nuclear transcription with cloned cDNA probes. Changes in the relative abundance of mitochondrial transcripts after stimulation of quiescent mouse fibroblasts.** *Exp Cell Res* 1985, **157**:127–143.

59. Wall SJ, Edwards DR: **Quantitative reverse transcription-polymerase chain reaction (RT-PCR): A comparison of primer-dropping, competitive, and real-time RT-PCRs.** *Anal Biochem* 2002, **300**:269–273.

60. Krussel JS, Huang HY, Simon,C, Behr B, Pape AR., Wen Y, Bielfeld P, Polan ML: **Single blastomeres within human preimplantation embryos express different amounts of messenger ribonucleic acid for beta-actin and interleukin-1 receptor type I.** *J Clin Endocrinol Metab* 1998, **83**:953–959.

61. Foss DL, Baarsch MJ, Murtaugh MP: **Regulation of hypoxanthine phosphoribosyltransferase, glyceraldehyde-3-phosphate dehydrogenase and beta-actin mRNA expression in porcine immune cells and tissues.** *Anim Biotechnol* 1998, **9**:67–78.

62. Carlyle WC, Toher CA, Vandervelde JR, McDonald KM, Homans DC, Cohn JN: **Changes in beta-actin mRNA expression in remodeling canine myocardium.** *J Mol Cell Cardiol* 1996, **28**:53–63.

63. Selvey S, Thompson EW, Matthaei K, Lea RA, Irving MG, Griffiths LR: **Beta-actin—An unsuitable internal control for RT-PCR.** *Mol Cell Probes* 2001, **15**:307–311.

64. Dirnhofer S, Berger C, Untergasser G, Geley S, Berger P: **Human beta-actin retropseudogenes interfere with RT-PCR.** *Trends Genet* 1995, **11**:380–381.

65. Raff T, van der Giet M, Endemann D, Wiederholt T, Paul M: **Design and testing of beta-actin primers for RT-PCR that do not co-amplify processed pseudogenes.** *Biotechniques* 1997, **23**:456–460.

66. Mutimer H, Deacon N, Crowe S, Sonza S: **Pitfalls of processed pseudogenes in RT-PCR.** *Biotechniques* 1998, **24**:585–588.

67. Dakhama A, Macek V, Hogg JC, Hegele RG: **Amplification of human beta-actin gene by the reverse transcriptase-polymerase chain reaction: Implications for assessment of RNA from formalin-fixed, paraffin-embedded material.** *J Histochem Cytochem* 1996, **44**:1205–1207.

68. Weisinger G, Gavish M, Mazurika C, Zinder O: **Transcription of actin, cyclophilin and glyceraldehyde phosphate dehydrogenase genes: Tissue- and treatment-specificity.** *Biochim Biophys Acta* 1999, **1446**:225–232.

69. Vandesompele J, De Preter K, Pattyn F, Poppe B, Van Roy N, De Paepe A, Speleman F: **Accurate normalization of real-time geometric averaging of multiple internal control genes.** *Genome Biol* 2002, **3**:11.

70. Hamalainen HK, Tubman JC, Vikman S, Kyrola T, Ylikoski E, Warrington JA, Lahesmaa R: **Identification and validation of endogenous reference genes for expression profiling of T helper cell differentiation by quantitative real-time RT-PCR.** *Anal Biochem* 2001, **299**:63–70.

71. Lowe DA, Degens H, Chen KD, Alway SE: **Glyceraldehyde-3-phosphate dehydrogenase varies with age in glycolytic muscles of rats.** *J Gerontol A Biol Sci Med Sci* 2000, **55**:B160–B164.

72. Ishitani R, Sunaga K, Tanaka M, Aishita H, Chuang DM: **Overexpression of glyceraldehyde-3-phosphate dehydrogenase is involved in low K^+-induced apoptosis but not necrosis of cultured cerebellar granule cells.** *Mol Pharmacol* 1997, **51**:542–550.

73. Kim JW, Kim TE, Kim YK, Kim YW, Kim SJ, Lee JM, Kim IK, Namkoong SE: **Antisense oligodeoxynucleotide of glyceraldehyde-3-phosphate dehydrogenase gene inhibits cell proliferation and induces apoptosis in human cervical carcinoma cell lines.** *Antisense Nucleic Acid Drug Dev* 1999, **9**:507–513.

74. Tajima H, Tsuchiya K, Yamada M, Kondo K, Katsube N, Ishitani R: **Over-expression of GAPDH induces apoptosis in COS-7 cells transfected with cloned GAPDH cDNAs.** *Neuroreport* 1999, **10**:2029–2033.

75. Mansur NR, Meyer-Siegler K, Wurzer JC, Sirover MA: **Cell cycle regulation of the glyceraldehyde-3-phosphate dehydrogenase/uracil DNA glycosylase gene in normal human cells.** *Nucleic Acids Res* 1993, **21**:993–998.

76. Calvo EL, Boucher C, Coulombe Z, Morisset J: **Pancreatic GAPDH gene expression during ontogeny and acute pancreatitis induced by caerulein.** *Biochem Biophys Res Commun* 1997, **235**:636–640.

77. Puissant C, Bayat-Sarmadi M, Devinoy E, Houdebine LM: **Variation of transferrin mRNA concentration in the rabbit mammary gland during the pregnancy-lactation-weaning cycle and in cultured mammary cells. A comparison with the other major milk protein mRNAs.** *Eur J Endocrinol* 1994, **130**:522–529

78. Yamada H, Chen D, Monstein HJ, Hakanson R: **Effects of fasting on the expression of gastrin, cholecystokinin, and somatostatin genes and of various housekeeping genes in the pancreas and upper digestive tract of rats.** *Biochem Biophys Res Commun* 1997, **231**:835–838.

79. Graven KK, Troxler RF, Kornfeld H, Panchenko MV, Farber HW: **Regulation of endothelial cell glyceraldehyde-3-phosphate dehydrogenase expression by hypoxia.** *J Biol Chem* 1994, **269**:24446–24453.

80. Lu S, Gu X, Hoestje S, Epner DE: **Identification of an additional hypoxia responsive element in the glyceraldehyde-3-phosphate dehydrogenase gene promoter.** *Biochim Biophys Acta* 2002, **1574**:152–156.

81. Zhong H, Simons JW: **Direct comparison of GAPDH, beta-actin, cyclophilin, and 28S rRNA as internal standards for quantifying RNA levels under hypoxia.** *Biochem Biophys Res Commun* 1999, **259**:523–526.

82. Ito Y, Pagano PJ, Tornheim K, Brecher P, Cohen RA: **Oxidative stress increases glyceraldehyde-3-phosphate dehydrogenase mRNA levels in isolated rabbit aorta.** *Am J Physiol* 1996, **270**:H81–H87.

83. Suzuki T, Higgins PJ, Crawford DR: **Control selection for RNA quantitation.** *Biotechniques* 2000, **29**:332–337.

84. Cale JM, Millican DS, Itoh H, Magness RR, Bird IM: **Pregnancy induces an increase in the expression of glyceraldehyde-3-phosphate dehydrogenase in uterine artery endothelial cells.** *J Soc Gynecol Investig* 1997, **4**:284–292.

85. Schmittgen TD, Zakrajsek BA: **Effect of experimental treatment on housekeeping gene expression: Validation by real-time, quantitative RT-PCR.** *J Biochem Biophys Methods* 2000, **46**:69–81.

86. Goidin D, Mamessier A, Staquet MJ, Schmitt D, Berthier-Vergnes O: **Ribosomal 18S RNA prevails over glyceraldehyde-3-phosphate dehydrogenase and beta-actin genes as internal standard for quantitative comparison of mRNA levels in invasive and noninvasive human melanoma cell subpopulations.** *Anal Biochem* 2001, **295**:17–21.

87. Tricarico C, Pinzani P, Bianchi S, Paglierani M, Distante V, Pazzagli M, Bustin SA, Orlando C: **Quantitative real-time reverse transcription polymerase chain reaction: Normalization to rRNA or single housekeeping genes is inappropriate for human tissue biopsies.** *Anal Biochem* 2002, **309**:293–300.

88. Bustin SA, Gyselman VG, Williams NS, Dorudi S: **Detection of cytokeratins 19/20 and guanylyl cyclase C in peripheral blood of colorectal cancer patients.** *Br J Cancer* 1999, **79**:1813–1820.

89. Rimarachin JA, Norcross J, Szabo P, Weksler BB: **GAPDH acts as an inducible not constitutive gene in cultured endothelial cells.** *In Vitro Cell Dev Biol* 1992, **28A**:705–707.

90. Oliveira JG, Prados RZ, Guedes AC, Ferreira PC, Kroon EG: **The housekeeping gene glyceraldehyde-3-phosphate dehydrogenase is inappropriate as internal control in comparative studies between skin tissue and cultured skin fibroblasts using Northern blot analysis.** *Arch Dermatol Res* 1999, **291**:659–661.

91. Hamalainen HK, Tubman JC, Vikman S, Kyrola T, Ylikoski E, Warrington JA, Lahesmaa R: **Identification and validation of endogenous reference genes for expression profiling of T helper cell differentiation by quantitative real-time RT-PCR.** *Anal Biochem* 2001, **299**:63–70.

92. Schrader M, Ravnik S, Muller-Tidow C, Muller M, Straub B, Diedrichs S, Serve H, Miller K: **Quantification of cyclin A1 and glyceraldehyde-3-phosphate dehydrogenase expression in testicular biopsies of infertile patients by fluorescence real-time RT-PCR.** *Int J Androl* 2002, **25**:202–209.

93. Savonet V, Maenhaut C, Miot F, Pirson I: **Pitfalls in the use of several "housekeeping" genes as standards for quantitation of mRNA: Tthe example of thyroid cells.** *Anal Biochem* 1997, **247**:165–167.

94. Zhu G, Chang Y, Zuo J, Dong X, Zhang M, Hu G, Fang F: **Fudenine, a C-terminal truncated rat homologue of mouse prominin, is blood glucose-regulated and can up-regulate the expression of GAPDH.** *Biochem Biophys Res Commun* 2001, **281**:951–956.

95. Wu YY, Rees JL: **Variation in epidermal housekeeping gene expression in different pathological states.** *Acta Derm Venereol* 2000, **80**:2–3.

96. Sabath DE, Broome HE, Prystowsky MB: **Glyceraldehyde-3-phosphate dehydrogenase mRNA is a major interleukin 2-induced transcript in a cloned T-helper lymphocyte.** *Gene* 1990, **91**:185–191.

97. Bereta J, Bereta M: **Stimulation of glyceraldehyde-3-phosphate dehydrogenase mRNA levels by endogenous nitric oxide in cytokine-activated endothelium.** *Biochem Biophys Res Commun* 1995, **217**:363–369.

98. Spanakis E: **Problems related to the interpretation of autoradiographic data on gene expression using common constitutive transcripts as controls.** *Nucleic Acids Res* 1993, **21**:3809–3819.

99. Oikarinen A, Makela J, Vuorio T, Vuorio E: **Comparison on collagen gene expression in the developing chick embryo tendon and heart. Tissue and development time-dependent action of dexamethasone.** *Biochim Biophys Acta* 1991, **1089**:40–46.

100. Goldsworthy SM, Goldsworthy TL, Sprankle CS, Butterworth BE: **Variation in expression of genes used for normalization of Northern blots after induction of cell proliferation.** *Cell Prolif* 1993, **26**:511–518.

101. Weisinger G, Gavish M, Mazurika C, Zinder O: **Transcription of actin, cyclophilin and glyceraldehyde phosphate dehydrogenase genes: Tissue- and treatment-specificity.** *Biochim Biophys Acta* 1999, **1446**:225–232.

102. Murphy RM, Watt KK, Cameron-Smith D, Gibbons CJ, Snow RJ: **The effects of creatine supplementation on housekeeping genes in human skeletal muscle using real time RT-PCR.** *Physiol Genomics* 2002, **12**:163–174.

103. Barroso I, Benito B, Garci-Jimenez C, Hernandez A, Obregon MJ, Santisteban P: **Norepinephrine, tri-iodothyronine and insulin upregulate glyceraldehyde-3-phosphate dehydrogenase mRNA during Brown adipocyte differentiation.** *Eur J Endocrinol* 1999, **141**:169–179.

104. Alexander MC, Lomanto M, Nasrin N, Ramaika C: **Insulin stimulates glyceraldehyde-3-phosphate dehydrogenase gene expression through *cis*-acting DNA sequences.** *Proc Natl Acad Sci USA* 1988, **85**:5092–5096.

105. Alexander-Bridges M, Dugast I, Ercolani L, Kong XF, Giere L, Nasrin N: **Multiple insulin-responsive elements regulate transcription of the GAPDH gene.** *Adv Enzyme Regul* 1992, **32**:149–159.

106. Nasrin N, Ercolani L, Denaro M, Kong XF, Kang I, Alexander M: **An insulin response element in the glyceraldehyde-3-phosphate dehydrogenase gene binds a nuclear protein induced by insulin in cultured cells and by nutritional manipulations *in vivo*.** *Proc Natl Acad Sci USA* 1990, **87**:5273–5277.

107. Rolland V, Dugail I, Le L, X, Lavau M: **Evidence of increased glyceraldehyde-3-phosphate dehydrogenase and fatty acid synthetase promoter activities in transiently transfected adipocytes from genetically obese rats.** *J Biol Chem* 1995, **270**:1102–1106.

108. Chao CC, Yam WC, Lin-Chao S: **Coordinated induction of two unrelated glucose-regulated protein genes by a calcium ionophore: Human BiP/GRP78 and GAPDH.** *Biochem Biophys Res Commun* 1990, **171**:431–438.

109. Freyschuss B, Sahlin L, Masironi B, Eriksson H: **The hormonal regulation of the oestrogen receptor in rat liver: An interplay involving growth hormone, thyroid hormones and glucocorticoids.** *J Endocrinol* 1994, **142**:285–298.

110. Desprez PY, Poujol D, Saez S: **Glyceraldehyde-3-phosphate dehydrogenase (GAPDH, E.C. 1.2.1.12.) gene expression in two malignant human mammary epithelial cell lines: BT-20 and MCF-7. Regulation of gene expression by 1,25–dihydroxyvitamin D3 (1,25-(OH)2D3).** *Cancer Lett* 1992, **64**:219–224.

111. Hazell AS, Desjardins P, Butterworth RF: **Increased expression of glyceraldehyde-3-phosphate dehydrogenase in cultured astrocytes following exposure to manganese.** *Neurochem Int* 1999, **35**:11–17.

112. Chen RW, Saunders PA, Wei H, Li Z, Seth P, Chuang DM: **Involvement of glyceraldehyde-3-phosphate dehydrogenase (GAPDH) and p53 in neuronal apoptosis: Evidence that GAPDH is upregulated by p53.** *J Neurosci* 1999, **19**:9654–9662.

113. Revillion F, Pawlowski V, Hornez L, Peyrat JP: **Glyceraldehyde-3-phosphate dehydrogenase gene expression in human breast cancer.** *Eur J Cancer* 2000, **36**:1038–1042.

114. Kim JW, Kim SJ, Han SM, Paik SY, Hur SY, Kim YW, Lee JM, Namkoong SE: **Increased glyceraldehyde-3-phosphate dehydrogenase gene expression in human cervical cancers.** *Gynecol Oncol* 1998, **71**:266–269.

115. Kitahara O, Furukawa Y, Tanaka T, Kihara C, Ono K, Yanagawa R, Nita ME, Takagi T, Nakamura Y, Tsunoda T: **Alterations of gene expression during colorectal carcinogenesis revealed by cDNA microarrays after laser-capture microdissection of tumor tissues and normal epithelia.** *Cancer Res* 2001, **61**:3544–3549.

116. Tricarico C, Pinzani P, Bianchi S, Paglierani M, Distante V, Pazzagli M, Bustin SA, Orlando C: **Quantitative real-time reverse transcription polymerase chain reaction: Normalization to rRNA or single housekeeping genes is inappropriate for human tissue biopsies.** *Anal Biochem* 2002, **309**:293–300.

117. Gong Y, Cui L, Minuk GY: **Comparison of glyceraldehyde-3-phosphate dehydrogenase and 28S-ribosomal RNA gene expression in human hepatocellular carcinoma.** *Hepatology* 1996, **23**:734–737.

118. Chang TJ, Juan CC, Yin PH, Chi CW, Tsay HJ: **Up-regulation of beta-actin, cyclophilin and GAPDH in N1S1 rat hepatoma.** *Oncol Rep* 1998, **5**:469–471.

119. Bhatia P, Taylor WR, Greenberg AH, Wright JA: **Comparison of glyceraldehyde-3-phosphate dehydrogenase and 28S-ribosomal RNA gene expression as RNA loading controls for Northern blot analysis of cell lines of varying malignant potential.** *Anal Biochem* 1994, **216**:223–226.

120. Tatton WG, Chalmers-Redman RM, Elstner M, Leesch W, Jagodzinski FB, Stupak DP, Sugrue MM, Tatton NA: **Glyceraldehyde-3-phosphate dehydrogenase in neurodegeneration and apoptosis signaling.** *J Neural Transm Suppl* 2000, **60**:77–100.

121. Jesnowski R, Backhaus C, Ringel J, Lohr M: **Ribosomal highly basic 23-kDa protein as a reliable standard for gene expression analysis.** *Pancreatology* 2002, **2**:421–424.

122. Epner DE, Coffey DS: **There are multiple forms of glyceraldehyde-3-phosphate dehydrogenase in prostate cancer cells and normal prostate tissue.** *Prostate* 1996, **28**:372–378.

123. Epner DE, Partin AW, Schalken JA, Isaacs JT, Coffey DS: **Association of glyceraldehyde-3-phosphate dehydrogenase expression with cell motility and metastatic potential of rat prostatic adenocarcinoma.** *Cancer Res* 1993, **53**:1995–1997.

124. Ripple MO, Wilding G: **Alteration of glyceraldehyde-3-phosphate dehydrogenase activity and messenger RNA content by androgen in human prostate carcinoma cells.** *Cancer Res* 1995, **55**:4234–4236.

125. Vila MR, Nicolas A, Morote J, de I, Meseguer A: **Increased glyceraldehyde-3-phosphate dehydrogenase expression in renal cell carcinoma identified by RNA-based, arbitrarily primed polymerase chain reaction.** *Cancer* 2000, **89**:152–164.

126. Bustin SA, Dorudi S: **Molecular assessment of tumour stage and disease recurrence using PCR-based assays.** *Mol Med Today* 1998, **4**:389–396.

127. Gelmini S, Tricarico C, Vona G, Livi L, Melina AD, Serni S, Cellai E, Magrini S, Villari D, Carini M, Serio M, Forti G, Pazzagli M, Orlando C: **Real-time quantitative reverse transcriptase-polymerase chain reaction (RT-PCR) for the measurement of prostate-specific antigen mRNA in the peripheral blood of patients with prostate carcinoma using the taqman detection system.** *Clin Chem Lab Med* 2001, **39**:385–391.

128. Bustin SA, Gyselman VG, Williams NS, Dorudi S: **Detection of cytokeratins 19/20 and guanylyl cyclase C in peripheral blood of colorectal cancer patients.** *Br J Cancer* 1999, **79**:1813–1820.

129. de Vries TJ, Fourkour A, Punt CJ, van de Locht LT, Wobbes T, van den BS, de Rooij MJ, Mensink EJ, Ruiter DJ, van Muijen GN: **Reproducibility of detection of tyrosinase and MART-1 transcripts in the peripheral blood of melanoma patients: A quality control study using real-time quantitative RT-PCR.** *Br J Cancer* 1999, **80**:883–891.

12

The qPCR Does Not Work?

Stephen A. Bustin and Tania Nolan

12

The qPCR Does Not Work?

Stephen A. Bustin[*] and Tania Nolan[†]

*Barts and The London, Queen Mary's School of Medicine
and Dentistry, University of London, London, United Kingdom
†Stratagene Europe, Amsterdam, The Netherlands*

12.1. Introduction

In theory, successful target amplification and quantification requires
only intact template, optimized protocols and reagents, a suitable instrument, and appropriate analysis. In practice, this is not always the case,
especially when performing RT-PCR assays. Unlike conventional PCR,
where troubleshooting can be exceedingly difficult, intelligent analysis
of amplification plots, multicomponent and raw spectrum views of real-
time assays will often allow an educated guess as to what might have
gone wrong.

If a qPCR reaction does not work, it is most likely to be due to the operator forgetting to add a component, using the wrong combination of primers and probes or the template being degraded. Viewing the multicomponent and raw spectrum will show whether probe and reaction buffer have been added, and can also reveal problems with the power supply (especially with the ABI 7700). It can also display whether too much template has been added which can swamp the PCR reaction or the detector and generate strange results.

If there was no obvious problem with reaction buffer, power supply, template amounts, and probe addition, the next step is to repeat the PCR, this time with a control template that is known to give a positive signal. If this works, then the problem may possibly reside with the original template. Genomic DNA samples may not be amplifiable when stored for long periods of time at 4°C. This may be due to degradation or the accumulation of inhibitory compounds because of repeated sampling. Degradation is easily checked by running the DNA on an agarose gel or the Agilent DNAChip. If the DNA is intact, new dilutions of the genomic DNA from stock solutions or by preparing fresh DNA samples from stored tissue will probably solve the problem. With RNA samples, the most likely suspect is degradation and it is best always to aliquot precious RNA samples and to store them at –70°C under ethanol. Therefore, the first thing to do is to repeat the PCR reaction, but adding an additional positive control template.

If this does not help, then the problem could be the primer/probe combination. Most likely, a wrong tube has been opened and the wrong probe has been added. However, if despite careful addition of the correct primers and probes, as well as of control template, no amplification is observed, it is worth rechecking the original primer/probe sequences that were ordered, as well as the product specification sheet sent with the oligonucleotides. We have cut and pasted from Primer Express (a Mac program) into Word for Windows and inexplicably lost part of the sequence, which (if we had not checked) would have resulted in a probe lacking three nucleotides from the middle.

12.2. Problem: What Is a Perfect Amplification Plot?

Fig. 12.1 provides an example of a perfect duplicate run of a sample with identical amplification plots and virtually identical C_ts. The multi-

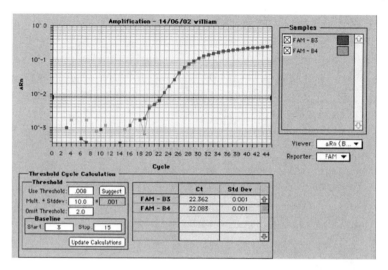

Figure 12.1. Perfect duplicate amplification plots.

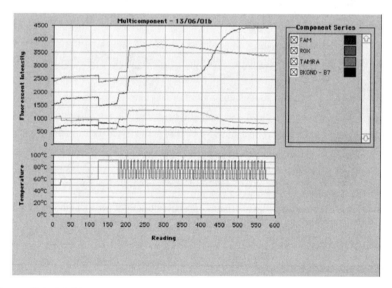

Figure 12.2. Multicomponent view. This demonstrates the increase in reporter dye and decrease in quencher dye characteristic of a successful qPCR assay.

component view (**Fig. 12.2**) shows the clear increase in the intensity of the fluorescent reporter (FAM). The raw spectra view (**Fig. 12.3**) also show the increase in the FAM peak due to probe hydrolysis.

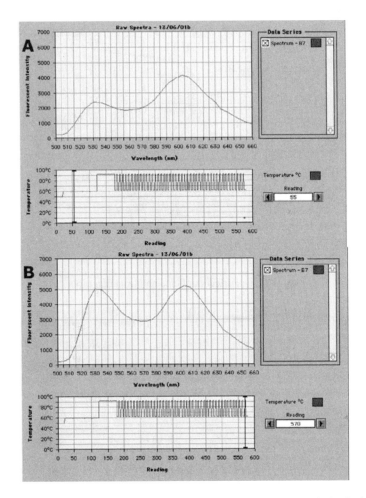

Figure 12.3. Raw spectra characteristics of successful qPCR assays at the beginning (**A**) and at the end (**B**) of a run. The increase in FAM (first peak) is obvious.

12.3. Problem: Too Much Target

It is not sufficient to rely on the experimental report for calculated C_t values or copy numbers. It may well report a C_t of 40, indicating that no amplification has taken place, even though the reaction has progressed perfectly satisfactorily. Typically, this happens when there is too much target and this overloads the assay (**Fig. 12.4**). The reason for this is that the first cycles are used to establish a baseline for the fluorescence and if that baseline is higher than the final fluorescence observed for low copy number targets, their C_ts are reported as 40. Excessively high fluorescence is also a "feature" of the SDS software on the ABI 7700 and occurs if the sample analysis includes wells that do not contain any reaction mix or if the negative control is analyzed together with the unknown samples.

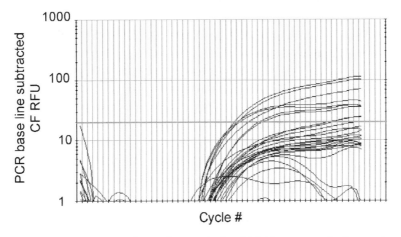

Figure 12.4. Too much template results in a high-fluorescence background.

12.3.1. Solution

Dilute template 1:100 to 1:1,000 and repeat assay. The threshold can be altered manually, either by dragging it down directly on the amplification plot or by changing the number of cycles that are used to establish the threshold definition. On the ABI 7700, analyze negative controls and unknown samples separately and always exclude wells that do not contain any reaction mix.

12.4. Problem: Amplification Plot Is not Exponential

Sometimes the automated assay report produces C_ts that appear to suggest genuine amplification but that on closer inspection turn out to result from nonexponential amplification plots. The amplification report derived from the amplification plot in **Fig. 12.5** reports a wide range of C_ts. However, inspection of the amplification plots reveals that two of the plots are not those expected of an exponential amplification.

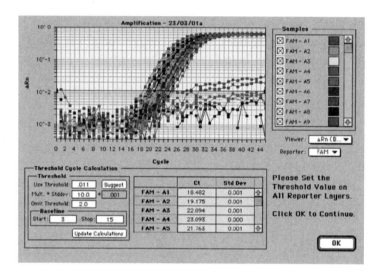

Figure 12.5. Amplification plot is not exponential.

12.4.1. Solution

The poor amplification is most likely caused by some inhibitor present in the sample. Therefore, a repeat of the amplification using a 1:10 or 1:100 dilutions may result in a proper amplification profile.

12.5. Problem: Duplicates Give Widely Differing C_ts

Sometimes the amplification plots of duplicates give widely differing C_ts. This should always result in a repeat of the assay. However, if there is no more sample, it may be possible to salvage something from the experiment by analyzing the amplification plots (**Fig. 12.6**). One duplicate has an apparent C_t of 40, the other of 24.48. However, the amplification plot of the second replicate does not generate a proper exponential curve.

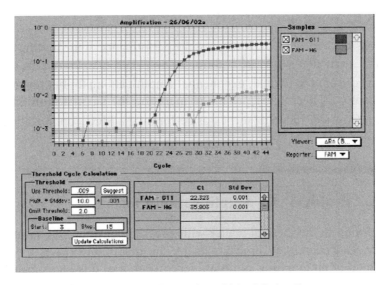

Figure 12.6. Duplicates give widely differing C_ts.

An inspection of the multicomponent view confirms that there is something wrong with the fluorescence of the sample giving a C_t of 40 (**Fig. 12.7**). This could be caused by uneven pipetting, uneven heating of the thermal block or the inadvertent contamination of the reaction tube with some inhibitor or due to the Monte Carlo effect (see **Section 11.5**).

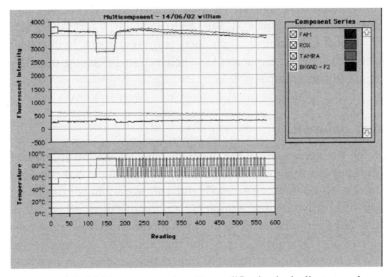

Figure 12.7. Multicomponent view. No amplification in duplicate sample.

12.5.1. Solution

If possible, repeat assay. If not, test the performance of the heating block at that particular well with a different duplicate sample. Accept the C_t derived from the normal, exponential amplification plot but report discordant C_t. Check the T_m of the primers and the thermal profile being used. Consider reducing the T_m or performing a $MgCl_2$ optimization.

12.6. Problem: No Amplification Plots

Returning to the thermal cycler with eager anticipation, the most dramatic and depressing problem facing the qPCR scientist is the total absence of an amplification plot. A description of this phenomenon is probably not required, but for those people fortunate enough not to have witnessed this yet, an example is provided (**Fig. 12.8**). In this experiment three genes (G1, G2, G3) are amplified in duplicate PCR reactions of identical cDNA (samples a and b). Additionally the amplification plot of a well containing no probe is shown (NPC). These data are the fluorescence values viewed relative to the ROX reference dye in each sample and baseline normalized (dR_n). In this case there is a clear difference between amplification positive samples—G1 (both a and b) and G2 (a alone), and amplification negative samples—G3 (a and b) and NPC. It is difficult to determine whether G2 sample b is genuinely amplified or not. In this case one problem is that the G2 duplicates have behaved so differently, making genuine quantification impossible.

12.6.1. Solution

1. In this example, some of the reactions have resulted in amplification. This suggests that there is no problem with the universal components of the reaction master mix used (and a strong argument for the inclusion of positive control samples). In circumstances where all reactions fail to amplify, there is the formal possibility that some component of the reaction mix has not functioned or was not included. dNTPs are sensitive to repeated freeze–thaw cycles and so would be the component to attract the first suspicion, especially if using an old

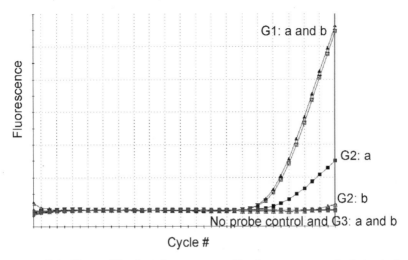

Figure 12.8. No amplification of some targets. The data are presented relative to the ROX reference dye and baseline normalized (ΔRn).

reagent batch. It is worth a check that the DNA polymerase used has a 5'–3' exonuclease function if hydrolysis assays are being performed.

2. By far the most common problem associated with reagents is operator error, especially failure to mix reaction cocktails, which will result in poor reproducibility and most drastically missing components leading to total failure. Therefore, repeat the reaction but make sure everything is properly mixed.

3. However often attempted or apparently cost-effective, PCR will not amplify in the absence of *Taq*! In the absence of an alternative explanation a repeat reaction often solves the problem.

4. The quality of the template can also adversely influence the reaction. Inhibition of PCR can occur due to various contaminants. This issue is specifically discussed at length elsewhere in this book. If all replicates of a particular sample fail to amplify alongside positive amplified samples of a different template, it would be advisable to repurify the nucleic acid and repeat the experiment. In the example given the same DNA sample is used throughout and so it is unlikely that sample contamination has caused the problems.

5. In most cases of a single qPCR assay, a test concentration of primers at 100 nM and probe at 200 nM will result in amplification. Occasionally, primer or probe concentration optimization may be required to pro-

duce any amplification. This is also discussed at length in **Chapter 13** and includes an example, which indicates that high concentration of primers was inhibitory to amplification. More is not always best!

6. Having eliminated operator errors and reaction mix issues, template impurity, and primer and probe concentration as the problem, the primer and probe operation must be investigated. At this stage of problem solving, a simple case of a reaction in which the probe is being correctly detected can be distinguished from a reaction in which the probe is absent, insufficiently, or not correctly labeled. Poorly labeled dual fluorophore probes often result from poor purification by the supplier, resulting in a mixture of labeled but not quenched, quenched but not labeled, and the desired dual-labeled oligonucleotide. The ratio of these oligonucleotides in the mixture will influence the quality of the data obtained. In order to investigate this, it is important to include a control reaction that does not include the fluorescent probe, this is particularly useful during the optimization steps of the PCR.

7. When the raw data are viewed (**Fig. 12.9**), it becomes clear that there are two different problems. In the G2 samples the background, or baseline level of the signal, is the same for a and for b, indicating that the probe has been added to both reactions. Since G2 is detected, the probe must be correctly and efficiently labeled. This begs the question as to the cause of the problem with reaction b. Failure of reaction b could be due to adding insufficient template, but note also the potential explanation that the observed lack of reproducibility could be an example of the Monte Carlo effect (**see Section 11.5**). In the G3 reactions there is no evidence of a background signal and no reaction, which is likely to indicate that the probe is absent or insufficiently or incorrectly labeled. However some chemistries produce remarkably low background signal and so the probe should be digested with DNase I in order to confirm that poor or absent label is the problem.

   At this stage the products of the PCR could be resolved by agarose gel electrophoresis but a negative result on a gel does not confirm that amplification has failed since qPCR is much more sensitive than endpoint detection. For sensitive assays, fragments that would be detected by qPCR may not be visible by EtBr staining. For this reason the most useful next, diagnostic, step is to repeat the reaction including the SYBR Green I DNA binding dye instead of the fluorescent probe and also to incorporate a melting curve reaction.

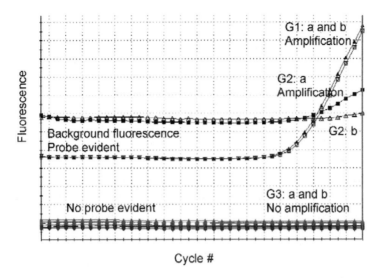

Figure 12.9. The same data presented as raw fluorescence counts. In this case, when the probe is absent, the fluorescence reading for the reaction is 4,000 counts. The background reading for the positive reaction containing G1 is around 11,000 counts increasing to 25,000 by cycle 40. The reaction containing G2 has a higher background at 16,000 counts indicating the presence of the probe in both reaction a and b. The slight amplification in G2 b is clearer from the raw data trace and indicated that template is the most likely problem in this case. The background readings for both reactions containing G3 are 4,000 counts—equivalent to the control reaction without probe. In this case it is likely that no probe was added, or that the probe has another label on it.

The SYBR Green I data will provide an extra level of troubleshooting information. If adequate amplification is detected using SYBR Green I, whereas no amplification was evident when a probe was included in the reaction, then the probe can be identified as the problem. Primer dimerization and nonspecific products can also be identified by melting curve analysis. A common, though often overlooked, cause of PCR failure is caused by the addition of too high a template concentration as well as too low. This may be perceived as counterintuitive but in order to address this possibility, the reaction should be repeated a serial dilution of 100 and 10 times more and also 1000, 100, and 10 times less template. SYBR Green I can also be used to diagnose high template concentration. This is discussed in greater detail elsewhere in this chapter.

8. PCR failure may be due to $MgCl_2$ sensitivity, which is best addressed by $MgCl_2$ optimization. Oligonucleotide annealing temperature algorithms are notoriously inaccurate and occasionally these can lead to

failed PCR reactions. This problem is usually identified and corrected by reducing the annealing temperature of the reaction by 5°C.

9. Complex three-dimensional folding of the amplicon is a problem, which occurs frequently in fragments containing runs of repeated sequences. This folding inhibits progression of the polymerase resulting in little or no product. There are a number of favorite tricks for overcoming this. Amongst these are addition of DMSO or glycerol and additions of mixtures of these using various ratios. A rapid solution is to swap from using commercial core reagents to commercially supplied master mix or *visa versa*. This can help since manufacturers add various additives (in addition to those included in core reagent kits) to their master mixes in order to make them useful for the broadest range of chemistry types possible and also to keep the enzyme stable. However, since the composition of master mixes varies between different commercial suppliers and it is rare that a detailed list of components will be provided, there is the risk that the problem will be solved only until the composition is altered.

10. A more lasting solution and flexible base for trouble shooting is to use a core reagent set and add "magic" ingredients as required. For a reaction, which is causing ongoing problems, it can take a fair amount of tweaking before a satisfactory solution is found. This is largely because the effect of changing reaction mix composition is amplicon specific. **Fig. 12.10** shows a comparison of qPCR using commercial master mix and core reagents for two amplicons. For the first sequence it is clear that using the master mix results in an increase in sensitivity and so lowers C_t and also increases product yield. However, the situation is entirely different for the second sequence where using master mix results in a huge improvement of sensitivity but a lower endpoint product.

While it is usual to select a set of favorite and familiar reagents and stick to these, it is clear that there are times when a little experimentation is required in order to persuade a difficult reaction to perform satisfactorily.

12.7. Problem: The Probe Doesn't Work!

The most usual diagnostic indicator that there is a problem due to some aspect of probe performance is successful amplification detected by SYBR

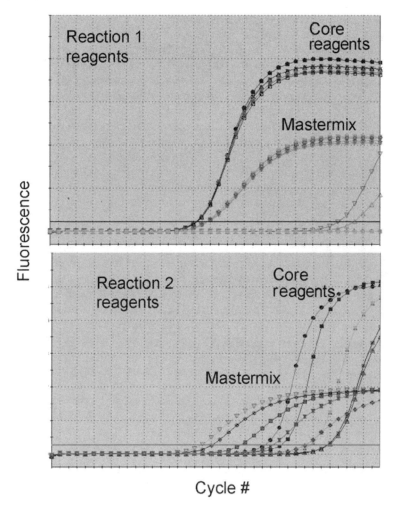

Figure 12.10. Effects of reaction mix components. In this comparison, two independent assays, reactions 1 and 2, were run using either only core reagents or a commercially available master mix. In reaction 1 it is clear that the use of the core reagents results in greater sensitivity by approximately two fold (or 1 C_t) while a significant decrease in C_t is apparent when using master mix for reaction 2. This is a clear demonstration that the components of the PCR reaction have an amplicon-specific effect on the efficiency of the reaction.

Green I but not by the probe. If after moving through the series of troubleshooting steps described above, the conclusion is that this probe does not work it is then useful to determine why the probe has failed.

Figs. 12.11 and **12.12** show classic examples of a very poor performing probe alongside a probe that is functioning well. **Fig. 12.11** uses the

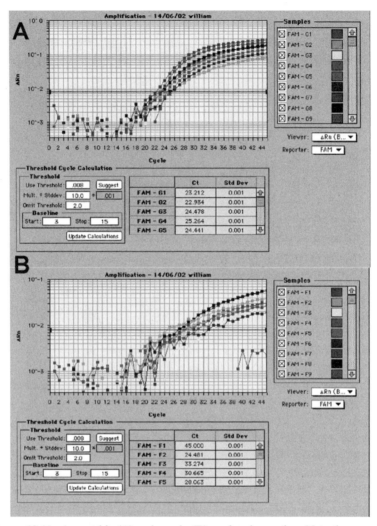

Figure 12.11. Acceptable (**A**) and poorly (**B**) performing probes. Note the poor ΔR_n value in B and the atypical amplification plot.

same probe for all samples and the resulting plots suggest that the C_ts from some of the samples are derived from exponential amplification plots with high ΔR_n values and some from nonexponential plots with low ΔR_n values. In **Fig. 12.12**, two probes are labeled and quenched in an identical manner and used on the same templates. It is clear that amplification is detected by probe 2; however the resulting increase in fluorescence is very inefficient suggesting that fewer fluorophores per amplicon are being released during the hydrolysis reaction containing probe 2 than in the reaction containing probe 1.

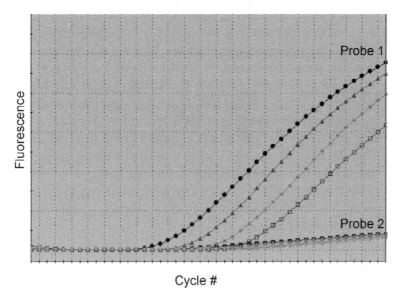

Figure 12.12. Poor-quality fluorescent probe. While the reaction containing probe 1 results in a significant increase in fluorescent signal, the final fluorescence of reactions containing probe 2 is barely changed.

12.7.1. Solution

Such results could be caused by PCR inhibitors in the sample, incorrect probe sequence, secondary structure in either the probe or the amplicon preventing hybridization, incorrect or absent label, and incorrect or absent quencher. Another potential reason for probe failure is that the assay conditions do not allow sufficient time for the probe to hybridize to the target before elongation from the primers. It is critical that TaqMan and Molecular Beacon probes are designed with a T_m of 7–10°C higher than the primers to ensure that the probe is hybridized well before the primes (see **Chapter 7**).

1. The problem in **Fig. 12.11** is not likely to be probe-related since the amplification of at least half the samples results in acceptable amplification plots. Instead, the problem is likely to be sample-related, with some of them containing an inhibitor of the PCR

reaction. Dilution of the template (1:10 or 1:1,000) should resolve this problem.

2. The problem in **Fig. 12.11B** is likely to be probe-related. One way to investigate the labeling and quenching of a potentially faulty probe is to perform a DNase I digest. Whichever single-molecule dual-labeled probe chemistry is used, DNase I digest will separate the dye from the quencher. If the probe is correctly labeled, this will result in a significant increase in specific dye fluorescence. The most important factor in this test is to include a positive control probe. This positive control probe must be labeled with the same dye and preferably quenched with the same molecule as the test probe. In addition, to identify incorrect labeling, collect emission data for as many wavelengths as the machine allows. It is interesting, though not essential, to monitor this experiment in real time.

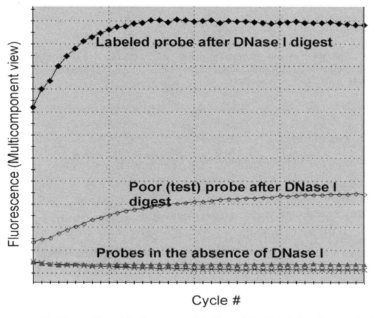

Figure 12.13. The quality of the fluorescent labeling of dual labeled probes can be investigated using a DNase I digest. In this example two probes were incubated both in the presence and in the absence of DNase I. Digestion of probe 1 resulted in a yield of 4,000 fluorescence units, while digestion probe 2 yielded only 2,000 units. Interestingly, probe 2 also has a much lower background fluorescence level, indicating that it is poorly labeled or poorly purified.

3. The labeling of each of the probes in **Fig. 12.12** was compared by digesting each with DNase I. It is much easier to interpret the results of such a digest if this is compared to the fluorescence level of the probe without digest. The level of raw fluorescence for each reaction is shown in **Fig. 12.13**. The fluorescence level of the undigested probe indicates the background fluorescence units after balancing the effect of both the quencher and the fluorescent label. In the example shown, the background is equivalent for both probes, which indicates that quenching is occurring in each case. After DNase I digestion, probe 1 produces fluorescence, which is twice that of probe 2 (15,000 units and 7,500 units respectively). This indicates that this probe has not been labeled and/or purified adequately and a replacement should be sought from the manufacturer. Having said that for many assays this may be sufficient to obtain the data required. This is achieved by viewing the amplification plots for each target (probe) individually to use the most appropriate fluorescence unit scale, baseline, and threshold setting.

12.8. Problem: The Data Plots Are Very Jagged

The uneven amplification plot is characteristic of data collected at very low fluorescence levels (**Fig. 12.14A**). In these cases the detection system is attempting to read at the lowest limits.

12.8.1. Solution

The data can be improved using algorithms to smooth the data plots if this is incorporated into the software (**Fig. 12.14B**). On the Stratagene instruments this function can be selected to perform automatically by applying the "moving average." This functions by selecting, e.g., five data points (the number of data points to average over is user determined), calculating the mean average of the C_t data, and then applying this value to the central, or third, data point of those chosen set. The set of data points encompassing the next five points is then selected and the process is repeated. While this makes acceptable data of poor-quality amplification plots, the ideal solution is to increase the fluorescence of the detection. This usually means ordering a better quality probe or an entire redesign of the assay.

12.9. Problem: The Amplification Plot for the Standard Curve Looks Great BUT……..

A standard curve is an excellent tool for examining the quality of the overall qPCR assay. In a perfect world, every amplicon will be replicated perfectly to generate a second copy during every amplification cycle. Assuming that a labeled probe binds to every single amplicon, each amplicon produced will result in one fluorophore molecule being released at each cycle. This means that a critical question is "what is the minimum number of molecules of fluorophore that can be detected?" If this were 1, it would detect 1 molecule at cycle 1. If it were 8 molecules that the instrument could detect, it would detect 1 template input molecule at cycle 4 and if it could detect only 512 molecules of label, it would take 10 cycles to detect a single template input molecule. For most instruments a ballpark figure of 10^{11} free FAM molecules can be detected with reasonable confidence above combined background noise. It is apparent that it will require 38 cycles of a perfect serial duplication PCR reaction to produce 1.4×10^{11} copies from an initial single template copy. Therefore, a plot of C_t vs. the log of the copy number of a perfect qPCR assay has a gradient (slope) of -3.3 and a y-intercept of around 38.

For the purposes of this discussion it is worthy of note that the R^2 is indicative of the fit of each data point to the line. A number of factors influence this value—the accuracy of the dilution series, pipetting reproducibility for each data point, contamination, or nonspecific fluorescence detection, lack of uniformity on the thermal block, and design of the assay including thermal characteristics. The R^2 values of poor assay will often be much lower than those for a good assay. With this in mind, the gradient, intercept, and R^2 values can be used as indicators of the efficiency, reproducibility, and sensitivity of the specific qPCR assay.

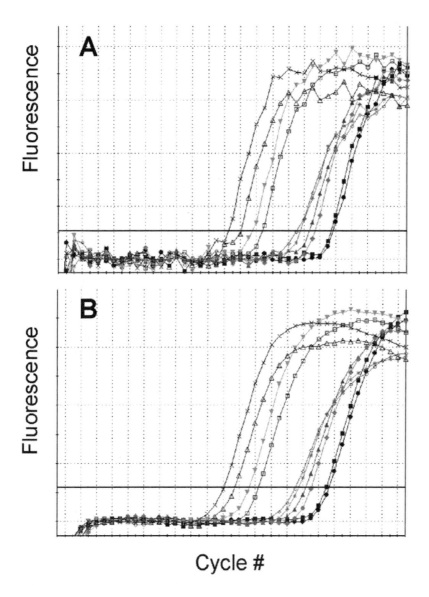

Figure 12.14 Jagged amplification plot. Some assays result in tremendously uneven amplification plots. This classically occurs when the assay is suboptimal (and usually just before submitting data for publication!). A smoothing algorithm is included in some software packages to enhance the appearance and also to make analysis meaningful. The data illustrated shows a before and after comparison of exactly the same assay. From this it can be seen that after the algorithm has been applied the linear regions of the amplification plots are more parallel making C_t measurements more accurate and the plateau regions are smoother.

12.9.1. ....The Gradient of the Standard Curve Is Greater Than –3.3

A gradient that is greater than –3.3 indicates that the qPCR reaction is less efficient than two fold per cycle or 100% (**Fig. 12.15**).

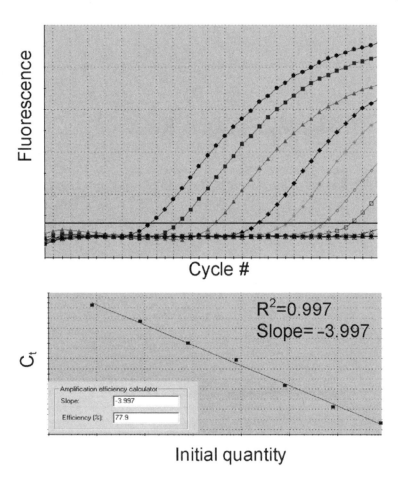

Figure 12.15. Standard curve problems (I). When a serial dilution results in a standard curve with a gradient of greater than –3.3, it indicates that the qPCR reaction is less efficient than two fold per cycle or 100%. In this example the standard curve is composed of a ten-fold dilution series. Ideally each sample would be 3.3 × C_t lower than the previous sample but these are closer to 4 × C_t apart. This results in a gradient of –3.99 and indicates a PCR efficiency of 77.9%.

12.9.1.1. Solution

A common source of error is a miscalculation in the dilution series constituting the standard curve. When a standard curve indicates an efficiency, which deviates unacceptably from –3.3, the first step should always be to repeat the serial dilution using fresh template material.

However, once simple dilution errors have been ruled out as the problem other factors must be investigated. PCR efficiency can be influenced by combinations of template contamination, Mg^{2+} concentration, oligonucleotide interactions, and secondary structure formation of the amplicon causing the *Taq* polymerase to fall off the template prematurely.

Sample inhibition can be identified by examination of a number of assays onto the same sample. The presence of an inhibitor is indicated if all assays using the same sample are inefficient. Often the C_t value for samples at low concentration is much lower than would be expected. This is usually because the inhibitory effect of the contaminant has also been diluted as the template has been diluted. In extreme cases high concentration template samples will fail entirely while lower concentrations will produce amplification (**Fig. 12.16**).

If a crude nucleic acid preparation technique has been used and inhibitors appear to remain, try to use a column-based technique for nucleic acid clean up. Detailed descriptions of template preparation and specific inhibition are presented elsewhere.

12.9.2. ....The Standards Aren't Diluting!

When the standard curve is constructed any contamination can result in inaccurate quantities being assigned to each sample. The standard curve shown in **Fig. 12.17** was constructed from cDNA. It can be seen that the lower 3 samples are of apparently the same concentration and are giving the same C_t.

12.9.2.1. Solution

Other than the obvious operator error in dilution or pipetting the most usual reason for this profile is contamination with genomic DNA. The effect of the contamination in samples with higher concentrations of specific target is less pronounced than in those with lower target copy numbers. The only solution to this problem is to re-purify the RNA and produce a fresh batch of cDNA. This is a clear illustration of how important it is to produce clean RNA samples for use in qPCR applications.

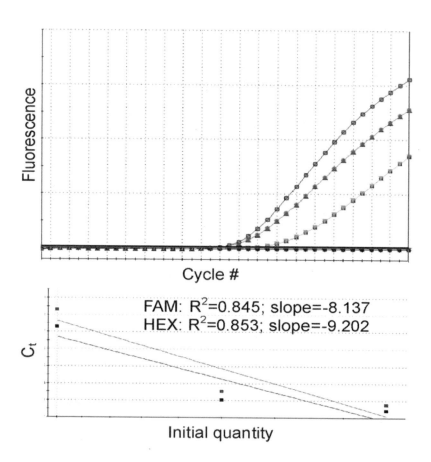

Figure 12.16. Standard curve problems (II). The presence of an inhibitor in the sample material is indicated when the C_t value for samples at high concentration is much higher than would be expected. This is usually because the inhibitory effect of the contaminant has also been diluted as the template has been diluted. In this extreme case the standard curve was produced from ten-fold serial dilutions of a crude genomic DNA preparation. For two independent assays the two high concentration samples give the same Ct while the lower concentration samples amplify but with a 4 × C_t increase and so less than 100% efficiency.

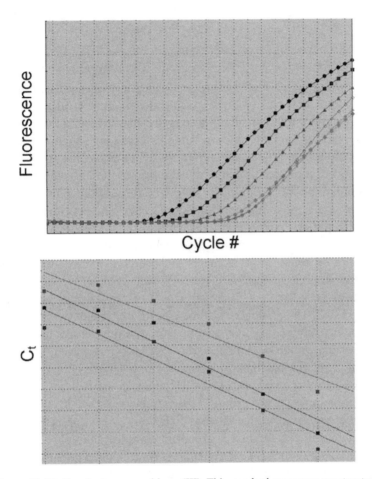

Figure 12.17. Standard curve problems (III). This standard curve was constructed from a ten-fold serial dilution of cDNA. It can be seen that the lower three samples are of apparently the same concentration and are giving the same C_t. This is a clear example of samples contaminated with genomic DNA. The effect of the contamination in samples with higher concentrations of specific target is less pronounced than in those with lower target copy numbers.

12.9.3. ………Using SYBR Green I, the Gradient of the Standard Curve Is Less Than –3.3

An efficiency of 179% is clearly impossible (according to our current understanding of the kinetics of PCR reactions).

12.9.3.1. Solution

Close examination of the standard curve in **Fig. 12.18A** reveals that the data points for samples of low concentration tend towards lower C_t values than would be predicted from the linear trend of samples at higher concentration. This lack of linearity indicates that nonspecific products are present and the influence of these is greater in the samples containing low starting template than in samples containing higher template concentration. In reactions containing SYBR Green I, this often occurs due to detection of products arising from primer dimers, which tend to form when template is absent or at low concentration. This is shown clearly by the dissociation profile **Fig. 12.18B**. The dissociation peak for the sample containing high concentration of template is at around 83.5°C. A higher melting temperature generally indicates a larger product (or higher relative GC content) and is indicative of the specific (hopefully desired) amplicon. The NTC and samples containing the template of very low concentration show a clear dissociation peak at around 79.5°C. This indicates that the amplification plot for these samples is a measurement of nonspecific, low melting temperature products, probably products produced from primer dimerization. However, examination of the profiles for samples 1 and samples 2 containing a reduced concentration show a mix of products consistent with the both the specific amplicon and primer dimer product.

Although it is evident that the amplicon component as determined by the area under the –R'(T) plot is proportional to the template concentration in the sample, such SYBR Green I assays cannot be used for reliable quantification since the fluorescence detected is proportional to all of the products formed, not only the specific product and the concentration of nonspecific products varies depending on the template concentration.

12.9.4. …….. Using a Sequence Specific Oligonucleotide Detection System the Gradient of the Standard Curve Is Less Than –3.3

A reaction with a standard curve of gradient –2.3 is shown in **Fig. 12.19A** and **B**. This gradient translates to an apparent efficiency of 171.9%, which is meaningless and indicates a serious problem with some aspect of the assay.

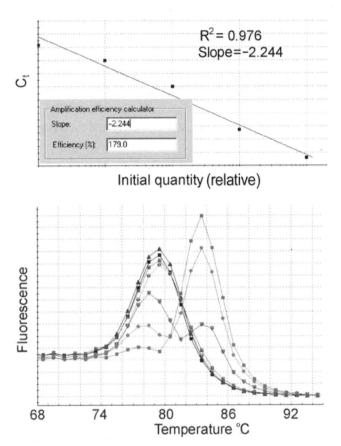

Figure 12.18. Standard curve problems (IV). This standard curve was produced from a ten-fold serial dilution of template. The efficiency of 179% is clearly impossible and the apparent gradient of –2.2 is a best estimate by the software to linearize a curve. Close examination of the data points reveals that the values for samples of low concentration tend towards lower C_t values than would be predicted from C_t values for samples at higher concentration. Products arising from primer dimers are shown by the dissociation profile. The dissociation peak for the sample containing high concentration of template is at around 83.5°C. The NTC and samples containing the template of very low concentration show a clear dissociation peak at around 79.5°C. This indicates that the amplification plot for these samples is a measurement of nonspecific, low melting temperature products, probably due to primer dimerization. However, examination of the profiles for samples 1 and samples 2 containing a reduced concentration show a mix of products consistent with the both the specific amplicon and primer dimer product.

12.9.4.1. Solution

As discussed previously, a very high efficiency can be indicated if the samples comprising the standard curve are incorrectly diluted. If the qPCR template is composed of either cDNA or gDNA, the standard curve can be validated by testing the efficiency of the reaction using an alternative, preferable validated, probe and primer set. If multiple assays appear to amplify with an efficiency that is apparently greater than 100% is likely that the dilution series is inaccurate and this should be freshly prepared. However, if the standard curve is composed of specific plasmid or oligonucleotide then a fresh dilution should be made automatically and the assay repeated.

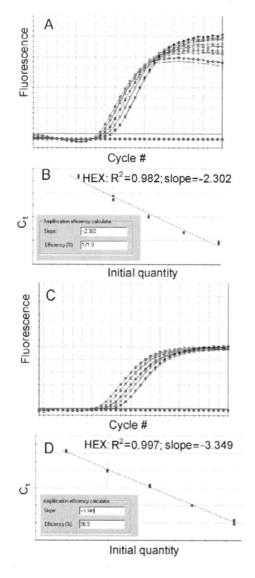

Figure 12.19. Standard curve problems (V). This standard curve has been constructed from samples that have very high concentrations of target. The baseline, or zero level, for the highest concentration probably occurs between cycles 3 and 12. (**A**) On the original amplification plot the default baseline is being set using the data from cycles 3 to 15 (the most usual default setting for qPCR machines) causing the plots to decrease below the baseline. (**B**) This results in a distortion of the plots and an apparently highly efficient reaction. (**C**) In order to use the correct cycles to set the baseline, the adaptive baseline algorithm has been applied. (**D**) All data points are normalized correctly and lie on a standard curve with a gradient of −3.349.

Having ruled out simple dilution problems, it is important to investigate the analysis of the amplification plot data. The amplification plots shown in **Fig. 19** illustrate a slight decrease below the baseline between cycles 7 and 13 before increasing again at cycle 14. This is characteristic of baseline setting problems. The baseline is the region of the amplification plot that represents the zero detection for that assay. Most qPCR machines select the ΔRn levels between cycles 3 and 15 and define these as being the baseline. Amplification is indicated by fluorescence readings (ΔRn), which are greater than those of the baseline. Therefore it is critical that the baseline cycles are correctly selected. If amplification occurs before the final baseline cycle selected, in this case cycle 15, a higher fluorescence reading is defined as zero. The effect of this is to cause the software to attempt to set this higher fluorescence as zero, in this way causing an apparent decrease below the baseline level of values, which are genuinely zero. This causes C_t values to be artificially high and on the standard curve the data points tend towards a curve rather than a linear relationship.

This is solved by simply selecting the appropriate cycles for which ΔRn is zero prior to amplification. An alternative analysis system offered by some software packages including the Stratagene Mx4000 is the adaptive baseline algorithm. This automatically examines each amplification plot and defines the region prior to amplification for each sample in each well. In **Fig. 12.19** it can be seen that after application of the adaptive baseline each amplification plot is normalized to zero ΔRn correctly and the gradient of the standard curve is –3.349.

12.10. Problem: The Amplification Plots Are Strange Wave Shapes

Occasionally the data from qPCR experiment appears so bizarre it is impossible to believe that any meaningful information can be derived from it. **Fig. 12.20A** is an example of such a weird experimental result. In this experiment SYBR Green I was used to attempt to quantify a plasmid template. The most concentrated samples result in the bizarre, wave

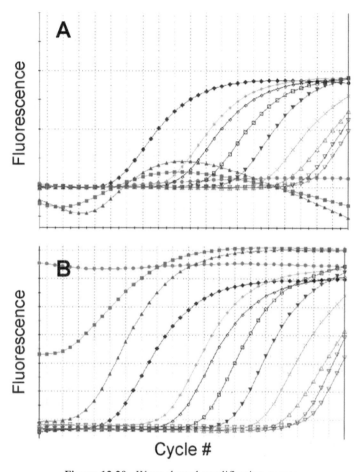

Figure 12.20. Wave-shaped amplification curves.

amplification plots on the ΔRn view. Any C_t value taken from these plots would be very misleading to say the least!

12.10.1. Solution

This is a further example of using the raw data plot to identify the most likely the cause of the problem. The very high background fluorescence level of the most concentrated samples along with very early amplification suggests that a high concentration of nucleic acid is present in the sample. In this case the highest sample concentration is even inhibitory to amplification. Analysis is difficult because there are very few cycles prior to amplification and so an accurate baseline cannot be set. The standard curve for the experiment contains samples that encompass the concentration of template in the unknown samples (**Fig. 12.20B**). Ideally C_t values would fall between 15 and 35. Although many researchers are using more cycles than this for highly sensitive applications, more concentrated samples should be diluted to give C_t values within this range.

12.11. Problem: The Amplification Plot Goes Up, Down and All Around

Sometimes it is clear that there is amplification, but the amplification plots are weird. Some go up suggesting increasing fluorescence reading after each cycle, others seem to go down which, of course, is not really possible (**Fig. 12.21A**).

12.11.1. Solution

This kind of problem typically occurs when running samples with a broad dynamic range. The most likely problem here is with the baseline setting. The instrument collects fluorescence readings during the first few cycles and of fluorescence spokes occur, the baseline will be adjusted to a level that generates these strange-looking amplification plots. Either change the settings to tell the instrument to collect baseline fluorescence data and exclude the cycle(s) causing the abnormal fluorescence readings, or use the adaptive baseline setting, where present. This fits the raw fluorescence data for each well and each path over a specified range of cycles using a linear least mean squares algorithm to produce a baseline. The value of the baseline function is calculated for every cycle and subtracted from the raw fluorescence to produce the baseline corrected fluorescence (ΔR) (**Fig. 12.21B**).

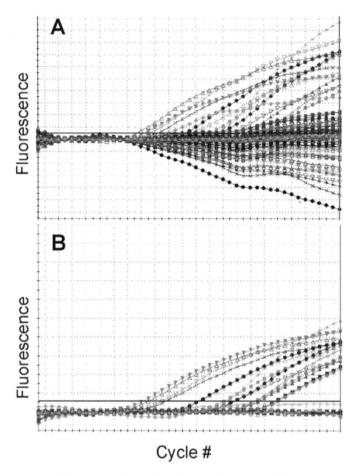

Figure 12.21. Amplification plot goes up and down.

PART III

SPECIFIC APPLICATIONS

13

Getting Started—The Basics of Setting up a qPCR Assay

Tania Nolan

13

Getting Started—The Basics of Setting up a qPCR Assay

Tania Nolan

Stratagene Europe, Amsterdam, The Netherlands

13.1. Introduction

After the long and painful process of securing sufficient funding to invest in the world of qPCR studies, the installation of a prized, new machine resembles Christmas celebrations. As the dust settles and the cardboard and wooden crates are disposed of, the awful truth dawns—the theory is sound but the practical knowledge is shaky to say the least. Still it is exciting and a new project will produce data for many publications, of course. Anxious to get started with real science and with the growing awareness of the costs associated with running this new toy, it becomes imperative to rationalize the number of experiments required to set up the technology prior to embarking on real science. Even before the optimization procedure can commence there are important decisions to be made. With an ever-increasing choice of fluorescent chemistries available, which approach is best for any particular application? As with all science there is not a definitive answer to this but there are a few guidelines that maybe helpful. Since most chemistry options are described at length in **Chapter 6**, the information is summarized and general advice is provided on the decision flowchart, **Table 13.1**.

Table 13.1. Decision flowchart for qPCR chemistries.

mRNA quantification High specificity and sensitivity are required to quantify low copy number mRNAs. Multiplex reactions are preferable if the sample is from a limited source. High throughput is not essential.	**1. Hydrolysis probe** **2. Molecular Beacon** **3. Scorpion**
Microarray validation Quantification of a large number of targets requires a low-cost approach. High sensitivity is not required, specificity (melting curves) is. High throughput is desirable. Final validation achieved with a specific chemistry.	**1. Intercalating dye** **2. Other "nonspecific" chemistries** **3. Hydrolysis probe**
SNP/Allelic discrimination High specificity and high throughput are critical. Use of LNA/PNA advisable. Duplex assays are desirable.	**1. Scorpion** **2. Molecular Beacon** **3. MGB hydrolysis probe**
Detection of occult disease High specificity and sensitivity are essential. Use of unique biological material makes multiplexing desirable. High throughput not required.	**1. Hydrolysis probe** **2. Scorpion** **3. Hybridization probe**
GMO/Pathogen detection High sensitivity and specificity are essential. Accurate quantification of a few genes from a limited sample source makes multiplexing desirable. High throughput is desirable.	**1. Scorpion** **2. MGB hydrolysis probe** **3. Wavelength-shifting MB (laser)**

Assay design is generally described in complex terms with many associated rules and regulations, some of which are more critical than others. Initially, the design process can appear so daunting that many novice qPCR scientists enter the field with trepidation. In fact, this process is as simple as designing a conventional PCR reaction and really nothing to be afraid of! The design procedure is described in easy to follow steps in **Chapter 7**. Once this has been achieved, the assays must be optimized.

13.2. Optimization

The vast majority of users skip this critical stage in their enthusiasm to get started with exciting science. However there are good reasons to invest in a couple of simple experiments. Optimization will generate data that show the quality of the assay design and often produces valuable information to indicate where problems may lie. By using the minimum primer and probe concentration to give the best assay conditions it is often possible to reduce the concentration of oligonucleotides included in the assays and so increase the assay's specificity and sensitivity as well as save much needed funds. The simple steps detailed in this chapter are designed to be as labor, time, and cost efficient as possible. Critically, if the dream is to eventually multiplex reactions these steps are required in order to have any hope of success!

The optimization process requires the use of a suitable template. This can be from any convenient source, but it is useful to have an excess supply and to be able to quantify the template. Commonly used target sources are cloned fragment in plasmid, purified PCR fragment, genomic DNA, or cDNA from cell culture (hence a ready supply).

> **Tip:** Closed circular plasmid can be an inefficient template and better results are usually obtained from linear molecules.

It is recommended that optimization of primers is carried out using SYBR Green I. Since SYBR Green I is a convenient and inexpensive approach, it provides reassurance that the primers are functioning and can (with a melting curve) also give a measure of the quality of the reaction. Should the primers fail, the wasted investment is minimal since the labeled oligonucleotide probes represent the major expense of the assay.

> **Tip:** Design a number of alternative assays around the sequence of interest and test several primer pairs before purchasing an internal oligonucleotide probe.

If the eventual assay requires incorporation of a hydrolysis (TaqMan) probe a decision must be made about the $MgCl_2$ concentration to use. In general the recommendation for hydrolysis assays is to increase the $MgCl_2$ in order to support the 5'–3' exonuclease function of *Taq* polymerase. Usually these assays are performed in 5 mM $MgCl_2$. However, this is a very high MgCl$_2$ concentration to use for SYBR Green I assays. Instead, it is better to use around 2.0 mM. A higher MgCl$_2$ concentration would be expected to promote primer dimer formation but then primer dimer products are not detected by the specific oligonucleotide! These caveats need to be considered when deciding which MgCl$_2$ concentration to use for the optimization procedure. In most cases it is adequate and informative to use 5 mM MgCl$_2$, if a probe is to be used at a later date, or 2.5 mM if SYBR Green I or other nonhydrolysis chemistries are to be used for subsequent experiments. Primer dimer products may be formed and will be visualized on the first derivative of the melting profile. These can be considered the worst-case scenario. Although primer dimer products are not detected using labeled internal oligonucleotide probes, substantial nonspecific product formation could inhibit the PCR reaction and result in reduced efficiency. For this reason it is imperative to select primer pairs that produce little or no nonspecific products in the PCR reaction.

13.3. Primer and Probe Optimization Protocol

For those biologists who are very reluctant mathematicians refer to Tables 13.2—13.5 to perform the following dilutions:

1. Dilute probe and primers to 100 µM for stock storage, aliquot, and store at –70 C.
2. Dilute primers to 10 µM for working solutions (store at –20°C).
3. Dilute probe to 5 µM for working solution (store at –20°C).

Table 13.2. Calculating oligonucleotide concentration.

To calculate 100 µM from the information supplied with the oligonucleotide:

start with the *µmolar concentration* = 20.25 µmol/l

$$volume\ to\ add\ for\ 100\ \mu M = \frac{\mu molar\ concentration \times 1000}{100}\ (\mu l)$$

volume (µl) to add for 100 µM = 202.5 µl

Table 13.3. Calculating primer volumes to add to the qPCR reaction.

Assuming that the primer stock concentration is 10 µM (from step 2 above) and using the equation:

stock concentration × µl volume of stock used = reaction (final) concentration × volume of reaction

e.g., for a final reaction concentration of a primer to be 100 nM in a 25 µl reaction;

[10 µM = 10,000 nM]

Using the equation:

stock concentration × µl volume of stock used = reaction (final) concentration × volume of reaction

$$10,000 \times vol\ stock\ used = 100 \times 25$$

$$vol\ stock\ used\ = \frac{100 \times 25}{10,000}$$

$$vol\ stock\ used = 0.25\ \mu l$$

For a final reaction concentration of a primer to be 100 nM in a 25 µl reaction use 0.25 µl primer stock at 10 µM.

Table 13.4. Calculating water volume to add to reaction master mix for optimisation experiment.

*Final volume in each tube is 60 µl.

Reagents volume for the primer optimization matrix using SYBR Green I, primers and/or water and reagents in master mix is 35.1 µl.

Reagents volume for the primer optimization m atrix using hydrolysis robe, primers and/or water and reagents in master mix is 39.9 µl.

Template *x* µl

*Water to make up to 60 µl = [60 − (template vol + reagents volume)]

4. Select template DNA that can be used for optimization.

The optimization experiments described in **Sections 13.4** and **13.7** consists of [2 × (26 reactions) + 2 × NTC; (use 50 nm/50 nm and 900 nm/900 nm primer combination for NTC)]: resulting in a total of 54 reactions. Each

Table 13.5. Calculating reaction volumes.

*Final volume in each tube is 60 μl.
Volume of this probe and/or water for the optimization matrix is 4 μl.
Primer volume = *x*.
Required reagents 15 μl.
Template = *y*.
*Water to make up to 50 μl = [50 − (*template vol* + *primer F vol* + *primer R vol* + 19)]

tube contains the stated primer concentration for a final volume of 60 μl. Use 10-μM stock of each primer and add volumes (in μl) as given **R**(everse)/**F**(orward) to each tube containing water as shown on **Table 13.6** (see color insert).

Note: Dilute primers 1/10 for 1 μM to use for the 50 nM concentrations to avoid pipetting low volumes. The volumes quotes are correct to result in the required concentration in 25-μl PCR reactions.

The optimal concentration of primers can range from 50 nM to 900 nM and so a matrix of reactions encompassing this range is performed. This procedure requires a single qPCR experiment of 52 samples plus controls and so is well worth the effort to avoid mysterious inhibition events occurring during real project experiments.

13.4. Optimization of Primers Concentration Using SYBR Green I

Run all optimization reactions in duplicate:

1. Set up a matrix of 0.5-ml tubes as shown on **Table 13.6** (see color insert). Each tube will eventually hold reaction mix to produce 2 × 25 μl (duplicate) optimization reactions. These will then be divided into individual 25-μl reactions. Whilst this is probably the most painstaking and fiddly approach, it does ensure the closest reproducibility between samples and reduces the possibility of pipetting errors leading to confusing or lost data. Since the rules of arithmetic often breakdown during pipetting, 60 μl of total volume will be made in each setup tube.

2. Make a reaction master mix by adding the reagents in the order shown in **Table 13.7**, mix gently, and then finally add *Taq* polymerase and mix gently again. Add 38.4 µl of the reaction mix to each primer/water setup tube in the matrix. Mix gently and then aliquot 25 µl of this into each of two instrument compatible microfuge tubes. Cap carefully, label tubes (if required, check that excitation and emission will not be obscured by the labeling), spin briefly, gently wipe the surface of each tube, and ease into the PCR block noting the orientation of the tubes.

3. Perform a qPCR assay and melting curve analysis as described in **Table 13.7**.

SYBR Green I data can be collected at either the extension stage or the latter half of the annealing stage. At the annealing stage the temperature is lower resulting in a greater fluorescence from the bound SYBR Green I. Comparison of data collected at both stages during the same reaction reveals that there is very little difference in C_t. The lower temperature may give a clearer impression of small, nonspecific products.

13.5. SYBR Green I Optimization Data Analysis

To select the optimal primer pairs, examine the amplification plots and select the combination that give the lowest C_t value. If identical C_t values result from multiple reactions, select the conditions, which give the highest ΔR_n value and then those using the lowest primer concentrations. An example of a primer optimization matrix is shown in **Plate 13.1**.

13.6. Examination of the Melting Curve

In order to perform a melting curve, all products from the PCR are held at 95°C to ensure that they are fully separated and then cooled to ensure complete hybridization. These duplex molecules are then subjected to incubations at increments of temperature. The period of hold and the temperature incremental steps influence the stringency of the data; a longer hold with smaller temperature steps results in a more stringent definition of the melting profile of the product.

Table 13.7. Primer optimization protocol 1.

Primer Optimization Protocol 1
Reagent Master mix for SYBR Green I reaction
Using the Stratagene Brilliant SYBR Green I Core reagent kits:

	1×60 μl reaction (μl)	27×60 μl
Master mix		
[Primers in matrix]	[21.6]	[583.2]
dH_2O	TBD*	TBD*
buffer (10×)	6	162
$MgCl_2$ (50 mM)	3	81
(2.5 mM final concentration)		
dNTP (20mM)	2.4	64.8
(0.8 mM final)		
ROX diluted $^1/_{200}$	0.9	24.3
SYBR Green I	0.6	16.2
(dilute 1/5000)		
Taq (5 U/μl)	0.6	16.2
template	TBD*	TBD*
(aim for 10^4 to 10^6 copies)		

Final volume　　**1620 μl**

* *TBD The volume of water to be added will depend upon the concentration of the template*

Tip: Remember to remove the reaction mix for the NTC before adding
template and add water to compensate.

Perform a qPCR protocol:

1 cycle:
95°C 10:00

40 cycles:
95°C 00:30
Annealing temp 01:00　　**Collect data**
　72°C 00:30　　**Collect data**

Followed by a melting profile:

1 cycle:
95°C 01:00

41 Cycles:　　**Collect data**
starting at 55°C hold for 00:30 and repeat incrementing temperature by 1°C per　cycle

Tip: Do not forget to collect data!

Tip: Use increments between 0.2°C to 1°C per cycle. Increments of less than 0.2°C per cycle do not improve stringency for most sequence differences.

The raw data from a melting profile are presented as a plot of fluorescence units against temperature (**Plate 13.2A**). This is not tremendously informative, however the first derivative view of the rate of change of fluorescence with respect to temperature, $-R'(T)$ (**Plate 13.2B**), provides a clear view of the rate of SYBR Green I loss and the temperature range over which this occurs. In order to illustrate this effect clearly, the data between 72°C and 90°C have been selected. The small peak corresponding to 74.5°C is, more than likely, due to primer dimer product formation since this is the only peak to occur in the NTC sample. The main peaks occur at around 85.55°C though there are some with a distinctly different profile and the next peak at 86.55°C. These distinct profiles represent different products in the final PCR product. The ideal, optimum assay has a single melting profile indicating a single product (**Plate 13.2C**), and so if multiple products are evident, it is recommended that alternative primer pairs are tested until a single dissociation product is produced (**Plate 13.2D**).

13.7. Optimization of Primer Concentration Using Fluorescent Probes

If a fluorescent probe is to be used and the preference is to optimize the assay using the probe, the initial step is to determine the optimal concentration of primers using a matrix of reactions as described for optimization using SYBR Green I. If Molecular Beacons or Scorpions are to be used the thermal characteristics of the reaction can be clearly defined by performing a melting curve analysis.

13.8. Molecular Beacon Melting Curve

If the application is using Molecular Beacons (or Scorpions), the thermal conditions can be more accurately determined using a melting curve and a specific target. If the application requires the discrimination of similar sequences, for example, as in allelic discrimination, a mismatched template can also be included in the experiment in order to define the optimum thermal conditions to distinguish the targets.

At high temperatures, the Molecular Beacon remains in an open conformation. As temperature decreases the Molecular Beacon closes and so the fluorescence decreases. As temperature decreases in the presence of a specific single-stranded oligonucleotide target, the Molecular Beacon will hybridize to the target and remain open continuing to emit fluorescence. The temperature at which half-maximum fluorescence is obtained gives the Tm for that Molecular Beacon. The ideal annealing temperature is that at which the Molecular Beacon will bind to its complementary target but will adopt a stem-loop conformation if no specific target is present. If target discrimination is required, an annealing temperature should be chosen at which the Molecular Beacon would bind to its complementary target but not to a mismatched target. Having determined the optimal thermal conditions for the Molecular Beacon assay, the primer and probe concentrations need to be optimized as described in **Section 13.9**.

13.9. Primer Optimization Reactions in Duplicate

1. Set up a matrix of 0.5-ml tubes as shown on **Table 13.6**. Each tube will eventually hold reaction mix to produce 2 × 25 μl (duplicate) optimization reactions. These will then be divided into individual 25-μl reactions. This is designed to ensure the closest reproducibility between samples and reduces the possibility of pipetting errors leading to confusing or lost data. Since the rules of arithmetic often breakdown during pipetting, 60 μl total volume will be made in each setup tube.

2. Make up the reaction master mix by adding the reagents in the order shown, mix gently, and then finally add *Taq* polymerase and mix gently again. Add 38.4 μl of the reaction mix to each primer/water setup tube in the matrix. Mix gently and then aliquot 25 μl of this into each of two instrument compatible microfuge tubes. Cap carefully, label tubes (if required), spin briefly, gently

wipe the surface of each tube, and ease the tubes fully into the PCR block, noting the orientation of the tubes.

3. For a Hydrolysis (TaqMan) Probe perform a two-step qPCR or, if using a Molecular Beacon or Scorpion, perform a three-step qPCR protocol as described in **Table 13.8**.

13.10. Primer Optimization Data Analysis

To select the optimal primer pairs, examine the amplification plots and select the combination that give the lowest C_t value. If identical C_t values result from multiple reactions, select the conditions, which result in the highest ΔR_n value and use the lowest primer concentrations. **Plate 13.1** shows an example of primers optimized in the presence of a hydrolysis probe. In this case a matrix of 100 nM to 900 nM was used. It is clear that high concentrations of forward primer are inhibitory to the reaction. The optimum primer pair concentration chosen was 300 nM forward and 900 nM reverse since this combination resulted in the lowest C_t value (22.58) and highest ΔR_n.

13.11. Optimization of Probe Concentration

Having chosen the most appropriate concentration for the primers, a second reaction is performed to determine the optimum probe concentration. These reactions include primers at the optimum concentration as determined previously. The optimum linear probe concentration is most likely to be within the range 50 nM to 300 nM, although Scorpions are usually used at the higher concentrations—from 250 nM to 500 nM.

Using **Table 13.9** as a guide, prepare a matrix of reaction preparation tubes. For a working solution of **1 μM probe**, add volumes of probe (in μl) and water as given in **Table 13.10**. Prepare the reaction master mix by adding the reagents in the order shown in **Table 13.9**, mix gently, and add 40 μl to each probe/water tube in the matrix. Mix gently

Table 13.8. Primer optimization protocol 2.

Primer Optimization Protocol 2 Using the Stratagene Brilliant Core reagent kits:		
Master mix	1×60 μl reaction (μl)	27×60 μl
[Primers in matrix]	[21.6]	[583.2]
dH$_2$O	TBD*	TBD*
buffer (10×)	6	162
MgCl$_2$ (50 mM)** (5 mM final conce ntration)	6	81
dNTP (20 mM) (0.8 mM final)	2.4	64.8
ROX diluted $^1/_{200}$	0.9	24.3
Probe (200 nM final) (From 100 μM stock)	2.4	64.8
template (aim for 10^4 to 10^6 copies)	TBD*	TBD*
Taq (5 U/μl)	0.6	16.2
	Final volume	**1620 μl**

* *TBD The volume of water to be added will depend upon the concentration of the template.*
** *The recommended starting concentrati on of MgCl$_2$ for Scorpion assays is 2.5 mM and for Molecular Beacons is 3.5 mM. Adjust as required.*

Tip: Remember to remove the reaction mix for the NTC before adding template and add water to compensate.

For a Hydrolysis (TaqMan) Probe perform a qPCR p rotocol of:

1 cycle:
95°C 10:00

40 cycles:
95°C 00:15
60°C 01:00   **Collect data**

OR
For a Molecular Beacon or Scorpion assay perform a qPCR protocol of:

1 cycle:
95°C 10:00

40 cycles:
95°C 00:15
Annealing temperature 01:00   **Collect data**
72°C 00:30

Table 13.9. Probe optimization protocol.

Probe Optimization Protocol

Using **Table 13.2** as a guide prepare a matrix of reaction set up tubes. Using a working solution of **1 µM probe**, add volumes of probe (in µl) and water as given in **Table 13.2**.

Using the Stratagene Brilliant Core reagent kits:

Master mix	1 × 60 µl reaction (µl)	10 × 60 µl (µl)
*dH$_2$O	TBD*	TBD*
buffer (10×)	6	60
MgCl$_2$ (50 mM)	6	60
(5 mM final)		
dNTP (20 mM)	2.4	24
(0.8 mM final)		
Primer F	TBD*	TBD*
Primer R	TBD*	TBD*
ROX diluted $^1/_{200}$	0.9	9
Taq (5 U/µl)	0.6	6
template	TBD*	TBD*
Final volume		**600 µl**

* *TBD The volume of water to be added will depend upon the concentration of the template.*

> **Tip:** Remember to remove the reaction mix for the NTC before adding template and add water to compensate.

For hydrolysis probe perform a qPCR protocol of:
1 cycle:
95°C 10:00

40 cycles:
95°C 00:30
60°C 01:00   **Collect data**

For Molecular Beacon or Scorpion perform a qPCR protocol of:
1 cycle:
95°C 10:00

40 cycles:
95°C 00:30
Annealing temp 01:00   **Collect data**
72°C 00:30

Table 13.10. Volumes of probe 1 µM and ddH$_2$O for probe optimization.

	(50 nM)	(100 nM)	(200 nM)	(300 nM)	NTC 1	NTC 2
ddH$_2$O	17	14	8	2	17	2
Probe 1 i M	3	6	12	18	3	18

and then aliquot 25 µl of this into each of 2 microfuge tubes. Cap carefully, spin briefly, and place into the machine noting the placement of the reactions.

13.12. Probe Optimization Data Analysis

To select the most appropriate probe concentration, examine the amplification plots and select the conditions that give the lowest C$_t$ value and the highest ΔR_n values. An example is shown on **Plate 13.3**. In this case it can be seen that reducing the probe concentration below 200 nM does not alter the C$_t$ but does result in reduced endpoint fluorescence. Increasing the probe concentration from 200 nM to 300 nM does not influence the data and so 200 nM was selected as the optimum probe concentration.

13.13. Testing the Efficiency of Reactions Using a Standard Curve

Having chosen the optimum concentration for primers and probe, the final stage of optimization is to determine the efficiency of the qPCR reaction. The use of the standard curve as a tool for determination of the quality of a qPCR reaction is described in **Section 12.9**. It is particularly important that the assay is reliable and of optimum efficiency, especially if multiple reactions are to be combined in multiplex or if the experiment will be run in the absence of a standard curve and a comparative quantification determination (or $\Delta\Delta C_t$) is to be used. Under ideal conditions a plot of C$_t$ vs. the log of the copy number of an efficient qPCR assay has a gradient (slope) of -3.3 and a y-intercept of around 38, and R^2 of greater than 0.98. Using suboptimal conditions for the qPCR and including an inappropriate T_m, will also result in low reproducibility of replicates (for further details refer to **Section 12.9**). The initial dilutions to use for the standard curve should encompass as large a range as possible and so for optimization purposes a three-fold to ten-fold dilution series over five to seven orders of magnitude usually serves best. Each sample should be run in triplicate.

The qPCR reaction conditions for both reaction master mix and thermal profile are identical to those used for probe optimization but, of course, using the primer and probe concentrations previously determined to be optimal.

An example of an ideal standard curve is shown in **Plate 13.4**. A three-fold serial dilution was used, and the gradient of -3.358 and 98.5% efficiency indicate that this is a well-optimized assay and suitable for application to experimental samples and quantification. In contrast, a less than desirable example is shown in **Plate 13.5**. This standard curve was constructed from a two-fold serial dilution of template. The gradient of -4.458 and efficiency 67.6% indicate that the reaction is very inefficient. It would not be advisable to use this assay for quantitative studies and would require a process of troubleshooting and possible redesign before proceeding.

14

Use of Standardized Mixtures of Internal Standards in Quantitative RT-PCR to Ensure Quality Control and Develop a Standardized Gene Expression Database

James C. Willey, Erin L. Crawford,
Charles A. Knight, Kristy A. Warner,
Cheryl R. Motten, Elizabeth Herness Peters,
Robert J. Zahorchak, Timothy G. Graves,
David A. Weaver, Jerry R. Bergman,
Martin Vondracek, and Roland C. Grafstrom

14

Use of Standardized Mixtures of Internal Standards in Quantitative RT-PCR to Ensure Quality Control and Develop a Standardized Gene Expression Database

James C. Willey,[*] Erin L. Crawford,[*] Charles A. Knight,[*]
Kristy A. Warner,[*] Cheryl R. Motten,[*] Elizabeth Herness Peters,[†]
Robert J. Zahorchak,[†] Timothy G. Graves,[*] Jerry R. Bergman,[*]
David A. Weaver,[*] Martin Vondracek,[‡]
and Roland C. Grafstrom[‡]

*Departments of Medicine and Pathology, Medical College of
Ohio, Toledo, Ohio; †Gene Express, Inc, Toledo, Ohio;
‡Division of Biochemical Toxicology and Experimental
Carcinogenesis, Institute of Environmental Medicine,
Karolinska Institutet, Stockholm, Sweden*

14.1. Introduction

Completion of the sequencing portion of the Human Genome Project
presents the opportunity to develop detailed understanding of normal

and pathologic human biology. With this increased understanding, there is the opportunity to develop clinical molecular tests that will improve prevention, diagnosis, and treatment of disease. Much of the promise is in the area of gene expression measurement. This promise already has inspired a very large investment from both the governmental and industrial sectors. Thus far, the methods used primarily in these efforts have been microarrays for initial screening experiments, and quantitative RT-PCR for follow-up confirmation of results. Successful application of gene expression measurement tools in clinical diagnostics will require careful quality control. In this chapter, we describe how quality control is implemented with standardized RT (StaRT)-PCR through the optimal use of a standardized mixture of internal standards in each gene expression measurement. These highly standardized and quality controlled data are suitable for building a standardized gene expression databank.

14.1.1. Controls Required for RT-PCR to Be Quantitative

For gene expression measurement to be useful in research and/or clinical applications it is necessary that it be quantitative. For clinical diagnostic tests an additional requirement is that the reproducibility, sensitivity, and specificity of a test be confirmed on a regular basis and that careful documentation of these tests be maintained.

There are several potential sources of variation in quantitative RT-PCR gene expression measurement, as outlined in **Table 14.1**. StaRT-PCR, by including a standardized mixture of internal standards (SMIS) in each gene-expression measurement, controls for each of these sources of variation. In contrast, using real-time RT-PCR without internal standards, or with internal standards that are not combined into a SMIS, it is possible to control for some, but not all of these sources of variation. These issues are discussed in the next sections (**Sections 14.1.2.–14.1.7.**).

14.1.2. Control for Variation in Loading of Sample into PCR Reaction

Rationale for Loading Control. Quantitative RT-PCR without a control for loading has been described.[1] According to this method, quantified amounts of RNA are pipetted into each PCR reaction. However,

Table 14.1. Sources of variation in quantitative RT-PCR gene-expression

Source of Variation	Control Methods	
	StaRT-PCR[1]	Real-time
cDNA loading: Due to variation in pipetting, quantification, or reverse transcription. Consequence: unreliable comparison of expression for same gene in two different samples	Multiplex Amplify with Reference Gene (e.g., beta-actin)	Multiplex Amplify with Reference Gene (e.g., beta-actin)
Amplification Efficiency **Cycle-to-Cycle Variation**: early slow, log linear, late slow plateau phases. Consequence: unreliable comparison of expression fo r same gene in different samples.	Internal standard CT for each gene in a Standardized Mixture of Internal Standards (SMIS)	Real-time measurement
Gene-to-Gene Variation: inefficiency of primers. Consequence: unreliable comparison of expression for diffe rent genes in the same or different sample .	Internal standard CT for each gene in a SMIS	External standard curve for each gene measured
Sample-to-Sample Variation: variable presence of an inhibitor of PCR. Consequence: unreliable comparison of expressi on for same or different gene in same or different samples .	Internal standard CT for each gene in a SMIS	Standard curve of reference sample compared to test sample[2]
Reaction-to-Reaction Variation: in quality and /or concentration of PCR reagents (e.g., primers). Consequence: unreliable comparison of expression for same or different gene in same or different samples.	Internal standard CT for each gene in a SMIS	None[2]
Reaction-to-Reaction Variation: in presence of an inhibitor of PCR. Consequence: un reliable comparison of expression for same or different gene in same or different samples.	Internal standard CT for each gene	None[2]
Position-to-Position Variation: in thermocycler efficiency Consequence: unreliable comparison of expression for same or different gene in same or different samples.	Internal standard CT for each gene	

[1] StaRT-PCR involves (a) the measurement at endpoint of each gene relative to its corresponding internal standard competitive template to obtain a numerical value and (b) comparison of expression of each target gene relative to the β-actin reference gene, to obtain a numerical value in units of molecules/10^6 β-actin molecules.

[2] With real-time RT-PCR, variation in the presence of an inhibitor in a sample may be controlled through use of standard curves for each gene in each sample measured and comparing these data to data obtained for each gene in a "calibrator" sample. However, variation in PCR reaction efficiency due to inhibitors in samples, variation in PCR reagents, or variation in position within thermocycler may be compensated only through use of an internal standard in the form of a SMIS for each gene measured. If an internal standard is included in a PCR reaction, quantification may be made at endpoint, and there is no need for kinetic (or real-time) analysis. If internal standards for multiple genes are mixed together in a SMIS and then used to measure expression for both the target genes and reference gene, this is the patented StaRT-PCR technology, whether it is done by kinetic (real-time) analysis or at endpoint. A SMIS fixes the relative concentration of each internal standard so that it cannot vary from one experiment to another.

there are two major quality control problems with this approach. *First*, there is no control for variation in reverse transcription (RT) from one sample to another and the effect will be the same as if unknown, unquantified amounts of cDNA were loaded into the PCR reaction. It is possible to control for variation in RT by including a known number of internal standard RNA molecules in the RNA sample prior to RT.[2] However, as described in the next section, as long as one controls for the amount of cDNA loaded into the PCR reaction, there is no need to control for variation in RT. *Second*, when gene expression values are related to the amount of RNA loaded into the RT reaction, there is no control for pipetting errors that may be generated at two points. Errors may occur when attempting to put the same amount of RNA from each sample into their respective RT reactions, and also when pipetting cDNA from the RT reaction into each individual PCR reaction. These sources of error also could be controlled at the RNA level if an internal standard RNA for both a reference gene and each target gene were included with the sample prior to RT. However, this is a very cumbersome process and it limits analysis of the cDNA to the genes for which an internal standard was included. Further, internal standards must be within 10-fold ratio of the gene-specific cDNA molecules. It is not possible to know ahead of time the proper amount of internal standard for each gene to include in the RNA prior to RT. For these and other reasons, it is most practical to control for loading at the cDNA level relative to a reference gene, as described below.

Control for cDNA loading relative to reference gene. With either realtime RT-PCR or StaRT-PCR, control for loading is best done at the cDNA level by amplifying a reference or "housekeeping" gene at the same time as the target gene. The reference gene serves as a valuable control for loading of cDNA into the PCR reaction if it does not vary significantly among the samples being evaluated. We, along with other investigators,[3] have determined that although RT efficiency varies from one sample to another, the representation of one gene to another in a sample does not vary among different reverse transcriptions. Thus, although it is necessary to control for loading at the cDNA level, it is not necessary to control for variation in efficiency of RT for each individual gene. When reference gene cDNA is measured along with target gene in each PCR reaction, it controls for variation in loading due to pipetting errors.

Choice of reference gene. Many different genes have been used as reference genes. No single gene is ideal for all studies. For example, β-actin varies little among different normal bronchial epithelial cell samples,[4] however it may vary several hundred-fold in samples from different tissues, such as bronchial epithelial cells compared to lymphocytes. With StaRT-PCR it is possible to gain understanding regarding intersample variation in reference gene expression by measuring two reference genes, β-actin and GAPDH, in every sample. We previously reported that there is a significant correlation between the ratio of β-actin/GAPDH expression and cell size.[5] This likely is due to the role of β-actin in cytoskeleton structure. If one determines that the variation in reference gene expression exceeds the tolerance level for a particular group of samples being studied, StaRT-PCR enables at least three alternative ways to normalize data among the samples.

Flexible reference gene. With StaRT-PCR, because the data are numerical and standardized, it is possible to use any of the genes measured as the one against which all of the others will be normalized. Thus, if there is a gene that appears to be less variable than β-actin, all of the data may be normalized to that gene by inverting the gene expression value of the new reference gene (to 10^6 β-actin molecules/molecules of reference gene) and multiplying this factor times all of the data, all of which are in the form of molecules/10^6 molecules of β-actin. As a result of this operation, the β-actin values will cancel out and the new reference gene will be on the denominator.

Interactive Gene Expression Indices. An ideal approach to intersample data normalization is to identify one or more genes that are positively associated with the phenotype being evaluated, and one or more genes that are negatively associated with the phenotype being evaluated. An interactive gene expression index (IGEI) may be derived, comprising the product of positively associated gene(s) (in units of mRNA/10^6 β-actin mRNA) on the numerator and the product of an equivalent number of the negatively associated gene(s) on the denominator. In these balanced ratios, the β-actin value is cancelled. This approach has been used successfully to identify IGEI that accurately diagnose bronchogenic carcinoma[6] and anti-folate resistance among childhood leukemias.[7]

Normalization against all genes measured. Because all of the data are standardized, if sufficient genes are measured in a sample, it is possible to normalize to all genes, as is commonly done with microarrays. The number of genes that must be measured for this approach to result in adequate normalization may vary depending on the samples and genes being studied.

14.1.3. Control for Variation in Amplification Efficiency

PCR amplification efficiency may vary from cycle to cycle, from gene to gene, from sample to sample, and/or from well to well within an experiment. The use of SMIS to control for these sources of variation in StaRT-PCR is described in **Sections 14.1.4** through **14.1.7**.

14.1.4. Control for Cycle-to-Cycle Variation in Amplification Efficiency

PCR amplification rate is low in early cycles because the concentration of templates is low. After an unpredictable number of cycles, the reaction enters a log-linear amplification phase. In late cycles, the rate of amplification slows, as the concentration of PCR products becomes high enough to compete with primers for binding to templates. With StaRT-PCR,[3-13] as with other forms of CT RT-PCR,[2,14-17] cycle-to-cycle variation in PCR reaction amplification efficiency is controlled through the inclusion of a known number of CT internal standard molecules for each gene measured. The ability to obtain quantitative PCR amplification at any phase in the PCR process, including the plateau phase, through the use of CT internal standards has been confirmed by direct comparison to real-time RT-PCR.[18,19]

In contrast, with real-time RT-PCR, cycle-to-cycle variation in amplification efficiency is controlled by measuring the PCR product at each cycle and taking the definitive measurement when the reaction is in log-linear amplification phase. A threshold fluorescence value known to be above the background and in the log-linear phase is arbitrarily established, and the cycle at which the PCR product crosses this threshold (C_t) is the unit of measurement.[20]

14.1.5. Control for Gene-to-Gene Variation in Amplification Efficiency

Oligonucleotide primers that are uniquely homologous to the gene of interest are essential for quantitative RT-PCR. These primers must hybridize to their target sequences with melting temperatures that fall within an optimized range (see **Section 14.3.** *Methods*), and they must be screened to ensure that they do not hybridize to any genes other than the targeted one. Finally, they must be tested to ensure that they amplify with high efficiency. Efficiency of PCR amplification as measured by lower detection threshold (LDT) using different 20-bp primers for the same gene may vary over greater than eight orders of magnitude. The best way to ensure that a pair of primers is highly efficient is to determine the lower detection threshold through serial dilution of a known number of molecules of a standard template. Gene-to-gene variation in efficiency is acceptable within certain range as long as it is controlled for. It is undesirable to use primers that are so inefficient that they cannot detect less than 100,000 cDNA molecules. On the other hand, a variation in lower detection threshold of 1–10 starting molecules is acceptable. Control for variation in amplification efficiency for primers that target different genes is essential if one is to confidently compare relative expression of multiple genes in the same sample. There are two ways to do this. One is to do use an external standard curve to quantify the efficiency of each set of primers. The alternative is to use internal standards. If one goes to the trouble to prepare a reagent that can be used in external standard curves, there are compelling reasons, described in this chapter, to use the same reagent as an internal standard within a SMIS. If one uses an internal standard, quantification can be done at endpoint and there is no need to do real-time analysis, as described above.

4.1.6. Control for Sample-to-Sample Variation in Amplification Efficiency

Variation in PCR amplification efficiency from sample-to-sample frequently is observed, [21] possibly due to variation in the presence of PCR reaction inhibitors, such as heme.[22,23] Importantly, amplification efficiency for different genes may be affected to different degrees in different samples.[21,24] Because of this, comparison of the target gene to a reference gene may not be a reliable control for cDNA loading, unless efficiency of amplification of the target gene and the reference gene is each controlled for. This type of control may be achieved using internal standards. With StaRT-PCR, inclusion of a SMIS in each PCR reaction controls for variation in amplification efficiency, both among samples within a single experiment as well as among samples evaluated in multiple different experiments in different laboratories[3-13,25] (**Plate 14.1**). In addition, the same SMIS is used to measure both the target gene and the reference gene in each sample, linking all of these data together. If there is variation in efficiency of primers for a particular gene, the efficiency of amplification of the corresponding internal standard for that gene is affected exactly the same. Because measurement of each gene is made relative to its internal standard, variation in efficiency does not alter the measurement. It is possible to include a SMIS with internal standard CTs for the target gene and reference gene in real-time PCR. For each gene, this would require preparation of one sequence-specific fluorescent probe for the native template (NT) and another for the CT. A probe specific to the NT would be homologous to the region that is in the NT but not in the CT. A probe specific to the CT would be homologous to the sequence formed when the reverse CT primer was incorporated (see below section and **Fig. 14.1**). Real-time RT-PCR using an internal standard for both a reference gene and a target gene would be StaRT-PCR, with the only difference being the method used to quantify the PCR products (endpoint densitometric measurement of electrophoretically separated, intercalator dye-labeled PCR products rather than densitometric measurement of sequence-specific fluorescent probe-labeled PCR products. Importantly, if a SMIS were included in the PCR reaction, it no longer would be necessary to monitor the reaction in real-time, because quantification can be made relative to the internal standards at any point in the PCR amplification process, including endpoint.[18,19,26]

14.1.7. Control for Reaction-to-Reaction Variation in Amplification Efficiency

Possible sources of reaction-to-reaction variation in amplification efficiency include the presence of an inhibitor in some reactions but not in others, variation in the temperature cycling among different regions of a thermocycler block, or variation in concentration or quality of important reagents, such as primers. When one of these sources of variation markedly reduces PCR amplification efficiency in a reaction, it is possible that no PCR product will be observed in that well. Using real-time RT-PCR without internal standards in each PCR reaction, it is not pos-

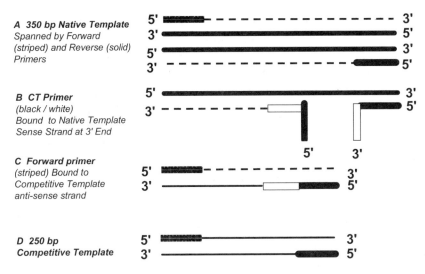

Figure 14.1. Preparation of internal standard competitive templates. **(A)** Forward (striped bar) and reverse (black bar) primers (approximately 20 bp in length) that span a 150–850 bp region are used to amplify the native template (NT) from cDNA. *Taq* polymerase will synthesize DNA (dashed lines) from these primers using the NT. **(B)** After confirming that native template primers work, a CT primer is designed. This is an approximately 40-bp primer with the sequence for the reverse primer (black bar) at the 5′ end, and a 20-bp sequence homologous to an internal native template sequence (white bar) at the 3′ end, collinear with the reverse primer sequence. The 3′ end of this 40-bp primer is designed to be homologous to a region approximately 50–100 bp internal to the reverse primer. The 5′ end of this 40-bp primer will hybridize to the region homologous to the reverse primer, while the 3′ end will hybridize to the internal sequence. Importantly, *Taq* polymerase will be able to synthesize DNA using only the primers bound at the 3′ end (dashed line). **(C)** In the next cycle of PCR, the DNA newly synthesized using the 40-bp primer hybridized to the internal sequence is bound to forward primer (striped bar), and a homologous strand is synthesized. **(D)** This generates a double stranded CT with the reverse primer sequence 100 bp closer to the forward primer than occurs naturally in the NT. This method is as previously described.[27]

sible to know whether to interpret absence of PCR products as absence of transcript or inefficient PCR amplification. An external standard curve would not be helpful because the PCR reactions would take place in different wells from the test sample. In contrast, by using a SMIS in each PCR reaction, it is immediately possible to decide between these two interpretations. The reagents for StaRT-PCR are carefully designed to amplify very efficiently such that for most genes a single molecule of CT or NT will be expected to give rise to detectable PCR product. The lowest concentration of internal standard CT molecules present in a StaRT-PCR reaction is 10^{-17} M with Mix F. In a 10-μl PCR reaction volume, 10^{-17} M represents sixty molecules. With sixty molecules of CT present in the PCR reaction and all of the components of the PCR reaction functioning properly, if a gene is not expressed in a sample, the PCR product for the internal standard CT will be observed but the PCR product for the NT will not. One can then conclude that the gene expression was so low that in the amount of cDNA included in the PCR reaction there were less than six molecules (10-fold less than the number of CT molecules) of cDNA representing that gene. On the other hand, if neither NT nor CT product is detectable, the PCR reaction efficiency was suboptimal and no interpretation can be made regarding level of expression.

14.1.8. Schematic Comparison of StaRT-PCR to Real-Time RT-PCR

A SMIS used in StaRT-PCR typically comprises internal reagents for 100–1,000 genes. In real time, the fluorescent PCR product is measured at each of 35–40 cycles. As many as four PCR products may be monitored simultaneously in real time, if four different fluors are used. In contrast to real-time RT-PCR, as few as one gene and as many as hundreds of genes may be measured in a sample or multiple samples in a single experiment. More importantly, because all StaRT-PCR data in every laboratory around the world going forward will be measured relative to the same SMIS, they comprise one large and growing multiplex experiment. All such data may be entered into the same database.

In **Plate 14.1** is a schematic presentation of the way quantitative measurements are made in the two forms of quantitative RT-PCR discussed here, real-time RT-PCR and StaRT-PCR. This plate shows the schematic depiction of simultaneous gene expression measurement by StaRT-PCR and real-time RT-PCR in two different samples. Although StaRT-PCR NT and CT products routinely are quantified by densitometry at endpoint of PCR following electrophoretic separation (as represented by the bands), if sequence-specific probes were prepared, they also could be quantified by real-time analysis and this schematic demonstrates how the reaction would look if measured at each cycle in real-time. For each real-time curve, the C_t is represented by a perpendicular black line. For sample 1, (see **Plate 14.1A**) there were about equivalent copies of β-actin NT and CT present at the beginning of the PCR reaction. Thus, following electrophoresis of the β-actin PCR products, the NT and CT bands were about equivalent and during real-time measurement, the fluorescent intensity for the NT was about the same as for the CT. The NT/CT ratio was the same at an early cycle as it was at a late cycle (endpoint). Similarly, the target gene NT band and CT band were about equivalent and the C_t value for the NT was about the same as for the CT. The target gene to β-actin gene ΔC_t was about 10. Methods for calculating numeric value for target gene expression using StaRT-PCR are presented in **Subsection 14.4.1.2**. In repeat analysis of sample 1 (**Plate 14.1B**), there was lower amount of cDNA loaded due to variation in pipetting. The NT/CT ratio for β-actin was lower, but the NT/CT ratio for target gene decreased commensurately, so that the odds ratio of target gene NT/CT divided by reference gene NT/CT and gene expression value, in terms of molecules/10^6 β-actin molecules, remained the same as in **Plate 14.1A**. Further, the ΔC_t was unchanged. Sample 1 analysis was repeated (**Plate 14.1C**), but with both larger amount of cDNA loaded due to variation in pipetting, and gene-selective low efficiency PCR, as might be caused by inhibitor in sample, inhibitor in well, or inappropriate concentration of reference gene primers. As a consequence of the gene-selective low efficiency amplification of β-actin, ΔC_t was reduced from 10 to 6. Thus, in real-time measurement the gene-selective inhibition would be associated with a decreased ΔC_t and erroneous measurement. However, in StaRT-PCR, both the variation in loading and variation in efficiency were controlled for by the internal standards. With the larger amount of cDNA loaded, the β-actin NT/CT ratio and the target gene NT/CT ratio increased commensurately. Because there was no change in NT/CT ratio for either reference or target gene, the odds ratio of target gene NT/CT divided by the reference gene NT/CT stayed the same as in **Plate14.1A** and **B**. For sample 2 (**Plate 14.1D**), the target gene is expressed at higher level than in sample 1 and ΔC_t was about 7. There were fewer copies of β-actin NT than CT present at the beginning of the PCR reaction. Thus, at the end of PCR the electrophoretically separated β-actin NT band was less dense than the CT band, and throughout real-time measurement the fluorescence value of the NT was less than that of the CT. However, even though less sample 2 cDNA was loaded into the PCR reaction compared to sample 1, the target-gene NT band was denser than the target-gene CT band, and the target-gene NT fluorescence value during real-time measurement was higher throughout PCR.

Thus, in StaRT-PCR, the products of endpoint PCR are electrophoretically separated and the shorter CT PCR product migrates faster than the NT PCR product. The PCR products are electrophoresed in the presence of fluorescent intercalating dye and densitometrically quantified. If there is more NT product than CT product, the NT band will emit more fluorescent light. If there is more CT product than NT product, the CT band will emit more fluorescent light. Importantly, the ratio of NT/CT that is present at the beginning of PCR will remain constant throughout PCR to endpoint. For this reason, with StaRT-PCR it is not necessary to monitor the PCR reaction in real time to ensure that the reaction is in log-linear phase (**Plate 14.1A**). In addition, measurement of both a reference and a target gene in every PCR reaction controls for loading from one sample to another (**Plate 14.1B**) or among replicate measurements of the same sample (**Plate 14.1D**). With StaRT-PCR, variation in PCR amplification efficiency caused by the presence of an inhibitor in the sample, an inhibitor in the PCR reaction vessel, defective PCR reagent, or wrong concentration of a PCR reagent is controlled for by the presence of internal standards in every PCR reaction (**Plate 14.1C**).

With real-time RT-PCR, it is possible to control for loading by measuring the target gene and reference gene in the same PCR reaction (**Plate 14.1A, B**, and **D**). The C_t for the reference gene and the target gene both may vary from one experiment to another, but the ΔC_t will not vary. However, real time may not control for well-to-well variation in the presence of inhibitors or quality of PCR reagents or sample-to-sample variation in PCR efficiency due to inhibitors (e.g., heme) (**Plate 14.1C**). Presence of an inhibitor may lead to variation in PCR amplification efficiency of one gene compared to another.[21] A bad lot or inappropriate concentration of primers for the reference gene or the target gene would cause variation in PCR amplification of one gene relative to another. As depicted here (**Plate 14.1C**), amplification efficiency of the reference gene in sample 1 is affected by low concentration of primer, but amplification efficiency of the target gene is normal. The result is that the ΔC_t is reduced from 10 in **Plate 14.1A** to 6 in **Plate 14.1C**, and the value for expression of the target gene is artifactually high. In contrast, with StaRT-PCR, because for each gene the amplification efficiency of the internal standard CT is affected the same way as the NT, the ratio is unchanged in **Plate 14.1A** and **Plate 14.1C** for either reference gene or target gene, and using the ratio of NT/CT for target gene relative to NT/CT for reference gene controls for variation in amplification efficiency. See **Section 14.3.** *Methods* for details of how StaRT-PCR data are calculated.

Thus, the key advantage in StaRT-PCR is the use of SMIS. Because the relative concentration of internal standards for each reference gene and target gene in the mixture is fixed, data from different experiments in different laboratories may be compared with confidence due to elimination of many sources of variation. Although StaRT-PCR data could be evaluated by homogenous real-time assays (as long as a CT-specific fluorescent probe were prepared for each gene), this becomes very difficult and expensive. Further, when standardized mixtures of internal standards are used, endpoint analysis is quantitative and when automated microfluidic devices are used, electrophoretic separation is high throughput, inexpensive and adds additional quality control.

14.2. Materials

StaRT-PCR reagents, including primers and SMIS are purchased from Gene Express, Inc. (GEI, Toledo, Ohio). PCR buffer (10×) for Idaho Rapidcycler air thermocycler (500 mM *Tris*, pH 8.3, 2.5 µg/µl BSA, 30 mM MgCl$_2$) is purchased from Idaho Technology, Inc. (Idaho Falls, ID). Buffer for block thermocyclers (Thermo 10×, 500 mM KCl, 100 mM *Tris*-HCl, pH 9.0, 1.0% Triton X-100) is purchased from Promega (Madison, Wisc.). *Taq* polymerase (5 U/µl), M-MLV reverse transcriptase, M-MLV RT 5× first strand buffer (250 mM *Tris*-HCL, pH 8.3; 375 mM KCl; 15 mM MgCl$_2$; 50 mM dithiothreitol), oligo dT primers, RNasin, pGEM size marker, and deoxynucleotide triphosphates (dNTPs) also are obtained from Promega. TriReagent is obtained from Molecular Research Center, Inc. (Cincinnati, Ohio). Ribonuclease (RNase)-free water and TOPO TA cloning kits are obtained from Invitrogen (Carlsbad, Calif.). GigaPrep plasmid preparation kits are purchased from Qiagen (Texas). Caliper AMS 90SE chips are obtained from Caliper Technologies, Inc. (Mountain View, Calif.). DNA purification columns were obtained from QiaQuick (Qiagen, Valencia, Calif.).

14.3. Methods

14.3.1. RNA Extraction and Reverse Transcription

RNA extraction and quantification. Cell suspensions are pelleted, the supernatant is poured off, and the pellet is dissolved in TriReagent and extracted according to manufacturer's instructions and previously recorded methods.[28] The quality of the RNase-free water is critical to efficient extraction of intact RNA. We have found that it is far more cost effective to purchase reliable RNase-free water from commercial sources than it is to prepare our own. Either inadequate DEPC treatment or inadequate removal of DEPC after treatment can inhibit reverse transcription and PCR. The RNA pellet is either stored under ethanol at –80°C, or suspended in RNase-free water, then frozen at –80° C. It may be safely stored in this condition for years. The quality of the RNA is evaluated on an Agilent 2100 Bioanalyzer using the RNA chip, according to manufacturer's instructions.

Reverse transcription. For RT, ideally 1 μg of total RNA is reverse transcribed using M-MLV RT and an oligo dT primer as previously reported.[29] For small amounts of RNA (e.g., less than 100 ng), the efficiency of reverse transcription is better with Sensiscript™ than with MMLV reverse transcriptase. We have obtained efficient RT of as little as 50 ng of RNA with Sensiscript™. The reaction is incubated at 37°C for 1 hour.

14.3.2. Synthesis and Cloning of Competitive Templates

CTs are constructed by Gene Express, Inc. (GEI) (Toledo, Ohio) based on previously described methods.[5,8,27]

Native Template Primer design. Use Primer 3.1 software.[30] Code available at http://www-genome.wi.mit.edu/genome_software /other/primer3.html). Designing primers with the same annealing temperature allows all StaRT-PCR reactions to achieve approximately the same amplification efficiency under identical conditions. If there is small variation in amplification efficiency from one gene to another, it does not cause variation in determination of quantitative value because the value is obtained from the ratio between the NT and CT for the same gene, and amplification efficiency of the NT and CT for the same gene is affected the same way.

Designing primers that amplify different sized products for different genes will support automation and high throughput applications, including capillary gel and microchannel capillary electrophoresis (CE). Primer sequences and Genbank accession numbers for genes designed by GEI are available at www.geneexpressinc.com.

Before the CT for each gene can be constructed, the primer pair must be demonstrated to efficiently amplify the native cDNA. Primers are tested using reverse transcribed RNA from a variety of tissues or individual cDNA clones known to represent the gene of interest. The presence of a single strong band after 35 cycles of PCR is verification that the primers are efficient and specific.

For primer pairs that fail to amplify the target gene in any tissue or the individual cDNA clone (less than 10% of the time) new ones are designed and the process repeated. Primers are designed such that they amplify from 200 to 850 bases of the coding region of targeted genes and have annealing temperature of 58°C (tolerance of ±1°C).

Competitive Template Primer Design. After suitable primers for NT amplification have been designed and tested, a CT primer then is prepared according to previously described methods,[27] as schematically presented in **Fig. 14.1**.

Competitive Template Primer Testing. The 40-bp CT primer is paired with the forward primer (designed to amplify the full-length native template) and used to amplify CT from native cDNA.

Competitive template-internal standard production. For each gene, five 10-μl PCR reactions using the native forward primer and the CT primer are set up and amplified for 35 cycles. The products of these five PCR reactions are combined, electrophoresed on a 3% NuSieve gel in 1× TAE, and the band of correct size is cut from the gel and extracted using the QiaQuick method. Purified PCR products are cloned into PCR 2.1 vector using TOPO TA cloning kits then transformed into HS996 (a T1-phage resistant variant of DH10B).

Selection of clones for large-scale preparation. After cloning, transformation, and plating on LB plates containing X-Gal, IPTG, and carbenicillin, three isolated white colonies are picked. Plasmid minipreps are made, *Eco*RI digestion performed, and digests electrophoresed on 3% SeaKem agarose. For those clones documented to have an insert by *Eco*RI digestion, the insert is confirmed to be the desired one by sequencing the same undigested plasmid preparation using vector specific primers. Only those clones with homology to the correct gene sequence and that have 100% matches for the primer sequences are allowed to proceed to large-scale CT preparation and to be included in the standard mixes. Those that pass this quality control assessment then continued to the next steps.

Large-scale plasmid preps. Each quality assured clone is prepared in quantities large enough (1.5 liter) to allow for more than 100 billion assays (approximately 2.6 mg). Plasmids are purified from resultant harvested cells using Qiagen GigaPrep kits. Plasmid yields are carefully quantified using a Hoeffer DyNAQuant 210 fluorometer. For each CT that passes all of the defined quality control steps described above, the sensitivity of the cloned CT and primers are assessed by performing PCR reactions on serial dilutions and determining the limiting concentration that still yields a PCR product. Only those preparations and primers that allow for detection of 60 molecules or fewer (a product obtained with 10^{-17} M CT in 10-μl PCR reaction volume) are continued for inclusion into standardized CT mixtures. The number of molecules at different molarities is a multiple of 6 as a consequence of Avogadro's Number (6.02×10^{23} molecules/Mole). More than 80% of the CTs developed have a sensitivity of 6 molecules or fewer. Thus, for these genes, it would be possible to measure as few as 10 molecules/10^{6} β-actin molecules.

14.3.3. Preparation of Standardized Mixtures of Internal Standards

1. Cloned and quantified CTs are combined into Standardized Mixtures of Internal Standards (SMIS) according to modifications of previously described methods.[5,8,27] Plasmids from quality assured preparations (see above in **Subsection 14.3.2**) are mixed into SMIS representing 24 genes. The concentration of the competitive templates in the 24 gene mixes is 4×10^{-9} M for β-actin CT, 4×10^{-10} M for GAPD (CT1), 4×10^{-11} M for GAPD (CT2), and 4×10^{-8} M for each of the other CTs.

2. Each 24 gene SMIS is linearized by *Not*I digestion. The SMIS is incubated with *Not*I enzyme at a concentration of 1 unit/µg of plasmid DNA in approximately 15 ml of buffer at 37°C for 12–16 hours.

3. Four linearized 24-gene SMIS are combined in equal amounts to yield 96-gene SMIS with a maximum concentration of 10^{-9} M for β-actin, 10^{-10} M GAPD (CT1), 10^{-11} M GAPD (CT2), and 10^{-8} M for the other CTs.

4. These highest concentration mixes are serially diluted with a reference gene CT mixture comprising β-actin CT (10^{-9} M) and two different GAPD CTs, GAPD CT1 (10^{-10} M), and GAPD CT2 (10^{-11} M). (The reason for two different GAPD CTs is that the expression of GAPD relative to β-actin may vary as much as 100-fold from one tissue type to another. Having two different concentrations of GAPD CT relative to β-actin enables comparison of GAPD to β-actin in all samples. These comparisons are helpful in determining intersample variation in expression of reference genes). This yields six stock SMIS (A–F) with β-actin, GAPD1 and GAPD2 at constant concentrations of 10^{-9} M, 10^{-10} M, and 10^{-11} M respectively while the concentration of the CTs for other genes in SMIS A–F respectively are 10^{-8} M, 10^{-9} M, 10^{-10} M, 10^{-11} M, 10^{-12} M, and 10^{-13} M.

5. These stock SMIS then are diluted 1,000-fold to working solutions with β-actin, GAPD1 and GAPD2 at concentrations of 10^{-12} M, 10^{-13} M, and 10^{-14} M, respectively while the concentration of the other CTs in SMIS A–F respectively are 10^{-11} M, 10^{-12} M, 10^{-13} M, 10^{-14} M, 10^{-15} M, and 10^{-16} M.

14.4. StaRT-PCR

StaRT-PCR is performed using previously published protocols[5,8] with a series of SMIS at different concentrations (A, B, C, D, E, and F) and gene-specific primers from GEI as described above. Briefly, StaRT-PCR is done by (a) including in each PCR reaction SMIS containing a known amount of competitive template (CT) for each gene measured, and (b) multiplex RT-PCR amplifying both the target gene native template (NT) and its respective CT and a reference gene (usually β-actin) NT and its respective CT for every gene expression measurement (**Plate 14.1**). These four templates may be amplified in the same tube[5,25] or, if the experiment is properly designed, the NT and CT pair for the target gene and the NT and CT pair for the reference gene may be amplified in separate tubes.[5]

14.4.1. Step by Step Description of StaRT-PCR Method

14.4.1.1. Sample Titration with β-Actin CT

For each cDNA sample, it is necessary to determine the dilution of the test cDNA that is approximately (within 10-fold range) in balance with 600,000 copies of β-actin (1 μl of SMIS containing β-actin CT at 10^{-12} M). This is approximately the amount of cDNA derived from 600–6,000 cells. This amount of cDNA is used in all subsequent experiments and is chosen to ensure that there is sufficient cDNA to quantify genes expressed at low levels. If the goal is to have at least 10 transcripts present at the beginning of PCR to avoid stochastic problems, this amount of cDNA will allow quantification of genes expressed as low as 1 transcript in every 10–100 cells. If less sensitivity is necessary, less cDNA could be used. Thus, one could choose to use the amount of cDNA in balance with 60,000 molecules of β-actin CT. This will not allow measurement of genes expressed at very low levels, but will be sufficient for analysis of most genes and will reduce consumption of cDNA 10-fold. This may be particularly useful when analyzing very small biopsy specimens for diagnostic tests. For each of the SMIS A–F, 1 μl of SMIS contains 600,000 molecules of β-actin CT, thus any of the SMIS could be used for this purpose of balancing cDNA with β-actin. The standard operating procedure is to use SMIS F.

A common mistake for beginning users of StaRT-PCR is to balance the cDNA with the β-actin in the SMIS initially, but then, when the target gene NT and CT are not in balance, to vary the amount of cDNA in the PCR reaction mixture in order to get the target gene NT/CT in balance. The proper method is to keep the amount of cDNA constant to keep the β-actin NT in balance with CT, and change the SMIS used as necessary to get the target gene NT and CT in balance. The SMIS have been prepared for measurement of genes across the full range of gene expression measurement (more than 6 orders of magnitude). Because the NT/CT ratio must be within 10-fold ratio in order to obtain reliable, reproducible quantification, six different CT mixes (A–F) have been prepared, containing 10-fold serial dilution of all target gene CTs relative to reference gene CT. Thus, if SMIS D were used to measure a target gene, and the β-actin NT and CT were in balance but the target gene NT was more than 10-fold greater than the CT, the next step would be to repeat the experiment with the same amount of cDNA, but using SMIS C, which has a 10-fold higher concentration of target gene CT.

14.4.1.2. Expression Measurement

With StaRT-PCR, as is clear in the schematic presented in **Fig. 14.2A**, expression of each normalizer gene (e.g., β-actin) or target gene (e.g., Gene 1–6) in a sample (for example, sample A) is measured relative to its respective internal standard in the SMIS. Because in each experiment the internal standard for each gene is present at a fixed concentration relative to all other internal standards, it is possible to quantify the expression of each gene relative to all others measured. Further, it is possible to compare data from analysis of sample A to those from analysis of all other samples, represented as B_{1-n}. The result is a continuously expanding virtual multiplex experiment. That is, data from an ever-expanding number of genes and samples may be entered into the same database. Because the number of molecules for each standard is known, it is possible to calculate all data in the form of molecules/normalizer gene molecules. In contrast, for other multi-gene methods, such as multiplex real-time RT-PCR or microarrays, represented in **Fig. 14.2B**, expression of each gene is directly compared from one sample to another and data are in the form of fold differences. Because of intergene variation in hybridization efficiency and/or PCR amplification efficiency, in the absence of internal standards to control for these sources of variation, it is not possible to directly compare expression of one gene to another in a sample or to obtain values in terms of molecules/molecules of reference gene.

Expression measurements steps:

1. **Combine and mix a volume of cDNA sample** (diluted to the level that is in balance with the amount of β-actin CT in 1 µl of SMIS, or 6×10^5 molecules, as described above) with an equal volume of the

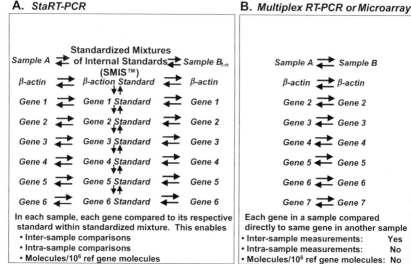

Figure 14.2. (**A**) Schematic diagram of the relationship among internal standards within the SMIS and between each internal standard and its respective cDNA from a sample. The internal standard for each reference gene and target gene is at a fixed concentration relative to all other internal standards within the SMIS. Within a polymerase chain reaction (PCR) master mixture, in which a cDNA sample is combined with SMIS, the concentration of each internal standard is fixed relative to the cDNA representing its respective gene. In the PCR product from each sample, the number of cDNA molecules representing a gene is measured relative to its respective internal standard rather than by comparing it to another sample. Because everyone uses the same SMIS, and there is enough to last 1,000 years at the present rate of consumption, all gene expression measurements may be entered into the same database. (**B**) Measurement by multiplex RT-PCR or microarray analysis. Using these methods each gene scales differently because of gene-to-gene variation in melting temperature between gene and PCR primers or gene and sequence on microarray. Consequently, it is possible to compare relative differences in expression of a gene from one sample to another, but not difference in expression among many genes in a sample. Further, it is not possible to develop a reference database, except in relationship to a non-renewable calibrator sample. Moreover, unless a known quantity of standard template is prepared for each gene, it is not possible to know how many copies of a gene are expressed in the calibrator sample, or the samples that are compared to the calibrator.

appropriate SMIS. A 1-µl volume of each is used for each gene expression assay to be performed. This is a key step that commonly is carried out incorrectly by users of StaRT-PCR. A primary purpose of the StaRT-PCR method is to standardize every gene expression measurement so that it is easily compared to all other StaRT-PCR measurements. The procedure described in this step allows one to compare the NT/CT ratio for the reference gene to the NT/CT ratio for the target gene in a reliable way that controls for variation in pipetting. The wrong way to do this step would be to aliquot SMIS sufficient for a single gene expression measurement into a separate PCR reaction mixture, and then aliquot cDNA for a single measurement into each tube. Due to pipetting errors, this would be associated with variation in the NT/CT ratio of each target gene relative to the NT/CT ratio for the reference gene, as well as that for other target genes.

The SMIS (A, B, C, D, E, or F) selected will be the one containing CT at the concentration most likely, based on previous experience, to be in balance (within 10-fold range) with the gene or genes being assessed.

2. **Combine cDNA/SMIS from previous step with other components of the PCR reaction mixture** (buffer, dNTPs, Mg^{2+}, *Taq* polymerase, H_2O).

3. **Prepare each well on microplates or each tube with a primer pair for a single gene.** If products are to be analyzed by PE 310 device, the primers should be labeled with appropriate fluor.

4. **Place aliquots of this PCR reaction mixture into individual tubes each containing primers for a single gene.** In the **Step 1** above, the ratios of CT for every gene in the SMIS relative to their corresponding NT in the cDNA are fixed simultaneously. When aliquots of this mixture are transferred to PCR reaction vessels, although variation in loading volume from one tube to another due to pipetting errors is unavoidable, there is no potential for variation in any target gene NT/CT ratio relative to reference gene NT/CT ratio. This method controls for loading. In addition, it enables standardized expression measurement. The choice of which SMIS to use is based on previous experience. For example, if among all previous samples, a gene has been expressed within a range of 10^1–10^4 molecules/10^6 β-actin molecules, the gene will be measured using SMIS E. In contrast, if among all previous samples, a gene has been expressed within a range of 10^4–10^7 molecules/10^6 β-actin molecules, the gene will be measured using SMIS C. Genes that are expressed at a level that causes the NT PCR product band density to be less than 1/10 that of the lowest concentration CT mix used, or greater than 10 times the highest concentration CT mix used may not be quantifiable and will need to be reassessed with the appropriate SMIS.

5. **PCR Amplification.** Each reaction mixture is cycled either in an air thermocycler (e.g., RapidCycler (Idaho Technology, Inc., Idaho Falls, Idaho; laboratory) or block thermocycler (e.g., PTC-100 block thermal cycler with heated lid, MJ Research, Inc., Incline Village, Nev.; laboratories) for 35 cycles. In either thermocycler, the denaturation temperature is 94°C, the annealing temperature is 58°C, and the elongation temperature is 72°C.

6. **Separation and Quantification of NT and CT PCR Products.** Electrophoresis may be in (1) an agarose gel, (2) capillary electrophoresis device (e.g., PE 310), or (3) microfluidic CE device (e.g., Agilent 2100 or Calipertech AMS 90 high-throughput system). If an agarose gel is used, electrophoresis is for one hour at 225 V through agarose gel. If a CE device or microfluidic CE device is used, electrophoresis is according to the manufacturer's instructions. Following electrophoresis, the relative amount of NT and CT is determined by densitometric quantification of bands that have been stained by an intercalating dye (e.g., ethidium bromide). Theoretically, the SMIS prepared for StaRT-PCR may be used to measure gene expression using any method capable of quantifying strands of DNA with different sizes and/or sequence, including solid-phase hybridization (microarrays and microbeads), MALDI-TOF and HPLC.

   (1) *Agarose gel.* Following amplification, the entire volume of PCR product (typically 10 μl) is loaded directly into wells of 4% agarose gels (3:1 NuSieve: SeaKem) containing 0.5 μg/ml ethidium bromide. Gels are electrophoresed for approximately one hour at 225 V in continuously chilled buffer, then visualized and quantified with an image analyzer (products available from Fotodyne, Bio-Rad).

   (2) *PE Prism 310 Genetic Analyzer CE Device.* PCR products are amplified with fluor-labeled primers in **Step 5** above. One microliter of each PCR reaction is combined with 9 μl of formamide and 0.5–0.1 μl of ROX size marker. Samples then are heated to 94°C for 5 minutes and flash cooled in an ice slurry. Samples are loaded onto the machine and electrophoresed at 15 kV, 60°C for 35–45 minutes using POP4 polymer and filter set D. The injection parameters are 15 kV, 5 seconds. Fragment analysis soft-

ware, GeneScan (Applied Biosystems, Inc., Foster City, Calif.) was used to quantify peak heights, which were used to calculate NT/CT ratios. No size correction was performed since each DNA molecule was tagged with one fluorescent marker from one labeled primer.

(3) *Microfluidic CE Device*

- *Agilent 2100 Bioanalyzer Microfluidic CE Device.* The DNA 7500 or DNA 1000 LabChip kit may be used. Following amplification, 1 µl of each 10 µl PCR reaction is loaded into a well of a chip prepared according to protocol supplied by manufacturer. DNA assay is run which applies a current to each sample sequentially to separate NT from CT. DNA is detected by fluorescence of an intercalating dye in the gel-dye matrix. NT/CT ratios are calculated from area under curve and a size correction is made. (See **Step 7** below.)

- Caliper AMS 90 Microfluidic CE Device. The PCR reactions are set up in wells of a 96- or 384-well microplate. Following amplification, the microplate is placed in the Caliper AMS 90. The protocol recommended by the manufacturer is followed. The AMS 90 removes and electrophoreses a sample from each well sequentially every 30 seconds. The NT and CT PCR products are separated and quantified. Because detection is through fluorescent intercalating dye, size correction is necessary.

7. **Calculation of gene expression.** Values are calculated in units of target gene cDNA molecules/10^6 β-actin cDNA molecules. In **Steps** *a–g* below, there are presented the computations used to calculate GST expression in Sample 238, based on densitometric measurement values for the electrophoretically separated NT and CT PCR products presented in **Fig.14.3**. The values were GST CT, 4.4; GST NT, 1.5; β-actin CT, 89; β-actin NT, 42.

   a. Correct NT PCR product pixel density to length of CT DNA.

   b. Correct HD PCR product pixel density to length of CT DNA.

   c. Determine ratio of corrected NT pixel density relative to CT pixel density.

   d. Multiply NT/CT value by number of CT molecules at beginning of PCR.

e. Calculation of β-actin molecules at start of PCR reaction:

42/89 (NT/CT) × 600,000 (β-actin CT molecules at start of PCR reaction) × *Size Correction Factor* = 150,000 β-actin NT molecules.

f. Calculation of GST molecules at start of PCR reaction:

1.5/4.4 (NT/CT) × 6,000 (GST CT molecules at start of PCR reaction) × *Size Correction Factor* = 930 GST NT molecules.

g. Calculation of GST molecules/ 10^6 β-actin molecules:

930 GST NT molecules/150,000 β-actin NT molecules = 6,200 GST molecules /10^6 β-actin molecules

The use of standardized mixtures of competitive templates and calculating gene expression in the manner described allows one to compare data from one laboratory to another and therefore enables development of a standardized expression measurement center and a standardized gene expression database.

14.5. The Standardized Expression Measurement Center

The Standardized Expression Measurement (SEM) Center recently was established at the Medical College of Ohio through a grant from the National Cancer Institute. The SEM Center is in operation and available for use at www.geneexpressinc.com.

Microarray technology often is the starting point for most large-scale gene transcript investigations. However, due to limits in lower detection threshold and sensitivity and lack of internal standards, microarray technology is most appropriately applied as a screening tool. Data obtained through microarray analysis must be followed by a more sensitive and quantitative method. Most investigators use a quantitative RT-PCR method for this purpose.

The purpose of the SEM Center is to provide standardized, reproducible, and inexpensive gene expression measurement as a service. The SEM Center uses StaRT-PCR for gene expression measurement because this method enables measurement of hundreds of genes simultaneously, and provides standardized, numerical data in the form of molecules/10^6 β-actin molecules, at relatively low cost. Because all

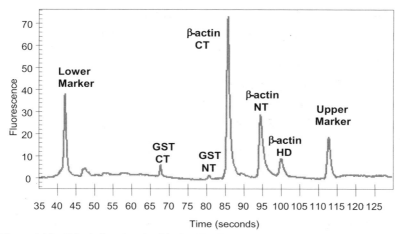

Figure 14.3. Calculations involved in StaRT-PCR measurement of GST gene expression relative to β-actin in an actual bronchial epithelial cell (BEC) sample. The native template (NT) PCR product was amplified from cDNA specific for the gene being measured; the competitive template (CT) is a PCR product for the internal standard for each respective gene. A known numbers of internal standard CT molecules for β-actin (600,000) and GST (6,000) were included at the beginning of the PCR reaction. Because for each gene the NT and CT amplify with the same efficiency, the β-actin gene NT/CT PCR product ratio allows determination of the number of β-actin NT copies at the beginning of PCR and the GST gene NT/CT ratio allows determination of the number of GST gene NT copies at the beginning of PCR. See text for steps used to calculate gene expression values.

StaRT-PCR data are measured with the same SMIS, all data obtained in laboratories around the world going forward may be entered into the same database. Further, StaRT-PCR is easily automated and subjected to quality control, which is critical for analysis of clinical specimens.

The SEM Center function is similar to that of a DNA sequencing service. Thus, users send their RNA or cDNA samples to the SEM Center for analysis. Users select a set of genes for measurement and send a requisition listing these selected genes (available at the SEM Center website) along with the samples.

14.6. Technology Incorporated by the SEM Center

14.6.1. Automated Preparation of StaRT-PCR Reactions

A PE Robotic liquid handler is used to prepare 10-μl PCR reactions in 96-well or 384-well microplates. First, the liquid handler is programmed to distribute 1 µl of primers for the requested genes into wells of the microplates. Second, for each cDNA a sufficient volume of PCR mixture for the anticipated number of gene expression measurements is prepared, containing buffer, *Taq* polymerase, dNTPs, cDNA, and internal standards. The robot then distributes 9 µl of this PCR reaction mixture into each well. Thus, in each well the internal standard CTs for each gene and cDNA are present in the same ratio, however, because only one pair of primers is present in each well, only one gene and its respective internal standard CT are amplified in each well. Following 35 cycles of PCR, each microplate is transferred to the Caliper AMS 90 for analysis.

14.6.2. Electrophoretic Separation of StaRT-PCR Products

When StaRT-PCR was first developed, products were separated on agarose gels.[5,25] This method is reliable but relatively costly, time consuming, and labor intensive. Through advances in capillary electrophoresis (CE), alternative methods for separation of StaRT-PCR products that are much faster and less expensive have become available. We compared separation of StaRT-PCR products on agarose gel, PE 310 CE, and Agilent 2100 Bioanalyzer microfluidic CE.[26] Each of these methods provided the same, reproducible results. Theoretically, the SMIS prepared for StaRT-PCR may be used to measure gene expression by any method capable of quantifying strands of DNA with different sizes, including HPLC and mass spectrometry.

The Caliper AMS 90 currently is used for high-throughput separation of StaRT-PCR products in the SEM Center. This device is capable of 1,000 gene expression assays in eight hours. The SEM Center employs a microfluidic chip with a sipper that moves from well to well of a microplate, aspirating and then electrophoretically separating StaRT-PCR products every 30 seconds. This allows analysis of a 384-well plate in approximately 3 hours, which is comparable to the throughput of the fastest real-time devices.

14.6.3. Design of High-Throughput StaRT-PCR Experiments

All of the genes that are to be measured in a given sample are PCR-amplified simultaneously. Due to the presence of the same SMIS in every PCR reaction, gene expression values for one sample then may be compared to gene expression values from another sample evaluated in a second experiment later the same day or another day.

PCR products (NT and CT) for as many as five genes may be electrophoresed (separated and quantified) in the same microfluidic channel of the AMS 90SE. Accomplishing this in the high-throughput SEM Center requires software that identifies which genes may be electrophoresed simultaneously based on the length in base pairs of the NT and CT PCR products. As described in **Section 14.3.** *Methods*, for each gene, the primers and CTs are designed to amplify PCR products that range from 150–850 bp. Thus, for every set of genes to be analyzed, the software must identify which genes may be electrophoresed together.

The calculation steps presented in the previous section have been incorporated into a spreadsheet. Thus, the user simply enters the raw values for the NT, CT, and heterodimer PCR products for each gene into the spreadsheet, and the expression value for the gene in molecules/10^6 β-actin molecules is automatically calculated. As described in **Section 14.6.** *The Standardized Expression Measurement Center*, software automatically enters the peak area values for each NT and CT PCR product into a spreadsheet. The spreadsheet automatically calculates expression value or, if the NT/CT ratio is not in balance, instructs the robotic liquid handler on how to set up the next experiment.

Acknowledgements

The author receives funding from NCI grants U01 CA 85147 and R24 CA 95806 and the George Isaak Cancer Research Center.

References

1. Zhang J, Day INM, Byrne CD: **A novel medium throughput quantitative competitive PCR technology to simultaneously measure mRNA levels from multiple genes.** *Nucleic Acids Res* 2002, **30**:e20.

2. Becker-Andre M, Hahlbrock K: **Absolute messenger-RNA quantification using the polymerase chain-reaction (PCR)—A novel-approach by a PCR aided transcript titration assay (patty).** *Nucleic Acids Res* 1989, **17**:9437–9446.

3. Loitsch SM, Kippenberger S, Dauletbaev N, Wagner TO, Bargon J: **Reverse transcription-competitive multiplex PCR improves quantification of mRNA in clinical samples—Application to the low abundance CFTR mRNA.** *Clinical Chem* 1999, **45**:619–624.

4. Crawford EL, Khuder SA, Durham SJ, et al.: **Normal bronchial epithelial cell expression of glutathione transferase P1, glutathione transferase M3, and glutathione peroxidase is low in subjects with bronchogenic carcinoma.** *Cancer Res* 2000, **60**:1609–1618.

5. Willey JC, Crawford EL, Jackson CM: **Expression measurement of many genes simultaneously by quantitative RT-PCR using standardized mixtures of competitive templates.** *Am J Respir Cell Mol Biol* 1998, **19**:6–17.

6. DeMuth JP, Jackson CM, Weaver DA, et al:. **The gene expression index c-*myc* x E2F1/p21 is highly predictive of malignant phenotype in human bronchial epithelial cells.** *Am J Respir Cell Mol Biol* 1998, **19**:18–24.

7. Rots MG, Willey JC, Jansen G, et al.: **mRNA expression levels of methotrexate resistance-related proteins in childhood leukemia as determined by a standardized competitive template-based RT-PCR method.** *Leukemia* 2000, **14**:2166–2175.

8. Crawford EL, Peters GJ, Noordhuis P, et al.: **Reproducible gene expression measurement among multiple laboratories obtained in a blinded study using standardized RT (StaRT)-PCR.** *Mol Diagn* 2001, **6**:217–225.

9. Crawford EL, Warner KA, Khuder SA, et al: **Multiplex standardized RT-PCR for expression analysis of many genes in small samples.** *Biochem Bioph Res Comm* 2002, **293**:509–516.

10. Mollerup S, Ryberg D, Hewer A, Phillips DH, Haugen A: **Sex differences in lung CYP1A1 expression and DNA adduct levels among lung cancer patients.** *Cancer Res* 1999, **59**:3317–3320.

11. Rots M.G, Pieters R, Peters GJ, et al.: **Circumvention of methotrexate resistance in childhood leukemia subtypes by rationally designed antifolates.** *Blood* 1999, **94**:3121–3128.

12. Allen JT, Knight RA, Bloor CA, Spiteri MA: **Enhanced insulin-like growth factor binding protein-related protein 2 (connective tissue growth factor) expression in patients with idiopathic pulmonary fibrosis and pulmonary sarcoidosis.** *Am J Respir Cell Mol Biol* 1999, **21**:693–700.

13. Vondracek MT, Weaver DA, Sarang Z, et al.: **Transcript profiling of enzymes involved in detoxification of xenobiotics and reactive oxygen in human normal and Simian virus 40 T antigen-immortalized oral keratinocytes.** *Intl J Cancer* 2002, **99**:776–782.

14. Gilliland G, Perrin S, Blanchard K, Bunn HF: **Analysis of cytokine mRNA and DNA: Detection and quantitation by competitive polymerase chain reaction.** *Proc Natl Acad Sci USA* 1990, **87**:2725–2729.

15. Wang AM, Doyle MV, Mark DF: **Quantitation of mRNA by the polymerase chain reaction.** *Proc Natl Acad Sci USA* 1989, **86**:9717–972.

16. Zhang J, Byrne CD: **A novel highly reproducible quantitative competitive RT-PCR system.** *J Mol Biol* 1997, **274**:338–352.

17. Zhou NM, Matthys P, Polacek C, Figen, P, Sato, A., Billiau A, and Froyen G: **A competitive RT-PCR method for the quantitative analysis of cytokine mRNAs in mouse tissues.** *Cytokine* 1997, **9**: 212–218.

18. Lyon E, Millson A, Lowery MC, et al.: **Quantification of HER2/neu gene amplification by competitive PCR using fluorescent melting curve analysis.** *Clin Chem* 2001, **47**:844–851.

19. Hirano T, Haque M, Utiyama H: **Theoretical and experimental dissection of competitive PCR for accurate quantification of DNA.** *Anal Biochem* 2002, **303**:57–65.

20. Livak KJ, Schmittgen TD: **Analysis of related gene expression data using real-time quantitative RT-PCR and the 2^{-DDCt} method.** *Methods* 2001, **25**:402-408.

21. Meijerink J, Mandigers C, van de Locht L, et al.: **A novel method to compensate for different amplification efficiencies between patient DNA samples in quantitative real-time PCR.** *J Mol Diagn* 2001, **3**:55–61, 2001.

22. Akane A, Matsuara K, Nakamura H, Takahashi S, Kimura K: **Identification of the heme compound co-purified with deoxyribonucleic acid (DNA) from blood stains, a major inhibitor of polymerase chain reaction (PCR) amplification.** *J Forensic Sci* 1994, **39**:362–372.

23. Zhu YH, Lee HC, Zhang L: **An examination of heme action in gene expression: Heme and heme deficiency affect the expression of diverse genes in erythroid K562 and neuronal PC12 cells.** *DNA Cell Biol* 2002, **21**:333–346.

24. Giulietti A, Overbergh L, Valckx D, Decallonne B, Bouillon R, Mathieu C: **An overview of real-time quantitative PCR: applications to quantify cytokine gene expression.** *Methods* 2001, **25**:386–401.

25. Apostolakos MJ, Schuermann WH, Frampton MW, Utell MJ, Willey JC: **Measurement of gene expression by multiplex competitive polymerase chain reaction.** *Anal Biochem* 1993, **213**:277–284.

26. Crawford E., Warner KA, Weaver DA, Willey JC: **Quantitative endpoint RT-PCR gene expression measurement using the Agilent 2100 Bioanalyzer and standardized RT-PCR.** http://www.chem.agilent.com/temp/rad6A17F/00029012.pdf, 2001.

27. Celi FS, Zenilman ME, Shuldiner AR: **A rapid and versatile method to synthesize internal standards for competitive PCR.** *Nucleic Acids Res* 1993, **21**:1047.

28. Chomczynski P, Sacchi N: **Single-step method of RNA isolation by acid guanidinium thiocyanate–phenol–chloroform extraction.** *Anal Biochem* 1993, **62**:156–159.

29. Willey JC, Coy EL, Frampton MW, Torres A, Apostolakos MJ, Hoehn G, Schuermann WH, Thilly WG, Olson DE, Hammersley JR, Utell MJ: **Quantitative RT-PCR measurement of cytochromes p450 1A1, 1B1, and 2B7, microsomal epoxide hydrolase, and NADPH oxidoreductase expression in lung cells of smokers and non-smokers.** *Am J Respir Cell Mol Biol* 1997, **17**:114–124.

30. Rozen S; Skaletsky H: **Primer 3 on the WWW for general users and for biologist programmer.** *Meth Mol Biol* 2000, **132**:365–386.

15

Standardization of qPCR and qRT-PCR Assays

Reinhold Mueller, Gothami Padmabandu, and Roger H. Taylor

Abstract

Quantitative RT-PCR and quantitative PCR experiments are expected to yield similar results whether repeated the next day, repeated the next month (intralaboratory variation), performed on another fluorescence real-time reader (platform), or carried out as part of an interlaboratory collaboration. Due to various factors, typical quantitation of input target quantity may vary considerably. Contributing factors may include pipetting irregularities, differences in instrumentation (e.g., platforms, optical calibration, variations in block temperature and cycling conditions), and different settings used in the analysis of data. Variation in data can be reduced by including one or more endogenous references (typically a relatively constant target, i.e., mRNA of a household gene or a gene known to be present in exactly one copy per cell) and a passive reference dye, which helps in minimizing tube-to-tube pipetting differences. To make comparisons between results obtained in different laboratories, a common or universal reference must be employed. Using a human reference total RNA control, qRT-PCR standard curves have been generated by hydrolysis probes that detect human β-2-microglubulin and TNF-α. The standard curves were generated and compared on two different instrumentation platforms. We have calculated the confidence intervals (CI) for each of the standard curves at a confidence level of 99%. Using the CI for each of the two standard curves, we quantified unknown samples. The predicted amounts from the standard curves for the unknown samples were comparable, but one platform showed larger variation (upper and lower CI values). Using a human reference total RNA and calculating the CI allows for the direct comparison of results obtained intra- or interlaboratory platforms and represents a step closer to "Universal Gene Transcript Quantification."

15

Standardization of qPCR and qRT-PCR Assays

Reinhold Mueller, Gothami Padmabandu, and Roger H. Taylor

Stratagene, La Jolla, California

15.1. Introduction

The quantification of target nucleic acid copy numbers in real-time qRT-PCR and qPCR assays can be (1) relative to some internal standard or (2) relative to an external standard generated with samples of known quantities. In the case of a relative comparison between treated and untreated samples, between healthy and diseased tissue, or between undifferentiated and differentiated cells, standardization is preferred but not required. To compensate for day-to-day or patient-to-patient differences in initial template concentration, a normalizer, usually a house-keeping gene, is included in the assay. Dilutions of the template are pre-pared, amplification plots for the normalizer and the gene of interest are generated, and a "standard" curve is calculated. The slopes of these dilution curves are indicators of amplification efficiency. When the amplification efficiencies for the normalizer and the gene of interest are identical, the dilution curve needs to be reestablished only when new components replace those that have been already tested. The result of a relative comparison is a ratio, which is unitless. Therefore, the data from this set are internally controlled. In theory, the results should be com-parable when performed on two different qPCR platforms. In practice, a number of assumptions about use of qPCR for relative comparison affect the quality of that comparison, as discussed in **Section 15.2.1** below.

A different set of controls and standards is necessary when the assay is used to determine, for example, how much of a specific mRNA is found in 1,000 laser-dissected cells, how many viral genomes are pres-ent in one milliliter of blood, or how many copies of a transgene have been successfully integrated in the host genome. First, the researcher has to take great care in quantifying the amount of target added to the reaction. In order to minimize the effect of variation in PCR and analy-sis, a standard curve for both the desired target and the reference needs to be generated every time an experiment is run, preferably as a multi-plex reaction. Values for the experimental samples, often called "unknown" samples, can then be extracted from the standard curve and will have a unit definition, such as copy number, nanomoles, or micro-grams. This method of determining input target concentration is often called "absolute quantification," although strictly speaking "absolute" quantification requires that one can actually count the number of input template molecules.

Quantitative RT-PCR and quantitative PCR experiments are expected to produce the same results when repeated the next day or in the lab down the hall. However, due to a number of adverse factors the input target quantity will vary. Adverse factors may include wrong estimates on the target concentration, pipetting irregularities, differences in instru-mentation (e.g., platforms, optical calibration, variations in block tem-perature and cycling conditions), and different settings used in the analy-sis of data. Some variation in results can be reduced by including one or more endogenous references (like a normalizer, an engogenous reference is typically a relatively constant target such as mRNA of a housekeeping gene or a gene that is known to be present in exactly one copy per cell) and a passive reference (dye). The use of a passive reference is recommended, so that tube-to-tube pipetting differences can be minimized. When making comparisons between results obtained in one laboratory with results in another laboratory, a universal standard must be used.

15.2. Platforms

From a technical point of view, four components are crucial for the success of a qPCR run: (1) a suitable instrument for thermal cycling and fluorescent signal acquisition (the platform), (2) an optimized detection chemistry, (3) good quality template, and (4) proper controls and standards.

Many thermal cyclers capable of detecting fluorescent signal are available on the market (see Bustin and Nolan **Section 8.2** of **Chapter 8**). Basic requirements for a suitable platform include the ability to multiplex, so that the sample (the "unknown"), endogenous control (the "reference"), and the passive reference dye can all be measured during the same experimental run. Once validated, most platforms should deliver comparable results using the methods described in **Section 15.3**. The validation of platforms often includes an assay with standard curve and two-fold discrimination. Validation of the platform is usually performed during installation. Subsequent validation may be performed by the user or by the manufacturer. For laboratories in a regulatory environment (using Good Laboratory Practices, Good Manufacturing Practices, and other international standards) some manufacturers offer a qualification service program.

15.2.1. Validation of Instrument Specification

For an optimized primer/probe set the following protocol may be used. The primer concentration is set at 600 nM each, the probe concentration is 300 nM, and the passive reference dye concentration is for a filter-based platform. The template is human genomic DNA and the target is β-actin.

1) Prepare enough master mix for 112 reactions: ddH$_2$O (2,830 µl), 10× Core Buffer (560 µl), 50 mM MgCl$_2$ (392 µl), 15 µM (each) of optimized primer mix (224 µl), 15 µM probe (112 µl), dNTPs (GATC at 5 mM each; 224 µl), 1 mM passive reference dye diluted 1:200 (84 µl), 5 U/µl hot start *Taq* (56 µl) for a total volume of 4,482 µl. Vortex gently.

2) Prepare 20,000-copies mix for 40.5 reactions: 10 ng/µl of human gDNA (405 µl), master mix (1,620 µl) for a total volume of 2,025 µl. Vortex gently.

3) Prepare 1× master mix by adding 714 µl of ddH2O to the remainder of the solution prepared in **step (1)**. Vortex gently.

4) Prepare serial dilutions by adding the appropriate volume of template to the 1× master mix from **step (3)**.

   - Prepare 10,000 copies for 68 reactions: 20,000 copies mix (1,700 µl), 1× master mix (1,700 µl) for a total volume of 3,400 µl.

   - Prepare 5,000 copies for 48.5 reactions: 10,000-copies mix (1,200 µl), 1× master mix (1,200 µl) for a total volume of 2,400 µl.

   - Prepare 2,000 copies for 7.5 reactions: 5,000-copies mix (150 µl), 1× master mix (225 µl) for a total volume of 375 µl.

   - Prepare 1,000 copies for 5 reactions: 2,000-copies mix (125 µl), 1× master mix (125 µl) for a total volume of 250 µl.

   - Prepare no-template control (NTC) for 5 reactions: 1× master mix (250 µl).

   - Vortex gently.

5) Pipette 50 µl each of the 10,000-copies mix into the wells of rows A to C. Pipette 50 µl of each of the 5,000-copies mix into the wells of rows F to H. Pipette 4 replicates, 50 µl each of NTC, 1,000-, 2,000-, 5,000-, 10,000-, and 20,000-copies mix into the wells of rows D and E.

6) Centrifuge the plate.

7) Run the samples using the appropriate cycling conditions.

8) Acquire fluorescent intensities at annealing for Molecular Beacons or at annealing/extension for TaqMan probes.

> **Note:** This setup has also been successfully used for SYBR
> Green I detection. In this case it is advisable to acquire
> data at the annealing and the extension steps.

A standard curve was generated with a β-actin primer/Molecular-Beacon set using the above protocol. In **Fig. 15.1**, the plot with the four replicates treated individually is shown. The R^2 is 0.995 (individually) and 0.999 (collectively). The slope of the curve is −3.217 (i.e., 104.6% efficiency; treated individually) or −3.219 (i.e., 104.5% efficiency; treated collectively).

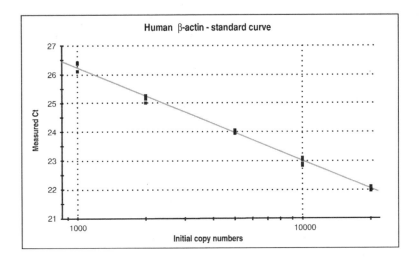

Figure 15.1. Standard curve for human β-actin.

Since the quality of the standard curve is critical for comparison of the same assay run on different platforms, it is worth establishing precisely. Criteria for evaluating a standard curve:

1. ***The linear range (critical).*** Most instrument manufacturers show data indicating a range in excess of six orders of magnitude. Linearity within that range allows for quantification of unknown samples with, e.g., 10^1 copies to 10^7 copies of target. It is important that the C_t of the unknown samples lies within the range of the standard curve, not beyond its highest or lowest point. One should not assume that the extrapolated part of the standard curve is linear.

2. *The standard deviation of replicate reactions and R^2-value (critical).* Accuracy in determining the C_t of replicates of standard curve dilutions influences the R^2-value and the confidence level. The R^2-value is a measure of the closeness of the data points to the best-fit line. The ideal value is 1; the smaller R^2 is the larger the assay's scatter and/or non-linearity and the larger the resulting confidence interval.

3. *The confidence interval (critical).* The confidence interval (CI) is the range beyond which one can be sure to a specified confidence that two measurements are different.

4. *The slope of the best-fit line.* In a semi-log (base 10) plot, the slope of the best-fit line is -3.32 for 100% PCR efficiency (exactly one doubling per cycle). The accuracy of data in standard curve quantification ("absolute" quantification) will probably not suffer much when the efficiency differs from 100% efficiency (lager or smaller) because the target in the unknown sample and in the standard will be affected equally.

   Note: In the case of using a standard curve for the relative comparison method matching the efficiency of target and reference is critical. The matching PCR efficiency is established by plotting the log of initial template amount over (*average C_t target*) – (*average C_t reference*). The efficiency of target and reference is called close enough when the slope of that line is less than 0.1 (Applied Biosystems: *User Bulletin* #2, 1997.)

5. *The y-axis intercept.* The slope and the *y*-axis intercept allow for comparison of two qPCR experiments. When the slope of the standard curve is close to -3.32, the *y*-axis intercept is a good indicator for the sensitivity of the assay.

We have found after running a number of different assays using a variety of detection chemistries on several platforms that the ranges of 0.980 to 1.000 for R^2-values and -3.1 to -3.5 for the slope of a standard curve generated by a probe-based assay are usual.

From the standard curve, the copy numbers of the unknowns for the above example, the human β-actin target, can be estimated. For this run, the mean is $10,172 \pm 1232$ (1σ) for the 10,000-copies sample and $4,776 \pm 516$ for the 5,000-copies sample. **Fig. 15.2** shows a β-actin

Molecular-Beacon assay run on about 100 different Stratagene Mx 4000 multiplex qPCR systems. The standard curve for each instrument was generated and the values for the 5,000- and 10,000-copies samples were extracted from the standard curve. This figure shows two important trends; there is variation in the "absolute" copy number in those 100 instruments, and the two-fold discrimination is not affected by the deviation from the apparent initial copy number. The deviation from the expected copy number is due to many factors, including instrumentation, chemistry, and operator.

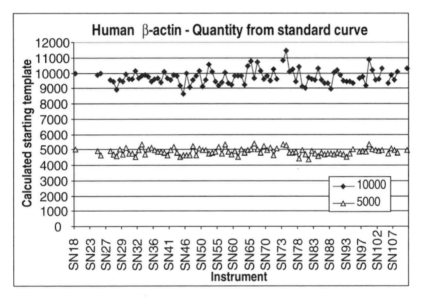

Figure 15.2. Quantification of 5,000 and 10,000 copies of the human β-actin target on a large number of Mx4000 fluorescence real-time readers.

With an assay as the one described above, an instrument can be, and in practice is, validated. Use of a standard curve reduces the impact of instrument and assay variation. Even in the event that one instrument has a much lower sensitivity than the next, the standard curve method will improve the accuracy of a comparison between results of the two instruments. As described above in this section, three standard curve parameters are more important for standardization of assays than others: the range of linearity of the curve, the standard deviation of the data points that are used for the generation of the curve, and the confidence interval. The reason will become apparent when comparing the same assay of two different platforms.

15.3. Detection Chemistries

The fluorescent signal, as detected in a real-time fluorescent reader, typically results from either a labeled probe that binds to a specific amplicon sequence, or a fluorescent dye (for example SYBR Green I) that binds nonspecifically to DNA. An important aspect in any qPCR assay is designing and optimizing the primers; this is described elsewhere in this book (see **Chapter 13.** *Getting Started-The Basics of Setting Up a qPCR Assay*). A good primer set in our experience will generate a very similar absolute and relative quantification for a given amount of target, regardless if this set is used in detection with SYBR Green I or with probe-based chemistries. Although the cost per reaction is low for SYBR Green I detection, the simultaneous detection of unknown sample and endogenous control is difficult, if not impossible. The unknown sample and the reference can be run in the two-tube format, but the disadvantages are obvious: The reaction volume is twice as large as in a multiplex reaction, and small differences in the unknown and reference wells may influence the quantitation.

In the following, a general protocol for multiplex setup is presented which may be used for coamplification of an unknown sample and the reference.

> **Tip:** Think master mix! Best results are achieved when all components of the assays are combined and then divided up, i.e., add water, 2× qRT-PCR master mix, primer/probe mixes, passive reference dye, and reverse transcriptase, then split this mixture into parts to which the template is added. After template addition the mixture is dispensed in to the replicate wells.

Setup of standard curves in multiplex (the reaction volume used here is 50 µl per reaction):

1. Prepare the master mix nuclease-free PCR-grade water to adjust the final total PCR volume
   - 25.0 μl of 2× qRT-PCR master mix (containing buffers, MgCl₂, dNTPs, and DNA polymerase;
   - 2.5 μl of 20× primer probe mix for β-2 microglobulin (ABI PDAR, *Cat. No. 4326319E*);
   - 2.5 μl of 20× primer probe mix for TNF-α (PDAR, *Cat. No. 4327055*);
   - Passive reference dye (300 nM for the Platform A and 75 nM for B);
   - Reverse Transcriptase (depending on manufacturer's recommendation).

2. Gently mix the reactions without creating bubbles (do not vortex).

3. Spin down droplets and split master mix into appropriate aliquots.

4. Prepare serial dilutions of the template to result in six to seven concentrations of the input template. It is advisable to add template in 5 μl or larger volumes to prevent any pipetting errors. The template used was PMA-treated Raji cell RNA (Stratagene, *Cat. No. 735408*).

5. Add *x* μl of experimental template (in this case 200 ng, and 5-fold serial dilutions thereof for each experimental reaction) to the appropriate aliquot (submaster mix).

6. Gently mix the reactions without creating bubbles (do not vortex).

7. Centrifuge the reactions briefly.

8. Pipette replicates from each submaster mix into wells.

9. Place the experimental and control reactions into real-time reader, in this case into two different platforms, A and B.

10. Two-step PCR profile (in this assay the RT step was 45 min and the annealing/extension step was 60°C:

Cycles	Duration of cycle	Temperature
1	30–45 minutes	50°C
1	10 minutes	95°C
45	15 seconds	95°C
	1 minute	50–60°C

An analysis of runs of the identical assay on two platforms (**Figs. 15.3** and **15.4**) makes it clear that one platform shows a slightly higher sensitivity (smaller y-axis intercept), whereas the other platform shows better precision (tighter confidence interval). The tighter the confidence interval around a standard curve, the more clearly the instrument can distinguish between differences in starting template. An instrument with higher sensitivity may be better than a lower sensitivity instrument at distinguishing between differences in small amounts of starting template. These two characteristics are interdependent and a precise, but less sensitive instrument may outperform a more sensitive but less precise instrument, even at low starting concentrations. By characterizing and accounting for both the precision and sensitivity of the instruments and assays, the standard curve method with confidence intervals provides a straightforward comparison of samples run on different platforms (**Table 15.1**).

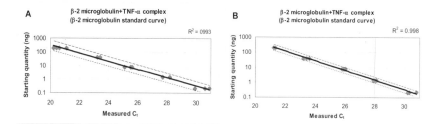

Figure 15.3. Standard curves for β-2-microglobulin in multiplex. The assay included 0.32, 1.6, 8, 40, and 200 ng of PMA-treated Raji total RNA, the target (TNF-α/FAM–PDAR), and the reference (β-2-microglobulin/VIC–PDAR), as well as passive reerence dye. Identical samples were run on two different platforms. In this figure the VIC standard curves are shown; platform A in the left panel and platform B in the right panel.

15.4. Conclusion

The quality of the standard curve is critical to the comparison of results from one platform to another. The R^2-value is a useful tool for the evaluation of the individual standard curve, but the confidence interval is more useful in comparing one assay with another. An assay with a large CI generates results that are difficult to distinguish from another assay. The goal

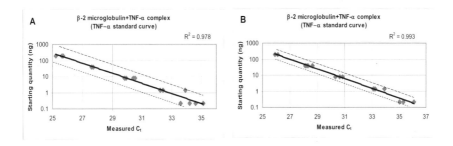

Figure 15.4. Standard curves for TNF α in multiplex. The assay included 0.32, 1.6, 8, 40, and 200 ng of PMA-treated Raji total RNA, the target (TNF-α/FAM–PDAR), and the reference (β-2 microglobulin/VIC–PDAR), as well as passive reference dye. Identical samples were run on two different platforms. In this figure the FAM standard curves are shown; platform A in the left panel and platform B in the right panel.

Table 15.1. Standard curve data acquired on two platforms.

Individual C_t values were obtained from the standard curves for TNF-α, shown in **Fig. 15.4**, and the average was calculated (column: *Average C_t*). The average C_t was compared to the standard curve for TNF-α. The resulting "Predicted Amount" is presented in the third column. The values for the upper and lower confidence interval (CI) are in the fourth and fifth columns.

Template Amount [ng]	Average C_t	Predicted Amount [ng]	Upper CI	Lower CI
Platform A				
200.00	25.43	189.58	569.29	63.13
40.00	27.63	41.84	121.33	14.43
8.00	30.10	7.67	21.95	2.68
1.60	32.67	1.31	3.82	0.45
0.32	34.37	0.41	1.22	0.14
Platform B				
200.00	26.07	184.15	344.10	98.55
40.00	28.27	42.19	77.35	23.01
8.00	30.56	9.10	16.56	5.00
1.60	33.36	1.40	2.56	0.76
0.32	35.68	0.30	0.55	0.16

is to define an algorithm that allows a statement of the statistical confidence level at which two predicted target amounts can be distinguished.

Other standard curve parameters provide additional information about the quality of the assay. The slope of the standard curve may indicate poor amplification, but this effect is minimized by the use of a standard curve. In other words, low PCR efficiency affects all data points on the standard curve equally. However, very poor efficiency may affect the precision of the assay. Using a standard curve with a (universal) reference coamplified with the unknown sample on a platform that has been validated, in the presence of a passive reference dye often provides a reliable method for comparing one run to another and one platform to another. A universal reference system may consist of a well-defined template and of qualified primers and probes. The appropriate primers and probes can be obtained from a group interested in standardizing assays (e.g., NIST, ASTM, DIN), from a group interested in comparing very special targets such as virus for determination of viral load (HIV, HBV, etc.) or from manufacturers providing qualified RNA and DNA primer and probe sets for the detection of reference and control targets. Using a universal reference DNA or RNA template with the appropriate primer and probe sets and applying the procedures described here will make the comparison of data more transparent and consistent.

16

Extraction of Total RNA from Formalin-Fixed Paraffin-Embedded Tissue

Fraser Lewis and Nicola J. Maughan

Abstract

The histopathology archive represents a well-characterized source of samples covering virtually every disease and is available for molecular biological investigation. The archive has become widely used for molecular genetic analysis and DNA can be routinely extracted from formalin-fixed, paraffin-embedded tissue. More recently, archival specimens have become a source of material for extensive analysis of mRNA expression utilizing real-time quantitative reverse transcriptase polymerase chain reaction (PCR). This should eventually lead to better diagnosis, better evaluation of prognosis, and better treatment through targeted therapeutic regimes.

16

Extraction of Total RNA from Formalin-Fixed Paraffin-Embedded Tissue

Fraser Lewis and Nicola J. Maughan

Histopathology, The Leeds Teaching Hospitals NHS Trust, Leeds, United Kingdom

16.1. Introduction

Histopathology departments house substantial archives of surgical material preserved by formalin fixation and embedded in paraffin wax. Archives of this material have been conserved for over a century and they represent a historical collection of virtually every disease and are an invaluable source of nucleic acids for application in new molecular technologies. With appropriate ethical consideration and consent, these specimens are available for investigation as new molecular assays develop for the elucidation, diagnosis, and prognosis of disease. The archive has already proved an invaluable source of DNA for molecular genetic analysis and identification of infectious agents and methods for the routine extraction of DNA from formalin-fixed, paraffin-embedded tissue are well documented.[1]

More recently it has become desirable to utilize archival specimens as a source of RNA in order to investigate the changes in expression of mRNA that occur during a disease process. There is now a requirement to identify up and down regulated genes using a number of emerging technologies including expression arrays and real-time quantitative reverse transcriptase polymerase chain reaction. These procedures require a reliable recovery of total RNA from the preserved tissue and new extraction methodologies have been proposed to accomplish this.

16.2. Extraction of RNA from Clinical Specimens

Provided that clinical specimens are rapidly received in the laboratory, total RNA can be readily extracted by several techniques including the use of a guanidinium thiocyanate—cesium chloride gradient[2] or a combined guanidinium thiocyanate acid-phenol chloroform procedure.[3] These methods reliably produce high yields of high-quality total RNA that can be utilized for further investigation. In addition, a number of simplified methods for RNA extraction have become available from numerous commercial suppliers to speed up the process without loss of quality of extracted RNA. These include RNeasy (Qiagen, Hilden, Germany), Purescript (Gentra Systems, Minneapolis, Minn.), Trizol (Invitrogen, Carlsbad, Calif.) and Totally RNA (Ambion, Austin, Tex.), which can be adapted for the extraction of RNA from most fresh clinical specimens to yield reasonable quantities of RNA at a quality suitable for reverse transcriptase PCR amplification procedures.

When applied to formalin-fixed, paraffin-embedded tissue, however, these methods generally result in failure to extract RNA in sufficient quantity to enable further investigation.

16.3. Effect of Fixation

The fixation procedure used to routinely preserve clinical specimens is an important consideration when attempting to extract RNA. The chemical nature of fixatives and fixation time can have a significant effect on the ability to extract macromolecules from processed tissues.[4,5] Successful extraction can be accomplished from tissues fixed in precipitating fixatives such as acetone, Clarke's and Carnoy's, and from cross-linking fixatives such as formalin, neutral buffered formalin, and paraformaldehyde. However, neither DNA nor RNA can be successfully extracted from highly cross-linking fixatives such as gluteraldehyde, modified formalins containing mercuric chloride and Bouin's fixative.[4]

It is probable that the histological specimens stored in Histopathology archives will have been routinely fixed in formalin although the length of time of fixation will not be known. Those specimens that occasionally fail to yield transcribable RNA or amplifiable DNA will have been fixed for longer than the acceptable time that ensures successful extraction of the nucleic acids. Generally, tissue fixed for 12–36 h will yield total RNA that can be reverse transcribed for further analysis.

The effect of formalin fixation on the structure of nucleic acids has indicated that all four bases show the addition of monomethylol (–CH(2)OH) groups at various rates with the additional dimerization of adenine groups by methylene bridging.[6] The majority of the methylol groups can be removed from the bases by simply elevating the temperature in a buffer solution. Methods that have been proposed for the isolation of total nucleic acids utilizing extended Proteinase K digestion of up to five days[1] may owe their success to the continuing removal of the monomethylol groups over the time period to restore their template activity. However, the inability to isolate mRNA by standard methods and prime reverse transcription reactions with poly (dT) indicates either a loss of polyA tails or their inaccessibility, which suggests that the dimerization of the adenine groups is difficult to reverse.

In addition, both DNA and RNA extracted from formalin-fixed, paraffin-embedded tissue are significantly degraded[7,8] and attempted amplification of long fragments should be avoided. It has been suggested that the fixation process is responsible for the degradation and this can be minimized if fixation is carried out at low temperatures or by the addition of EDTA to the fixative.[9]

16.4. Extraction of Total RNA from Formalin-Fixed, Paraffin-Embedded Tissue

A number of successful methods have been proposed including a guanidium thiocyanate acid-phenol chloroform method for the extraction of Hepatitis C RNA from stained sections of liver tissue,[10] and the use of Trizol has similarly been successfully employed for the extraction of this RNA virus.[11] However, in order to improve the yield of total RNA from formalin-fixed, paraffin-embedded tissue, a number of procedures have been proposed.

Chelex-100 extraction has been shown to be successful in extracting RNA from around 84% of sections tested,[12] and the use of a procedure utilizing sonication and oligo(dT)$_{25}$ paramagnetic beads also resulted in successful RT-PCR.[13] A method that results in the binding of RNA to acid-treated glass beads in the presence of high molarity guanidinium salt[14] is highly successful for acetone-fixed specimens but less successful for formalin-fixed specimens.

The most successful methods for the recovery of total RNA from formalin-fixed, paraffin-embedded tissue use a Proteinase K digestion prior to acid-phenol chloroform extraction and carrier precipitation.[1,6,8] A similar method is also employed in a commercial kit—Paraffin Block RNA Isolation Kit (Ambion). Chaotropic agents, such as guanidinium hydrochloride, do not readily solubilize dewaxed sections from formalin-fixed, paraffin-embedded tissue, whereas digestion in Proteinase K results in their complete solubility.[6]

The subtilase, Proteinase K, isolated from the fungus *Tritirachium album limber*,[15] is classed as a subtilisin-related serine protease with a molecular weight of around 27–29 Kd calculated by gel electrophoresis and active site labeling.[16] It is one of the most active endopeptidases known and does not exhibit any cleavage specificity. It hydrolyzes peptide or ester bonds adjacent to the carboxy groups of aromatic and hydrophobic aliphatic amino acids. Proteinase K degrades glycoproteins and peptides as well as native proteins and is especially suitable for use in the isolation of DNA and RNA from tissue and cells. This is in part due to its rapid inactivation of endogenous nucleases such as RNases and DNases, particularly in the presence of SDS.[17-19] The enzyme also promotes cell lysis by activation of a bacterial autolytic factor. As a subtilisin, proteinase K exhibits several advantages over other proteolytic enzymes such as pepsin, trypsin, and pronase. It is not inactivated by metal ions, chelating agents such as EDTA, sulfhydryl reagents, or trypsin or chymotrypsin inhibitors.[20] It can, however, be inactivated by phenylmethylsulfonyl fluoride and by mercuric ions.[21] The enzyme's resistance to inactivation can therefore be advantageous in its application to formalin-fixed, paraffin-embedded tissue, which might be contaminated with molecules that may be inhibitory to some enzymes. In addition, activity is stable over a very wide range of pH from 6.5 to 9.5.[20] The enzyme experiences stimulation of activity in the presence of denaturing agents such as SDS and urea. For example, it has been shown that by including SDS in the reaction mixture a seven-fold increase in the activity of Proteinase K is observed.[18] It also exhibits a wide temperature range for activation (25°C to 65°C) with activity at 65°C twelve times that at 25°C.[2] It is also significantly more active than other enzymes; for example, three times more active than trypsin and six times more active than pronase.[20] As a result, Proteinase K has been utilized as a most effective protease for digesting tissue sections prior to extraction.

The enzyme readily destroys proteins and this property appears to be little affected by the highly cross-linked nature of the proteins following formalin fixation. The result of incubation of the sections in Proteinase K is the release of RNA from the cross-linked matrix enabling its purification by acid-phenol chloroform extraction. The extremely low yields of RNA obtained result in very dilute aqueous solutions, which require the addition of a precipitant carrier such as glycogen or linearized acrylamide to ensure its precipitation.

16.5. Use of RNase Inhibitors

The recommendation that all glassware and reagents should be treated with diethyl pyrocarbonate (DEPC), as a precaution against potential RNase activity, should be avoided. Trace amounts of DEPC will modify purine residues in RNA by carboxymethylation and this carboxymethylated RNA will transcribe with extremely low efficiency producing very low yields of cDNA. Effectively, the DEPC poisons the RNA extract by the introduction of inhibitory effects. Although the use of DEPC is recommended for the destruction of endogenous nucleases, in formalin-fixed material these will have become totally inactivated by cross-linking during the fixation process. Furthermore, digestion with Proteinase K ensures that this cross-linked enzyme is totally destroyed thus avoiding any potential reactivation during reversal of the fixation in aqueous buffers. Potentially, the only source of RNase is from glassware, buffers, and human contact during the extraction procedure. The use of high-quality reagents, RNase-free water, and ultraclean glassware is sufficient to minimize all problems associated with this ubiquitous source of RNase.

16.6. Protocol for the Extraction of Total RNA from Formalin-Fixed, Paraffin-Embedded Tissue

With all of the above considerations in mind, we have developed a reliable method for the extraction of total RNA from routinely formalin-fixed, paraffin-embedded tissue based on an earlier method described by Jackson et al.[1] The resulting RNA can be utilized successfully in real-time RT-PCR assays and in array analysis for measurement of relative gene expression, although success with this latter application is dependent on the type of expression array being utilized.

16.6.1. Method

Cut ten 5-μm sections from the block onto standard microscope slides and hotplate at 60°C for 10 min on a slide-drying hotplate. Do not heat for longer than this to avoid destruction of the RNA. Dewax the sections in xylene at 37°C for 30 min, twice in xylene at room temperature for 10 min each and dehydrate through graded ethanols at 100% twice, 70%, 50%, and 25% to water over a 10 min period. Scrape the sections, or appropriate parts of each section where microdissection is required, into a screw top microcentrifuge tube. Resuspend the tissue in a suitable volume of 10 mM *Tris*-HCl pH 8.0, 100 mM NaCl, 25 mM EDTA, 0.5% SDS, containing 2 mg/ml Proteinase K (Amresco, Solon, Ohio). The volume of digestion reagent used should be kept to a minimum as over dilution of the RNA will hamper its recovery by precipitation. Generally, 200–500 µl of digestion reagent is used and is dependent on the size of the sections being extracted. Incubate the resuspended sections in digestion mixture at 37°C for five days with gentle end over end rotation using a rotator such as the Heto Mastermix (Jouan Nordic, Allerod, Denmark). Following the digestion, extract the sample twice with an equal volume of phenol/chloroform (5:1 pH 4.5 (Amresco)) and then once with an equal volume of chloroform/isoamyl alcohol mixture (24:1). During the extraction, separate the organic and aqueous phases by brief centrifugation (2 min) at no more than $4,000 \times g$. After the final extraction transfer the aqueous phase to a clean microcentrifuge and add 1 µl glycogen at 20 mg/ml (Roche Applied Science, Lewes, UK) or 1 µl linear acrylamide (Ambion) and 2.5 volumes of 100% ethanol and leave at –20°C overnight to precipitate the RNA. Centrifuge at high speed $(21,000 \times g)$ for 10 minutes, drain off the ethanol, wash once with 70% ethanol, and dry briefly at room temperature. Resuspend the RNA pellet in 30 µl of molecular biology grade water and aliquot into 5-µl aliquots for storage and store at –80°C.

The successful extraction of total RNA from archival specimens results in low yields of highly degraded product (**Fig. 16.1**). It is possible, however, to utilize this RNA in a variety of molecular assays, which can be used as a template for a large number of applications.

Figure 16.1. Extracts from a fresh colon (A) were compared with extracts from formalin-fixed, paraffin-embedded normal and tumor tissues (other lanes) by electrophoresis on a 2% agarose gel. The result shows significant degradation of the RNA extracted from the paraffin sections.

16.7. Reverse Transcription of Total RNA from Paraffin Sections

Priming the reverse transcription reaction with poly(dT) rarely results in the formation of cDNA from total RNA extracted from paraffin tissue sections. This is due to the loss of the polyA tails on mRNA, which results from the combined effects of formalin fixation and the extraction procedure. In addition, it has been observed that the severe fragmentation of the mRNA renders sequences at both the 5' and 3' ends unsuitable for the design of assays for real time quantitative PCR. Loss of the sequence at the 3' end is the main reason why cDNA derived from these extracts does not hybridize successfully to arrays constructed with short oligonucleotide sequences designed to the 3' ends of mRNA.

Reverse transcription of the total RNA derived from paraffin sections is successful using random hexamers to prime the reaction and reverse transcriptase enzymes such as Superscript (Invitrogen). Most reverse transcriptase procedures recommend the inactivation of the reverse transcriptase enzyme after the reaction by heating to 70°C for 5–15min. This step should be avoided as, in our experience, total loss of the synthesized cDNA occurs (**Plate 16.1**). The reason for this observation is not known.

16.7.1. Method

Mix a 5-µl aliquot of total RNA with 1 µl of random hexamer (10 pmoles) and heat at 70°C for 10 min. Cool the tube on ice for 5 min and add 4 µl of first strand buffer, 2 µl of DTT, 1 µl of 10 mM dNTP mix (10 mM each of dATP, dCTP, dGTP and dTTP), and 6 µl of sterile molecular biology grade water. Incubate at 37°C for 2 min then add 1 µl of Superscript (200 units). Mix the contents by pipetting gently up and down then incubate at 37°C for 1 h. Immediately following the reaction, store the cDNA at –20°C until required for real-time PCR. 2.5 µl of cDNA are used in each PCR reaction.

16.8. Design of Real-Time PCR Assays

Attempts to amplify fragments longer than 120 bp from RNA extracted from formalin-fixed, paraffin-embedded tissue are usually unsuccessful. In our experience, amplification of fragments in a range 70-120 bp generally results in a success rate of greater than 95%. **Plate 16.2** illustrates a typical result from a series of eighteen colorectal cancers, extracted, simultaneously using the procedures described above. Real-time amplification of thymidilate synthase was carried out in the presence of SYBR Green I. Amplification failed in only one of the extracts tested.

As discussed, careful extraction from just 10×5-μm sections of formalin-fixed, paraffin-embedded tissue enables total RNA to be reverse transcribed to yield sufficient cDNA to perform around 48 PCR assays. Special considerations have to be made if the reverse transcription step is to succeed and careful design of the assay has to be undertaken for the success of the subsequent PCR.

References

1. Jackson DP, Lewis FA, Taylor GR, Boylston AW, Quirke P: **Tissue extraction of DNA and RNA and analysis by the polymerase chain reaction.** *J Clin Pathol* 1990, 43(6):499–504.

2. Mehra M: **RNA isolation from cells and tissue.** In: *Laboratory Guide to RNA: Isolation, Analysis, and Synthesis.* Krieg PAA, ed. New York, NY: Wiley-Liss, 1996:1–20.

3. Chomczynski P, Sacchi N: **Single-step method of RNA isolation by acid guanidinium thiocyanate-phenol-chloroform extraction.** *Anal Biochem* 1987, 162(1):156–159.

4. O'Leary JJ, Browne G, Landers RJ, Crowley M, Healy IB, Street JT, Pollock AM, Murphy J, Johnson MI, Lewis FA, Mohamdee O, Cullinane C, Doyle CT: **The importance of fixation procedures on dna-template and its suitability for solution-phase polymerase chain-reaction and PCR *in-situ* hybridization.** *Histochem J* 1994, 26:337–346.

5. Goldsworthy SM, Stockton PS, Trempus CS, Foley JF, Maronpot R: **Effects of fixation on RNA extraction and amplification from laser capture microdissected tissue.** *Mol Carcinog* 1999, **25**:86–91.

6. Masuda N, Ohnishi T, Kawamoto S, Monden M, Okubo K: **Analysis of chemical modification of RNA from formalin-fixed samples and optimization of molecular biology applications for such samples.** *Nucleic Acids Res* 1999, **27**:4436–4443.

7. Stanta G, Schneider C: **RNA extracted from paraffin-embedded human tissues is amenable to analysis by PCR amplification.** *Biotechniques* 1991, **11**:304, 306, 308.

8. Krafft AE, Duncan BW, Bijwaard KE, Taubenberger JK, Lichy JH: **Optimization of the isolation and amplification of RNA from formalin-fixed, paraffin-embedded tissue: The armed forces institute of pathology experience and literature review.** *Mol Diagn* 1997, **2**:217–230.

9. Tokuda Y, Nakamura T, Satonaka K, Maeda S, Doi K, Baba S, Sugiyama T: **Fundamental study on the mechanism of DNA degradation in tissue fixed in formaldehyde.** *J Clin Pathol* 1990, **43**:748–751.

10. Saito K: **Morphology and molecular pathology: Detection of hepatitis C virus RNA sequences in stained sections by microscopy-directed selective extraction.** *Rinsho Byori* 1998, **46**(1):49–55.

11. Greenson JK, Svoboda-Newman SM, Merion RM, Frank TS: **The histologic progression of recurrent hepatitis C in liver transplant allografts.** *Am J Sur Pathol* 1996, **20**:731–738.

12. Coombs NJ, Gough AC, Primrose JN: **Optimisation of DNA and RNA extraction from archival formalin-fixed tissue.** *Nucleic Acids Res* 1999, **27**:e12.

13. Houze TA, Gustavsson B: **Sonification as a means of enhancing the detection of gene expression levels from formalin-fixed, paraffin-embedded biopsies.** *Biotechniques* 1996, **21**:1074–1078, 1080, 1082.

14. Koopmans M, Monroe SS, Coffield LM, Zaki SR: **Optimization of extraction and PCR amplification of RNA extracts from paraffin-embedded tissue in different fixatives.** *J Virol Methods* 1993, **43**:189-204.

15. Roelcke D, Uhlenbruck G: **Proteinase K: A new serological effective protease from fungi.** *Z Med Mikrobiol Immunol* 1969, **155**:156–170.

16. Jany KD, Mayer B: **Proteinase K from *Tritirachium album* Limber. I. Molecular mass and sequence around the active site serine residue.** *Biol Chem Hoppe Seyler* 1985, **366**, 485–492.

17. Mendelsohn SL, Young DA: **Inhibition of ribonuclease. Efficacy of sodium dodecyl sulfate, diethyl pyrocarbonate, proteinase K and heparin using a sensitive ribonuclease assay.** *Biochim Biophys Acta* 1978, **519**:461–473.

18. Hilz H, Wiegers U, Adamietz P: **Stimulation of proteinase K action by denaturing agents: Application to the isolation of nucleic acids and the degradation of 'masked' proteins.** *Eur J Biochem* 1975, **56**:103–108.

19. Rauber NR, Jany KD, Pfleiderer G: **Ribonuclease A digestion by proteinase K.** *Z Naturforsch [C]* 1978, **33**:660–663.

20. Ebeling W, Hennrich N, Klockow M, Metz H, Orth HD, Lang H: **Proteinase K from *Tritirachium album* Limber.** *Eur J .Biochem* 1974, **47**:91–97.

21. Muller A Saenger W: **Studies on the inhibitory action of mercury upon proteinase K.** *J Biol Chem* 1993, **268**:26150–26154.

22. Tullis RH, Rubin H: **Calcium protects DNase I from proteinase K: A new method for the removal of contaminating RNase from DNase I.** *Anal Biochem* 1980, **107**:260–264.

17

Cells-to-cDNA II: RT-PCR without RNA Isolation

Quoc Hoang and Brittan L. Pasloske

Abstract

The analysis of RNA by RT-PCR from cells grown in tissue culture or from small tissue samples is a multistep process. The rate-limiting step of this process is usually the up-front purification of the RNA which is in itself, a multistep procedure. In addition to the time disadvantage of RNA isolation, another drawback related to the multistep procedure includes sample loss. Poor recovery is an especially important consideration when processing samples that contain only a few picograms of RNA.

This chapter describes the Cells-to-cDNA™ II technology, a method for performing RT-PCR directly from a cell lysate, thus eliminating the need for RNA isolation and maximizing the recovery of the RNA from the sample and greatly simplifying the analysis of the RNA by RT-PCR. Cells-to-cDNA II is quantitative from a single cell to thousands of cells and can be used in a variety of different applications including real-time PCR, automated (robotic) 96-well analysis, the analysis of laser captured microdissected samples, and the analysis of formalin-fixed cells.

17

Cells-to-cDNA II: RT-PCR without RNA Isolation

Quoc Hoang and Brittan L. Pasloske

Ambion, Inc., Austin, Texas

17.1. Introduction

The most commonly used method to study mRNA levels from cells is the reverse transcription polymerase chain reaction (RT-PCR). In this process, complementary DNA (cDNA) is first transcribed from mRNA with a reverse transcriptase. The cDNA is then amplified by PCR and the concentration of the mRNA is correlated with the accumulation of the PCR product. Generally, the substrate for RT-PCR is RNA purified from a biological sample such as a tissue or cells from tissue culture.

RNA isolation is often a tedious and multistep process involving phenol extraction or the capture of the RNA on a glass filter or magnetic beads. These procedures use a strong denaturant to lyse the cells which can be inhibitory to downstream applications, including DNase I treatment and reverse transcription, if they are not properly removed from the RNA during the isolation procedure. Denaturants, such as guanidinium, are needed to inactivate ribonucleases (RNases) in the sample. Active RNases in the sample will lead to the degradation of the RNA.[1] Sample loss can be expected during any or all the steps of RNA isolation including cell lysis, RNA extraction, and RNA recovery.

With Cells-to-cDNA™ II, a crude cell lysate with as many as 2,500 cells/µl is used directly in reverse transcription or one-step RT-PCR, effectively by-passing the RNA isolation protocol. Briefly, cells are added to a Cell Lysis Buffer and heated. During the heating step, the cells are simultaneously lysed and the RNases inactivated. The cell lysate can be DNase I treated, thereby degrading the contaminating genomic DNA. The lysate is then added to a reverse transcription reaction followed by PCR or a one-step RT-PCR reaction. By eliminating the RNA isolation step, the total time from cells to a final PCR product is greatly reduced.

Cells-to-cDNA II is ideal for samples with a few cells such as those obtained by laser capture microdissection (LCM) or fluorescence activated cell sorting (FACS). LCM and FACS are used to isolate cell populations with specific phenotypes, down to a single cell. Due to the low number of cells used in these experiments, RNA isolation is impractical since loss of RNA can only be expected and yields are often variable. The streamlining of the process of going from cells to a PCR product also makes Cells-to-cDNA II well suited for automated, 96-well plate applications.

This chapter describes a typical experiment using real-time RT-PCR to establish the optimal, maximum cell concentration with Cells-to-cDNA II using a serial dilution of cells from tissue culture and an Armored RNA® control. Armored RNA consists of a specific RNA sequence protected by a bacteriophage coat protein.[2] When included in the initial lysis step, it will release its protected RNA in concert with the RNA from the cells. The Armored RNA concentration is constant in each reaction while the cell concentration is varied. A drop in the Armored RNA PCR signal indicates that the higher concentration of cell debris inhibited the reverse transcriptase reaction and/or that the RNases were not completely destroyed in the cell lysis procedure. By using this control, it is straightforward to establish the highest cell concentration that can be used in Cells-to-cDNA II that does not inhibit RT-PCR. GAPDH will be detected from each lysate concentration to show the linearity obtained with this protocol.

17.2. Materials

17.2.1. Materials Supplied with Cells-to-cDNA II

The Cells-to-cDNA II kit (Ambion, Inc., Austin, Texas) contains the reagents for cell lysis and RNase inactivation, DNase treatment, and reverse transcription:

> 1× phosphate buffered saline (PBS);
> Cell Lysis Buffer;
> Nuclease-free water;
> DNase I;
> 10× RT Buffer;
> dNTP mix;
> Oligo dT primers;
> Random decamers;
> RNase inhibitor;
> MMLV-RT;
> Armored RNA control;
> Armored RNA primers;
> β-actin primers (see **Note 1**).

17.2.2. Materials for Real-Time PCR (see Note 2)

1. SuperTaq Real-Time (Ambion, Inc.) comes complete with *Taq* DNA polymerase, 10× Real-Time PCR buffer, $MgCl_2$, dNTP mix, and 50× ROX passive reference.

2. Primers and probes specific for each target that is to be amplified.

3. Instrumentation to perform real-time PCR such the 7900HT (Applied Biosystems) or the Mx 4000 (Stratagene).

17.2.3. Heating Sources (see Note 3)

Heating sources will be needed for 75°C, 37°C, and 42°C incubations. Confirm that these instruments were calibrated. It is critical that the incubator for cell lysis is at least 75°C.

17.3. Method

17.3.1. Lysis and DNase I Treatment

HeLa cells are grown in Dulbecco's Modified Eagle Medium with 10% fetal bovine serum in a tissue culture flask until the cells have grown to 50–75% confluency. The medium is removed and then the cells are incubated with trypsin (0.05% trypsin, 0.53 mM EDTA) for 5 minutes at 37°C. The trypsin is inactivated by suspending in medium with 10% fetal bovine serum. Cell concentration is established using a hemacytometer. Collect 6 million cells based on the cell concentration. Pellet the cells at 3,000 rpm for 5 minutes and remove the medium. Wash the cells once with 1 ml of cold PBS and pellet the cells again at 3,000 rpm for 5 minutes. Remove the PBS. Suspend the cells in 60 µl of PBS. Make a serial dilution of cells at 1×10^5, 5×10^4, 2.5×10^4, 1.25×10^4, 5×10^3, 1×10^3, 200, 40, and 10 cells/µl in PBS. Add 10 µl of each cell dilution to 90 µl Cell Lysis Buffer for final concentrations 1×10^4, 5×10^3, 2.5×10^3, 1.25×10^3, 500, 100, 20, 4, and 1 cells/µl. 2 µl of the Armored RNA control is included in each sample with one sample with only 100 µl Cell Lysis Buffer as a positive control. The samples are incubated at 75°C for 10 minutes and then cooled to 37°C. 2 µl of DNase I is added to the cell lysate, incubated at 37°C for 15 minutes and then incubated at 75°C for 5 minutes to inactivate the DNase I (see **Note 5**). The cell lysate is now compatible for reverse transcription and PCR.

17.3.2 Reverse Transcription

- Run a reverse transcription for each of the cell lysates. Include an RT(–) reaction for each concentration in which no reverse transcriptase is included to the reaction. Also include a negative control-lacking template (cell lysate or RNA), called the template minus control. No signal is expected for the negative controls.
- Transfer 5 µl of the cell lysates to a fresh tube and place on ice.
- Add to each tube:
  - 5 µl of RNase-free water;
  - 4 µl of dNTP mix;
  - 2-µl Random Decamer Primers.
- Incubate 70°C, 3 minutes in water bath or temperature block to denature the RNA. Remove the tubes and place on ice.
- Add:
  - 2 µl of 10× RT buffer;
  - 1 µl of RNase Inhibitor;
  - 1 µl MMLV-RT.
- Incubate at 42°C for 15 to 60 minutes to reverse transcribe the RNA. Incubate at 92°C for 10 minutes to inactivate the MMLV-RT. Store at –20°C until amplification.

17.3.3. Real-Time PCR

Assemble the following for Real-Time PCR using primers and TaqMan probes for GAPDH and the Armored RNA control:

Components	RT(–) PCR Control (µl)		RT(+) PCR Control (µl)		Template (–) Control (µl)	
	GAPDH	*AR	GAPDH	AR	GAPDH	AR
RT(–) Reaction – GAPDH	5	–	–	–	–	–
RT(–) Reaction – *AR	–	5	–	–	–	–
RT(+) Reaction – GAPDH	–	–	5	–	–	–
RT(+) Reaction – AR	–	–	–	5	–	–
RNase Free Water	9.8	9.8	9.8	9.8	14.8	14.8
10× PCR Buffer	2.5	2.5	2.5	2.5	2.5	2.5
25 mM MgCl$_2$	3.0	3.0	3.0	3.0	3.0	3.0
dNTP Mix	2	2	2	2	2	2
50× ROX	0.5	0.5	0.5	0.5	0.5	0.5
GAPDH Primer Pair	1	–	1	–	1	–
AR Primer	–	1	–	1	–	1
GAPDH Probe	1	–	1	–	1	–
AR	–	1	–	1	–	1
SuperTaq (5 U/µl)	0.2	0.2	0.2	0.2	0.2	0.2

* Armored RNA

Set cycling parameters for the ABI 7900HT:

> 94°C (5 minutes);
> 40 cycles;
> 94°C (20 seconds);
> 60°C (40 seconds);

17.3.4 Data Analysis

The real-time amplification data were plotted for both GAPDH and the Armored RNA control. A plot of the threshold cycle (C_t) against cell concentration was linear up to 2,500 cells/µl with GAPDH (**Plate 17.1**). GAPDH signal was detected at 5,000 and 10,000 cells/µl but inhibition of the RT-PCR by these cell concentrations was observed. The C_t values were higher for the Armored RNA control at these cell concentrations compared to the lower cell concentrations (**Fig. 17.1**). The signals from the Armored RNA control was constant from cell lysate concentrations less than 2,500 cells/µl.

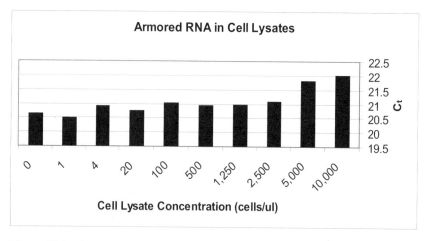

Figure 17.1. The results of the Armored RNA experiment to find an optimal, maximum concentration of cell lysate for the Cells-to-cDNA II process with HeLa cells. The Armored RNA concentration is the same for each cell concentration. The increase in C_t values evident at 10,000 and 5,000 cells/µl indicates that there was some inhibition from the lysates at these concentrations. The optimal cell concentration is therefore 2,500 cells/µl.

The cDNA synthesis reactions that did not include MMLV-RT [the RT(–) control] did not generate PCR signal indicating that the genomic

DNA was degraded to undetectable levels and that signals produced by RT-PCR are attributable solely to the amplification of the cDNA.

17.4. Notes

Note 1

Cells-to-cDNA II includes an endogenous primer pair used to amplify β-actin from human, mouse, or rat RNA samples. To use this endogenous primer pair, add 1 μl of the primers to the PCR reaction. This will yield a PCR product that is 294 base pairs. The β-actin primers function with all the cell lines that we tested including including HeLa S3 (human cervical adenocarcinoma), 3T3 (Swiss mouse embryo fibroblast), MCF-7 (human mammary gland adenocarcinoma), K-562 (human chronic myelogenous leukemia), and J-558 (mouse plasmacytoma).

Note 2

The use of real-time PCR has become a convenient way to quantify RNA by RT-PCR. Cells-to-cDNA II is well suited for real-time PCR in either a one-step or two-step RT-PCR assay. Many methods for real-time PCR are available including TaqMan probes, molecular beacons, and SYBR Green I. The method described in this chapter is with the use of a TaqMan probe. The use of a TaqMan probe requires the design of primers and probes specific for each target. Contact Ambion (techserv@ambion.com) to obtain sequences for primers and probes used in this chapter.

Note 3

The initial 75°C incubation is absolutely critical in obtaining reliable data. If your reactions produce no signal or PCR product, then confirm that the actual temperature of the sample reaches 75°C during the cell lysis step. The temperature of the heat supply will need to be adjusted accordingly. For example, we have found that it is necessary to set a heating tile to between 85 and 95°C when using a flat-bottom, 96-well plate to insure that the sample temperature reaches 75°C. We have also found that some thermocyclers do not reach the temperature indicated and have been the cause of failed reactions. Monitor incubator temperatures with a calibrated thermometer when possible! Negative results using Cells-to-cDNA II can often be explained by the improper heating of the sample.

Note 4

The duration of the Cells-to-cDNA process can be substantially decreased by eliminating the DNase I treatment. Designing PCR primers that only amplify the cDNA and not the genomic DNA usually enables this strategy. This may be accomplished by designing the primers that span one or more introns found in the genomic sequence and not in the cDNA sequence. However, some genes do not have introns or there are pseudogenes that can be amplified and therefore, this strategy will be void. To confirm that a gene does not have pseudo-genes, try amplifying the genomic DNA and cDNA with the specially designed primers. If the genomic DNA generates a PCR product the same size as the cDNA, then there is at least one pseudogene. If the PCR product amplified from the genomic DNA is substantially larger than the cDNA, then this strategy should be feasible because the shorter PCR product generated from the cDNA will be amplified in preference to the larger genomic DNA product. To confirm this, after performing RT-PCR using a cell lysate without DNase I treatment, fractionate the products in an agarose gel. If only the product from the cDNA is visible, then this strategy is feasible.

Note 5

Cellular or genomic DNA contamination can produce false positive results in RT-PCR. To eliminate genomic DNA, a DNase I treatment after cell lysis is performed. For each sample, an RT-minus control should be run in which no reverse transcriptase is added to the reverse transcription reaction. If genomic contamination continues to be a prob-lem even after the DNase I treatment, it may be necessary to double the

DNase concentration or perform the DNase I incubation on a shaker as the lysates can be viscous at high cell concentrations.

Note 6

Cells-to-cDNA II is easily adaptable to one-step RT-PCR.[3] In these reactions, the reverse transcription reaction is coupled with the PCR to make a one-tube, one-buffer system that greatly reduces the overall time to perform RT-PCR and increases convenience. The RT buffer supplied with the kit is compatible with both reverse transcriptase and *Taq* DNA polymerase. To perform these reactions, a 25-μl reaction is assembled on ice as follows:

- 2.5 μl   10× RT Buffer;
- 4 μl   dNTP Mix;
- 1 μl   RNase Inhibitor;
- 1 μl   MMLV-RT;
- 1 μl   Gene specific primer mix (10 μM each);
- 0.2 μl   *Taq* Polymerase (5 U/μl);
- 5 μl   Cell lysate;
- To 25 μl Nuclease-free water.

Set a thermocycler to perform a 15-minute incubation at 42°C to produce the cDNA by reverse transcriptase and then set the PCR temperature profile to follow.

Note 7

Laser Capture Microdissection (LCM) is a powerful technique for isolating small numbers of specific cells for gene expression.[4] Generally, 5–10 μm frozen sections of a specific tissue such as mouse kidney are embedded with OCT medium then fixed and stained with Hematoxylin and Eosin. LCM samples are captured using a system such as the PixCell™ (Arcturus). With this system the cells are captured to a plastic cap. For Cells-to-cDNA II, the plastic layer on the LCM cap is lifted with a pair of tweezers, added directly to the Cell Lysis Buffer and then subjected to the Cells-to-cDNA II procedure. We have used sections of mouse kidney as large as 1 mm² in Cells-to-cDNA II successfully.

Note 8

Fluorescence activated cell sorting (FACS) is a technique for isolating pure cell populations down to a single cell for gene expression studies.[5] In this method, cells are sorted according to biochemical or molecular markers that are specific to one cell type. Cells can be sorted by FACS directly into a PCR plate that is preloaded with as little as 4 µl of Cell Lysis Buffer. The plate can then be heated in a PCR machine to 75°C for 10 minutes and, the lysate can then be DNase I treated according to the Cells-to-cDNA II protocol. This lysate is then ready to be used directly in a reverse transcription reaction or one-step RT-PCR.

Note 9

The streamlining of RT-PCR with Cells-to-cDNA II makes it well suited for high-throughput applications. Cells-to-cDNA II has been automated using robotic platforms including the BioMek 2000 (Beckman) and the MultiPROBE II (PerkinElmer Life Sciences). The programs for both platforms can be directly downloaded from the Ambion website (www.ambion.com). **Fig. 17.2** shows the reproducibility of running a 96-well plate on an automated platform such as the BioMek2000. The final cell lysate concentration should be kept below 2,500 cells/µl. This means that the final cell number should not exceed 250,000 cells per well for a 96-well plate with 100 µl of lysis buffer.

Note 10

The fixation of cells with such fixatives as formalin may be desired if the processing of cells and reverse transcription cannot be performed shortly after one another. For example, cells should be fixed before sorting by FACS.

Formalin fixation is generally performed with 1–10% formalin in PBS at 4°C for 1 to 24 hours. By fixing the cells, RNases are inactivated and the RNA expression profile is preserved without actually lysing the cells. Prior to the addition of Cell Lysis Buffer, wash the fixed cells at least twice with PBS to remove formalin from any downstream applications. The cells can then be used with the Cells-to-cDNA protocol.

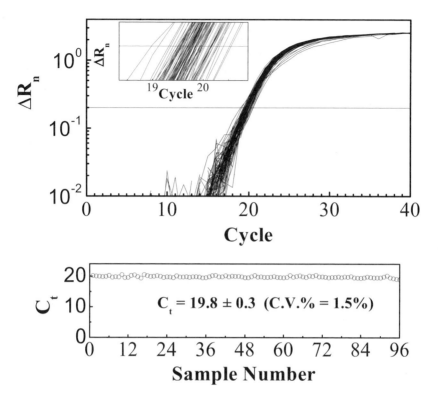

Figure 17.2. Reproducibility of Cells-to-cDNA II on an automated platform. 5,000 HeLa S3 cells were plated in each well of a 96-well tissue culture plate and grown overnight at 37°C. The plate was placed on the BioMek 2000 (Beckman) platform and then an automated protocol was started that performed the cell washing, cell lysis, DNase I treatment and the DNase I inactivation of the Cells-to cDNA II procedure. The last step involved the assembly of the single-step RT-PCR reactions for GAPDH. The reactions were then transferred manually to the ABI 7900 HT to run the RT-PCR. Similar results are also obtained using the MultiPROBE II (PerkinElmer Life Sciences).

References

1. O'Leary TJ: **Reducing the impact of endogenous ribonucleases on reverse transcription-PCR assay systems.** *Clin Chem* **1999**, 45:449–450.

2. Pasloske BL, WalkerPeach CR, Obermoeller RD, Winkler M, DuBois DB: **Armored RNA technology for the production of ribonuclease resistant viral RNA controls and standards.** *J Clin Microbiol* 1998, **36**:3590–3594.

3. Monpoeho S, Dehee A, Mignotte B, Schwartzbrod L, Marechal V, Nicolas JC, Billaudel S, Ferre V: **Quantification of enterovirus RNA in sludge samples using single tube real-time RT-PCR.** *Biotechniques* 2000, **29**:88–93.

4. Fink L, Kinfe T, Stein MM, Ermet L, Hanze J, Kummer W, Seeger W, Bohle RM: **Immunostaining and laser-assisted cell picking for mRNA analysis.** *Laboratory Invest* 2000, **80**:327–333.

5. Oselin K, Mrozikiewicz PM, Pahkla R, Roots I: **Quantitative determination of the human MRP1 and MRP2 mRNA expression in FACS-sorted peripheral blood CD4+, CD8+, CD19+, and CD56+.** *Eur J Haematol* 2003, **71**:119–123.

18

Optimization of Single and Multiplex Real-Time PCR

**Marni Brisson, Shannon Hall,
R. Keith Hamby, Robert Park,
and Hilary K. Srere**

Abstract

Real-time PCR has become the tool of choice for many researchers studying gene expression, allelic discrimination, viral load as well as many other applications. The goal of this chapter is to help the researcher understand and optimize real-time PCR reactions, both singleplex and multiplex, in order to have the highest confidence in the final data obtained with real-time PCR.

18

Optimization of Single and Multiplex Real-Time PCR

Marni Brisson,[‡] S. Hall,[†] R. Keith Hamby,[†] Robert Park,[†] and Hilary K. Srere[†]

[†]Bio-Rad Laboratories, Hercules, California
[‡]University of Pittsburgh School of Medicine, Department of Pharmacology, Pittsburgh, Pennsylvania

18.1. Introduction

Multiplex PCR is the amplification of more than one target in a single reaction tube. Successful multiplexing is not a simple matter of combining all primers and templates in the same tube because amplification of any one target can influence the amplification of the other targets. However, with careful experimental design and optimization of reaction conditions, the simultaneous amplification of up to twenty targets is achievable. Design and optimization are particularly important for multiplexed real-time PCR applications in which the reaction kinetics are monitored throughout the course of the experiment. Depending on the type of real-time PCR instrumentation chosen, it is possible to amplify and quantify as many as four targets in the same reaction tube. The goal of multiplex optimization for real-time PCR is to demonstrate that the results obtained in the multiplex experiment are identical to the results obtained from separate individual reactions. Optimization of each individual reaction before combining it into a multiplex reaction is necessary. In this chapter, strategies for design and optimization of both individual and multiplex real-time PCR reactions are presented. Data demonstrating the simultaneous amplification of four targets from genomic DNA in a single tube and the quantitative amplification of two targets when the starting concentrations differ by ten million fold will also be presented.

18.1.1. Why Multiplex?

There are a number of reasons, both practical and scientific, that might compel one to multiplex. These include limited quantities of starting tissue, or limited accessibility to samples. Multiplexing reduces the handling of samples and the opportunities for laboratory contamination; in addition, laboratory throughput can be increased, and reagent costs concomitantly reduced.

The detection of pathogens is an application in which multiplexing is valuable. Multiplexing can be used to amplify a control target within each sample reducing concerns about false-negatives or to detect multiple pathogens in a single sample. Similarly, researchers detecting known single nucleotide polymorphisms (SNPs) can identify multiple polymorphisms with a single sample or use multiple probes (i.e., one probe for wild type and one or more others for any mutants) to unambiguously assign genotypes.[1]

In gene expression analysis done by RT-PCR, PCR amplification follows a cDNA synthesis step and the amount of starting message is inferred either by endpoint analysis (e.g., Northern blot) or, more accurately, by real-time quantification. In either case, the gene of interest is quantified in comparison to another reference or housekeeping gene thought to be expressed at a relatively constant level. Though the PCR reactions can be carried out in separate reaction tubes, when the two targets are amplified in the same tube, concerns about using the same amount of cDNA starting template and any other potential differences in the reaction conditions, are relieved. For example, the carryover of some trace inhibitor from the template preparation will be reflected in both amplifications in a multiplex reaction and not necessarily found uniformly in the separate ones.

18.2. Getting Started—Proper Laboratory Technique

18.2.1. Avoiding Contamination

1. Proper laboratory technique is an important and sometimes overlooked step toward successful multiplexing. While contamination is always a concern with PCR, the effects are more pronounced in real-time PCR, resulting in inaccurate quantification of target concentration. There are several ways to avoid this type of contamination: workstations should be wiped down with dilute solutions of bleach or with commercially available decontamination solutions, pipettes should be cleaned often with a dilute solution of bleach and frequent changing of gloves during sample preparation can also prevent carryover of contaminating nucleic acids.

2. Samples should be prepared in a designated clean room, hood or bench-top workstation equipped with a UV lamp, separate from the location of the instrument. Take care to avoid contaminating these areas with plasmids or amplicons. Post-amplification samples should never be brought into the clean room. This can be accomplished by providing separate areas for preparing samples and for running and analyzing reactions.

3. There are laboratory supplies that reduce the potential for contamination during reaction assembly. These include screw-cap tubes, aerosol-barrier pipette tips, and hot-start DNA polymerases. Screw-cap tubes prevent spraying of reagents and template when opening and closing reaction tubes. Aerosol-barrier tips provide protection against pipette contamination. Hot-start polymerases prevent indiscriminate amplification before the start of the PCR reaction.

18.2.2. Improving Reliability

In order to minimize statistical variation in experimental results, samples and standards (if any) should all be analyzed in replicate. Reactions should be prepared from master mixes, which are further subdivided into submaster mixes for each set of replicate samples. Ideally, pipette only once into each well or sample tube. All reagents should be aliquoted appropriately to reduce repetitive freezing and thawing. Finally, to ensure that contamination is not present, no-template controls should always be included in the analysis.

18.3. Designing Probes for Multiplexing

18.3.1. Types of Probes

Multiplexing requires a specific fluorescently labeled probe or primer for each target or allelic variant. There are both linear probes (e.g., TaqMan) and probes with secondary structure (e.g., Molecular Beacons) used either for quantification (sensitivity) or for detecting a particular nucleotide sequence, deletion, or insertion (specificity). The ultimate use of the probe must be taken into consideration when specifying the probe sequence and length. There are also real-time PCR strategies that employ labeled primers with secondary structure (e.g., Scorpions). Each probe or primer strategy has advantages and disadvantages, but theoretically any of them can be used to carry out multiplex PCR so long as the probes or primers can be labeled with distinct fluorophores. The tactics for optimization presented in this chapter are universal and can be applied to any detection approach. In practice, linear probes for either sensitivity or specificity are typically simpler to design and sometimes simpler to manufacture, though there are several software packages available to aid in design of all types of probes and primers.

18.3.2. Reporters and Quenchers

Reporter fluorophores should be selected so that the individual emission spectra have minimal overlap. Multicolor real-time PCR instruments such as the iCycler iQ®, use pure dye calibration data to separate fluorescent measurements into the individual contributions of each fluorophore. The more distinct the emission spectra and the less overlap of signal, the more robust the spectral analysis. The effects of incorrect calibrations, small variations in illumination due to light-source aging, or slight disparities resulting from different probe syntheses will be minimized. For example, separating the emission signals from FAM-labeled (Em_{max} = 520 nm) and TET-labeled (Em_{max} = 536 nm) probes is more vulnerable to inaccurate calibration than when the TET-labeled probe is replaced by a Texas Red-labeled (Em_{max} = 603 nm) one. For a four-color multiplex reaction, probes labeled with the following fluorophores provide high signal intensities with the minimal spectral overlap:

Emission Max (nm)	
FAM	520
HEX	556
Texas Red	603
Cy5	667

We have also successfully used the combination of FAM, HEX, TAMRA (Em_{max} = 568 nm), and Texas Red.

Fluorescent signal intensity is another important factor when choosing fluorophores for probes. Fluorophores with high quantum efficiencies are preferred because they will provide a strong signal in the reaction. Fluorophores with low quantum efficiencies should be avoided.

Quenchers for linear probes can be either fluorescent moieties (e.g., TAMRA) or so-called "dark" molecules (e.g., Black Hole Quenchers). Dark quenchers dissipate the energy received from the reporter as heat without emitting fluorescence. In most applications, the dark quenchers are preferable to the fluorescent ones. The combination of high quantum efficiency reporters and dark quenchers provide excellent signal-to-noise ratios over a wide spectral range. This allows higher sensitivity for quantification of target nucleic acids. Dark quenchers can be used as distance quenchers (linear probes) and as mechanical quenchers (Molecular Beacons). The emission from fluorescent quenchers like

TAMRA contributes to the overall background and diminishes the signal-to-noise ratio, reducing the limits of detection in quantification experiments. **Plate 18.1** shows a comparison between two probes identical in every aspect except that one is quenched by TAMRA and the other is quenched by Black Hole I. The reactions using the probe synthesized with the dark quencher reach threshold cycle significantly earlier, have more reproducible behavior, and have a much higher final fluorescence.

18.3.3. Analyzing Probe Quality

One important consideration in obtaining accurate quantitative real-time PCR data is probe quality. Even a perfectly designed probe will fail if the probe is improperly synthesized or purified. Two probes with identical sequences and identical fluorophore labels can be measurably different when synthesized by different suppliers or even at different times by the same supplier. It is recommended that aliquots of each probe be saved for direct comparisons with newly synthesized probes.

Probes will typically fail to produce a good fluorescent signal because of high background or noise. These problems arise from improper removal of uncoupled fluorescent label, low efficiency coupling, and/or poor quenching. This causes a low signal-to-noise ratio resulting in decreased sensitivity and dynamic range.

Real-time PCR instrumentation systems that allow visualization of the experimental plate, like the iCycler iQ, provide a straight-forward way to evaluate probe quality. Probe can be pipetted into a few wells of an experimental plate and the background fluorescence can be assessed by collecting plate images (e.g., **Fig. 18.1**) at different exposure times. A probe that is properly synthesized and purified will have a low background signal that will only be detected at the longest camera exposures of 640 or 1280 ms. In **Plate 18.2**, images of wells containing 100 nM of a VIC-labeled, TAMRA-quenched probe were taken at varying exposure times. At 640 ms, the signal from the VIC/TAMRA probe was completely saturated due to a high level of background. Not until the exposure time was reduced to 40 ms were unsaturated signals collected. Because of the high level of background noise, the sensitivity and dynamic range with this particular probe are compromised.

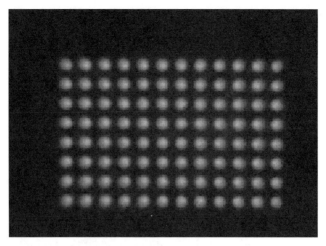

Figure 18.1. Screen shot of Imaging Services.

18.4. Standard Curves

18.4.1. Interpreting Standard Curves

Accurate quantification using real-time PCR is dependent on constructing a good standard curve. There are several ways to construct a functional standard curve. One of the most common ways is to create a dilution series with a known concentration of target (e.g., nanograms of genomic DNA or copies of plasmid DNA). Another common method is to make a serial dilution of a nonquantified sample (e.g., cDNA). The threshold cycle (C_t) for each dilution (and its replicates) is plotted against the log of the starting concentration. A best-fit linear regression line is then fit to these data. The correlation coefficient, r, and the slope of this linear regression are then calculated (**Fig. 18.2**).

The correlation coefficient (*r*) of a standard curve represents how well the actual data fit the predicted values. A significant difference in observed C_t values between replicates will lower the correlation coefficient and decrease the usefulness of the standard curve.

The ideal dilution series will result in amplification curves that are equally spaced. The spacing is determined by the equation $2^n = fold\ dilution$, where $n = C_t$ cycles apart. For example, the threshold cycles of amplifi-

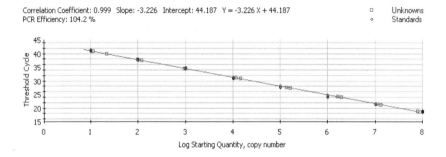

Correlation Coefficient: 0.999 Slope: -3.226 Intercept: 44.187 Y = -3.226 X + 44.187   □   Unknowns
PCR Efficiency: 104.2 %   ○   Standards

Figure 18.2. An example of a standard curve generated by real-time PCR amplification of a ten-fold serial dilution of DNA from 10^8–10^1 copies of DNA. The C_t values at each DNA dilution were plotted against the log of the starting quantity of DNA.

cation traces for a two-fold serial dilution of DNA should be separated by one cycle (i.e., $2^n = 2$, so $n = 1$. Refer to **Fig. 18.3**). If the DNA is not properly diluted or the samples are contaminated, the amplification traces will be unequally spaced resulting in an anomalous slope of the standard curve.

The slope of the standard curve can be related to the amplification efficiency of the individual target by the equation:

$$\eta = 10^{-1/\text{slope}} - 1 \, ,$$

where η is an efficiency.

The slope of the standard curve can provide useful information about the efficiency of amplification for a target. It is important to maximize and equalize amplification efficiencies, not only for multiplex reactions, but also for any type of direct comparison between samples (e.g., gene of interest relative to a housekeeping gene). A direct comparison using the $\Delta\Delta C_t$ method[2] can only be made if the efficiencies of both amplifications are equal. If the efficiencies are not equal, then a mathematical correction must be made to compare the two reactions.[3] Standard curves are important tools for accurate quantification of starting DNA amounts in both individual and multiplex reactions.

18.4.2. Proper Use of Standards

For quantification of DNA from standard curves, it is important to amplify standards and unknowns under the same reaction conditions

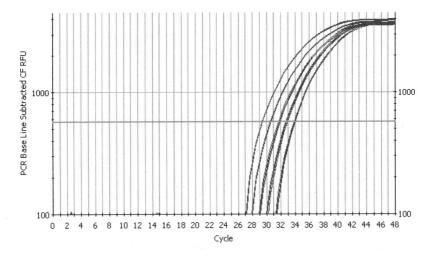

Figure 18.3. Amplification of a two-fold serial dilution of human genomic DNA from 3.2 ng to 100 pg using primers for the Factor VIII gene (300 nM of each primer). Amplification was detected with a Cy5-labeled, BH2-quenched linear probe (200 nM) specific for Factor VIII. Real-time PCR conditions: denature, 95°C × 3 min; anneal/extend 50 cycles at 95°C × 10 s, 60°C × 45 s.

and from the same source of DNA. For example, if the unknown target is amplified from genomic DNA, it is inappropriate to quantify these samples using a standard curve generated with a plasmid DNA serial dilution. Genomic DNA is a more complex target than plasmid DNA, and the thermodynamics of primer binding to genomic DNA are different than when binding to a plasmid target. The amplification efficiency and the probability of amplifying nonspecific, secondary products can vary between plasmid and genomic DNA.

Accurate determination of the concentration of the standard being used in the dilution series is also a key part in obtaining reliable quantification from the standard curve. Traditionally, DNA and RNA concentrations are determined by measuring the UV absorbance at 260 nm and 280 nm. These measurements provide only an estimate of the concentration and purity of the samples. The overall sensitivity of this method is low, especially when using lower concentrations of nucleic acids. Absorbance readings cannot distinguish single-stranded from double-stranded DNA. Since quantification of DNA by real-time PCR requires that the concentrations of each standard must be accurate, DNA and RNA samples should be quantified using a nucleic acid-specific dye-binding assay (e.g., Hoechst dye or PicoGreen® for double-stranded DNA) and a fluorimeter. Additionally, RNA quality and amount can be accurately assessed and quantitated with the Agilent 2100 Bioanalyzer or with the NanoDrop spectrophotometer. Both instruments use microliter volumes for quantitation.

Finally, as with standard curves for any assay type (e.g., protein determination assay), the unknown samples must fall within the range of the curve itself. A standard curve with a dynamic range of 10^9 to 10^5 copies should not be used to determine unknown DNA concentrations less than 10^5 or more than 10^9 copies.

In summary, reaction conditions should be optimized for individual targets, producing the best quality standard curve, in order to accurately quantify unknown samples both in individual and multiplex reactions.

18.5. Optimizing Individual Reactions before Multiplexing

To ensure that quantification of targets does not differ if the analysis is performed individually or in a multiplex reaction, each individual PCR must be optimized before it can be analyzed in a multiplex reaction. Optimization of individual reactions can be achieved by maximizing amplification efficiency while ensuring specificity of the primers and probes for each target.

18.5.1. Definition of Efficiency

Maximum efficiency is necessary for accurate quantification of DNA over a wide range of concentrations. The efficiency of a PCR is related to the slope of the standard curve by the following equation:

$$\text{Efficiency} = (10^{-1/\text{slope}^*}) - 1 \, ,$$

where *slope is derived from a graph of C_t values versus log starting concentration.

A slope of -3.32 indicates an amplification efficiency of 100%.

We have found that an amplification efficiency of greater than 90% is desired for each individual reaction before combining in a multiplex reaction. Efficiencies less than 90% can be the result of poor primer design. Efficiencies much greater than 100% (e.g., greater than 110%) are an indication of nonspecific amplification (e.g., primer dimers or secondary products). Individual reactions in which the efficiency has not been optimized may have an even lower efficiency in a multiplex reaction.

18.5.2. Designing Primers for Maximum Amplification Efficiency

Two main factors to consider when optimizing efficiency in a real-time PCR experiment are amplicon size and primer placement. Amplicons in real-time PCR reactions should be designed to be 100–150 bp or less. The shorter the amplicon, the higher the amplification efficiency tends to be.

The location of the primers in the template DNA will also affect efficiency. Sometimes the nature of the experiment dictates placement of the primers, as in the case of RT-PCR where it is often desirable to span the junction of two exons to ensure against amplification of contaminating genomic DNA. If at all possible, primers should be designed to hybridize to the template in locations outside of significant secondary structure. Secondary structure present within the amplicon itself can be determined using computer algorithms available through the Internet. The MFold program (http://www.bioinfo.rpi.edu/applications/mfold/old/dna/), allows the user to "fold" a DNA sequence at the annealing/extension temperature used in the PCR. This predicts the amplicon secondary structure at the temperature at which the primers will hybridize to the target sequence. An example of how secondary structure in the amplicon affects amplification efficiency is shown in **Plate 18.3A**. The reverse primer in this example hybridizes in a region of significant secondary structure in the amplicon. When a dilution series is amplified with this primer set, an amplification efficiency of only 66.3% is obtained (**Plate 18.3B**). When the reverse primer is placed in a different location of the amplicon (**Plate 18.3C**) and the same dilution series is amplified, the efficiency of the reaction increases dramatically. During the first round of amplification, the reverse primer still binds in an area of secondary structure in the target DNA. However, this reaction will produce a linear amplicon without secondary structure in the second and subsequent rounds of amplification, allowing the reverse primer to easily hybridize to its target (**Plate 18.3D**).

18.5.3. Designing Primers for Maximum Specificity

PCR amplification efficiency is also influenced by the specificity of the primers. Primers should be designed with the intent of amplifying a unique target. Nonspecific binding of primers can cause amplification of secondary products. Primers can also hybridize to one another, resulting in the formation of primer dimers. Any type of nonspecific product formation, including primer dimers, reduces the amplification efficiency of the specific product.

Primer dimers are deleterious because they directly compete for reagents in the amplification reaction. Primer dimers not only affect the efficiency of amplification of the specific target, but they affect it in a concentration-dependent manner. Lower starting DNA concentrations are more significantly affected by primer dimer formation than higher DNA concentrations. When high amounts of target DNA are present (more than 2,000 copies in the example below), the template DNA is able to compete with primer-dimer formation. While with low amounts of starting template DNA, the primer-dimer formation occurs more readily, competing for reaction components while depleting the available primers for amplification of the target gene.

Many software and Internet programs are available to assist in designing primers with the lowest probability of primer-dimer formation. Avoiding runs of the same nucleotide (e.g., GGG), particularly at the 3' ends of the primers helps to prevent primer-dimer formation. Once a primer pair has been chosen, it is important to check the specificity of this pair against the template sequence. The BLAST (Basic Local Alignment Search Tool) program provided by the NIH (http://www.ncbi.nlm.nih.gov/BLAST/) is a powerful means for evaluating primer sequences. The primer sequences are compared to the other DNA sequences in the database or the user may import sequences using a Genbank accession number. Primers chosen to amplify an individual target can be compared to the other DNA templates that will be used in a multiplex reaction to ensure that each primer set only amplifies its intended target. BLAST is also a good tool to verify the specificity of the probe sequences chosen to detect each target.

Plate 18.4 shows the importance of eliminating primer dimers from real-time PCR experiments. A set of primers was designed to amplify the IL1-beta gene from plasmid DNA. A five-fold dilution series of plasmid DNA from 10,000 to 16 copies was analyzed. The amplification plot reveals that the replicates for each dilution are spread and it is difficult to resolve one dilution from the next. Only the two highest DNA concentrations can be resolved. The standard curve shows a poor correlation coefficient ($r = 0.937$) and the efficiency is 152% (**Plate 18.4 inset**). Efficiencies in excess of 100% (110% and higher) can indicate the presence of nonspecific products. The amplification was followed by a melting curve analysis[4] to determine the number of products (**Fig. 18.4**). Looking at the two highest DNA concentrations, only one product peak is detected at a melting temperature (T_m) of 89°C (**Fig. 18.4A and B**). The lower concentration reactions revealed two major product peaks with T_m values of 89°C and 78°C (**Fig. 18.4C**). An amplified product with a low T_m can indicate the presence of primer dimers. The no-template control was also analyzed, and (**Fig. 18.4D**) a large amount of product was present with the same T_m of 78°C. Gel electrophoresis performed on these samples confirmed that the secondary product present in these amplifications was indeed primer dimers (data not shown).

It has been suggested that when primer dimers are known to be present, fluorescent monitoring should be done at a temperature above which the primer dimers are melted, but the specific target amplicons are still intact.[5] **Plate 18.5** shows the same experiment performed as described in **Plate 18.4**, with the exception that the data were collected at a temperature at which the primer dimers are denatured (82°C). Only the specific product should be detected at this temperature. There is an improvement in the amplification efficiency ($\eta = 90\%$) because the reporter fluorescence is no longer skewed by the primer-dimers in the reaction, however, the standard curve still shows a poor correlation coefficient ($r = 0.953$, **Plate 18.5 inset**). There is still spread in the replicates and the dilutions are still poorly resolved on the standard curve. These results suggest that even when primer-dimers do not contribute to the measured fluorescence, their presence still impacts the amplification reaction by competing for reaction components and the impact varies from tube to tube, depending on the amount of starting template present. The proper solution to primer-dimer formation is to redesign the

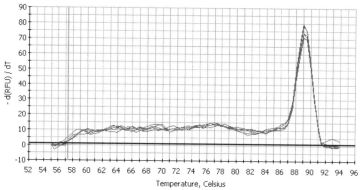

A

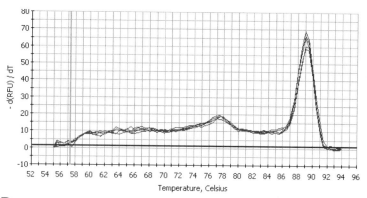

B

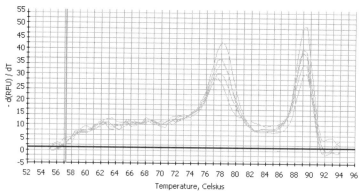

C

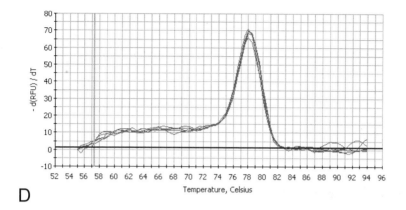

D

Figure 18.4. Melting curves (95°C to 55°C) generated from the amplifications in Plate 18.4. At the highest concentrations of plasmid DNA (10,000 copies), only one major amplified product was detected with a T_m of 89°C (**A**). The same product was detected with 2,000 copies of DNA, as well as a small amount of a secondary product at a T_m of 77°C (**B**). At lower DNA concentrations (400 copies), a 1:1 ratio of each product was detected (**C**). The appearance of amplified product at the T_m of 77°C in the no-template controls (**D**).

primers to eliminate the dimers. In this case, shifting the primer-binding site by a few bases eliminated them, resulting in tight replicates, a clear dilution series and an accurate standard curve (r = 1.000, η = 101%, **Plate 18.6**).

18.5.4. Equalizing Amplification Efficiencies

We have observed that when combining targets that amplify with disparate efficiencies into a multiplex reaction, the differences in efficiency become exaggerated. The gene targets with the highest amplification efficiencies compete more efficiently for the reaction components than the lower efficiency target amplifications (data not shown). In order to make valid comparisons over a wide dynamic range, the efficiencies of the individual reactions must be approximately equivalent.

Plate 18.7A shows the standard curves from four individual targets amplified in a multiplex real-time PCR. The upper trace has a distinctly different amplification efficiency than the other three targets in the reaction as judged by its slope. The differences in threshold cycle between the top trace and any of the other traces at the same starting template concentration is not constant across the entire range of input. This makes it impossible to confidently make conclusions about the relative expression levels based solely on threshold cycles - the only comparisons that can be made are when standard curves are constructed and absolute quantification is determined. In this experimental system, the reactions were optimized to balance the efficiencies, making it possible to make comparisons regardless of the input target concentrations (**Plate 18.7B**).

18.6. Optimization of Multiplex Reactions

The steps described previously are essential for optimizing individual reactions, however, further strategies may still be required when combining the reactions in a multiplex assay. A common challenge for multiplex real-time PCR combines targets of significantly different concentrations. This is typical of gene expression studies when comparing a gene of interest to a control gene.

18.6.1. Comparing Individual and Multiplexed Reactions

It is important to compare multiplex amplification results to the results from the individual reaction. The most important factor in comparing these results is to ensure that there is no significant difference in the observed threshold cycle (**Plate 18.8A and B**). Differences detected in the level of fluorescence at the end of the amplification are not significant since final fluorescence values are not used for quantitative analysis.

18.6.2. Optimizing Reaction Conditions

There are two strategies for optimizing the multiplex reaction: increasing concentrations of reaction components (e.g., polymerase, dNTPs, and magnesium) or limiting the primer concentrations for the targets that are present in excess. An example of each approach is presented below.

Two example assays are presented below to demonstrate the application of the first strategy. In the first example assay, samples with 10^5–10^2 copies of GAPDH were amplified alone and compared with a multiplex reaction where the same GAPDH concentrations were coamplified in the presence of a high concentration of alpha-tubulin (10^9 copies). The GAPDH amplification was undetectable in all dilutions when coamplified with α-tubulin using 300 nM of each primer and 200 μM of each probe in a 1× concentration of a commercially available supermix consisting of 1.25 U of *Taq* polymerase, 3 mM of Mg^{2+}, and 200 nM of each dNTP in a 50 μl reaction. (**Plate 18.9A**). The alpha-tubulin reaction proceeds at maximum efficiency, consuming the available reagents resulting in the GAPDH reactions proceeding at very poor efficiencies. When the polymerase, dNTPs, and Mg^{2+} concentrations were increased to 2.5 U, 400 μM of each, and 4 mM, respectively, the GAPDH signal was detected in all of the dilutions of DNA (**Plate 18.9B**). However, the analysis revealed a suboptimal correlation coefficient ($r = 0.988$) and a low amplification efficiency ($\eta = 79.4\%$) (**Plate 18.9B inset**). When the concentrations of these reaction components were further increased to 3.5 U of polymerase, 450 μM of each dNTP and 5 mM of Mg^{2+}, the re-sults demonstrated an optimal standard curve ($r = 0.999$, $\eta = 99\%$) (**Plate 18.9C and inset**).

In the second example assay, GAPDH, α-tubulin, Factor VIII, and IL1-beta are coamplified in a single reaction. The amplification efficiencies for each target had previously been maximized and equalized to approximately 95%. Upon combining these targets in a multiplex reaction, a significant difference in the threshold cycles was observed when compared to the results of the individual reactions. The initial reaction mix contained: 500 ng of genomic DNA, 300 nM of each primer, and 200 nM of each probe in a 1× concentration of a commercially available supermix (consisting of 1.25 U of *Taq* polymerase, 3 mM of Mg^{2+}, and 200 nM of each dNTP in a 50-μl reaction). To obtain optimized multiplex results (**Fig. 18.5**), it was necessary to optimize the concentrations of the components of the reaction mix for the multiplex reaction in the same manner as above.

Increasing the concentrations of the reagents makes it possible to achieve quantitative data in multiplex reactions. The amount of reagent needed for each multiplex experiment is dependent on the number of targets to be amplified, the concentration differences between the individual targets, and the amount of template. Reaction components should be optimized each time an individual target is changed in a multiplex reaction.

It is also possible to achieve optimized multiplex reactions by limiting the primers for one or more targets. For comparison, the first assay was optimized by titrating the concentration of the alpha-tubulin primers. Observed threshold cycles and the resulting standard curve for each titration were compared to the results of the GAPDH reactions alone. The optimal α-tubulin primer concentrations were determined to be 25 nM each. All of these amplifications were done using 1× concentrations of all reagents without supplementation (**Plate 18.10**).

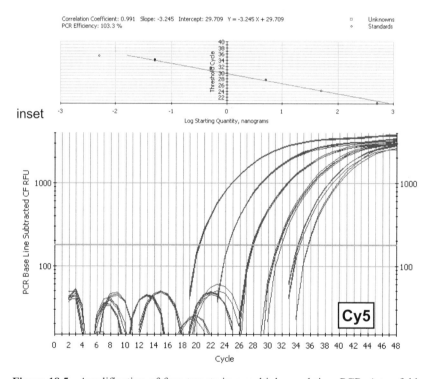

Figure 18.5. Amplification of four targets in a multiplex real-time PCR. A ten-fold dilution series (500 ng—5 pg) of human genomic DNA and primers (300 nM each) designed to specifically amplify Factor VIII, IL1-β, GAPDH, and α-tubulin. Amplification of each target was detected by specific linear probes (200 nM each): FAM–Factor VIII–BH1, HEX–GAPDH–BH2, Texas Red–IL1-β–BH2, and Cy5-α–tubulin–BH2. Real-time PCR conditions: denature, 95°C × 3 min; anneal/extend 50 cycles of 95°C × 10 s, 60°C × 45 s.

Fig.18.5 continued on next pages.

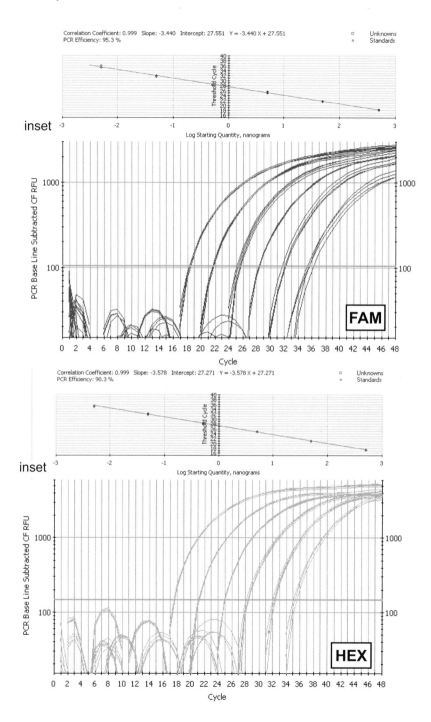

inset

inset

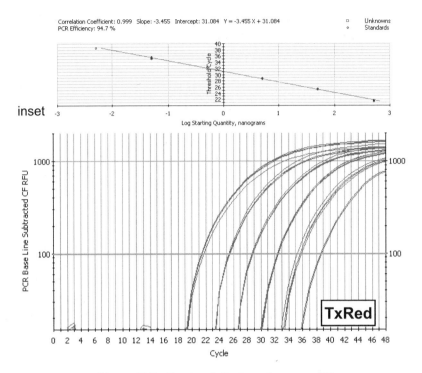

Figure 18.5. *Continued. See legend on page 638.*

Though reducing the concentration of the α-tubulin primers produced the same results seen when increasing the reagent concentrations, there may be disadvantages to the limiting primers technique. The complexity of achieving the optimal balance in primer concentrations increases as the number of targets in the multiplex assay increases. In this example, it was more difficult to get reproducible results with the limiting primer strategy. Increasing reagent concentrations in the multiplex reactions is simpler and faster than trying to optimize primer concentrations, although the cost per reaction is greater. These strategies may not be mutually exclusive. If optimization proves difficult, a combination of both strategies may be necessary.

18.7. Summary

Multiplex real-time PCR offers both practical (e.g., throughput, limited handling) and scientific (e.g., quantification compared to a reference, internal controls, multipoint mutation detection) advantages. Optimal design of primers and probes is essential to successful real-time PCR and requires additional consideration when designing for multiplex real-time PCR assays. Robust and consistent fluorescent signals can be achieved via selection of reporters with minimal spectral overlap and "dark" quenchers.

Much of the appeal of real-time PCR comes from the ability to achieve quantitative evaluation of starting template material. Accurate quantification relies upon construction of a good standard curve. This can be derived from known concentrations of target or from serial dilutions of a reference sample. It is important to amplify standards and unknown samples using the same reaction conditions and the same source of DNA.

Reactions should be optimized individually prior to combining in a multiplex. This is achieved by maximizing amplification efficiency while ensuring specificity of the primers and probes for each target. Equalization of efficiencies of individual assays that will be multiplexed ensures more accurate relative quantification. Establishment of consistent efficiency is an alternative solution when equalization is not possible.

Once targets are combined into a multiplex reaction, the results of the individual and multiplex reactions for each target should be compared to ensure that the reaction efficiency of each target is not affected by the multiplex.

It is not uncommon to find that reaction efficiencies are affected by multiplexing. In this case, two strategies exist to ameliorate the differences in efficiencies. The first strategy is to increase the concentration of the reaction components to ensure availability of components for each target. This strategy increases the costs of each reaction but requires very little time to implement, making it suitable for optimizing assays. The second strategy is to limit the primer concentration of the more abundant target. This strategy requires a commitment of several assays to titrate primer concentrations, may not be as reproducible over time, and the complexity of the optimization increases as more targets are added to the multiplex reaction. However, it could result in lower costs per assay once titration of the primer concentrations is complete. The appropriate strategy to follow is dependent on the assay and the individual goals of the researcher.

References

1. Ugozzoli LA, Chinn D, Hamby K: **Fluorescent multicolor multiplex homogeneous assay for the simultaneous analysis of the two most common hemochromatosis mutations.** *Anal Biochem* 2002, **307**:47–53.

2. Livak KJ, Schmittgen TD: **Analysis of relative gene expression data using real-time quantitative PCR and the 2(-delta delta C(T)) method.** *Methods* 2001, **25**:402–408,.

3. Pfaffl MW: **A new mathematical model for relative quantification in real-time RT-PCR.** *Nucleic Acids Res* 2001, **29**:E45.

4. Ririe KM, Rasmussen RP, Wittwer CT: **Product differentiation by analysis of DNA melting curves during the polymerase chain reaction.** *Anal Biochem* 1997, **245**:154–160.

5. Morrison TB, Weis JJ, Wittwer CT: **Quantification of low-copy transcripts by continuous SYBR Green I monitoring during amplification.** *Biotechniques* 1998, **24**:954–958, 960, 962.

19

Evaluation of Basic Fibroblast Growth Factor mRNA Levels in Breast Cancer

Pamela Pinzani, Carmela Tricarico, Lisa Simi, Mario Pazzagli, and Claudio Orlando

Abstract

bFGF has been studied extensively as having a potential role as an epithelial mitogen in a variety of human cancers. We developed a quantitative real-time RT-PCR assay based on the TaqMan technology to quantify bFGF mRNA levels in tumor samples. We used this technique to measure bFGF gene expression in a series of 73 unilateral invasive primary breast tumor RNAs and in the adjacent non-neoplastic tissues. bFGF mRNA was detected in all sample tissues analyzed, with mRNA levels significantly higher in adjacent normal tissue (median 7.03×10^7 molecules/µg total RNA; range 1.1×10^{12}) compared with cancer samples (median 2.4×10^7 molecules/µg total RNA; range 4.2×10^{10}; $p < 0.005$). Results of real-time RT-PCR measurements were analyzed on the basis of the clinical features of the patients involved in the study. Node-positive tumors show a significant decrease of bFGF levels in comparison to both the adjacent normal tissue ($p < 0.05$) and the node-negative tumor samples ($p < 0.005$). In less differenziated cancers (G3), a significant decrease of bFGF mRNA expression was found in tumor tissue in comparison to the adjacent normal tissue ($p < 0.01$). We also determined, on a subset of 63 breast cancer samples and normal tissues from the same patients, whether bFGF mRNA levels correlated with the expression levels of an other important angiogenic factor, VEGF, as determined previously using a real-time PCR method. Linear regression analysis of bFGF versus VEGF data gave a significantly positive result in normal tissue from breast cancer patients, while no correlation was found when plotting bFGF and VEGF results from tumor tissues of the same patients.

19

Evaluation of Basic Fibroblast Growth Factor mRNA Levels in Breast Cancer

Pamela Pinzani, Carmela Tricarico, Lisa Simi, Mario Pazzagli, and Claudio Orlando

Department of Clinical Physiopatology, Clinical Biochemistry Unit, University of Florence, Florence, Italy

19.1. Introduction

Angiogenesis plays an important role in the growth, progression, and metastasis of solid tumors.[1] The switch of a tumor to the angiogenic phenotype is believed to involve a change in the local equilibrium between angiogenic inducers.[2] Many angiogenic factors have been described in the last years.[3] Some of the best-understood and most important ones are vascular endothelial growth factor (VEGF), acidic and basic fibroblast growth factor (bFGF), and platelet-derived endothelial cell growth factor (PDECGF). bFGF belongs to a family of nine this far identified growth-regulatory proteins, which induce proliferation and differentiation of a wide range of cells of epithelial, mesodermal, and neuroectodermal origin.[4-6] It is expressed in vascular endothelium during tumor neovascularization and angioproliferative diseases and it has diverse biological functions, which include involvement in cellular growth differentiation, embryogenesis, wound healing, plasminogen activator synthesis, invasion, and angiogenesis.[6-11] Several of these functions could influence the progression of cancer by encouraging cell growth or metastasis, and FGFs have consequentely been studied in several cancers. bFGF has been studied extensively as having a potential role as an epithelial mitogen in a variety of human cancer including colonic adenocarcinoma,[12] bladder cancer,[13] rhabdomyosarcoma,[14] ovarian cancer,[15] pancreatic carcinoma,[16] renal cell carcinoma,[17] and oesophageal carcinoma.[18] However, lower levels of bFGF mRNA have been found in malignant human breast biopsies than in normal and benign breast tissues[19] and this has since been confirmed at the protein level.[20,21] Moreover, higher levels of bFGF are associated with improved overall and disease-free survivals.[21] Recently, besides the numerous conflicting reports on the effect of bFGF on cell lines growth *in vitro*, bFGF was shown to exert multiple effects when over expressed in MCF-7 cells, which may all contribute to a tumor suppression role in breast cancer.[22]

Immunohistochemistry of human breast sections[23] and analysis of mRNA and protein extracted from purified normal human breast cell populations[24] have identified the myoepithelial cell as the main source of bFGF in the breast and this cell type is lost in the progression to neoplasia, suggesting a role of myoepithelial-derived bFGF in control of epithelial cell growth. Almost all the data available on bFGF expression in tumors derive from immunohistochemistry based studies at the protein level. Northern blotting is not sensitive enough to detect low-level expression of bFGF mRNA and not accurate enough to quantify its mRNA levels. Northern blotting is also time-consuming, requires large amounts of RNA, and uses radioactive reagents which means it cannot be used routinely in laboratories. An amplification step is therefore required to determine the bFGF mRNA copy number in small amounts of tumor RNA (small early-stage tumors or cytopuncture specimens). We developed a quantitative real-time RT-PCR assay based on the

TaqMan technology to address these problems and to quantify bFGF mRNA levels in tumor samples. Quite apart from its potential to become a reference in terms of performance, accuracy, sensitivity, wide dynamic range, and high throughput capacity, this method is suited for the development of new target gene assays with a view to achieving high levels of interlaboratory standardization and yielding statistical confidence values. We used this technique to measure bFGF gene expression in a series of 73 unilateral invasive primary breast tumor RNAs and in the adjacent non-neoplastic tissues. Results of real-time RT-PCR measurements were analyzed on the basis of the clinical features of the patients involved in the study. We also determined, on a subset of 63 breast cancer samples and normal tissues from the same patients, whether bFGF mRNA levels correlated with the expression levels of an other important angiogenic factor, VEGF, as determined previously using a real-time PCR method.[25]

19.2. Materials And Methods

19.2.1. Cancer Samples

Samples of breast tissue were collected from a consecutive series of 73 patients undergoing surgery in the Surgical Department of Careggi Hospital (Florence, Italy). From each surgical specimen, a random sample was collected from the tumor mass and from the normal tissue. The sample was taken from the center of the tumor mass after dividing it at the maximum diameter. The nontumoral tissue was chosen from adjacent breast tissue after conservative treatment or from the opposite quadrant after total mastectomy. Tumor samples were examined histologically for the presence of tumor cells. A tumor sample was considered suitable for this study if the proportion of tumor cells was greater than 60%.

19.2.2. Materials

Oligonucleotide, primers and probes, and reaction kits were obtained from ABI (Foster City, Calif.). DNase was purchased from Promega (Madison, Wisc.).

19.2.3. Sample Preparation

Total RNA was extracted from surgical or bioptical specimen of the breast tumors with RNeasy Kit (Qiagen S.p.A., Milan, Italy). The concentration and purity of the RNA were determined spectrophotometrically after DNase treatment.

19.2.4. Quantitative Evaluation of bFGF mRNA Expression

i) **Oligonucleotide primers and probe.** The primers for bFGF RNA quantification for use with the ABI Prism 7700 Sequence Detection System were designed by the proprietary software Primer Express. The upstream PCR primer corresponds to the region from base 692 to base 721 (sequence, 5' GGAGTGTGTGCTAACCGTTACCTGGCTATG 3'). The reverse primer corresponds to the region from base 905 to base 934 (sequence 5' TCAGCTCTTAGCAGACATTGGAAGAAAAAG 3'). The internal oligonucleotide probe was labeled with the fluorescent dyes 5-carboxyfluorescein (FAM) on the 5' end and N,N,N', N'-tetramethyl-6-carboxyrhodamine (TAMRA) on the 3' end. The internal probe hybridizes within the 25-bp region amplified by the PCR primers and has the sequence 5'-(FAM)- CTGCCCAGTTCGTTTCAGTGCCACA-(TAMRA)-3'.

(ii) **Reverse transcription and PCR conditions.** 400 ng of total RNA was reverse-transcribed by random hexamer priming according to the ABI protocol. The PCR mixture consisted of 12.5 µl of universal master mix (ABI), primers 308 and 309 (300 mM each), 200 nM TaqMan probe in a final volume of 25 µl. Amplification and detection were performed on the ABI 7700 system with the following profile: 1 cycle of 50°C for 2 min, 1 cycle of 95°C for 10 min, and 40 cycles of 95°C for 30 s and 60°C for 1 min. The ROX signal was used to standardize the reaction.

(iii) **Standard curve.** Standard curves were generated from 10-fold serial dilutions of RNA of known starting concentration extracted from cells over expressing bFGF mRNA.

19.2.5. Statistical Analysis

Expression of bFGF mRNA in tumor samples is expressed as molecules bFGF mRNA/µg total RNA and reported as mean ± standard error of the mean (SEM). Median and range of data are also reported. Statistical analyses used SPSS software (SPSS for Windows, version 6.1.3). Significance of the differences was evaluated by nonparametric Wilcoxon pair rank and Kruscal Wallis tests.

19.3. Results

19.3.1. Intra-Assay and Inter-Assay Variability

To determine the accuracy of the assay, 10 replicates of one RNA sample extracted from a breast carcinoma tissue were reverse transcribed and amplified on three separate days. The mean C_t values, standard deviations and the coefficient of variation (CV) were calculated for each day to obtain intra-assay precision. Mean C_t values $\pm$ SD for each day were found to be 28.2 ± 0.43, 28.6 ± 0.26 and 28.8 ± 0.40 with an intra-assay precision of target amplification of 1.55, 0.92, and 1.40% CV respectively. The inter-assay variation of amplification for the three days ($n = 30$) was also calculated and found to be 1.5%.

19.3.2. Quantification of bFGF and VEGF mRNA Levels

bFGF mRNA was detected in all samples tissues analyzed, with mRNA levels significantly higher in adjacent normal tissue (median 7.03×10^7 molecules/µg of total RNA; range 1.1×10^{12}) compared with cancer samples (median 2.4×10^7 molecules/µg of total RNA; range 4.2×10^{10}); ($p < 0.005$). When bFGF expression levels in paired tumor and adjacent normal biopsies from the same patient were compared, we observed reduced or substantially unaffected expression in the tumor in most of the cases investigated (51/73; 70%). However, 22/73 samples (30%) clearly showed higher bFGF expression in tumor tissue (**Fig. 19.1**). VEGF mRNA levels were quantitated in 63 of the breast samples subjected to bFGF measurement and, as expected, higher VEGF levels were found in the tumor samples (median 4.6×10^7 molecules/µg total RNA; range 2.4×10^9) when compared to the adjacent normal tissue (median 1.3×10^7 molecules/µg total RNA; range 8.6×10^8) ($p = 0.001$).

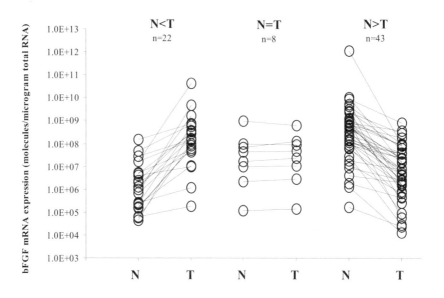

Figure 19.1. bFGF expression in breast cancer patients. bFGF mRNA levels were measured in paired tumor (T) and adjacent normal (N) biopsies from the same patient ($n = 73$).

19.3.3. Clinicopathologic Characteristics

Analysis of the bFGF result on the basis of clinicopathologic characteristics of tumors are summarized in **Table 19.1**. Biopsies from node negative cancers expressed bFGF mRNA at significantly higher levels (median 7.1×10^7 molecules/µg total RNA; range 1.3×10^4–4.2×10^{10}) than biopsies from node positive ones (7.2×10^6 molecules/µg total RNA; range 2.3×10^4–4.6×10^9; $p < 0.005$). There was no difference between menopausal status, tumor histology, grade or stage, or estrogen receptor (ER) or progesterone receptor (PGR) status.

Analysis of the VEGF mRNA results in the subset of 63 breast carcinomas revealed no significant differences based on the different clinicopathological features of the cancers. Interestingly, there was significant less VEGF mRNA in the adjacent normal tissue of patients with node-positive cancers (3.8×10^6 molecules/µg total RNA) compared with adjacent normal tissue of node-negative patients (3.2×10^7 molecules/µg total RNA); ($p < 0.005$).

Table 19.1. Analysis of bFGF mRNA expression as determined in normal (N) and neoplastic (T) breast tissue.

	n	MEDIAN (N)	RANGE	MEDIAN (T)	RANGE	p
Total	73	7.03×10^{7}	1.10×10^{12}	2.40×10^{7}	4.20×10^{10}	0.004
Menopausal status						
Pre	20	1.07×10^{8}	4.90×10^{9}	2.36×10^{7}	4.60×10^{9}	0.332
Post	53	6.20×10^{7}	1.10×10^{12}	2.40×10^{7}	4.20×10^{10}	0.008
		0.466		0.683		
Stage						
T1	48	3.65×10^{7}	1.10×10^{12}	4.70×10^{7}	4.20×10^{10}	0.070
T2	20	1.27×10^{8}	3.00×10^{9}	7.88×10^{6}	1.62×10^{9}	0.048
T3+T4	5	1.50×10^{8}	8.98×10^{8}	2.40×10^{7}	3.48×10^{8}	0.225
		0.647		0.543		
Lymphnodes						
N-	38	1.29×10^{8}	1.10×10^{12}	7.06×10^{7}	4.20×10^{10}	0.058
N+	33	6.20×10^{7}	1.04×10^{10}	7.20×10^{6}	4.60×10^{9}	0.029
		0.281		0.003		
Grading						
G1	12	8.40×10^{6}	8.60×10^{9}	3.52×10^{7}	8.10×10^{8}	0.938
G2	26	9.24×10^{7}	4.90×10^{9}	2.40×10^{7}	4.60×10^{9}	0.104
G3	35	1.08×10^{8}	1.10×10^{12}	2.40×10^{7}	4.20×10^{10}	0.009
		0.258		0.681		
Histology						
Ductal	56	9.24×10^{7}	1.10×10^{12}	2.40×10^{7}	4.60×10^{9}	0.003
Others	17	4.67×10^{7}	4.90×10^{9}	3.63×10^{7}	4.20×10^{10}	0.523
		0.917		0.855		
ER status						
ER-	17	1.60×10^{7}	1.04×10^{10}	1.12×10^{7}	7.20×10^{8}	0.287
ER+	52	9.24×10^{7}	1.10×10^{12}	3.01×10^{7}	4.20×10^{10}	0.007
		0.415		0.786		
PGR status						
PGR-	21	1.60×10^{7}	1.00×10^{10}	1.62×10^{7}	7.20×10^{8}	0.339
PGR+	46	9.99×10^{7}	1.10×10^{12}	2.40×10^{7}	4.20×10^{10}	0.008
		0.253		0.299		

Breast cancer patients with estrogen receptor positive status expressed a significantly higher level of VEGF mRNA in the tumor tissue when compared to adjacent non-neoplastic tissue (**Table 19.2**). This difference was absent between adjacent normal and tumor tissue from breast cancer patients with estrogen receptor negative status (**Table 19.2**). In contrast, in both progesterone receptor positive and negative samples there were significant differences in VEGF mRNA levels between adjacent normal and cancer biopsies (**Table 19.2**).

Table 19.2. Analysis of VEGF mRNA expression as determined in normal (N) and neoplastic (T) breast tissue.

	n	MEDIAN (N)	RANGE	MEDIAN (T)	RANGE	p
Total	63	1.30×10^7	8.60×10^8	4.60×10^7	2.40×10^9	0.001
Menopausal status						
Pre	18	1.45×10^7	8.60×10^8	5.45×10^7	2.40×10^9	0.094
Post	45	1.10×10^7	7.90×10^8	4.60×10^7	1.20×10^9	0.005
		0.229		0.970		
Stage						
T1	39	1.40×10^7	8.60×10^8	1.00×10^8	1.90×10^9	0.004
T2	20	9.85×10^6	1.80×10^8	3.20×10^7	2.40×10^9	0.030
T3+T4	4	6.65×10^7	3.80×10^8	1.38×10^7	4.30×10^8	0.593
		0.642		0.226		
Lymphonodes						
N-	30	3.15×10^7	7.90×10^8	7.35×10^7	2.40×10^9	0.096
N+	31	3.75×10^6	8.60×10^8	3.50×10^7	1.90×10^9	0.004
		0.059		0.299		
Grading						
G1	9	2.30×10^5	3.00×10^8	4.50×10^6	3.80×10^8	0.025
G2	22	3.05×10^7	8.60×10^8	3.80×10^7	1.90×10^9	0.126
G3	32	9.90×10^6	7.90×10^8	9.80×10^7	2.40×10^9	0.017
		0.050		0.109		
Histology						
Ductal	47	1.40×10^7	8.60×10^8	1.10×10^8	2.40×10^9	0.001
Others	16	5.60×10^6	4.60×10^8	2.20×10^7	7.00×10^8	0.408
		0.130		0.016		
ER status						
ER-	16	1.45×10^7	5.80×10^8	1.10×10^8	2.40×10^9	0.088
ER+	43	1.30×10^7	8.60×10^8	3.00×10^7	1.90×10^8	0.017
		0.695		0.062		
PGR status						
PGR-	18	8.88×10^6	5.80×10^8	9.80×10^7	2.40×10^9	0.035
PGR+	38	1.40×10^7	8.60×10^8	3.50×10^7	1.90×10^9	0.023
		0.299		0.207		

Linear regression analysis of bFGF versus VEGF results gave a significantly positive result in normal tissue from breast cancer patients ($r = 0.435$, $n = 63$, $p < 0.001$), while no correlation was found when plotting bFGF and VEGF results from tumor tissues of the same patients ($r = 0.175$, $n = 63$, $p = 0.170$).

19.4. Discussion

The growth and development of a cancer is not only determined by the tumor cells themselves, but also by the microenvironment including various neighboring cell types and the products they release such as growth factors and cytokines. In the normal breast, bFGF is predominantly expressed and released by myoepithelial cells,[24] which are considered to be part of the host defense against cancer,[26] whereas tumors lose their myoepithelial cells and their derived bFGF.

The present study is important because: 1) it provides a quantitative estimate of bFGF and VEGF expression in a large cohort of breast carcinomas; 2) it reports the simultaneous determination of bFGF and VEGF in tumor as well as in the neighboring normal tissue. In this study we observed a decrease in bFGF mRNA expression in tumor samples of patients affected by breast cancer when compared to the corresponding non-neoplastic tissues. The observed decrease in bFGF expression in breast cancers may partly be due to the loss of myoepithelial cells that occurs in malignant disease. *In vitro* studies on cell lines suggest that bFGF has a role in maintaining the differentiated state of the duct rather than promoting cell proliferation. This is consistent with the high levels of bFGF that we have shown to be present in the normal breast tissues. If this is the case, then loss of bFGF might lead to more aggressive tumors. In fact node-positive tumors show a significant decrease of bFGF levels in comparison to both the adjacent normal tissue and the node-negative tumor samples (**Table 19.1**). Alternatively, loss of bFGF expression may not be causal in increasing the malignancy of breast cancer cells but may be a marker of less differentiated cancers (see **Table 19.1** grading).

The positive correlation between bFGF and VEGF values in normal tissues from breast cancer patients can confirm that these angiogenic factors act synergistically, but it seems that in the neoplastic tissue this relationship is no longer valid.

References

1. Folkman J: **Clinical applications of research on angiogenesis.** *N Engl J Med* 1995, **333**:1757–1763.

2. Hahanan D, Folkman J: **Patterns and emerging mechanisms of the angiogenic switch during tumorogenesis.** *Cell* 1996, **86**:353–364.

3. Scott PAE, Harris AR: **Current approaches to targeting cancer using antiangiogenesis therapies.** *Cancer Treat Rev* 1994, **20**:393–412.

4. Gospodarowicz D, Neufeld G, Schweigerer L: **Fibroblast growth factor: Structural and biological properties.** *J Cell Physiol* 1987, **5**:15–26.

5. Basilico C, Moscatelli D: **The FGF family of growth factors and oncogenes.** *Adv Cancer Res* 1992, **59**:115–116.

6. Klagsbrun M: **The fibroblast growth factor family: Structural and biological properties.** *Prog Growth Factor Res* 1989, **1**:207–235.

7. Montesano R, Vassalli JD, Baird A, Guillemin R, Orci L: **Basic fibroblast growth factor induces angiogenesis in vitro.** *Proc Natl Acad Sci USA* 1986, **83**:7297–7301.

8. Gospodarowicz D: **Biological activities of fibroplast growth factors.** *Ann NY Acad Sci* 1991, **638**:1–8.

9. Sato Y, Rifkin DB: **Autocrine activities of basic fibroblast growth factor: Regulation of endothelial cell movement, plasminogen activator synthesis, and DNA synthesis.** *J Cell Biol* 1988, **107**:1199–1205.

10. Tsuboi R, Rifkin DB: **Recombinant basic fibroblast growth factor stimulates wound healing in healing-impaired db/db mice.** *J Exp Med* 1990, **172**:245–251.

11. Tsuboi R, Sato Y, Rifkin DB: **Correlation of cell migration, cell invasion, receptor number, proteinase production and basic fibroblast growth factor levels in endothelial cells.** *J Cell Biol* 1990, **110**:511–517.

12. New BA, Yeoman LC: **Identification of basic fibroblast growth factor sensitivity and receptor and ligand expression in human colon tumor cell lines.** *J Cell Physiol* 1992, **150**:320–326.

13. Allen LE, Mahaler PA: **Expression of basic fibroblast growth factor and its receptor in an invasive carcinoma cell line.** *J Cell Physiol* 1993, **155**:368–375.

14. Schweigerer L, Neufeld G, Mergia A, Abraham JA, Fiddes JC, Gospodarowicz D: **Basic fibroblast growth factor in human rhabdomyosarcoma cells: Implications for the proliferation and neovascularization of myoblast-derived tumors.** *Proc Natl Acad Sci USA* 1987, **84**:842–846.

15. Crickard K, Gross JL, Crickard U, Yoonessi M, Lele S, Herblin WF, Eidsvoog K: **Basic fibroblast growth factor and receptor expression in human ovarian cancer.** *Gynaecol Oncol* 1994, **55**:277–284.

16. Leung HY, Gullick WJ, Lemoine NR: **Expression and functional activity of fibroblast growth factors and their receptors in human pancreatic cancer.** *Int J Cancer* 1994, **59**:667–675.

17. Emoto N, Isozaki O, Ohmura E, Ito F, Tsushima T, Shizume K, Demura H, Toma H: **Basic fibroblast growth factor (FGF-2) in renal cell carcinoma, which is indistinguishable from that in normal kidney, is involved in renal cell carcinoma growth.** *J Urol* 1994, **152**:1626–1631.

18. Iida S, Katoh O, Tokunaga A, Terada M: **Expression of fibroblast growth factor gene family and its receptor gene family in the human upper gastrointestinal tract.** *Biochem Biophys Res Commun* 1994, **199**:1113–1119.

19. Luqmani YA, Graham M, Coombes RC: **Expression of basic fibroblast growth factor , FGFR1, and FGFR2 in normal and malignant human breast and comparison with other normal tissue.** *Br J Cancer* 1992, **66**:273–280.

20. Smith J, Yelland A, Baillie R, Coombes RC: **Acidic and basic fibroblast growth factors in human breast tissue.** *Eur J Cancer* 1994, **30A**:496–503.

21. Yiangou C, Gomm JJ, Coope RC, Law M, Luqmani YA, Shousha S, Coombes RC, · Johnston CL: **Fibroblast growth factor 2 in breast cancer: Occurrence and prognostic significance.** *Br J Cancer* 1997, **75**:28–33.

22. Liu D, Buluwela L, Ali S, Thomson S, Gomm JJ, Coombes RC: **Retroviral infection of the FGF2 gene into MCF-7 cells induces branching morphogenesis, retards cell growth and suppresses tumorigenicity in nude mice.** *Eur J Cancer* 2001, **37**:268–280.

23. Gomm JJ, Smith J, Ryall GK, Baillie R, Turnbull L, Coombes RC: **Localization of basic fibroblast growth factor and transforming growth factor beta 1 in the human mammary gland.** *Cancer Res* 1991, **51**:4685–4692.

24. Gomm JJ, Browne PJ, Coope RC, Bansal GS, Yiangou C, Johnston CL, Mason R, Coombes RC: **A paracrine role for myoepithelial cell-derived FGF2 in the normal human breast.** *Exp Cell Res* 1997, **234**:165–173.

25. Tricarico C, Salvadori B, Villari D, Nicita G, Della Melina A, Pinzani P,Ziche M, Pazzagli M: **Quantitative RT-PCR assay for VEGF mRNA in human tumors of the kidney.** *Int J Biol Markers* 1999, **14**:247–250.

26. Sternlict MD, Barsky SH: **The myoepithelial defense: A host defense against cancer.** *Medical Hypothesis* 1997, **48**:37–46.

20

Detection of "Tissue-Specific" mRNA in the Blood and Lymph Nodes of Patients without Colorectal Cancer

Stephen A. Bustin and Sina Dorudi

Abstract

The RT-PCR assay, especially in its real-time format, is widely seen as having
the potential to augment significantly conventional histopathological staging of
colorectal cancer. Its conceptual simplicity and technical specificity and sensitivity combined with the ability to quantitate tumor tissue-specific target markers has led to an explosion of reports claiming to be able to offer rapid, reliable
and routine prognostic information for individual cancer patients. However, the
expectation that in the absence of tumor-specific markers a single, or even two
or three tissue-specific markers, might be able to predict tumor behavior is
proving to be too simplistic an expectation.

20

Detection of "Tissue-Specific" mRNA in the Blood and Lymph Nodes of Patients without Colorectal Cancer

Stephen A. Bustin[*,†] and Sina Dorudi[†]

[*]Centre for Academic Surgery, [†]Barts and The London, Queen Mary's School of Medicine and Dentistry, University of London, London, United Kingdom

20.1. Introduction

Colorectal cancer causes over 19,000 deaths every year in the United Kingdom alone[1] and nearly a third of colorectal cancer patients undergoing supposedly curative surgery develop distant metastatic disease. Some of these patients can be identified during post-operative patient follow-up by monitoring plasma levels of carcinoembryonic antigen

(CEA). Although an elevated postoperative CEA is an adverse prognostic indicator, knowledge of an elevated CEA does not appear to alter patient survival or quality of life.[2] CEA levels are generally associated with macroscopic disease and only a small percentage of patients with established liver metastases are suitable for surgery.

There is an urgent need for a more accurate surveillance assay capable of detecting circulating tumor cells, especially since the emergence of effective adjuvant chemotherapy protocols.[3] This has prompted the evaluation of reverse transcription PCR (RT-PCR) assays as molecular surveillance tools.[4] However, although RT-PCR is a sensitive and rapid technique capable of detecting the presence of viable tumor cells in the circulation, the clinical benefit of using RT-PCR to detect circulating tumor cells during postoperative surveillance of cancer patients remains unclear. Furthermore, the detection of circulating tumor cells, *per se,* without any information about their metastatic potential, may not be sufficiently informative. The assay relies on the detection of tumor or tissue-specific transcription in tissue compartments commonly investigated for the presence of micrometas-tases. However, unlike hematological malignancies, colorectal cancers are not defined by specific genetic alterations. Therefore, the specificity of RT-PCR assays relies on their ability to detect colon epithelium-specific mRNA in a background of native blood cells. Cytokeratin 20 (Genbank accession no X73501) has been reported as one such tissue-specific marker[5] whose expression is retained in most colorectal cancers and their metastases.[6,7] Detection of its mRNA has been widely used to identify tumor cells in the blood of colorectal[8-11] as well as other cancer patients.[12-17] However, some recent reports have challenged its specificity and suggest that illegitimate transcription of ck20 can be detected in blood samples from healthy controls.[18-21] These contradictory results have not allowed an accurate assessment of the biological significance of the detection of ck20 in peripheral blood.[4]

The introduction of the fluorogenic 5'-nuclease (TaqMan) real-time RT-PCR assay[22] offers several advantages over conventional RT-PCR protocols to the clinical investigator. It produces fully quantitative results and obviates the need for gel electrophoresis or blot-ting. Levels of sensitivity are equivalent to those obtained with nested PCR protocols, but its specificity is superior.[20] With appropriate instrumentation, it permits full quantification and analysis of the PCR reaction without the need for gel electrophoresis and is being evaluated as a tool in routine clinical screening.[20,23,24]

This chapter describes the use of a real-time RT-PCR assay to investigate the tissue specificity of ck20 mRNA expression and reveals that its mRNA can be detected in a wide range of samples taken from different tissues: these include liver, kidney, keratinocytes, normal peripheral blood, and lymph node tissue, and that the lack of colon tissue specific-ity renders ck20 useless as a marker for the postoperative surveillance of colorectal cancer patients.

20.2. Materials and Methods

20.2.1. Patients and Controls

This study was approved by the Local Research Ethics Committee of the East London and City Health Authority. Venous blood samples were taken from 51 patients with colorectal cancer at the time of operation. Further samples were obtained from patients at the time of their follow-up visits. Relevant patient data are summarized in **Table 20.1**. Blood samples were also taken from four patients with benign gastrointestinal disease and 42 healthy control subjects. In each case 3-ml samples of peripheral blood were obtained and stored in sterile lithium heparin vacutainers for a maximum of 2 h before RNA was extracted. In our hands use of heparinized containers, combined with the RNA extraction protocol detailed below, did not inhibit the subsequent RT-PCR reaction.

20.2.2. Tumors and Lymph Nodes

10–15-mg sections of tumors from 32 colorectal cancer patients were removed, washed in distilled water, blotted dry, and weighed. Sections of pituitary tissue were obtained in a similar fashion. 24 lymph nodes were collected from eight patients with benign epithelial disease as previously described.[20]

Table 20.1. Clinical status of patients with colorectal carcinoma. P = poorly, M = medium, W = well differentiated. * indicates synchronous tumours, one staged as Dukes B, the other as Dukes C.

Patient Number	Age	Sex	Stage	Differentiation Status
1	63	M	B	M
2	68	M	A	M
3	61	F	B	W
4	55	F	A	M
5	53	M	B	M
6	63	M	C	P
7	43	F	B+C*	M
8	61	M	B	M
9	68	F	B	M
10	85	M	B	M
11	75	M	B	M
12	68	M	B	M
13	45	F	B	M
14	45	F	B	M
15	76	M	B	M
16	68	M	B	M
17	77	F	B	W
18	73	F	C2	P
19	66	F	B	M
20	78	F	B	M
21	65	M	B	M
22	77	F	B	P
23	75	F	D	M
24	47	M	C2	M
25	43	F	B+C	M
26	78	M	A	M
27	77	M	B	M
28	67	F	B	W
29	61	M	B	W
30	64	F	B	M
31	65	M	B	P
32	78	M	B	P

20.2.3. RNA Extraction

All RNA extractions were carried out in a separate room in a class 2 containment hood as described.[20] RNA was quantitated using a GeneQuant II spectrophotometer (Pharmacia). The RNA quality of some selected samples was assessed using RNA Chips together with an Agilent 2100 Bioanalyzer.

20.2.4. Primers and Probes

Cytokeratin 20 primers and probes were designed using Primer Express software (PE Applied Biosystems, Warrington, United Kingdom). The primers (5'-GCGACTACAGTGCATATTACAGACAA and 5'-GCAGGACACACCGAGCATTT) bind to exons 1 and 2, generating an amplicon of 86 bp.

The probe (5'-TGAGCATCCTTAATCTGACTTCGCAGCTCTTC-3), labeled with a fluorescent dye (6-carboxyfluorescein, FAM) and a quencher (6-carboxy-tertramethyl-rhodamine, TAMRA), hybridizes to both exons. The GAPDH (*Genbank accession No. J04038*) probe/primer set spans introns 2 and 3, generates an amplicon of 226 bp and the probe binds to exon 3. It is identical to the PE-ABI set (402869), except that the probe was synthesized with the same reporter dye (FAM) as the cytokeratin probes.

20.2.5. RT-PCR Reactions

We have previously shown that the ck-20 one-tube/one enzyme RT-PCR protocol can be as sensitive as a separate reverse transcription step followed by PCR.[25] Following the reverse transcription, the PCR reaction is carried out in the presence of a single-stranded oligonucleotide that is complementary to the amplicon. This probe contains a fluorescent reporter at its 5' end and a quencher dye at its 3' end. Without target amplification, the probe remains intact and the proximity of reporter and quencher dyes results in suppression of reporter fluorescence. However, if target is amplified during PCR, the probe anneals to the amplicon. The 5'–3'-nuclease activity of *Taq* DNA polymerase displaces and cleaves any hybridized primer it encounters during DNA replication.[26] The amount of product resulting in detectable fluorescence at any given cycle within the exponential phase of PCR is proportional to the initial number of template copies. The number of PCR cycles (threshold cycle—C_t) needed to detect the amplicon is therefore a direct measure of template concentration. Reactions were recorded and analyzed using the ABI 7700 Prism Sequence detection system (ABI, Warrington, United Kingdom).

20.2.6. Quantification

Accurate quantification of each potential marker requires that the "absolute" quantities of each transcript be known by some independent means. This was achieved by serial dilutions of T7 RNA polymerase-transcribed GAPDH or ck20 RNA and generation of standard curves as previously described.[20] 1 µg of an average 1,000 bp mRNA contains 1.9×10^{12} molecules. Serial dilutions of the T7 transcripts were carried out in duplicate from 1×10^9 molecules down to 10 molecules and used in RT-PCR reactions. Reactions were carried out four times, each one in triplicate. By plotting the log (input copy number) against the threshold cycle, a standard curve was obtained for each amplicon (**Fig. 20.1**). The copy numbers of unknown samples were calculated from the respective regression lines.

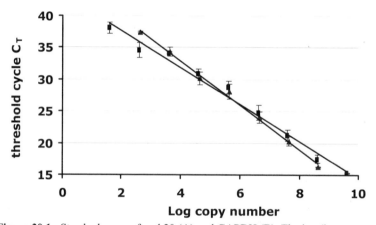

Figure 20.1. Standard curves for ck20 (**A**) and GAPDH (**B**). The log (input copy numbers) is plotted against the threshold cycles. The curves show at least six orders of linear dynamic range. Error bars show the 95% confidence intervals at each point.

20.2.7. Normalization

The TaqMan system contains a passive reference to normalize for non-RT-PCR-related fluctuations in fluorescence signal. Copy numbers of the GAPDH housekeeping gene mRNA vary significantly between individuals and cannot be used to normalize ck20 mRNA copy numbers for comparative proposes.[20] Instead, for quantification of ck20 mRNA from tumor tissue and lymph nodes, copy numbers were standardized relative to total RNA concentration and expressed as copy number/µg RNA. Copy numbers of ck20 mRNA transcribed in blood were more conveniently expressed in terms of copy numbers/ml blood.

20.2.8. Quality Standards

All serial dilutions were carried out in duplicate. The reactions to generate standard curves were repeated four times, each time in triplicate. All clinical samples were tested in triplicate. For quantification, the average value of the triplicates was used.

RNA is labile in the complex mixture of cells and proteins present in a blood sample. Therefore, blood samples were kept at 4°C for a maximum of two hours after collection. Two no-template controls were included with every amplification run; one was prepared before opening all the tubes and dispensing the various reagents, the other at the end of the experiment. This allowed us to monitor any contamination arising during the handling of the reagents.

20.3. Results

20.3.1. ck20 mRNA in Colorectal Cancers

RNA was successfully isolated from all 32 cancer samples. GAPDH mRNA levels showed the wide range reported previously (median copy number 3.1×10^7/µg RNA, range $1.2 \times 10^4 - 2.4 \times 10^{10}$/µg RNA). ck20 mRNA was detected in all tumor samples, with a median copy number of 4.2×10^4 copies/ µg RNA (range: $2.5 \times 10^2 - 1.4 \times 10^8$) (**Fig. 20.2**).

20.3.2. ck20 mRNA in the Peripheral Blood of Patients

ck20 mRNA was detected in all 51 preoperative (median 4.5×10^3 copies RNA/ml blood, range $3.4 \times 10^2 - 1.6 \times 10^6$) (**Fig. 20.3A**) as well as 57 postoperative (median 4.2×10^3 copies RNA/ml blood, range

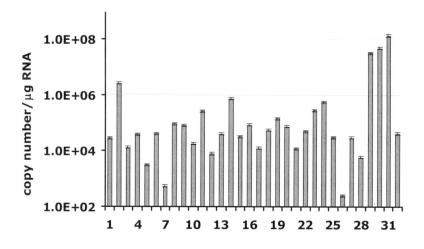

Figure 20.2. Range of ck20 mRNA levels in 32 colorectal tumours. Copy numbers of ck20 mRNA are expressed relative to total RNA concentration. Error bars indicate standard deviations.

1.3×10^2–1.6×10^8) (**Fig. 20.3B**) blood samples from colorectal cancer patients. It was also detected in the blood from all four patients with benign disease (median 3.1×10^4 copies RNA/ml blood, range 2.5×10^3–8.2×10^4) (**Fig. 20.3C**). The no-template controls included with each amplification run were always negative.

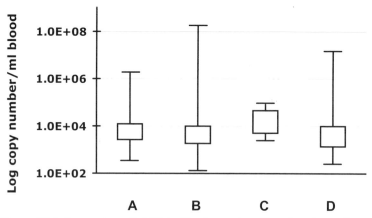

Figure 20.3. Expression of ck20 in blood samples. The plot shows the range of mRNA copy numbers, and the upper and lower quartiles. (**A**) Preoperative ($n = 51$). (**B**) Postoperative ($n = 7$). (**C**) Benign disease ($n = 4$). (**D**) Healthy controls ($n = 42$).

20.3.3. ck20 mRNA in the Peripheral Blood of Healthy Volunteers

ck20 transcription was detected in the peripheral blood samples from all 42 healthy controls (median 4.1×10^3 copies RNA/ml blood, range $2.6 \times 10^2 - 1.3 \times 10^7$). These copy numbers are not significantly different from the copy numbers observed in either the pre-operative or the follow-up samples from colorectal cancer patients (**Fig. 20.3D**).

20.3.4. ck20 Expression in Lymph Nodes

Molecular detection of micrometastases in lymph nodes has the advantage that histological lymph nodes involvement already is an accepted prognostic marker. Our analysis of lymph nodes from eight patients undergoing surgery for benign gastrointestinal disease shows that ck20 mRNA can be detected in all 24 lymph nodes (median 3.2×10^4 copies/µg RNA, range 4×10^2 to 2.2×10^7 copies/µg RNA (**Fig. 20.4A**).

20.3.5. ck20 Expression in Other Human Tissues

Although immunological methods suggest that ck20 expression is restricted to the gastro-intestinal tract, the urothelium, and Merkel cells, this has not been validated using the superior sensitivity of the RT-PCR.

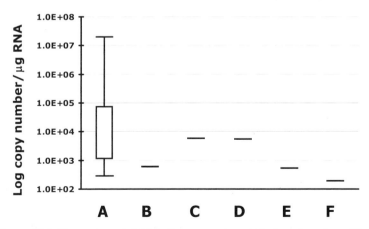

Figure 20.4. Expression of ck20 in tissue samples. (**A**) Lymph nodes. (**B**) Liver. (**C**) Kidney. (**D**) Keratinocyte. (**E**) Pituitary. (**F**) Fibroblast.

Therefore, RNA prepared from cells derived from a number of human tissues was analyzed for ck20 mRNA transcription. The results (**Fig. 20.4B–F**) show that this mRNA could be detected in every tissue investigated, with ck20 mRNA copy numbers ranging from more than 1×10^3–1×10^6 copies/µg RNA.

20.4. Discussion

The RT-PCR assay has the potential to detect rare tumor cells in a background of native cells in blood.[27] Importantly, this technique identifies viable cells and is more sensitive[28] as well as technically easier to carry out than immunohistochemical assays.[29] While the use of the RT-PCR in routine clinical diagnostics is feasible in principle, in practice there are problems associated with its use and the clinical value of this technique as a tool for the detection of occult disease remains unclear.[30-32]

The first problem concerns the methodology of the assay. In particular, sample processing,[33] standardization of the technique and quality control management[34,35] are vital issues, which have hindered the translation of results into clinical practice.[36,37]

The second relates to the difficulties in obtaining quantitative information from conventional RT-PCR assays. Several protocols for conventional quantitative RT-PCR have been developed, but all are laborious and require extensive optimization.[38] The development of the TaqMan assay[22] represents a significant advance in nucleic acid quantification and we have previously applied it to the detection of three mRNAs in the blood of colorectal cancer patients.[20]

A third problem concerns the lack of truly tissue-specific markers.[4] There are several potential tissue-specific RNA targets appropriate for colorectal cancer. The use of cytokeratins has been investigated intensively and cytokeratin 20 showed great initial promise for the detection of colorectal cancer cells. Immunocytochemical data suggested that its expression is restricted to the gastrointestinal tract, the urothelium, and Merkel cells.[7] Several investigators have used RT-PCR to show that detection of ck20 mRNA in the peripheral blood may be a marker for hematogenic tumor dissemination in colorectal[8-11] as well as other cancer patients.[12-17] At least one group used three-step nested RT-PCR to show an apparent absence of ck20 mRNA transcription in the blood of normal controls.[9,10] However, there are three reports describing illegitimate transcription[39] of ck20 in the blood of healthy volunteers. One group used conventional RT-PCR to detect it in 1/12 samples,[18] the other nested RT-PCR to identify it in 8/8 samples.[19] Indeed, the presence of ck20 transcripts in blood has been shown recently to be due to stable background tran-scription in granulocytes.[21] Our own work using conventional, non-nested RT-PCR did not detect ck20 in the blood of healthy controls,[25] but when we applied the TaqMan RT-PCR assay, we found ck20 mRNA detected in 21/21 control blood samples.[20] Such con-tradictory results question the prognostic significance of detecting ck20 mRNA in blood.

The results presented here, obtained from a larger number of control bloods, provide clear evidence that ck20, like ck1830 and ck19,[40] is transcribed in the peripheral blood of healthy volunteers. Our 1-ml blood samples contained between 1×10^6 and 7×10^6 nucleated cells and transcribed a median of 5×10^3 (range $4 \times 10^2 - 2 \times 10^6$) copies of ck20 mRNA. Whether such low transcription levels are due to illegitimate transcription or whether translation occurs under certain conditions is unclear. It is interesting to note that translation of ck20 mRNA has been identified in the blood and bone marrow of healthy controls using an anti-ck20 antibody.[41,42] Clearly, there is sufficient template present to permit the amplification of ck20 mRNA resulting in false positives during conventional RT-PCR assays. The detection of ck20 mRNA tran-scription in the peripheral blood of 1/12 normal blood samples using conventional, non-nested RT-PCR has been described recently.[18] It is likely that a more sensitive assay such as ours would have resulted in the detection of ck20 mRNA in more of these samples. More surprising is that the use of nested[13] and three-step nested[9,10] PCR techniques did not result in the amplification of ck20 mRNA from the blood of healthy controls.

For similar reasons, the choice of ck20 mRNA as a marker to investigate the contribution of surgical manipulation to hematogenic tumor dissemination[11] is not advisable. In combination with conventional, nonquantitative RT-PCR it is likely to overestimate the effect of surgery on the release of tumor cells. Indeed, spillage of tumor cells into the mesenteric circulation after surgical manipulation of primary colorectal cancer is probably uncommon, as confirmed by a recent report.[43]

Transcription of ck20 by breast cancer cell lines as well as primary tumors has been reported previously.[14] We now extend this to the detection of ck20 mRNA in other human tissues. mRNA levels in kidney (6.1×10^3) and keratinocytes (5.5×10^3) are approximately ten-fold lower than those found in colon epithelial cells $(4.2 \times 10^4$ copies/μg RNA). Transcription levels in the pituitary tumor, liver, and fibroblasts are significantly lower $(5.4 \times 10^2, 6.1 \times 10^2,$ and $2 \times 10^2/$μg RNA), and may be due to illegitimate transcription in those cells.

In conclusion, the detection of significant levels of transcription of ck20 mRNA in all control peripheral blood samples makes its use as a marker for the detection of circulating tumor cells in peripheral blood invalid. Whether it is of any more use in detecting the presence of micrometastases in lymph nodes or bone marrow remains to be seen. Certainly, our detection of ck20 mRNA in all 24 lymph nodes from 8 patients with benign disease is in contradiction with at least one previous report[44] but in agreement with another.[45] Our data emphasize that if PCR is to have any predictive power, it must be fully quantitative and permit distinction between background levels of "tissue-specific" gene expression caused by illegitimate transcription and true expression from rare circulating tumor cells. Perhaps more importantly, RT-PCR may simply be detecting cells of no biological significance as the presence of occult disease *per se* does not necessarily lead to successful tumor colonization at a distant site. The pivotal issue is the identification of a cancer's underlying potential for successful growth at a distant site. Clearly, this can only be answered by studying the transcriptome of the cancer in more detail to obtain an expression profile that reveals molecular markers predictive for successful metastasis.

Acknowledgement

We would like to thank Marta Korbonits, Mark Fear, and Mohammed Ikram for their gifts of liver and kidney RNA, fibroblast RNA, and keratinocyte RNA respectively. This research was supported by grants from Bowel and Cancer Research and the Special Trustees of the Royal London Hospital.

References

1. *OPCS: Mortality Statistics, Cause, 1993.* HMSO, Series DH2, London: Bernan Assoc, 1995, No.22.

2. **Clinical Practice Guidelines for the Use of Tumor Markers in Breast and Colorectal Cancer.** *J Clin Oncol* 1999, **14**:2843–2877.

3. Stewart JM, Zalcberg JR: **Update on adjuvant treatment of colorectal cancer.** *Curr Opin Oncol* 1998, **10**:367–374.

4. Bustin SA, Dorudi S: **Molecular assessment of tumour stage and disease recurrence using PCR-based assays.** *Mol Med Today* 1998, **4**:389–396.

5. Burchill SA, Bradbury MF, Pittman K, Southgate J, Smith B, Selby P: **Detection of epithelial cancer cells in peripheral blood by reverse transcriptase-polymerase chain reaction.** *Br J Cancer* 1995, **71**:278–281.

6. Moll R, Zimbelmann R, Goldschmidt MD, Keith M, Laufer J, Kasper M, Koch PJ, Franke WW: **The human gene encoding cytokeratin 20 and its expression during fetal development and in gastrointestinal carcinomas.** *Differentiation* 1993, **53**:75–93.

7. Moll R, Lowe A, Laufer J, Franke WW: **Cytokeratin 20 in human carcinomas. A new histodiagnostic marker detected by monoclonal antibodies.** *Am J Pathol* 1992, **140**:427–447.

8. Soeth E, Vogel I, Roder C, Juhl H, Marxsen J, Kruger U, Henne-Bruns D, Kremer B, Kalthoff H: **Comparative analysis of bone marrow and venous blood isolates from gastro-intestinal cancer patients for the detection of disseminated tumor cells using reverse tran-scription PCR.** *Cancer Res* 1997, **57**:3106–3110.

9. Funaki NO, TanakaJ, Itami A, Kasamatsu T, Ohshio G, Onodera H, Monden K, Okino T, Imamura M: **Detection of colorectal carcinoma cells in circulating peripheral blood by reverse transcription-polymerase chain reaction targeting cytokeratin-20 mRNA.** *Life Sci* 1997, **60**:643–652,.

10. Funaki NO, Tanaka J, Ohshio G, Onodera H, Maetani H, Imamura M: **Cytokeratin 20 mRNA in peripheral venous blood of colorectal carcinoma patients.** *Br J Cancer* 1998, **77**:1327–1332.

11. Weitz J, Kienle P, Lacroix J, Willeke F, Benner A, Lehnert T, Herfarth C, von Knebel DM: **Dissemination of tumor cells in patients undergoing surgery for colorectal cancer.** *Clin Cancer Res* 1998, **4**:343–348.

12. Weber W, Holting T, Weitz J, Amann K, Klar E, Herfarth C, Doerr HW: **Detection of cytokeratin 20 mRNA in thyroid carcinomas and peripheral blood by RT-PCR. Langen-becks.** *Arch Surgery* 1999, **S1**:205–208.

13. Kawamata H, Uchida D, Nakashiro K, Hino S, Omotehara F, Yoshida H, Sato M: **Haematogenous cytokeratin 20 mRNA as a predictive marker for recurrence in oral cancer patients.** *Br J Cancer* 1999, **80**:448–452.

14. Bostick PJ, Chatterjee S, Chi DD, Huynh KT, Giuliano AE, Cote R, Hoon DS: **Limitations of specific reverse-transcriptase polymerase chain reaction markers in the detection of metastases in the lymph nodes and blood of breast cancer patients.** *J Clin Oncol* 1998, **16**:2632–2640.

15. Chausovsky G, Luchansky M, Figer A, Shapira J, Gottfried M, Novis B, Bogelman G, Zemer R, Zimlichman S, Klein A: **Expression of cytokeratin 20 in the blood of patients with disseminated carcinoma of the pancreas, colon, stomach, and lung.** *Cancer* 1999, **86**:2398–2405.

16. Fujii Y, Kageyama Y, Kawakami S, Kihara K, Oshima H: **Detection of disseminated urothelial cancer cells in peripheral venous blood by a cytokeratin 20— Specific nested reverse transcriptase-polymerase chain reaction.** *Jpn.J Cancer Res* 1999, **90**:753–757.

17. Weber T, Lacroix J, Weitz J, Amnan K, Magener A, Holting T, Klar E, Herfarth C, von Knebel DM: **Expression of cytokeratin 20 in thyroid carcinomas and peripheral blood detected by reverse transcription polymerase chain reaction.** *Br J Cancer* 2000, **82**:157–160.

18. Wyld DK, Selby P, Perren TJ, Jonas SJ, Allen-Mersh TG, Wheeldon J, Burchill SA: **Detection of colorectal cancer cells in peripheral blood by reverse-transcriptase polymerase chain reaction for cytokeratin 20.** *Int J Cancer* 1998, **79**:288–293.

19. Denis MG, Lipart C, Leborgne J, LeHur PA, Galmiche JP, Denis M, Ruud E, Truchaud A, Lustenberger P: **Detection of disseminated tumor cells in peripheral blood of colorectal cancer patients.** *Int J Cancer* 1997, **74**:540–544.

20. Bustin SA, Gyselman VG, Williams NS, Dorudi S: **Detection of cytokeratins 19/20 and guanylyl cyclase C in peripheral blood of colorectal cancer patients.** *Br J Cancer* 1999, **79**:1813–1820.

21. Jung R, Petersen K, Kruger W, Wolf M, Wagener C, Zander A, Neumaier M. **Detection of micrometastasis by cytokeratin 20 RT-PCR is limited due to stable background transcription in granulocytes.** *Br J Cancer* 1999, **81**:870–873.

22. Heid CA, Stevens J, Livak KJ, Williams PM: **Real time quantitative PCR.** *Genome Res* **6**: 1996, 986–994.

23. Gelmini S, Orlando C, Sestini R, Vona G, Pinzani P, Ruocco L, Pazzagli M: **Quantitative polymerase chain reaction-based homogeneous assay with fluorogenic probes to measure c-erbB-2 oncogene amplification.** *Clinical Chemistry* 1997, **43**:752–758.

24. Gerard CJ, Olsson K, Ramanathan R, Reading C, Hanania EG: **Improved quantitation of minimal residual disease in multiple myeloma using real-time polymerase chain reaction and plasmid-DNA complementarity determining region III standards.** *Cancer Research* 1998, **58**:3957–3964.

25. Dorudi S, Kinrade E, Marshall NC, Feakins R, Williams NS, Bustin SA: **Genetic detection of lymph node micrometastases in patients with colorectal cancer.** *Br J Surg* 1998, **85**: 98–100.

26. Holland PM, Abramson RD, Watson R, Gelfand DH: **Detection of specific polymerase chain reaction product by utilizing the 5'----3' exonuclease activity of *Thermus aquaticus* DNA polymerase.** *Proc Natl Acad Sci USA* 1991, **88**:7276–7280.

27. Johnson PW, Burchill SA, Selby PJ: **The molecular detection of circulating tumour cells.** *Br J Cancer* 1995, **72**:268–276.

28. Mattano LA Jr, Moss TJ, Emerson SG: **Sensitive detection of rare circulating neuroblastoma cells by the reverse transcriptase-polymerase chain reaction.** *Cancer Res* 1992, **52**:4701–4705.

29. Pelkey TJ, Frierson HF Jr, Bruns DE: **Molecular and immunological detection of circulating tumor cells and micrometastases from solid tumors.** [Review] [163 refs]. *Clin.Chem* 1996, **42**:1369–1381.

30. Zippelius A, Kufer P, Honold G, Kollermann MW, Oberneder R, Schlimok G, Riethmuller G, Pantel K: **Limitations of reverse-transcriptase polymerase chain reaction analyses for detection of micrometastatic epithelial cancer cells in bone marrow.** *J Clin Oncol* 1997, **15**:2701–2708.

31. Foss AJ, Guille MJ, Occleston NL, Hykin PG, Hungerford JL, Lightman S: **The detection of melanoma cells in peripheral blood by reverse transcription-polymerase chain reaction.** Br J Cancer 1995, 72:155–159.

32. Hanekom GS, Johnson CA, Kidson SH: **An improved and combined reverse transcription-polymerase chain reaction assay for reliable detection of metastatic melanoma cells in peripheral blood.** *Melanoma Res* 1997, **7**:111–116.

33. Burchill SA, Lewis IJ, Selby P: **Improved methods using the reverse transcriptase polymerase chain reaction to detect tumour cells.** *Br J Cancer* 1999, **79**:971–977.

34. Lambrechts AC, 't Veer LJ, Rodenhuis S: **The detection of minimal numbers of contaminating epithelial tumor cells in blood or bone marrow: Use, limitations and future of RNA-based methods.** *Ann Oncol* 1998, **9**:1269–1276.

35. Raj GV, Moreno JG, Gomella LG: **Utilization of polymerase chain reaction technology in the detection of solid tumors.** *Cancer* 1998, **82**:1419–1442.

36. Keilholz U, Willhauck M, Rimoldi D, Brasseur F, Dummer W, Rass K, de Vries T, Blaheta J, Voit C, Lethe B, Burchill S. **Reliability of reverse transcription-polymerase chain reaction (RT-PCR)-based assays for the detection of circulating tumour cells: A quality-assurance initiative of the EORTC Melanoma Cooperative Group.** *Eur J Cancer* 1998, **34**:750–753.

37. Schittek B, Blaheta HJ, Urchinger G, Sauer B, Garbe C: **Increased sensitivity for the detection of malignant melanoma cells in peripheral blood using**

an improved protocol for reverse transcription-polymerase chain reaction. *Br J Dermatol* 1999, **141**:37–43.

38. Orlando C, Pinzani P, Pazzagli M: **Developments in quantitative PCR.** *Clin Chem Lab Med* 1998, **36**:255–269.

39. Chelly J, Concordet JP, Kaplan JC, Kahn A: **Illegitimate transcription: Transcription of any gene in any cell type.** *Proc Natl Acad Sci USA* 1989, **86**:2617–2621.

40. Dingemans AM, Brakenhoff RH, Postmus PE, Giaccone G: **Detection of cytoker-atin-19 transcripts by reverse transcriptase-polymerase chain reaction in lung cancer cell lines and blood of lung cancer patients.** *Lab Invest* 1997, **77**:213–220.

41. Litle VR, Lockett SJ, Pallavicini MG: **Genotype/phenotype analyses of low fre-quency tumor cells using computerize image microscopy.** *Cytometry* 1996, **23**:344–349.

42. Litle VR, Warren RS, Moore D, Pallavicini MG: **Molecular cytogenetic analysis of cytokeratin 20-labeled cells in primary tumors and bone marrow aspirates from colorectal carcinoma patients.** *Cancer* 1997, **79**:1664–1670.

43. Sales JP, Wind P, Douard R, Cugnenc PH, Loric S: **Blood dissemination of colonic epithelial cells during no-touch surgery for rectosigmoid cancer.** *Lancet* 1999, **354**:392.

44. Gunn J, McCall JL, Yun K, Wright PA: **Detection of micrometastases in colorec-tal cancer patients by K19 and K20 reverse-transcription polymerase chain reaction.** *Lab Invest* 1996, **75**:611–616.

45. Soong R, Beyser K, Basten O, Kalbe A, Rueschoff J, Tabiti K: **Quantitative reverse transcription-polymerase chain reaction detection of cytokeratin 20 in noncolorectal lymph nodes.** *Clin Cancer Res* 2001, **7**:3423–3429.

21

Optimized Real-Time RT-PCR for Quantitative Measurements of DNA and RNA in Single Embryos and Their Blastomeres

Cristina Hartshorn, John E. Rice, and Lawrence J. Wangh

Abstract

Female 8-cell mouse embryos contain *Xist* RNA localized on the inactive X chromosome of every cell, as seen by fluorescent *in situ* hybridization. But by the blastocyst stage, the cells of the inner mass have lost this pattern, while trophoblasts maintain it, suggesting that the levels of *Xist* RNA in blastomeres of the 8-cell stage may be predictive of the later lineages. To investigate this novel hypothesis, we have used real-time PCR in conjunction with methods developed or optimized in our laboratory for analysis and quantification of RNA and DNA at very low copy numbers. *Xist* transcript accumulation was initially quantified in single whole mouse embryos at different stages of development, and the embryos' sex was identified with a parallel assay detecting the presence/absence of *Sry* DNA. In a second phase, our technique was enhanced to permit simultaneous sexing and precise counting of the number of *Xist* transcripts present in each isolated blastomere of an 8-cell embryo. Our method, discussed in detail in this chapter, is designed to preserve intact RNA during isolation of the blastomeres, and is quantitative and sensitive down to the level of one molecule of template, allowing us to conclude that *Xist* RNA levels in individual blastomeres vary as early as at the 8-cell stage. This study is the first step toward a larger analysis of cell lineage in early mouse embryos.

21

Optimized Real-Time RT-PCR for Quantitative Measurements of DNA and RNA in Single Embryos and Their Blastomeres

Cristina Hartshorn, John E. Rice, and Lawrence J. Wangh

Department of Biology, Brandeis University, Waltham, Massachusetts

21.1. Introduction

Early gene expression in mammalian embryos is currently the subject of intensive investigation summarized in numerous reviews.[1-6] Differential patterns of expression or protein distribution among cleavage-stage blastomeres or between the cells of the inner cell mass and trophecto-derm within the blastocyst have received particular attention because they mark the loss of developmental totipotency and the commitment to cellular differentiation. Stem cell research has further spurred interest in this line of investigation, with particular attention being given to the responses of early embryonic cells to extracellular factors, as discussed by Czyz and Wobus.[7] However, quantitative analysis of transcription levels in single cells or small numbers of cells remains technically difficult.

In the past, RNA levels in pooled embryos or in pooled cell types have been quantified in relative terms. More recently, absolute RNA levels in individual samples have been calculated by applying the strategy of competitive reverse transcription-polymerase chain reaction (RT-PCR). The merits and pitfalls of this and other quantitative approaches to mRNA analysis have been reviewed in depth by Bustin.[8-9] Briefly, an exogenous competitor with extensive sequence homology to the target transcript of interest is added to each reaction over a range of competitor:target ratios. The efficiency with which the competitor is reverse transcribed and amplified provides an indirect measure of the efficiency of the same processes as they apply to the target transcript. This experimental strategy, however, is labor intensive and may generate artifacts if the target and competitor amplicons form heteroduplexes whose presence influences the amplification efficiency of either.

Neither competitive RT-PCR, nor the use of commercially available exogenous RNA standards (such as Ambion's Armored RNA®) provides any insight into the efficiency of RNA extraction from small samples. One approach designed to circumvent this problem involves normalizing the amount of the target RNA relative to the level of a particularly abundant housekeeping gene such as glyceraldehydes-3-phosphate-dehydrogenase (GADPH), β-actin, or one of the ribosomal RNAs. This experimental design assumes that different RNA sequences are recovered, reverse transcribed, and amplified with equal efficiency, although this is not the case.[10] It is also complicated by the fact that differences in housekeeping genes transcription levels exist between individuals and, in particular, these levels have not reached steady state during very early embryonic development. Studies describing these findings are exemplified by references[11-12] and are reviewed by Bustin.[8-9]

We have developed an alternative method aimed at overcoming many of these difficulties. Our approach involves the use of a genomic DNA sequence chosen to be equal to the cDNA sequence under study, as an internal control for nucleic acids recovery and real-time RT-PCR of both DNA and RNA in individual embryos and single embryonic cells. This genomic sequence also serves as a control for quantification of RNA molecules, as detailed in the following sections. The present chapter describes the challenges and discusses the pitfalls that we encountered in applying two versions of this strategy to quantitative analysis of *Xist* and *Sry* RNA and DNA in male and female mouse embryos, **Fig. 21.1**. Version I involves *Xist* real-time PCR analysis of two aliquots of the same sample, prepared with (+RT) or without (no-RT) reverse transcription. The amplified products are detected using the nonspecific fluorescent probe SYBR® Green (FMC BioProducts, Rockland, Maine). Version II is a multiplex real-time RT-PCR assay that employs two specific fluorescent probes to simultaneously measure *Xist* and *Sry* genomic DNA and RNA copies extracted from samples as small as a single cell.

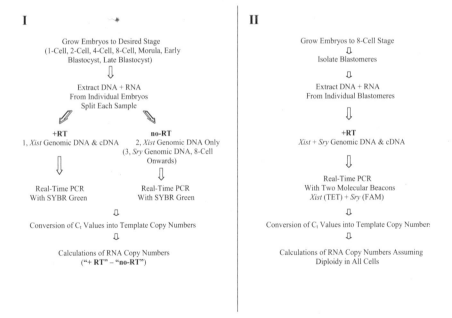

Figure 21.1. Flowcharts of the two methods used to study *Xist* expression in preimplantation mouse embryos by real-time RT-PCR. In both cases embryos were sexed based on the presence/absence of the *Sry* gene. **(I)** Single embryos aliquots (RT/no-RT) were analyzed with a SYBR Green-based PCR assay. **(II)** Molecular Beacons technology allowed simultaneous amplification of *Xist* and *Sry* in individual blastomeres from 8-cell embryos.

In Version I, the no-RT aliquot is used to quantify the number of genomic *Xist* DNA copies present in the sample, while the +RT aliquot is used to measure the total level of genomic *Xist* DNA plus *Xist* cDNA. *Xist* cDNA copy numbers, hence the amount of *Xist* RNA, are then calculated as the difference between these two values. Sexing of the embryos is achieved based on the knowledge that only female embryos contain *Xist* RNA and by counting genomic *Xist* copy numbers, and is confirmed by determining the presence/absence of *Sry* genomic DNA in a third aliquot (female cells contain two copies of the *Xist* gene, one on each X chromosome, and male cells contain one copy of *Xist* on the X chromosome and one copy of *Sry* on the Y chromosome). Thus, Version I of our method uses genomic sequence amplification as an internal standard for nucleic acid recovery and PCR efficiency, but it is only suitable for analysis of samples that are large enough to be subdivided, such as whole mouse embryos.[13]

In contrast, Version II of our method is useful for analysis of the RNA content of samples as small as single blastomeres. This improvement is accomplished by employing multiplex real-time RT-PCR to simultaneously measure both *Sry* DNA and total *Xist* DNA + RNA copies (*Sry* cDNA would also be amplified with this assay, but *Sry* is not expressed in 8-cell stage embryos). Embryos are sexed as in Version I and *Xist* RNA accumulation in individual female cells is then deduced from total *Xist* template numbers by subtracting the two genomic *Xist* copies.[14]

21.2. Key Features of Real-Time RT-PCR

The theory and practice of real-time PCR are described elsewhere in this volume. The following key features are relevant to the findings presented in this chapter:

1) Real-time PCR is a quantitative method that provides an indication of the amount of the starting target sequence based on how many PCR cycles it takes to amplify a detectable amount of the expected product, as reviewed by Walker.[15] The cycle at which the fluorescent signal rises above background is called the C_t value.

2) Under conditions of efficient amplification of one or more amplicons, each ten-fold increase in the number of target molecules

present at the start of the reaction causes the real-time PCR signal to reach the C_t value 3.2 cycles earlier.

21.3. Primer Design

Rigorous quantitative accuracy of real-time PCR depends on efficient amplification of the intended sequences only. Amplicon specificity, in turn, depends on primer design, as well as optimization of the PCR temperatures and cycle times. We design sets of PCR primers based on the general features suggested by software programs such as Oligo® 6 (Molecular Biology Insights, Inc., Cascade, Colo.). When primer pairs are multiplexed they have to be examined for specificity and efficiency under the same $MgCl_2$ concentration and PCR conditions. In addition, the sequences of all primers in a reaction have to be analyzed for possible primer-dimer formation, since amplification of such dimers competes with amplification of the intended sequence. For the work described in this chapter as Version II we created a "superamplicon" formed by fusing the chosen *Xist* and *Sry* sequences and imported it into Oligo 6 as a new sequence. All four selected primers were then analyzed against each other for possible dimerization using this program.

Primer specificity for the genes under study was additionally investigated by performing BLAST searches on the available mouse genomic sequences (http://www.ncbi.nlm.nih.gov/BLAST/). While this kind of search never definitively rules out the possibility of mispriming, it is useful in pointing to sequences that belong to conserved families and pose particular challenges for the design of primers, as in the case of the HMG box within the *Sry* gene.

21.4. Avoidance of the HMG Box within *Sry*

The highly conserved HMG box within the *Sry* gene encodes a 79 amino acid DNA-binding motif having at least 50% amino acid identity with any member of the *Sox* (*Sry*-box) gene family. This group includes at least 30 identified members, 15 of which are in mammals. In the mouse, the X chromosome-linked gene *Sox3* presents the highest (67%) nucleotide identity to *Sry* within the HMG box, while the HMG sequence of the autosomal *Sox9*, required for gonadal development and sexual differentiation, is 59% identical to that of *Sry*.[16] Specific amplification of the *Sry* gene is, therefore, problematic because its translated sequence is largely comprised of the HMG box and a glutamine-rich repetitive domain.[17] We tested several pairs of primers within the murine HMG box and found that they generated specific amplicons when 1-to-100 male genomes were used as templates. In the presence of small numbers of female genomes these same primers generated no amplified product, but they did yield discrete amplicons when tested against 100 female genomes. However, the real-time PCR signals from female genomes arose approximately seven cycles later than from 100 male genomes, indicating nonspecific primer initiation with decreased efficiency. (It is important to note that these alternate amplicons were never generated in male genomes.) In order to minimize nonspecific initiation we shifted one of our *Sry* primers to a unique sequence 3' to the HMG box. This new pair of primers virtually eliminated nonspecific amplification from female genomic DNA. The use of sequence-specific probes (see **Section 21.6.** *Molecular Beacons Design*) further guaranteed the reliability of real-time PCR signals for specific quantification of the intended amplicons.

21.5. Amplicon Selection and Verification

Real-time PCR is accurate for determining the number of target molecules present in a sample over a range of 1 to 1,000,000 molecules. It is therefore ideally suited for comparing a sample that contains as little as one gene copy to a sample that potentially contains a great many cDNA molecules in addition to the chromosomal DNA. We have applied this rationale to the study of embryonic *Xist* RNA levels, choosing to amplify a sequence within exon 1 of the *Xist* gene. *Sry*, on the other hand, is an intronless gene. In both cases, therefore, the genomic DNA sequence is identical to the cDNA sequence and both templates can be amplified and measured together. (As mentioned earlier in this chapter, *Sry* RNA is not produced in cleavage stage embryos and only *Sry* DNA was amplified in the present work, but this general strategy can be applied to the study of other genes.)

Other considerations are involved in the selection of sequences to be amplified during PCR. The chosen amplicons should present the least possible amount of secondary structure at annealing temperature (the http://bioinfo.math.rpi.edu/~mfold/dna/form1.cgi site can be used to visualize theoretical folding of DNA at the desired temperature), in order to be available for primer binding. It should be also kept in mind that successful detection of amplified DNA sequences depends on their length and on the type of fluorescent probe used for real-time PCR. While the nonspecific fluorescent probe SYBR Green interacts with double-stranded DNA of any length, sequence-specific Molecular Beacons require amplicons of about 150 nucleotides or less.

Real-time PCR in the presence of SYBR Green is useful in determining the purity and specificity of each amplicon before multiplexing. The product, or products, accumulated at the end of PCR are analyzed by increasing the temperature to produce a "melting profile"[18] typical of each amplicon and determined by its nucleotide composition. A single peak at the expected melting temperature (T_m) shows specific amplification (see **Inset** of **Plate 21.1**). We also recommend analysis of the PCR product by agarose gel electrophoresis to confirm its size. The combined characteristics of size and T_m can be considered unique for each amplicon. (Melting profile analysis is also useful for identifying the occurrence of primer dimerization during PCR, addressed in the **Section 21.3.** *Primer Design*. Primers dimers usually form a peak at T_m lower than that of the amplicon, which is also found in "blank" assays, devoid of DNA template.) The melting profile of multiplexed amplicons is also informative, provided that the two (or more) templates have different T_m and that the peaks do not overlap. Real-time PCR in the presence of SYBR Green cannot, however, be used to quantify multiplex amplicons because the probe binds nonspecifically to all amplicons generated (and also to primers dimers if they are present). Sequence-specific Molecular Beacon probes are, therefore, employed for quantitative multiplex real-time PCR or RT-PCR. Detection of real-time PCR products with sequence-specific probes further eliminates the risk of misinterpretation of the data because amplicons alternative to the intended template(s) are not labeled by this kind of probes (see **Section 21.4.** *Avoidance of the HMG Box within Sry*).

21.6. Molecular Beacons Design

Analysis of the amplicon's secondary structure is particularly useful as a prelude to designing Molecular Beacons because it reveals whether the sequence to which the probe will bind is likely to be single stranded under reaction conditions (see below in this section).

Two or more Molecular Beacons conjugated to fluorophores emitting at different wavelength can be used in order to successfully detect and measure multiplex amplification products generated during real-time PCR. Applications of this strategy in our laboratory are described by Pierce et al.[19] and by Hartshorn et al.[14] These probes offer great specificity and very low background fluorescence, as first shown by Tyagi and Kramer[20] and reviewed by Bustin,[8] but they are expensive due to the required synthesis procedure and also because optimal binding cannot be entirely predicted based on thermodynamic considerations and is usually achieved by testing a family of molecules.

Some of the challenges encountered when using Molecular Beacons are illustrated by our experience with *Xist* probes. **Plate 21.1** compares results obtained with probes B-1 and G-B1 during real-time PCR of the selected *Xist* amplicon (see also **Plate 21.2**). Probe B1 is one of a set of five Molecular Beacons synthesized in accord with the recommended thermodynamic characteristics (http://www.molecular-beacons.org/). These Molecular Beacons consist of an extended loop whose T_m is 7–11°C higher than the PCR annealing temperature, and of a stem with a T_m higher than the loop. The stem serves to keep unbound beacon molecules in the closed, nonfluorescent "lollipop" conformation at annealing temperature, thus minimizing background fluorescence. Loop sequences are 22 to 23 nucleotides long and, in all cases, interact with a portion of the *Xist* amplicon that is predicted to be completely single-stranded at the chosen PCR annealing temperature, as shown for B1 in **Plate 21.2**. Nevertheless, each probe in this family yielded a very low fluorescent signal under the chosen PCR conditions. Addition of a single G nucleotide to the Beacon's loop (G-B1 probe), however, greatly boosted the fluorescent signal, although the loop's T_m of this new probe is slightly higher than the stem's T_m and part of the amplicon's target sequence participates in secondary structure (see **Plates 21.1** and **21.2**).

As stated above, Molecular Beacons are expensive, but they are also finicky to synthesize and must be purified by high-pressure liquid chromatography. For low-volume laboratories, such as our own, we recommend use of commercially prepared, highly purified probes with optimized signal-to-background ratio (compare end fluorescence of in-house synthesized G-B1 beacon, shown in **Plate 21.1**, with that of Research Genetics, Inc., Huntsville, Ala., G-B1 beacon, **Plate 21.4**). A list of licensed vendors can be found at http://www.molecular-beacons.org.

Care should also be taken in setting the concentration of the Molecular Beacon in the PCR assay. In fact, depending on their sequence, some Molecular Beacons are still partially bound to their target during the elongation step (J.E. Rice, personal communication) and can actually interfere with amplification when used at high concentrations. **Fig. 21.2** illustrates such a concentration-dependent effect produced by B2-NEG, our *Sry* probe of choice, in the presence of 3.5 mM $MgCl_2$. The selected *Xist*-specific beacon, G-B1, does not display similar behavior in spite of presenting very similar general characteristics. In addition, it is interesting to note that B2-NEG interferes with ampli-

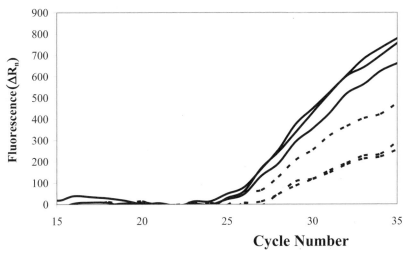

Figure 21.2. Molecular Beacon FAM-2NEG's (Research Genetics, Inc) concentration effect on *Sry* amplification. Solid line—0.3 µM probe; broken line—0.6 µM probe (one hundred genome copies were used as templates in each assay). In specific cases such as this, Molecular Beacons can interfere with PCR when used above a certain concentration. This inhibitory effect is enhanced by Mg^{2+} (3.5 mM $MgCl_2$ was added in the PCR assay shown above).

fication even though it binds to its target strand sixty-eight nucleotides down stream from the anti-sense primer, while G-B1, a sense probe, does not interfere with amplification even though it hybridizes only two residues downstream from the upper primer (see **Plate 21.2**). A more pronounced interference with elongation might be anticipated in the second case but is actually observed in the first case, indicating that the amplicon's sequence plays a major role in determining this phenomenon. In our experience, a final concentration of 0.3 μM for each Molecular Beacon usually gives the best results.

As in the case of primers, interactions between the two beacons selected for multiplex signal detection, as well as between these probes and the four primers must be avoided in order to prevent nonspecific binding and fluorescence generation. To this end all the sequences must be checked by using the BLAST program, as specified in **Section 21.3.** *Primer Design.* Furthermore, the chosen Molecular Beacons must be able to optimally and specifically bind to the respective amplicons under the same ionic and temperature conditions. If possible, independent amplification of each selected genomic sequence should be initially measured by real-time PCR in the presence of the nonspecific fluorescent probe SYBR Green and these results should be compared to those generated with the respective Molecular Beacon. Once the efficiency of Molecular Beacon detection is established, multiplex amplification of the two (or more) genes of interest can be examined.

21.7. Multiplex Optimization

After primers and fluorescent probes have been independently tested on real-time PCR of each of the two amplicons under study, these reagents are combined in a single reaction mixture. Amplification of the two desired sequences needs to be evaluated once again, in order to establish that both amplicons are produced with very similar efficiency. Not infrequently, in fact, one amplicon tends to "take over" the reaction, particularly in reactions initiated with low numbers of templates. Ensuring reproducible coamplification and detection of both the desired templates is essential for reliable results and may require additional adjustments. Magnesium concentration can be varied between 2 and 4 mM, and primers ratios can be changed in order to favor the initial amplification of the "weakest" amplicon. **Plate 21.3** illustrates the effect of varying concentration of our *Xist* and *Sry* primers on multiplex real-time PCR detection of *Sry* (upper panel) and *Xist* (lower panel) obtained from 3, 10, and 100 male genome copies (BALB/C mouse DNA, Sigma Chemical Company, St. Louis, Mo.). In this example, increasing the ratio of *Sry* primers to *Xist* primers was not beneficial because it led to suboptimal *Xist* amplification. We concluded that an equimolar concentration of 0.3 μM for all primers gave the best results for both gene sequences at any copy numbers. A higher primer concentration led to a lower C_t values, but also increased the scatter among replicate reactions, particularly in terms of their final fluorescence ("fanning effect").

Another consideration to keep in mind is the volume of the reaction; this is particularly important when performing RT-PCR because the RT buffer needs to be diluted as much as possible in the PCR cocktail, which implies performing PCR in the largest volume allowed by the real-time cycler (usually 100 μl). Scaling up the assay volume from 25 to 100 μl does not constitute a problem when SYBR Green is used as a detector, because SYBR Green binds to double-stranded DNA after the elongation step. In contrast, for reactions containing Molecular Beacons the lengths of the steps in PCR may have to be adjusted when scaling up. This is because the Molecular Beacon hybridizes to one strand of the amplicon during the annealing step and thus competes with both elongation of the primer binding to that same strand and reannealing of the amplicon strands. Increasing the reaction volume decreases template concentrations and therefore suggests the use of longer annealing and elongation times, but excessively long PCR steps may favor amplicons reannealing and displacement of bound beacons. **Fig. 21.3** illustrates this point by showing changes in *Xist* C_t values in the multiplex *Xist*/*Sry* PCR assay, when this assay was performed in a 25 μl volume with short PCR steps (10" denaturation, 45" annealing, and 15" elongation), in a 100 μl volume with the same PCR profile, and in a 100 μl volume with longer PCR steps (20" denaturation, 60" annealing, and 30" elongation; further increasing the steps duration did not improve the results). Fluorescent signals appear later in the larger volume assays, but the reaction efficiency is largely restored by increasing the length of the PCR steps.

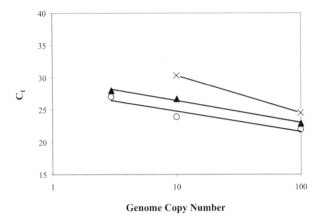

Figure 21.3. Effects of assay volume and PCR steps duration on *Xist* C_t values during real-time PCR of a *Xist/Sry* multiplex (0.3 µM *Xist* TET-G-B1 beacon). Circles—25-µl assay, short PCR steps (see text for details); crosses—100-µl assay, short PCR steps (3-genome samples did not generate a product); triangles—100-µl assay, long PCR steps. C_t values were averages of three determinations; 3, 10, and 100 male mouse genomes were used as templates. Linear regression trendlines are plotted in the chart. A similar assay volume/PCR steps duration effect was observed on *Sry* C_t values (not shown).

Under optimized conditions *Xist* and *Sry* signals rise above the threshold almost simultaneously at each template concentration (**Plate 21.4**, male samples and inset). Moreover, in both cases ten-fold increases in the number of template molecules decrease the C_t value by about 3.2 cycles, as expected for efficient exponential amplification. Comparison of these data with *Xist* amplification in the female genome demonstrates that generation of *Xist* signals in the male is not affected by the co-amplification of *Sry*, **Plate 21.4**.

21.8. Blastomere Isolation

We started our investigation by using SYBR Green to detect *Xist* and *Sry* amplicons in separate aliquots prepared from individual embryos (see Version I, **Section 21.1.** *Introduction*). Once we had determined average levels of *Xist* RNA in female (expressing) and male (non-expressing) embryos at different developmental stages, we turned to an analysis of *Xist* expression in single blastomeres prepared from 8-cell stage embryos.

While this second part of our investigation (designated as Version II in **Section 21.1.** *Introduction*) provided us with new insight in the biology of the embryos, it also shows utility in supporting the validity of our experimental strategy. In fact, if all (or most) blastomeres from an embryo are recovered and their RNA content is measured for a specific gene, the sum of these values should be similar, in the average, to the results obtained for whole embryos at the same developmental stage. If this is the case, it is implied that the specific transcripts are recovered from both whole embryos and individual cells without undergoing degradation. The procedure selected for blastomere isolation is important for preserving intact RNA, and in the present section we describe our findings relative to *Xist* RNA recovery in blastomeres harvested with two methods.

Advantages and disadvantages of the currently available techniques for blastomere isolation have been described elsewhere.[21] In order to ablate the desired blastomeres from the embryo, it is first necessary to remove at least partially the surrounding *zona pellucida*. This goal has been traditionally achieved by quick exposure to acidic Tyrode's solution, either of the whole embryo (when all blastomeres from the sample need to be analyzed) or of a small area of the *zona* (when a single blastomere is removed for genetic analysis). The effects of this transient acidification on the cells health have been questioned, but do not appear to interfere with genomic DNA amplification. In our experience, however, this harsh chemical treatment may affect RNA recovery.

In order to collect as many cells as possible from each 8-cell embryo (**Fig. 21.4A**), samples are immersed for 10 seconds in acidic Tyrode's solution (pH 2.5) containing 0.4% polyvinyl pyrrolidone (PVP), according to a procedure initially developed by Nicolson et al.[22] The denuded embryo is immediately transferred to Dulbecco's PBS (devoid of calcium and magnesium chloride) containing 0.4% PVP (all products from Sigma Chemical Company), and the clustered cells are then separated by repeated pipetting in thin glass capillaries (**Fig. 21.4D–F**). We found that, while genomic *Xist* and *Sry* signals are generated by the majority of single blastomeres isolated with this procedure, even when present as a single copy in the male cells, *Xist* cDNA is only occasionally amplified from female cells. This result conflicts with our previous knowledge that female embryos at this stage contain hundreds of *Xist* transcripts.[13] (Details on *Xist* and *Sry* genomic and cDNA copies quantification will be given in the **Section 21.12.** *Real-time PCR and*

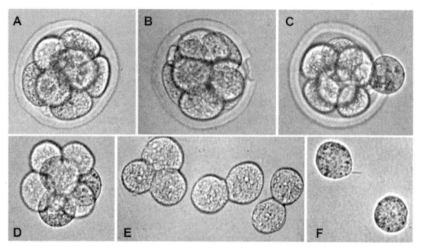

Figure 21.4. Alternative procedures for blastomere isolation from mouse 8-cell embryos. Embryos were cultured from the 2-cell stage (as detailed in the text) and processed before reaching compaction. (**A**) Intact 8-cell embryo. (**B**) Laser-drilling of the *zona pellucida* was achieved by three 1-ms pulses aimed at adjacent areas of the zona. (**C**) Blastomeres were released one at a time in the outside medium by gentle pipetting. (**D**) According to a well-established technique, *zonae* can be chemically dissolved by quick exposure to acidic Tyrode's solution. (**E**) and (**F**) Blastomeres were dissociated from the cluster by repeated pipetting with glass capillaries of progressively decreasing diameter.

Quantification of Genomic DNA and cDNA Templates in Single Blastomeres).

An alternative protocol, developed in our laboratory, overcomes this problem and allows a quicker, cleaner, and easier way to isolate all cells from noncompacted embryos. This approach, however, requires the investment of purchasing a laser system. We had excellent results with a ZILOS (zona infrared laser optical system; beam = 1480 nm) (Hamilton Thorne Research, Inc., Beverly, Mass.). A particularly helpful feature of this system's software is the inclusion of color-coded Isotherm Rings™. Visualization of the isotherm peaks allows precise cutting of the *zona* in the desired position, as the limits of the hole produced by firing the laser correspond to the 140°C ring (more information can be found at http://www.hamiltonthorne.com/research/ivf/). Embryos are placed in Dulbecco's PBS + 0.4% PVP and the *zona* is drilled by carefully aiming three 140-mW pulses of 1 ms each in close proximity to each other (**Fig. 21.4B**). Blastomeres are then extruded one-by-one through gentle pipetting of the embryo still enveloped by the *zona* and thus protected from mechanical shearing (**Fig. 21.4C**). By repeating this procedure, all cells are collected sequentially. As it will be better explained later in this chapter, *Xist/Sry* RT-PCR analysis of nucleic acids extracted from blastomeres isolated with this method confirms that *Xist* RNA levels measured in single female cells from one embryo add up to the amount expected for whole embryos at the 8-cell stage. On this ground, we recommend using the laser approach for harvesting embryonic cells.

21.9. DNA and RNA Isolation

RT-PCR requires recovery of RNA as well as, in our protocol, DNA and is technically more challenging than preparation of genomic DNA alone. A survey of the literature indicates that RNA extraction is largely performed using various improvements of the acid guanidinium thiocyanate-phenol-chloroform method first described by Chomczynski and Sacchi.[23] Commercially available kits based on this approach include the Micro RNA Isolation Kit (Stratagene, La Jolla, Calif.), the TRIzol® Reagent (Invitrogen, Life Technologies, Carlsbad, Calif.), and the ToTALLY RNA™ Total RNA Isolation Kit (Ambion, Inc., Austin, Tex.). A wide array of other approaches to total RNA isolation includes the use of RNA-binding glass fiber filters (RNAqueous™ Kit, Ambion) and silica-gel membranes (RNeasy System, Qiagen, Inc., Valencia, Calif.). Alternatively, mRNA molecules can be specifically extracted by interaction of their poly(A) tails with oligo(dT) attached to cellulose (Poly(A)Pure™, Ambion; Poly(A) Quik®, Stratagene), resins or beads (Oligotex Resin, Qiagen). This list of products, however, is by no means comprehensive and it is only intended as a sampler of commonly used RNA isolation strategies.

Most of these methods work well when the starting sample is comprised of hundreds of cell, or many more, but are not suitable for nucleic acids extraction from single cells. We attempted adapting the RNeasy Mini Kit to nucleic acids extraction from individual embryos, but were not successful in recovering all RNA while keeping the elution volume very small (when a whole sample needs to be analyzed in one real-time RT-PCR assay, nucleic acids have to be resuspended in a minimal volume, so that RT and the following steps of dilution and PCR can be carried out in a single tube. The maximal volume of water for RNA/DNA resuspension allowed by our experimental design is of 5.5 µl, or 6 µl if reverse transcription primers are already diluted in the water). Other commercial kits, advertised for RNA extraction at the single-cell level (such as the QuickPrep Micro mRNA Purification Kit from Amersham Pharmacia Biotech, Piscataway, NJ, and the newly released Absolutely RNA™ Nanoprep kit from Stratagene), also require an elution step (the Stratagene kit offers the possibility of 10-µl elution volume). These kits are expensive for studies such as ours that involve processing large numbers of samples.

The Micro RNA Isolation Kit, employed for this study, is comparatively inexpensive and permits resuspension of the purified nucleic acids to any desired volume. When applied to many specimens this method becomes rather cumbersome, but it is reliable and offers several other advantages. The collected samples are immediately transferred to a denaturing solution that inactivates all RNases and they can be stored frozen for prolonged periods of time, thus allowing the harvesting of embryos on different days prior to nucleic acids extraction. In addition, the guanidinium thiocyanate-phenol-chloroform method protocol leads to the recovery of total RNA, rather than mRNA only, bypassing the need for poly(A) tail-binding to a matrix. This step would be of concern in dealing with the *Xist* transcript because of its unusual length (17.4 kb), which increases the possibility of shearing of the molecules during the preparation.

We followed the procedure recommended by the manufacturer (using the minimal volume for each sample, i.e., 100 µl of Denaturing Solution), except for the amount of chloroform:isoamyl alcohol added to the phenol phase. Mixing 35 µl of chloroform:isoamyl alcohol (instead of the suggested 20 µl) with 100 µl of phenol produces, in our experience, a much better separation of the two phases after centrifugation (we found no difference in RNA recovery between 35 and 45 µl of chloroform:isoamyl alcohol). A clear separation is obviously critical because nucleic acids recovery needs to be as thorough as possible when quantifying sequences from a very small number of cells. Following extraction we add 10 µg/assay of tRNA (Sigma Chemical Company), rather than glycogen, as a DNA/RNA co-precipitant.

Considering that DNA partitions at the interface of the two phases, it is virtually impossible to collect all RNA molecules without introducing

DNA contamination. Our experimental strategy overcomes this hurdle, as we aim at extracting both kinds of nucleic acids together. As mentioned earlier in this chapter, the genomic *Xist* and *Sry* sequences provide an excellent quantitative internal control for numerous stages of our procedure. When investigating whole embryos at different developmental stages, we recovered, on average, the expected number of genomes (as shown by the no-RT-PCR assays).[13] In our more recent work on single blastomeres, we were able to amplify single *Xist* or *Sry* genes from most, although not all, male cells. While these results are very encouraging, they do not rule out the possibility that some DNA or RNA molecules are lost during extraction and precipitation. Only a protocol that eliminated these steps entirely would bypass this problem. Ambion's Cells-to-cDNA™ Kit was devised as a one-tube system for cell lysis followed by reverse transcription. The challenge in this case is to attain complete protein removal from the nucleic acids while avoiding detergent interference during RT or PCR. Preliminary tests in our laboratory indicated a lower efficiency for this kit when compared to our present procedure; however we are currently testing the new Cells-to-cDNA II Kit to see if it meets our quantitative standards.

With the Micro RNA Isolation Kit, cellular RNA is protected from RNases from the moment of sample harvesting until the aqueous/organic phase separation. At any later time, RNases carried over or newly introduced in the tube (i.e., from the investigator's skin or from other lab samples) will readily degrade the transcripts. For this reason, extreme care should be taken when handling preparations for both nucleic acids extraction and reverse transcription. It is advisable to set aside a clean area and dedicated instrumentation and pipettes. Disposable pipette tips and tubes, as well as the water and all other reagents used, should be DNase- and RNase-free. We wipe all surfaces, containers, micropipettes, and equipment with RNaseERASE (ICN Biomedicals, Inc., Irvine, Calif.) prior to each experiment, and expose them to UV light if possible.

An additional concern has to be kept in mind when processing cells for RT-PCR if the genes under study are differently distributed or expressed between male and female samples, such as in the *Xist/Sry* case. Not only are these genes present in different copy numbers in the two sexes (see **Section 21.1.** *Introduction*), but female cells express *Xist* RNA while male do not. It is very important, therefore, to avoid contamination between samples, particularly single-cell samples, because their gender is unknown until PCR is performed and the introduction of a single *Sry* sequence into a female sample can lead to erroneous identification of sex. Conversely, *Xist* cDNA mistakenly carried over from a female cell could be interpreted as *Xist* expression in a male cell. (Of course, contamination can also derive from poor disposal of previous PCR assays, considering that many millions of copies of the sequences of interest are generated during PCR.) For this reason, fresh gloves should always be used to open microfuge tubes containing unknown samples.

21.10. Reverse Transcription

The success of RT-PCR studies depends in some cases on which reverse transcriptase is used to synthesize cDNA. We found that ThermoScript™ (Invitrogen, Life Technologies) was particularly effective and more reliable in producing *Xist* cDNA than either SuperScript™ (Invitrogen, Life Technologies) or M-MLV Reverse Transcriptase (Cells-to-cDNA Kit, Ambion). This result is likely due to the unusual length of the *Xist* transcript which leads to folding of the molecule and the presence of secondary structure even at relatively high temperature (42°C), thus preventing efficient primer binding and reverse transcription. Because ThermoScript is engineered to be active at higher incubation temperatures (50–65°C) than most other enzymes, a more linear conformation of the *Xist* mRNA molecule allows better reverse transcription. But this strategy does not necessarily apply to other RNAs. For instance, ThermoScript was completely ineffective in a RT-PCR assay for the heat-shock protein gene *hsp 70.1*. In parallel reactions, thousands of copies of *hsp 70.1* mRNA were amplified from heat-shocked embryos when RT had been carried out with M-MLV Reverse Transcriptase, while none were detected in ThermoScript-treated samples (A. Anshelevich, C. Hartshorn, and L.J., Wangh, manuscript in preparation). We, therefore, recommend testing different reverse transcriptases if a specific cDNA fails to be amplified during PCR and RNase contamination can be excluded.

Nam et al.[24] reported that oligo(dT) primers generate a high frequency of truncated cDNA and this problem could be even more pronounced for a long transcript like *Xist*. Conversely, we found that random hexamers were excellent primers for this transcript. We followed the ThermoScript reverse transcription procedure suggested by the manufacturer, but omitted DTT from the reaction mixture. DTT is required for maintaining activity of the ribonuclease inhibitor included in the kit (RNaseOUT™) but considerably delays the emergence of the fluorescent signal during real-time PCR (**Fig. 21.5**). We found that extremely careful handling of the samples prevented RNase contamination problems and overcame the need for DTT. DTT inhibitory effect probably occurs during the PCR assay performed after reverse transcription and depends on the final concentration of this reducing agent in the PCR mixture.[25]

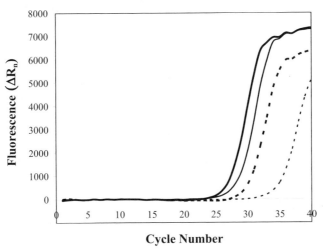

Cycle Number

Figure 21.5. DTT effect on *Xist* real-time PCR. Reverse transcription was carried out on all samples with the ThermoScript kit, as detailed in this section. DTT was added to a set of samples at the concentration recommended by the manufacturer (broken lines) and omitted from a second set (solid lines). 6 µl of RT mixture (thick lines, 2-embryo equivalents) or 3 µl of RT mixture (thin lines, 1-embryo equivalents) were then added to the PCR mixture (the final volume of each PCR assay was 100 µl). Embryo equivalents were calculated from 20 pooled blastocyst. SYBR Green was used as a fluorescent probe for this experiment.

The cDNA Synthesis Mix:PCR Mix ratio recommended by the manufacturer is 2 µl:50 µl. This ratio, however, cannot be maintained when working with very small samples, such as single embryos or single blastomeres. The minimal volume attainable for each ThermoScript RT reaction is 10 µl (we reduced by half all the components of the suggested cDNA synthesis mixture. Nucleic acids were resuspended in 5.5 µl of H_2O + 0.5 µl of random hexamer primers and, after a short preincubation, the other components were added to 10 µl). The maximum volume for each real-time PCR assay is 100 µl (we used an ABI Prism® 7700 Sequence Detector, Applied Biosystems, Foster City, Calif., for this study). Therefore our RT Mix:PCR Mix ratio is 1:10 rather than 1:25. This is not a problem as long as the same volume of RT mixture is added to all the assays, including the genomic standards used to quantify the results obtained from real-time PCR, in order to take in account the increase in ionic concentration (Mg^{2+} concentration is particularly elevated in the ThermoScript System buffer). The RT mixture used to this end needs to contain all components except the enzymes, including nucleotides and primers that bind Mg^{2+}, and is also subjected to all the RT incubation steps.

Reverse transcription protocols found in the literature often begin with a DNase digestion of the nucleic acids after extraction, with the goal of eliminating genomic DNA from the preparation. Experiments in our laboratory, however, indicate that some RNA degradation occurs during DNase treatment of the samples, even when recommended protocols are followed very carefully. In addition, genomic DNA provides an excellent control for nucleic acids extraction and amplification, and for copy number quantification, as explained earlier. We, therefore, chose to avoid performing DNase digestion of our samples. According to Version I of our strategy (**Fig. 21.1, I**), a portion of the nucleic acids from each embryo is used to prepare a no-RT-PCR assay that allows measurement of the copy number of the genes being studied (in parallel with the RT-PCR assay that also measures transcript numbers). During reverse transcription, designated no-RT-PCR aliquots are processed together with the RT-PCR samples and exactly in the same way, except for the omission of ThermoScript from the RT cocktail.

21.11. Real-time PCR and Quantification of Genomic DNA and cDNA Templates in Single Embryos

Xist is expressed almost exclusively in female cells because it mediates X chromosome inactivation and dosage compensation.[26-29] Sexing of the embryos to be analyzed is thus essential for a correct interpretation of the results when counting *Xist* RNA copies. For the same reason, averaging measurements in individual embryos is more precise than using pooled samples in which an equal distribution of males and females is usually assumed but statistically unlikely for small numbers of embryos.

We, therefore, approached the study of *Xist* developmental profile in female and male mouse embryos by parallel real-time PCR analyses of both *Xist* (genomic DNA + cDNA) and *Sry* (genomic DNA) in multiple single embryos. Embryos comprised by eight or more cells were sexed based on the presence/absence of *Sry*, while *Xist* RNA levels plus the number of *Xist* genomic copies were calculated for samples at all developmental stages.

This analysis allowed us first of all to conclude that embryos at the 8-cell stage onwards that lack *Sry* consistently display *Xist* RNA, as expected for female cells carrying one inactive X chromosome. Thus, *Xist* gene expression can be used as a reliable assay of embryo gender. (We could not perform *Sry* PCR on embryos comprised of fewer than eight cells because this additional assay required samples to be divided in at least three aliquots.) As shown below, this conclusion is valid for single blastomeres as well, but depends on the use of a *Xist/Sry* multiplex assay suitable for sexing of embryos at any developmental stage.

Second, we counted genomic *Xist* DNA and *Xist* RNA copies in multiple single embryos at different developmental stages. In order to determine the absolute numbers of template molecules present in an experimental sample, the C_t value(s) of the sample has to be compared to a standard curve correlating C_t values with known template numbers. This curve is the basis for quantification and needs to be as accurate as possible. We recommend using genomic DNA, rather than plasmid DNA, for constructing such a scale because it ensures that the chosen primers are specific for the desired amplicon, even when the presence of homologous sequences could cause mispriming. As detailed previously in this chapter, SYBR Green melting profiles provide a convenient way to establish product purity. Standard curves should be linear (such as the ones shown in **Plate 21.4, inset**), particularly at low template copy numbers in order to ensure an efficient detection of even single copies of a gene (**Plate 21.5A**). A line with a slope shallower than 3.2 cycles for each 10-fold decreases in template copy number (see **Section 21.2.** *Key Features of Real-Time RT-PCR*) indicates that PCR amplification is inefficient for some reason.

At each stage of development the average number of *Xist* genomic DNA copies per female embryo was found to be about twice the average number for male embryos at the same stage. This finding is consistent with the presence of two X chromosomes in female cells and one X chromosome in male cells and provides strong demonstration of the capacity of our real-time PCR-based procedure to accurately extract and count gene copies. In our experience such an analysis requires averaging values from at least 10–20 individually processed embryos, because embryos at the same stage vary in terms of their actual cell number and position in the cell cycle.

The average number of *Xist* genomic DNA copies in female and male embryos at each developmental stage also nicely matched the known number of cells at that stage. The number of cells in embryos at early stages was counted under the microscope before samples were collected. At later stages these numbers were estimated based on morphology and time in culture.

The results in the previous paragraphs further validated the accuracy of our methods and gave us confidence in our ability to count the number of genomes per embryo, even when individual cell boundaries are no longer distinct. This was particularly useful because mammalian embryos undergo endoreduplication[30] during formation of giant trophectodermal cells of the late blastocyst. These considerations, in turn, led us to conclude that it is most accurate to describe the pattern of *Xist* gene expression in female embryos both as the number of RNA molecules per whole embryo and as the number of RNA molecules per genome, as hundreds of genome copies can be present in a single cell.

21.12. Real-time PCR and Quantification of Genomic DNA and cDNA Templates in Single Blastomeres

Our analysis of female embryos demonstrated that the number of *Xist* RNA copies per genome peaks at the 16-cell stage and then declines, as RNA synthesis reaches a steady-state but DNA replication continues. This result, in turn, posed the question, is *Xist* RNA equally distributed in all cells of an embryo? We, therefore, developed a new strategy for the second part of our work in order to compare *Xist* RNA levels among individual blastomeres of single 8-cell stage female embryos (**Fig. 21.1**, Version **II**). In the course of this analysis we could not independently measure the number of *Xist* genomic copies present in each cell because reverse transcription had to be carried out in all samples. This number, however, is known for male and female blastomeres, as mentioned earlier, and can be subtracted from the total genomic *Xist* DNA + *Xist* cDNA copies in order to calculate *Xist* transcript levels. We have previously shown that male blastomeres at this developmental stage do not contain measurable amounts of *Xist* RNA. Thus, only one copy of *Xist* template is expected to be amplified during real-time RT-PCR of nucleic acids from a single male blastomere at the 8-cell stage, corresponding to a single copy of the *Xist* gene. It is also known that *Sry* is not expressed in cleavage stage embryos[31] and, therefore, all *Sry* signals are generated by genomic DNA sequences and also reflects the presence of a single copy in each male cell.

Based on this knowledge, we devised a multiplex RT-PCR assay for *Xist* and *Sry* by taking advantage of two sequence-specific Molecular Beacons conjugated to different fluorophores (the technical challenges encountered in developing this assay are described earlier in this chapter). While our goal was to measure *Xist* RNA levels in isolated female blastomeres, analysis of male blastomeres served to validate the method (**Plate 21.5A**). Although some male samples were missing either a *Sry* or a *Xist* signal (it is difficult to avoid losing a chromosome occasionally during the extraction procedure), signals from the recovered male DNA were remarkably consistent and served to establish the mean C_t value of a single copy of either the *Sry* or the *Xist* gene. This value, in turn, allowed us to calculate the expected C_t value of the two *Xist* genes present in each female sample. As anticipated, none of the female blastomeres exhibited a *Sry* signal and all had *Xist* signals with lower C_t values than any male blastomere, indicating the presence of *Xist* cDNA (**Plate 21.5B**). Numerous analyses were performed on cells isolated from several male and female embryos and the resulting C_t values were converted into numbers of *Xist* RNA copies per cell. Determinations in female blastomeres, in turn, were used to calculate total *Xist* RNA levels per embryo. These *Xist* RNA levels per embryo, calculated as the sum of single-cell values, were then compared to total *Xist* transcript accumulation directly measured in whole female 8-cell embryos. Whole embryos assays were run with either of the two strategies summarized in **Fig. 21.1** (Version **I** and Version **II**), providing two independent controls. These three sets of data (two from whole embryos, one from the sum of individual cells) overlapped, suggesting that our single-cell *Xist* RNA measurements were reliable. This finding was important in light of the fact that *Xist* RNA accumulation in individual cells of the same female embryo varied widely (*Xist* signals in **Plate 21.5B**, do not have the same C_t, unlike the single-copy male *Xist* signals in **Plate 21.5A**, indicating different levels of *Xist* RNA in the cells), and, in all embryos analyzed, two cells consistently contained the largest *Xist* RNA fraction.[14]

In conclusion, application of real-time RT-PCR to the study of *Xist* RNA levels in single embryos and individual blastomeres of single embryos allowed us to gain a considerable amount of new information. We could not only calculate average *Xist* RNA copy numbers for different developmental stages, but also establish that these numbers are quite variable within each group, maybe in relation to the individual sample's developmental rate. Moreover, we found wide differences in the *Xist* RNA content of blastomeres from the same 8-cell embryo and are presently investigating their possible connection with lineage differentiation. As shown by this example, quantification of gene expression by real-time RT-PCR holds great potential for the study of embryonic development, carcinogenesis, and many other fields.

References

1. Schultz RM, Davis W Jr, Stein P, Svoboda P: **Reprogramming of gene expression during preimplantation development.** *J Exp Zool* 1999, **285**:276–282.

2. Levy R: **Genetic regulation of preimplantation embryo survival.** *Int Rev Cytol* 2001, **210**:1–37.

3. Pesce M, Scholer HR: **Oct-4: Gatekeeper in the beginnings of mammalian development.** *Stem Cells* 2001, **19**:271-278.

4. Reik W, Dean W, Walter J: **Epigenetic reprogramming in mammalian development.** *Science* 2001, **293**:1089–1093.

5. Watson AJ, Barcroft LC: **Regulation of blastocyst formation.** *Front Biosci* 2001, **6**:D708–D730.

6. Zernicka-Goetz M: **Patterning of the embryo: The first spatial decisions in the life of a mouse.** *Development* 2002, **129**:815–829.

7. Czyz J, Wobus A: **Embryonic stem cell differentiation: The role of extracellular factors.** *Differentiation* 2001, **68**:167–174.

8. Bustin SA: **Absolute quantification of mRNA using real-time reverse transcription polymerase chain reaction assays.** *J Mol Endocrinol* 2000, **25**:169–193.

9. Bustin SA: **Quantification of mRNA using real-time reverse transcription PCR (RT-PCR): trends and problems.** *J Mol Endocrinol* 2002, **29**:23–39.

10. Liu W, Saint DA: **Validation of a quantitative method for real time PCR kinetics.** *Biochem Biophys Res Commun* 2002, **294**:347–353.

11. Krussel JS, Huang HY, Simon C, Behr B, Pape AR, Wen Y, Bielfeld P, Polan ML: **Single blastomeres within human preimplantation embryos express different amounts of messenger ribonucleic acid for beta-actin and interleukin-1 receptor type I.** *J Clin Endocrinol Metab* 1998, **83**:953–959.

12. Kowalik A, Liu HC, He ZY, Mele C, Barmat L, Rosenwaks Z: **Expression of the insulin-like growth factor-1 gene and its receptor in preimplantation mouse embryos; Is it a marker of embryo viability?** *Mol Hum Reprod* 1999, **5**:861–865.

13. Hartshorn C, Rice JE, Wangh LJ: **Developmentally-regulated changes of *Xist* RNA levels in single preimplantation mouse embryos, as revealed by quantitative real-time PCR.** *Mol Reprod Dev* 2002, **61**:425–436.

14. Hartshorn C, Rice JE, Wangh LJ: **Differential pattern of *Xist* RNA accumulation in single blastomeres isolated from 8-cell stage mouse embryos following laser zona drilling.** *Mol Reprod Dev* 2003, **64**:41–51.

15. Walker NJ: **A technique whose time has come.** *Science* 2002, **296**:557–559.

16. Bergstrom DE, Young M, Albrecht KH, Eicher EM: **Related function of mouse SOX3, SOX9, and SRY HMG domains assayed by male sex determination.** *Genesis* 2000, **28**:111–124.

17. Koopman P: *Sry* and *Sox9*: **Mammalian testis-determining genes.** *Cell Mol Life Sci* 1999, **55**:839–856.

18. Bernard PS, Lay MJ, Wittwer CT: **Integrated amplification and detection of the C677T point mutation in the methylenetetrahydrofolate reductase gene by fluorescence resonance energy transfer and probe melting curves.** *Anal Biochem* 1997, **255**:101–107.

19. Pierce KE, Rice JE, Sanchez JA, Brenner C, Wangh LJ: **Real-time PCR using molecular beacons for accurate detection of the Y chromosome in single human blastomeres.** *Mol Hum Reprod* 2000, **6**:1155–1164.

20. Tyagi S, Kramer FR: **Molecular beacons: probes that fluoresce upon hybridization.** *Nat Biotechnol* 1996, **14**:303–308.

21. De Vos A, Van Steirteghem A: **Aspects of biopsy procedures prior to preimplantation genetic diagnosis.** *Prenat Diagn* 2001, **21**:767–780.

22. Nicolson GL, Yanagimachi R, Yanagimachi H: **Ultrastructural localization of lectin-binding sites on the zonae pellucidae and plasma membranes of mammalian eggs.** *J Cell Biol* 1975, **66**:263–274.

23. Chomczynski P, Sacchi N: **Single-step method of RNA isolation by acid guanidinium thiocyanate-phenol-chloroform extraction.** *Anal Biochem* 1987, **162**:156–159.

24. Nam DK, Lee S, Zhou G, Cao X, Wang C, Clark T, Chen J, Rowley JD, Wang SM: **Oligo(dT) primer generates a high frequency of truncated cDNAs through internal poly(A) priming during reverse transcription.** *Proc Natl Acad Sci USA* 2002, **99**:6152–6156.

25. Pierce KE, Rice JE, Sanchez JA, Wangh LJ: **QuantiLyse™: Reliable DNA amplification from single cells.** *Biotechniques* 2002, **32**:1106–1111.

26. Lyon MF: **Gene action in the X chromosome of the mouse (Mus musculus L.).** *Nature* 1961, **190**:372–373.

27. Borsani G, Tonlorenzi R, Simmler MC, Dandolo L, Arnaud D, Capra V, Grompe M, Pizzuti A, Muzny D, Lawrence C, Willard HF, Avner P, Ballabio A: **Characterization of a murine gene expressed from the inactive X chromosome.** *Nature* 1991, **351**:325–329.

28. Brockdorff N, Ashworth A, Kay GF, Cooper P, Smith S, McCabe VM, Norris DP, Penny GD, Patel D, Rastan S: **Conservation of position and exclusive expression of mouse *Xist* from the inactive X chromosome.** *Nature* 1991, **351**:329–331.

29. Sheardown SA, Duthie SM, Johnston CM, Newall AE, Formstone EJ, Arkell RM, Nesterova TB, Alghisi GC, Rastan S, Brockdorff N: **Stabilization of *Xist* RNA mediates initiation of X chromosome inactivation.** *Cell* 1997, **91**:99–107.

30. Edgar BA, Orr-Weaver TL: **Endoreplication cell cycles: More for less.** *Cell* 2001, **105**:297–306.

31. Cao QP, Gaudette MF, Robinson DH, Crain WR: **Expression of the mouse testis-determining gene *Sry* in male preimplantation embryos.** *Mol Reprod Dev* 1995, **40**:196–204.

22

Single Cell Global RT and Quantitative Real-Time PCR

Ged Brady and Tania Nolan

Abstract

Increasingly, mRNA expression patterns established using a variety of molecular technologies such as cDNA microarrays, SAGE, and cDNA display are being used to identify potential regulatory genes and as a means of providing valuable insights into the biological status of the starting sample. Until recently, the application of these techniques has been limited to mRNA isolated from millions, or at very best, several thousand cells thereby restricting the study of small samples and complex tissues. To overcome this limitation a variety of amplification approaches have been developed which are capable of broadly evaluating mRNA expression patterns in single cells. This review will describe approaches that have been employed to examine global gene expression patterns either in small numbers of cells or, wherever possible, in actual isolated single cells. The first half of the review will summarize the technical aspects of methods developed for single-cell analysis and the latter half of the review will describe the areas of biological research, which have benefited from single-cell expression analysis.

22

Single Cell Global RT and Quantitative Real-Time PCR

Ged Brady[*] **and Tania Nolan**[†]

[*]Epistem Ltd., Manchester, United Kingdom
[†]Stratagene Europe, Amsterdam, The Netherlands

22.1. Introduction

Following enormous advances in the area of genomics and the complete sequencing of the human genome, the current challenge to biologists is to learn how the products of the 30,000–150,000 identified genes interact to produce the complexity exhibited by higher eukaryotes. Although an examination of mRNA or protein expression patterns alone does not directly address function, the knowledge of when and where a gene is expressed can provide valuable insights as to the potential role of a gene and has historically been instrumental in the discovery of developmentally regulated genes. For example, the earliest cDNA cloning experiments were based on the knowledge of tissue-specific expression and led to the isolation of cDNA clones for globin[1] and lysozyme.[2] Subsequent to the isolation of highly expressed genes such as globin, cDNA subtraction strategies were developed in order to reveal lower abundance differentially expressed genes and led to the discovery of biologically important genes such as the T cell receptor[3,4] and the myoD transcription regulator.[5]

Recognition of the value of the examination of expression patterns led to the development of a plethora of more advanced technologies such as cDNA microarrays,[6] SAGE,[7] and cDNA display[8] aimed at the simultaneous measurement of tens to several thousand genes in the target samples. However, a major restriction of most mRNA profiling approaches is the relatively large amount of starting mRNA required thus limiting studies to the examination of pools of several million or at best several thousand cells. The ability to apply expression profiling to smaller samples including single cells would be beneficial for both basic research and clinical molecular diagnosis. However, since the total RNA content of mammalian cells ranges between 20–40 pg[9,10] and only 0.5–1 pg of this is mRNA any attempt at single-cell profiling must be capable of dealing with a total of 10^5–10^6 starting mRNA molecules. Despite this considerable limitation, over the last decade a multitude of amplification procedures have been developed in order to tackle mRNA expression profiling specifically at the level of a single mammalian cell (for a general review see reference).[11] This chapter will specifically deal with the use of a global cDNA amplification protocol (*PolyAPCR*) to amplify and characterize representative total cDNAs from single cells.

22.2. *PolyAPCR* Overview

PolyAPCR was designed to preserve the relative abundance of the transcripts present in the starting RNA sample.[12] In order to preserve relative abundance during the PCR step and avoid biased amplification of cDNAs due to size, the reverse transcriptase reaction has been tailored to create produce cDNA strands to around 100–700 bases regardless of the size of the original RNA template. To simplify the amplification process and to make it suitable for single-cell analysis, cDNA amplification is achieved by the sequential addition of reagents to the starting cell(s) thereby avoiding any losses associated with sample purification.[12,13] Although the simplicity and representative nature of *PolyAPCR* lends itself to multiple single-cell analysis[12,14-17] and quantitative studies,[12,18-21] it must be noted that the 3' nature of the PCR product (*PolyAcDNA*) makes it unsuitable for the analysis of changes in the 5' end. Due to the speediness and simplicity of the *PolyAPCR* method can be readily applied to hundreds of samples[17] and the resultant *PolyAcDNA* products have been widely used as probes in differential screening approaches. For example, *PolyAcDNA* probes have been prepared from microdissected mouse embryo tissues,[22] antibodiy fractionated human hematopoietic precursors,[23] single murine hemopoietic precursors,[24,25] and more recently *PolyAcDNA* probes have been used for high density microarray screening.[26,27]

22.3. Ensuring Ratio of RNAs in Is Equal to Ratio of cDNAs out

Although *PolyAcPCR* is both sensitive and quantitative (*op cit*), it is important that the reagents used are effective. One of the most direct means of doing so is to apply *PolyAcPCR* to a set of RNA standards containing defined proportions of a target gene(s). A convenient set of RNA standards can be prepared using total RNA from a non-erythroid tissue and commercially obtainable globin RNA.[12,20] Following amplification of cDNAs prepared from the RNA standards the proportion of target sequences present can be evaluated by Southern hybridization or quantitative PCR.[12,20,21]

22.4. Why Carry out Single-Cell Analysis?

Single-cell expression profiling studies enable researchers to tackle the cellular complexity of higher eukaryotes and represent one of the few approaches, which are suitable for the examination of rare, biologically important, cell types such as stem cells.[28-30] However, although single-cell RT-PCR approaches such as *PolyAPCR* are achievable, they are nevertheless extremely technically demanding and should be employed when there is a clear benefit in examining gene expression at a single cell level. For example, there is a clear benefit in analyzing individual tumor or leukemic cells if they are surrounded by nonmalignant cells but single-cell analysis would not be warranted if homogeneous or clonal populations of neoplastic cells are available. The following descriptions are intended to provide examples of when single-cell analysis is justified.

In addition to aiding the study of tumors and leukemia, single-cell profiling approaches have been particularly useful in examining hemopoiesis. For hemopoiesis studies the existence of well-characterized culture conditions has allowed the identification and molecular characterization of individual cells on the basis of their developmental capacity.[15,17,19] The general principle of this approach (known as sibling analysis—see reference[15] for details) is to grow individual precursors *in vitro* under none-restrictive growth conditions and allow them to divide two or five times to generate a "colony start" of 4 to 32 cells. From each colony start, one or more cells are withdrawn for global amplification and the remaining sibling cells are grown separately to generate secondary colonies. The differentiation capacity of the lysed cell(s) used for RT-PCR is then inferred from the colony types arising from the living siblings. Since the total number of hematopoietic precursors analyzed by sibling analysis generally amounts to less than 1% of starting hematopoietic tissues, it is unlikely that the expression patterns uncovered would be detected using expression methods applied to bulk populations.

Another field, which has benefited from single-cell profiling, is the study of early embryos particularly including the study of individual oocytes, eggs, and one-cell embryos.[18,31,32] Expression studies of oocytes, eggs, and one-cell embryos is greatly helped by the fact that they are relatively large and contain around 50–100 fold more mRNA than somatic cells ($1-3\times10^7$ mRNAs/cell—see discussion in the paper).[18] In some instances examination of RNA extracted from fractionated cellular compartments has facilitated the study of gene regulation due to alterations in adenylation of existing mRNAs or recruitment of mRNAs to the transcriptional machinery.[18,20]

A useful and striking feature of single-cell expression analysis is its ability to detect transient expression patterns, which would not be detected through studies of large cell populations. For example, single-cell analysis of revealed that the imprinted tumor suppressor gene H19 is transiently expressed specifically at the onset hemopoietic lineage commitment and is low or undetectable at earlier or later stages of differentiation.[23] In a similar vein analysis of the expression of retinoic acid receptors (RAR), α and γ in enriched populations, single cells revealed transient expression predominantly in cells destined to become granulocytes.[33] This latter observation led to the analysis of hematopoietic precursors in RAR α and γ null animals and the discovery of a requirement for RAR α and γ expression during terminal granulocytic maturation.[33]

22.5. Picking the "Right" Single Cell

The most obvious and important factor in single-cell expression profiling is the correct identification and isolation of the target cell. The exact means of identification and isolation will vary depending on the target but will be generally based on characteristics such as morphology, cell location, presence of surface epitopes, physiological function, and the behavior of sibling cells. Clearly, stringent cell identification criteria will reduce the likelihood of choosing an incorrect cell which will cloud later expression analysis. Whenever possible cell identification criteria should be used which allow direct visualization of the target cell such as the presence of immunologically detectable cell-surface markers, which have been used by Trumper and colleagues to apply *PolyAPCR* to individual Hodgkin's and Reed-Sternberg cells isolated from patients with Hodgkin's disease.[14,34] For solid tumors laser capture microdissection (LCM) offers one of the most promising means of isolating cells based on direct microscopic visualization of tissue sections.[35] In addition to direct visualization, the presence of known expression markers in the target cell will prove extremely valuable for checking both the accuracy of cell selection and the efficiency of global single-cell amplification.

As well as clearly identifying individual cells, it is equally important to ensure that the process of cell isolation has not brought about unavoidable changes in gene expression. Although, as Werner Heisenberg made clear,[36] we cannot avoid influencing any observed result, there are some precautions, which can minimize potential artifacts. Since most, if not all, cells from multicellular organisms are programmed to self-destruct if deprived from a source of survival factors, it is essential that these factors are present at all stages of cell isolation. This is particularly important when handling low cell densities where individual cells may not receive sufficient survival factors from their neighbors. Another common problem encountered when handling cells in small volumes is a lethal increase in pH often brought about by using phosphate buffered media in low CO_2 (atmospheric) conditions. This can often be avoided by using an isotonic solution buffered with biological buffer such as HEPES.

22.6. Experimental Details of *PolyAPCR*

22.6.1. Global Amplification of cDNA to Copy All Polyadenylated RNAs (*PolyAPCR*)

Details of *PolyAPCR* have been previously described.[13,21] Briefly in general, total RNA (1–100 ng) or fresh cell lysate (1–200 cells) in a volume of 1 μl, is added to 10 μl of first lyse buffer (600 units/ml Prime RNase Inhibitor (5'-3' Inc), 50 mM *Tris*-HCl pH 8.3, 75 mM KCl, 3 mM $MgCl_2$, 0.5% Nonidet P-40, 10 μM dNTPs, 23 nM dT24 oligo) incubated at 65°C for 1 minute, cooled to room temperature (23°C), and transferred to wet ice. Subsequent to the addition of 12.5 units of AMV reverse transcriptase (Boehringer Mannheim), the reverse transcription reaction is initiated by transferring the samples from ice to 37°C. After incubation at 37°C for 15 minutes, the reverse transcriptase is inactivated by incubation at 65°C for 10 minutes and samples were then returned to ice. Addition of a 5'-priming site is achieved by performing a terminal transferase reaction by adding 10 μl of 2× tailing buffer (200 mM potassium cacodylate pH 7.2, 4 mM $CoCl_2$, 0.4 mM DTT, 1 mM dATP) containing 10 units of terminal deoxynucleotide transferase (Gibco BRL).

Samples are after that incubated at 37°C for 15 minutes, the enzyme then is heat inactivated at 65°C for 10 minutes, and samples are returned to ice. For the PCR, 20 µl of PCR mix (23.5 mM *Tris*-HCl pH 8.3; 117.4 mM KCl, 8.2 mM $MgCl_2$, 2.2 mM dNTPs, 0.23% Triton X-100, 47 µg/ml BSA, 85 units/ml *Taq* polymerase (Boehringer Mannheim), 8.33 µM Oligo Not1dT40 (Genosys), **Table 22.1**) is added to 10 µl of tailed reaction, and amplification performed using two linked programs, each of 25 cycles. The first 25 cycles consist of denaturation at 94°C for 1 minute, primer annealing at 42°C for 2 minutes and extension at 72°C for 6 minutes. The second 25 cycles consist of denaturation at 94°C for 1 minute, primer annealing at 42°C for 1 minute, and extension at 72°C for 2 minutes. The *PolyAPCR* products (*PolyAcDNA*) can be evaluated by agarose gel electrophoresis and samples adjusted to a final concentration of approximately 0.5 µg/ml. Subsequent amplifications of *PolyAcDNA* can be carried out on approximately 1 ng of target *PolyAcDNA* products in 50 µl reactions containing 1.5 µM oligonucleotide Not1dT40 (**Table 22.1**), 2.5 units *Taq* Polymerase (Boehringer Mannheim) and 0.25 mM dNTPs in buffer supplied by the manufacturer. A typical reamplification PCR reaction would consist of 25 cycles of denaturation at 94°C for 1minute, primer annealing at 42°C for 1 minute, and extension at 72°C for 2 minutes.

Table 22.1. Examples of PCR primers and fluorogenic TaqMan™ PCR

Gene	Oligo	Primer and probe sequence 5' to 3'
PolyAPCR	Oligo Not1 dT40	CATCTCGAGCGGCGGC (TTT)$_8$
Rabbit á globin	RG-QF	GCGCACAAGCTGCGGGTG
	RG-QR	CCACTCACTCAGACTTTATTC
	RG-F	CATGCCTCCCTGGACAAGTT
	RG-R	CCAGGCTCCAGCTTAACGATA
	RG-T	*FAM*–CCAACGTGAGCACCGTGCTGACC – *TAMRA*
GAPDH	Gap-QF	CCAGCAAGAGCACAAGAGGAAGAG
	Gap-QR	AGCACAGGGATACTTTATTAGATG
	Gap-F	ACACTCAGACCCCCACCACA
	Gap-R	CATAGGCCCCTCCCCTCTT
	Gap-T	*FAM*–TCTCCCTCCTCACAGTTGCCATGTAGA – *TAMRA*

TaqMan™ sets = F—forward primer, R—reverse primer, and T—probe.
Probes are labeled at 5' with the reporter dye FAM (6-carboxyfluorescein, emission λ_{max} = 518 nm) and at 3' end with the quencher dye TAMRA (6-carboxytetramethylrhodamine, emission λ_{max} = 582 nm).

22.6.2. Preparation of Gene Specific Quantity Standard Series

Specific PCR primers are required for each gene studied. These should be directed towards the mRNA sequence within 300 bp of the PolyA$^+$ addition site, as described previously.[23] Example primer sequences are presented in 5' to 3' orientation and are listed in **Table 22.1**. For genes with only one quantification primer listed, the second primer was used for both conventional and TaqMan™ PCR. Simple gene-specific PCR reactions are carried out in a total volume of 25 µl and contained 1 ng of *PolyAcDNA*, 0.33 µM of each oligonucleotide PCR primer, 0.5 units of *Taq* Polymerase (Boehringer Mannheim), and 0.25 mM dNTPs in buffer supplied by the manufacturer. Gene-specific PCR products can be purified using a Qiagen PCR purification kit as recommended by the manufacturer. Purified fragments can then be resolved by agarose gel electrophoresis, visualized by ethidium bromide staining, and the concentration can be determined by densitometric analysis using a GS-700 imaging Densitometer (Bio-Rad) and Molecular Analyst Software version 1.5 (Bio-Rad). The purified fragments can then be used to generate a gene-specific quantity standard series (GSQS) ranging from 1.5×10^{10} molecules/ml to 1.5×10^4 molecules/ml,[23] diluted in TE (10 mM *Tris*-HCl pH 8.0, 1mM EDTA).

22.6.3. TaqMan™ Real-Time Quantitative PCR Used to Quantify Specific Gene Expression

PCR primers and probes, for use in real real-time quantitative PCR, were designed using Primer Express™ Software (PE Applied Biosystems, Foster City, Calif., version 1.0) and are listed in **Table 22.1**. Primers and fluorogenic probes (5' FAM and 3' TAMRA) were supplied by either PE Applied Biosystems or MWG-Biotech. For each gene, PCR reactions are applied to approximately 1 ng *PolyAcDNA* derived from each patient sample and also to 10 µl of each gene-specific quantity standard (diluted to maintain the equivalent of 3×10^7 molecules to 30 molecules). The PCR reaction is typically carried out in a total volume of 25 µl using a TaqMan™ Gold kit as recommended by the manufacturer. Briefly, *PolyAcDNA* is diluted to 1 ng in 10 µl and dispensed into optical 96-well plates (Advanced Biotechnologies). A PCR master mix of 15 μl containing probe and primers is then aliquoted onto each target sample. Sample data is then analysed using a suitable real-time detection system such as an ABI Prism 7700 Sequence Detection System (PE Applied Biosystems).

Acknowledgement

I would like to thank the editor for his patience.

References

1. Maniatis T, Kee SG, Efstratiadis A, Kafatos FC: **Amplification and characterization of a beta-globin gene synthesized *in vitro*.** *Cell* 1976, **8**:163–182.

2. Sippel AE, Land H, Lindenmaier W, Nguyen-Huu MC, Wurtz T, Timmis KN, Giesecke K, Schutz G: **Cloning of chicken lysozyme structural gene sequences synthesized *in vitro*.** *Nucleic Acids Res* 1978, **5**:3275–3294.

3. Yanagi Y, Yoshikai Y, Leggett K, Clark SP, Aleksander I, Mak TW: **A human T cell-specific cDNA clone encodes a protein having extensive homology to immunoglobulin chains.** *Nature* 1984, **308**:145–149.

4. Hedrick SM, Nielsen EA, Kavaler J, Cohen DI, and Davis MM: **Sequence relationships between putative T-cell receptor polypeptides and immunoglobulins.** *Nature* 1984, **308**:153–158.

5. Davis RL, Weintraub H, Lassar AB: **Expression of a single transfected cDNA converts fibroblasts to myoblasts.** *Cell* 1987, **51**:987–1000.

6. Duggan DJ, Bittner M, Chen YD, Meltzer P, Trent JM: **Expression profiling using cDNA microarrays.** *Nature Genetics* 1999, **21**:10–14.

7. Velculescu VE, Zhang L, Vogelstein B, Kinzler KW: **Serial analysis of gene expression.** *Science* 1995, **270**:484–487.

8. Liang P, Pardee: **Differential display of eukaryotic messenger RNA by means of the polymerase chain reaction.** *Science* 1992, **257**:967–971.

9. Uemura E: **Age-related changes in neuronal RNA content in rhesus monkeys (Macaca mulatta).** *Brain Res Bull* 1980, **5**:117–119.

10. Roozemond RC: **Ultramicrochemical determination of nucleic acids in individual cells using the Zeiss UMSP-I microspectrophotometer. Application to isolated rat hepatocytes of different ploidy classes.** *Histochem J* 1976, **8**:625–638.

11. Brady G: **Expression profiling of single mammalian cells—Small is beautiful.** Comp Funct Genomics: *Yeast* 2000, **17**:211–217.

12. Brady G, Barbara M, Iscove NN: **Representative *in vitro* cDNA amplification from individual hemopoietic cells and colonies.** *Meth Mol Cell Biol* 1990, **2**:17–25.

13. Brady G, Iscove NN: **Construction of cDNA libraries from single cells.** *Methods Enzymol* 1993, **225**:611–623.

14. Trumper LH, Brady G, Bagg A, Gray D, Loke SL, Griesser H, Wagman R, Braziel R, Gascoyne RD, Vicini S, Iscove NN, Cossman J, Mak TW: **Single-cell analysis of Hodgkin and Reed-Sternberg cells: Molecular heterogeneity of gene expression and p53 mutations.** *Blood* 1993, **81**:3097–3115.

15. Brady G, Billia F, Knox J, Hoang T, Kirsch IR, Voura EB, Hawley RG, Cumming R, Buchwald M, Siminovitch K, Miyamoto N, Boehmelt G, Iscove NN: **Analysis of gene-expression in a complex differentiation hierarchy by global amplification of cDNA from single cells.** *Current Biology* 1995, **5**:909–922.

16. Berardi AC, Wang AL, Levine JD, Lopez P, Scadden DT: **Functional isolation and characterization of human hematopoietic stem-cells.** *Science* 1995, **267**:104–108.

17. Ziegler BL, Muller R, Valtieri M, Lamping CP, Thomas CA, Gabbianelli M, Giesert C, Buhring HJ, Kanz L, Peschle C: **Unicellular-unilineage erythropoietic cultures: Molecular analysis of regulatory gene expression at sibling cell level.** *Blood* 1999, **93**:3355–3368.

18. Rambhatla L, Patel B, Dhanasekaran N, Latham KE: **Analysis of G protein alpha subunit mRNA abundance in preimplantation mouse embryos using a rapid, quantitative RT-PCR approach.** *Molecular Reproduction And Development* 1995, **41**:314–324.

19. Cheng T, Shen HM, Giokas D, Gere J, Tenen DG, Scadden DT: **Temporal mapping of gene expression levels during the differentiation of individual primary hematopoietic cells.** *Proc Natl Acad Sci USA* 1996, **93**:13158–13163.

20. Wang QX, Latham KE: **Translation of maternal messenger ribonucleic acids encoding transcription factors during genome activation in early mouse embryos.** *Biology of Reproduction* 2000, **62**:969–978.

21. Al Taher A, Bashein A, Nolan T, Hollingsworth M, Brady G: **Global cDNA amplification combined with real-time RT-PCR: Accurate quantification of multiple human potassium channel genes at the single cell level.** *Yeast* 2000, **17**:201–210.

22. Varmuza S, Tate P: **Isolation of epiblast-specific cDNA clones by differential hybridization with polymerase chain reaction-amplified probes derived from single embryos.** *Molecular Reproduction And Development* 1992, **32**:339–348.

23. Núnêz C, Bashein AM, Brunet C, Hoyland J, Freemont T, Buckle A-M, Murphy C, Cross M, Lucas G, Bostock VJ, Brady G: **Expression of the imprinted tumour-suppressor gene H19 is tightly regulated during normal hematopoiesis and is reduced in hematopoietic precursors of patients with** *Polycythemia Vera*. *Journal of Pathology* 2000, **190**:61–68.

24. Claudio JO, Liew CC, Dempsey AA, Cukerman E, Stewart AK, Na E, Atkins HL, Iscove NN, Hawley RG: **Identification of sequence-tagged transcripts differentially expressed within the human hematopoietic hierarchy.** *Genomics* 1998, **50**:44–52.

25. Weaver DL, Núñez C, Brunet C, Bostock V, Brady G: **Single-cell RT-PCR cDNA subtraction.** In: *Molecular Embryology: Methods and Protocols*, P. Sharpe and I. Mason, eds. Totowa, NJ, USA: Humana Press, 1999, pp. 601–609.

26. Bryant Z, Subrahmanyan L, Tworoger M, LaTray L, Liu CR, Li MJ, vandenEngh G, RuoholaBaker H: **Characterization of differentially expressed genes in purified Drosophila follicle cells: Toward a general strategy for cell type- specific developmental analysis.** *Proc Natl Acad Sci USA* 1999, **96**:5559–5564.

27. Iscove NN, Barbara M, Gu M, Gibson M, Modi C, Winegarden N: **Representation is faithfully preserved in global cDNA amplified exponentially from sub-picogram quantities of mRNA.** *Nat Biotechnol* 2002, **20**:940–943.

28. van der Kooy D, Weiss S: **Why stem cells?** *Science* 2000, **287**:1439–1441.

29. Weissman IL: **Translating stem and progenitor cell biology to the clinic: Barriers and opportunities.** *Science* 2000, **287**:1442–1446.

30. Bach SP, Renehan AG, Potten CS: **Stem cells: The intestinal stem cell as a paradigm.** *Carcinogenesis* 2000, **21**:469–476.

31. Adjaye J, Daniels R, Bolton V, Monk M: **cDNA libraries from single human preimplantation embryos.** *Genomics* 1997, **46**:337–344.

32. Jurisicova A, Antenos M, Kapasi K, Meriano J, Casper RF: **Variability in the expression of trophectodermal markers beta-human chorionic gonadotrophin, human leukocyte antigen-G and pregnancy specific beta-1 glycoprotein by the human blastocyst.** *Human Reproduction* 1999, **14**:1852–1858.

33. Labrecque J, Allan D, Chambon P, Iscove NN, Lohnes D, Hoang T: **Impaired granulocytic differentiation** *in vitro* **in hematopoietic cells lacking retinoic acid receptors alpha 1 and gamma.** *Blood* 1998, **92**:607–615.

34. Trumper LH, Brady G, Vicini S, Cossman J, Mak TW: **Gene expression in single Reed Sternberg cells of Hodgkin's disease: Results from PCR generated single cell cDNA libraries.** *Ann Oncol* 1992, **3** Suppl 4:25–26.

35. Emmert-Buck MR, Bonner RF, Smith PD, Chuaqui RF, Zhuang Z, Goldstein SR, Weiss RA, Liotta LA: **Laser capture microdissection.** *Science* 1996, **274**:998–1001.

36. Heisenberg, W: **Über den anschaulichen Inhalt der quantentheoretischen Kinematik und Mechanik.** *Zeitschrift für Physik* 1927, **43**:172–198.

23

Single Nucleotide Polymorphism Detection with Fluorescent MGB Eclipse Probe Systems

Irina A. Afonina, Yevgeniy S. Belousov,
Mark Metcalf, Alan Mills, Silvia Sanders,
David K. Walburger, Walt Mahoney,
and Nicolaas M. J. Vermeulen

Abstract

The MGB Eclipse Probe Systems are ideally suited to unambiguously detect single nucleotide polymorphisms (SNP) with post-amplification melting curves. Assays are easy to perform, capable of high throughput and can be performed on any amplified target. Since the probes are not degraded during amplification, reactions could be archived. This chapter describes the design of probes and primers to analyze three SNPs in "easy" and "problematic" AT- and GC-rich regions. Probes and primers are designed with the newly developed MGB Eclipse™ Design Software that has the ability to incorporate an MGB moiety and three Superbases into the probes and primers to address stability or self-association.

23

Single Nucleotide Polymorphism Detection with Fluorescent MGB Eclipse Probe Systems

Irina A. Afonina, Yevgeniy S. Belousov, Mark Metcalf, Alan Mills, Silvia Sanders, David K. Walburger, Walt Mahoney, and Nicolaas M. J. Vermeulen

Epoch Biosciences, Inc., Bothell, Washington

23.1. Introduction

Single-nucleotide polymorphism analysis has become increasingly important in basic fundamental research, pharmacogenomics, and molecular diagnostics.[1] Melting curve analysis for the detection of polymorphisms including SNPs, viral types, deletions, and insertions was developed as an important adjunct to homogenous real-time fluorescent detection assays. The technique is simple, is performed post-amplification, and requires a probe or probes that are stable during amplification. Homogeneous assay formats based on melting curve analysis such as dynamic allele-specific hybridization (DASH),[2] melting curve single-nucleotide polymorphism (McSNP),[3] and FRET-based melting curves have been reported.[4] These assays are setup as typical amplification reactions; the only difference is that analysis is performed post-amplification.

We recently developed fluorogenic 2'-deoxyribonucleotide probes containing a MGB Eclipse™ Dark Quencher (DPI$_3$-Q) at the 5' end and a fluorophore (Fl) at the 3' end, known as MGB Eclipse™ Probe Systems[5] (MGB™ and Eclipse™ are trademarks of Epoch Biosciences; www.epochbio.com). The MGB ligand consists of a dihydrocyclopyrroloindole (DPI$_3$) minor groove binder, which stabilizes AT-rich duplexes preferentially.[6] The 5'-MGB-quencher group also prevents 5'-nuclease digestion by *Taq* polymerase during homogeneous amplification.[5] These probes fluoresce upon hybridization to the complementary target (**Plate 23.1**). In absence of amplified target, the probe exists in a random coil conformation with extremely low fluorescence. In a real-time PCR assay, these probes displayed a dynamic range of 7 orders of magnitude, with an ultimate sensitivity of better than 5 copies per sample.

The MGB ligands conjugated to oligonucleotides form hyperstabilized duplexes with complementary DNA.[7,11] The sequence specificity of these conjugates provides a significant advantage for high temperature PCR applications.[11] The nonfluorescent dark quencher (Eclipse™ Dark Quencher, www.epochbio.com) in combination with the MGB moiety in probes (MGB-Q-Oligo-Fl) allows for low-fluorescence backgrounds.[8] Performance of some probes and primers in G- and AT-rich regions can be improved significantly by the appropriate substitution of G, A, and T with Super G™, Super A™ or Super T™ (www.epochbio.com), respectively.[9]

Since 5'-MGB-Q-Oligo-Fl probes are not cleaved by 5'-nuclease activity during amplification, they are ideal to differentiate SNPs through melting curve analysis post-amplification. Typically, two probes complementary to a wild-type and mutant alleles respectively are designed using the MGB Eclipse Design Software (www.epochbio.com) with similar or identical T$_m$s, but labeled with two fluorophores with different emission wavelengths. The wild-type probe is labeled with fluorophore A and the mutant one with fluorophore B. In the analysis of samples, both probes are added to each sample. When amplification is completed, the first derivative melting curve for each probe duplex is determined at two different emission wavelengths specific for two different fluorophores, respectively. If only homozygous wild-type target is present, a melting curve with only the fluorophore-A-labeled wild-type probe is observed in the A-channel with a lower than match T_m melting curve in the B channel. Similarly, if only homozygous mutant target was present, a melting curve with only the fluorophore-B-labeled probe was obtained (curve in the A channel with lower than match melting curve in the A channel was sometimes observed). However, in the case of a heterozygous target, melting curves with both the fluorophore-A- and fluorophore-B-labeled probes, with the T_m of a match (homozygous) sample, were observed in both channels. The presence of a melting curve in the appropriate channel at the expected T_m allows for unambiguous interpretation. Most instruments, like the Rotor-Gene 2000 (www.corbettresearch.com) and ABI PRISM® 7700 and 7900 (www.appliedbiosystems.com), have the ability to perform melting curves and to compile the curves of different samples in each channel. The post-amplification detection strategy allows archiving of amplified samples for further analysis.

This chapter describes the analysis of single nucleotide polymorphisms of IL13-02, IL5, and DIO2 (http://snp500cancer.nci.nih.gov) in DNA samples obtained from Coriell Institute of Medical Research (http://arginine.umdnj.edu) (See **Section 23.7**, *Note 1*). The IL13-02 and IL5 alleles are examples of mismatches in G- and AT-rich regions, respectively.

23.2. General Discussion

The detection of A/C alleles in the G-rich IL13-02 gene by post-amplification melting curve analysis for a wild-type, heterozygous, and mutant samples is shown in **Plate 23.2**. PCR amplification was performed with primers (oligos # 1 and # 2, see **Table 23.1**) and probes for both alleles in each sample tube; the wild-type probe (oligo # 3) was labeled with

fluorescein (FAM) and the mutant allele probe (oligo # 4) was labeled
with 5'-tetrachlorofluorescein (TET; www.glenresearch.com). These
probes were designed with the MGB Eclipse Design 2.3 Software to
have similar melting temperatures and required the inclusion of Super
G™ (see **Section 23.7**, *Note 2*). When amplification was completed, the
first derivative melting curve for each probe duplex was determined at
two different emission wavelengths specific for FAM and TET, respectively (**Plate 23.2A–C**).

Table 23.1. Sequence of primers and probes for allele discrimination studies.

Oligo #	Type	Sequence[a]
IL13-02		
1	L-primer	GTGGGAGATGCCGTGGGC
2	E-primer	GTGCCTGGAGTGCCG
3	"A"-Probe	MGB-Q-CCGTAG**A**GGgGTCACA-FAM
4	"C"-Probe	MGB-Q-CGTAG**C**GGgGTCACA-TET
IL5		
5	L-primer	CTTGCtttTTCCTGCTGCTCAT
6	E-primer	CATCCTTGGGCACCTTTCC
7	"C"-Probe	MGB-Q-TACATA**C**aGaTCCaG-FAM
8	"T"-Probe	MGB-Q-TACATA**T**aGatCCaG-TET
DIO2-02		
9	L-primer	CATGTGGCTCCCTCAGCTATCTTCT
10	E-primer	AGGTGAAATTGGGTGAGGATGC
11	"C"-Probe	MGB-Q-CCTTCTG**C**ACTGGA-FAM
12	"T"-Probe	MGB-Q-CCTTCTG**T**ACTGGAGA-TET

[a] The SNP is in bold and underlined. "a" is Super A and "t" is Super T. TET is 5'-tetra-
chlorofluorescein. Q is the Eclipse™ Dark Quencher. L is limiting (0.2 μM final
concentration) and E is excess (2.0 μM final concentration).

The homozygous wild-type allele yields a melting curve with only the
FAM-labeled wild-type probe in the FAM-channel (**Plate 23.2A**), with
no melting curve in the TET-channel. Similarly, the homozygous
mutant target presents a melting curve, with the expected T_m in the TET-
channel and a low T_m melting curve in the FAM-channel (**Plate 23.2C**).
However, in the case of the heterozygous target, melting curves with
both the FAM- and TET-labeled probes are observed in both channels
(**Plate 23.2B**). The insignificant hybridization of the mutant probe with

the wild-type target in the FAM channel (**Plate 23.2C**) represents a small melting curve with a lower T_m than that of the perfect match, allowing unambiguous interpretation.

The IL5 single nucleotide polymorphism is located in an AT-rich region. One primer (oligo # 5) required the substitution of T_s with Super T™ while the two probes (oligo # 6 and # 7) needed substitution of A with Super A, to achieve the required stability for a functional assay (**Plate 23.3**, **Section 23.7**, *Note 2*). The DNA samples were unambiguously typed as containing ten wild-type, four heterozygous, and one mutant allele. As shown in **Plate 23.3B**, the small melting curves with a lower T_m in the TET-channel were obtained due to slight hybridization of the wild-type probe to the mutant target.

The single-nucleotide polymorphism, DIO2-02, represents a case where no modification of primers and probes is required in the analysis (**Plate 23.4**).

All the samples could be typed unambiguously. X and Z are examples of samples that do not amplify well. In scatter plots based on traditional endpoint real-time fluorescence, these samples more than likely would have been incorrectly typed. Since only one melting curve was observed for each of these samples in either the FAM- or TET-channels that coincided with match T_ms, they are unambiguous, typed as wild-type and mutant alleles, respectively. The small melting curves in the TET-channel with a lower T_m, represent slight hybridization by wild-type probe to the mutant allele.

The 5'-nuclease stability of the MGB Eclipse probes allows a post-amplification detection strategy and makes archiving of amplified samples for further analysis possible.

23.3. Materials

23.3.1. Preparation of Nucleic Acids

(See **Section 23.7**, *Note 1*)

The samples used in this chapter are human genomic DNAs purchased from Coriell Institute for Medical Research (Camden, N.J.).

23.3.2. Primers and Probes

(See **Section 23.7**, *Note 2*)

The MGB Eclipse Design Software 2.3 (www.epochbio.com) was used to design MGB Eclipse primers and probes. There are several suppliers that synthesize primers. MGB modified probes and primers that contain Superbases™ are available from Epoch Biosciences. Limiting and reverse primers (0.2 and 2 μM final concentration) could be mixed together and should be stored at –20°C. The sequences of the primers and probes used are shown in **Table 23.1**.

23.3.3. Amplification Enzyme

(See **Section 23.7**, *Note 3*)

JumpStart™ *Taq* Polymerase (www.sigma-aldrich.com) is used at a concentration of 0.8 U per reaction volume. The amount of enzyme can be changed proportionally to the desired volume.

23.3.4. Amplification Solutions

(See **Section 23.7**, *Note 4*)

PCR buffer should be prepared as a 2× master mix (40 mM Tris-HCl pH 8.7, 100 mM NaCl, 10 mM $MgCl_2$), 0.25 mM dATP, 0.25 mM dCTP, 0.25 mM dGTP, 0.5 mM dUTP, 2× MasterAmp PCR Enhancer (www.epicenter.com) and 0.02× of 1 U/μl of AmpErase® Uracil *N*-glycosylase (www.appliedbiosystems.com)).

23.4. Methods

23.4.1. Amplification

(See **Section 23.7**, *Note 5*)

1. Set up each 10-μl reaction per tube/well as shown in **Table 23.2**. One tube should be reserved for no-template control.

2. Cap the 0.1-ml tubes (plate) and ensure that they are properly sealed.

3. Transfer the tubes (plate) to thermocycler and perform PCR as described in **Table 23.3**.

Table 23.2. Amplification reaction mixture.

Reaction Components	Volume/Reaction	Final Concentration
DNase-free sterile water	3.18 µl	
2× Master mix	5 µl	1×
20× Primer Mix	0.5 µl	1×
Taq DNA polymerase (2.5 U/ì l)	0.32 µl	0.8 U/reaction
Template genomic DNA	1.0 µl	1 pg–2 µg/reaction
Total Volume	10 µl	

Table 23.3. PCR amplification conditions.

Stage	1	2	3 (40–50 cycles)		
Temp., °C	50	95	95	58*	76
Time, s	120	120	5	15	20

* Fluorescence is optionally measured in the annealing step.

23.4.2. Melting Curve Analysis

(See **Section 23.7**, *Note 6*)

1. Assign sample names to each tube or well (i.e., unknown, no-template control).

2. Both probes can be added (both into each sample) at the end or after the first amplification step to a final concentration of 0.2 µM.

3. Start melting curve analysis by holding at 95°C for 25 s and at 45°C for 15 s and then heat to 80°C at a rate of 1°C per 5 s for the Rotor-Gene 2000 instrument. The ramp rates for the ABI PRISM® 7700 and 7900 are 5 min and 10%, respectively. Consult instrument manuals for the proper dissociation curve presentation. Deselect "normalization" option, if possible.

4. The instrument analyzes the data and calculates the first derivative melting curve for each sample. It plots the $\Delta F/\Delta T$ against temper-

ature for each sample in the two selected fluorescence emission channels.

5. The experimental data report display analyzes data for each sample and displays all the melting curves in a compiled format for each channel (**Plates 23.2–23.4**).

23.5. Instruments

(See **Section 23.7**, *Note 7*)

We have used Rotor-Gene 2000 and ABI PRISM® 7700 and 7900 for the melting curve analysis.

23.6. Data Interpretation

(See **Section 23.7**, *Note 8*)

23.6.1. Rotor-Gene

a) The melting curve for each sample in each channel is inspected. A melting curve with the labeled probe for wild type and a melting curve with a second labeled probe for the mutant in their respective channels at the T_ms expected for a match probe, unambiguously indicate the presence of a wild-type and mutant alleles, respectively. A sample showing melting curves with both these probes in both channels corresponding to the expected T_ms, unambiguously indicates the presence of a heterozygous allele.

b) In the case of the Rotor-Gene 2000 instrument, each sample can be selected to visually assign the allelic type.

c) The Rotor-Gene 2000 has since been replaced with the Rotor-Gene 3000 with improved performance characteristics.

23.6.2. Other Instruments

The analysis is performed in a similar fashion as that used in the Rotor-Gene 2000 instrument and according to the manufacturer's instructions (see **Section 23.7**, *Note 7*).

23.7. Notes

Note 1

Although we have used purified DNA in this study, we also have prepared DNA samples for other studies with commercial extraction kits. We have used the IsoQuick Extraction kit (Orca Research, Bothell, Wash.) successfully for the extraction of DNA from blood.

Note 2

The T_m melting analysis requires asymmetric PCR amplification. This limits the competition between the probe and the amplicon strand for binding to the excess target strand (see *Note 3*). The MGB Eclipse Design Software has the ability to incorporate not only the MGB moiety, but also three different modified bases into probes as the sequence dictates. Super G is used to substitute G in probe and primer sequences containing more than three Gs in a row (see probes # 3 and # 4) to eliminate self-association.[10] The incorporation of the DPI_3 moiety into the probe stabilizes AT-rich sequence preferentially allowing the design of short probes with excellent mismatch discriminatory properties.[11] Super A and Super T when substituted for A and T increase the T_m respectively with about 2.5 to 5.5 and 1.5 to 3.0°C per incorporation, depending on the nearest neighbors. MGB Eclipse Probes Systems containing Super A and T are available from Epoch Biosciences. The MGB Eclipse Design Software automatically designs primers, for this study, with T_ms in the range of 61–69°C.

The MGB-probes are designed with a T_m between 64–68°C and a length of between 11 and 18 bases long. In cases where additional stabilization on top of that supplied by the MGB group is required (oligos # 7 and # 8), modified base is incorporated automatically by the software or manually by the operator. The design program takes into consideration interactions between probes and primers; so that in the final design there are no detrimental secondary structures in probes and primers. The accuracy of the program is ±2°C for primers and probes. MGB Eclipse probes and primers are delivered in ready to use 20× formulations and should be stored at −20°C.

Note 3

Enzymes from a licensed vendor should be used. The Jumpstart™ *Taq* polymerase (Sigma Aldrich, *Cat. No. D9307*) functions well with the MGB Eclipse Hybridization Buffer. Polymerases from other PCR vendors have been evaluated with MGB Eclipse Probe System. FastStart *Taq* DNA polymerase (Roche, Indianapolis, Ind.) works only with the manufacturer's FastStart buffer. Both the Platinum® *Taq* DNA polymerase with the Platinum *Taq* Antibody (Invitrogen, Carlsbad, Calif.) and Titanium *Taq* DNA polymerase (Clontech, Palo Alto, Calif.) also perform well only with the manufacture's buffer. AmpliTaq® Gold (www.appliedbiosystems) performs well only if used in combination with MasterAmp™ PCR Enhancer (www.epicentre.com). It was determined that HotStartTaq® (Qiagen, Valencia, Calif.) performs well in the Qiagen buffer. The magnesium concentration should be adjusted if necessary to achieve the required concentration, see *Note 4*.

Note 4

PCR is covered by patents owned by Hoffman-La Roche, Inc. and Hoffman-La Roche Ltd. AmpErase Uracil *N*-glycosylase is used with dUTP (instead of TTP) in all PCR reactions as a PCR product carryover prevention measure. The correct magnesium ion concentration assures satisfactory amplification and should be between 2 and 5 mM.

The higher extension temperature at 76°C is used to assure that no clamping occurs due to MGB Eclipse probes during extension.

Note 5

Amplification volumes can be adjusted for other instruments, e.g., 5 and 25 µl for the ABI PRISM® 7900 and 7700 respectively. If desired, amplification can be performed in a nonfluorescent thermocycler, followed by melting curve analysis in a fluorescent thermocycler.

In this study the amplification mixtures are thoroughly mixed during amplification by the centrifugal force of the Rotor-Gene 2000 Real-Time Amplification System. In other instruments care should be taken to assure that samples are properly prepared and mixed as required. If no melting curve signal is observed, we typically run a gel to determine if amplification of the intended target occurred. If the gel indicates no or little amplification, a number of parameters should be checked:

a) The number of cycles may be too low—increase number of cycles.

b) Extension temperature may not be properly set at 76–78°C.

c) Check that the final optimum magnesium concentration is between 2 and 5 mM.

d) Data is not properly analyzed.

Note 6

If no fluorescence signal is observed make sure that (a) the instrument is set to read fluorescence at the required emission wavelengths of the two fluorophores and (b) that the "Normalize to" option should be deselected. Passive reference, such as ROX, should be deselected if ROX is present in the buffer.

A typical melting curve analysis with all the samples takes about 5–10 minutes after completion of amplification.

Note 7

To perform melting curves on the ABI PRISM 7700, MGB Eclipse Probe Systems utilize the ABI PRISM Dissociation Curve Analysis Software. This program uses the Multicomponent data exported from the SDS software v. 1.7 to display the dissociation curves for each sample. Though the primary purpose of the ABI PRISM Dissociation Curve Analysis Software is to provide melting curve analysis on SYBR Green dye assays run on the ABI PRISM 7700, any dye loaded on the system can be analyzed in the software. The ABI PRISM Dissociation Curve Analysis Software is available free of charge from the Applied Biosystems website. It is important to note that SDS software v. 1.7 or higher is required for use with the ABI PRISM Dissociation Curve Analysis Software. The most current SDS software is also available free of charge from the Applied Biosystems website (www.appliedbiosystems.com/support/software/7700/updates.cfm).

In the case of the AB PRISM® 7900 melting curve analysis with the MGB Eclipse Probes systems can be performed as described in the manual. Alternatively, summarized protocols to perform melting curve analysis with these probes on these instruments are available from Epoch Biosciences. For high-throughput applications we have developed a macro that automatically genotypes samples based on melting curve analysis (available from www.epochbio.com\support).

Note 8

SNP analysis with endpoint real-time PCR methods based on fluorescent values, on occasion erroneously types alleles as manifested by overlapping scatter plot assignments.[9] Since the assignment of alleles based on melting curves is dependent on its presence in one or both of the analyzing channels and not on fluorescent values, allele typing is unambiguous. The assignment of allele is further confirmed by the presence of the melting curve with designed T_m. Occasionally a probe complementary to one allele (wild-type) hybridizes slightly to another allele (mutant). This leads to a small melting curve with a lower T_m than that of the perfect match, still allowing unambiguous allele assignment.

23.8. Summary

The MGB Eclipse Probe Systems are ideally suited to unambiguously detect single nucleotide polymorphisms (SNP) with post-amplification melting curves. Assays are easy to perform, capable of high throughput and can be performed on any amplified target. Since the probes are not degraded during amplification, reactions could be archived. This chapter described the design of probes and primers to analyze three SNPs in "easy" and "problematic" AT- and GC-rich regions. Probes and primers were designed with newly developed design software that has the ability to incorporate MGB technology and three Superbases into the probes and primers to address stability of self-association.

References

1. Shi MM: **Enabling large-scale pharmacogenetic studies by high-throughput mutation detection and genotyping technologies.** *Clin Chem* 2001, **47**:164–172.

2. Howell WM, Jobs M, Gyllensten JU, Brookes AJ: **Dynamic allele-specific hybridization. A new method for scoring single nucleotide polymorphysims.** *Nat Biotechnol* 1999, **17**:87–88.

3. Akey JJ, Sosnoski D, Parra E, Dios S, Hiester K, Su B, Monilla C, Jin L, Shriver MD: **Melting curve analysis of SNPs (McSNP®): A gel-free and inexpensive approach for SNP genotyping.** *Biotechniques* 2001, **30**:358–367.

4. Espy MJ, Uhl JR, Michell PS, Thorvilson JN, Svien KA, Wold AD, Smith TF: **Diagnosis of Herpes Simplex Virus infections in the clinical laboratory by Light Cycler PCR.** *J Clin Micorbiol* 2000, **38**:795–799.

5. Afonina IA, Reed MW, Lusby E, Shishkina IG, Belousov YS: **Minor groove binder-conjugated DNA probes for quantitative DNA detection by hybridization-triggered fluorescence.** *BioTechnniques* 2002, 32:940–949.

6. Kutyavin EV, Lukhtanov EL, Gamper HB, Meyer RB: **Oligonucleotides with conjugated dihydropyrrooindole tripeptides: Base composition and backbone effects on hybridization.** *Nucleic Acids Res* 1997, **25**:3718–3723.

7. Lukhtanov EA, Kutyavin IV, Gamper HB, Meyer RB: **Oligodeoxynucleotides with conjugated dihydropyrroloindole oligopeptides: Preparation and hybridization properties.** *Bioconj Chem* 1995, **6**:418–426.

8. Lukhtanov EL, Metcalf M, Reed MW: **Fluorogenic DNA probes for multicolor hybridization assays.** *Am Biotechnol Lab* 2001, **19**:68–69.

9. Afonina I, Belousov E, Metcalf MS, Mills A, Sanders S, Kutyavin I, Walburger D, Gorn V, Shishkina I, Adams D, Ahmadian M, Dempcy R, Milesi D, Reed MW, Vorobiev A, Wald A, Scarr N, Yau E, Vermeulen N: **Single nucleotide polymorphism detection with MGB Eclipse™ assays.** *J Clin Ligand Assay* 2002, **25**:268–275.

10. Kutyavin IV, Lokhov SG, Afonina IA, Dempcy R, Gall AA, Gorn VV, Lukhtanov E, Metcalf M, Mills A, Reed MW, Sanders S, Shishkina I, Vermeulen NMJ: **Reduced aggregation and improved specificity of G-rich oligonucleotides containing pyrazolo[3,4-d]pyrimidine guanine (PPG) bases.** *Nucleic Acids Res* 2002, **30**:4952–4959.

11. Kutyavin IV, Afonina IA, Mills A, Gorn VV, Lukhtanov EA, Belousov ES, Singer MJ, Walburger DK, Lokhov SG, Gall AA, Dempcy R, Reed MW, Meyer RB, Hedgpeth J: **3'-Minor groove binder-DNA probes increase sequence specificity at PCR extension temperatures.** *Nucleic Acids Res* 2000, **28**:655–661.

24

Genotyping Using MGB-Hydrolysis Probes

Jane Theaker

Abstract

This chapter describes the latest chemistries, plasticware, and protocols associated with the development of genotyping assays, which use MGB hydrolysis probes. The commonly encountered phenomenon of "ROX baseline drift," is explained, with some solutions to the problem. The formulation of master mixes for genotyping is described. Various assay-design and analysis programs are covered; some freely available on the web. The application of melting curves to troubleshooting assays, of various types, is discussed. Finally, a useful laboratory tool: A Total Human DNA Quantification Assay based on the Apo B gene is presented.

24

Genotyping Using MGB-Hydrolysis Probes

Jane Theaker

AstraZeneca Pharmaceuticals, Alderley Park, Macclesfield, United Kingdom

24.1. Introduction

The accurate detection of polymorphisms, especially SNPs using various molecular techniques has become an essential precursor for human genotyping. Real-time PCR methods are particularly suited for diagnostic assays, designed to detect known mutations or polymorphisms. The 5'-nuclease (TaqMan) assay is the most widely used of the real-time methods and, through its combination of the amplification and analysis steps, makes genotyping a simple, reliable process with the potential for high throughput. In this chapter, I refer to TaqMan probes, which are only available from ABI and make the distinction between these probes and "dual-labeled" probes from other manufacturers.

24.1.1. Improved Chemistries

In the recent past, the success of hydrolysis-based (TaqMan and dual-labeled probe) genotyping assays could be unpredictable, especially when using probes designed to anneal to AT-rich sequence. They were prone to cross-hybridize to the "wrong" amplicon, generating a non-specific signal. One solution to this problem is the use of allele-specific Minor Groove Binder (MGB) TaqMan probes labeled with different fluorescent dyes (**Fig. 24.1**). Another historical problem when optimizing a genotyping or multiplex assay was the considerable spectral overlap of fluorophores, with the resultant spectral crosstalk affecting the robustness of the assays. Novel chemistries have, once again, come to the rescue, and a typical fluorophore combination for a genotyping or multiplex assay uses FAM and VIC, which are spectrally, relatively distant.

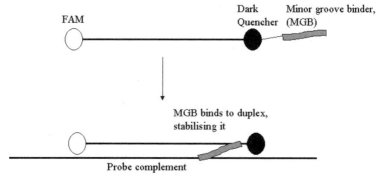

Figure 24.1. When the probe encounters its complement, it hybridizes to the latter. The MGB moiety at the 3' end of the probe is then able to nestle in the minor groove, which is only generated in the duplex state. The binding of the MGB moiety stabilizes the duplex state, raising the T_m of the duplex. What was once a 25-mer probe can now be designed to be a 16-mer MGB probe. For an allele-specific probe, the benefit is that one mismatched base in 16 bases is more destabilizing, than one base in 25 bases. Hence, allele specificity is improved by using a short MGB probe.

24.1.2. Dark Quenchers

All TaqMan and dual-labeled probes must have a quencher moiety at the 3' end to prevent the probe signaling in the uncleaved state. TAMRA, the traditional choice, uses Fluorescent Resonance Energy Transfer (FRET) to quench any fluorescence from the FAM reporter fluorophore at the 5' end of the probe. Light energy harvested by the FAM reporter is donated to the TAMRA FRET-quencher, which re-emits the energy, at a slightly increased wavelength. In contrast, dark quenchers, for example, BlackHole Quencher™, or BHQ, (Biosearch Technologies, Inc.) and ElleQuencher™ from Eurogentec, work by accepting the light energy of the FAM reporter and "vibrating" it away as heat-energy, without re-emitting it as light. Why is this important? It means that where there is a fluorescent signal from TAMRA, this no longer occurs with a dark quencher probe. Therefore, there is more "room" in the spectrum for the fluorophores, in which we are interested—FAM and VIC. Other dark quenchers, such as methyl red, do not re-emit fluorescent energy around 580 nm, which would coincide with VIC or TAMRA, but at a much higher wavelength. Consequently, it makes sense that MGB probes should be synthesized with dark, not FRET quenchers.

24.1.3. Single-Tube Genotyping Assay Design Recommendations

When designing large numbers (greater than 25) of genotyping assays at once, Applied Biosystems, Inc. (ABI) will design and synthesize MGB assays under their "Assays-by-Design^{SM} Service." The Assays-by-Design^{SM} Service is an assay development service that designs, synthesizes, formulates, and delivers analytically quality-controlled primer and probe sets for single nucleotide polymorphism (SNP) genotyping and gene expression assays based on sequence information submitted by the customer.

It goes without saying, that all reagents, machines, plasticware, and conditions should be ABI approved for the assays to function as the user intends. The service is aimed at large-scale genotyping operations rather than smaller institutions. The Assays-on-Demand™ service supplies prevalidated MGB assays with increasing coverage of the genome, as time goes by. The quality of the assays is always excellent. When designing a small number of assays (less than 25), ABI's software, Primer Express™, version 1.5 or higher, is recommended. Using FAM/VIC MGB probe technology will improve assay success. It is suggested that designing the MGB allele-specific probes with the allele-variant base, in the middle or 3' end of the probe will gain maximal allele specificity. In addition, there are several assay design recommendations, namely:

A. Probe Design Rules

- no Gs next to the reporter (G acts as a fluorescence quencher);
- more Cs than Gs;
- probe T_m 7°C higher than the primers;
- less than 4 contiguous Gs;
- 13–20 bases long MGB;
- allele-variant base in the middle or 3' end of the probe.

B. Amplicon Design Rule

- 50–150 bp in length.

C. Primer Design Rules

- T_m is 58–60°C;
- 20–80% GC content;
- less than 2°C difference in T_m between the two primers;
- maximum of 2/5 G or C at 3' end;
- length 9–40 bases;
- As close as possible to the probe without overlapping.

24.2. Evaluation of a Single-Tube Genotyping Assay

To evaluate a single-tube genotyping assay you need to have:
- Forward and reverse primers;
- FAM/dark quencher MGB probe (A-specific probe);
- VIC/dark quencher MGB probe (B-specific probe);
- Homozygous Allele A template DNA @ 25 ng/μl;
- Heterozygous Allele B template DNA @ 25 ng/μl;
- Heterozygous A/B template DNA @ 25 ng/μl;

- Universal master mix (UMM);
- Water.

Prepare the three reaction mixes described below.

Mix 1

A-specific FAM probe (200 nM final), UMM (1× final), forward and reverse primers (900 nM final), and water to bring volume to 25 µl/well.

Mix 2

B-specific VIC probe (200 nM final), UMM (1× final), forward and reverse primers (900 nM final), and water to bring volume to 25 µl/well.

Mix 3

A-specific FAM probe (200 nM final), B-specific VIC probe (200 nM final), UMM (1× final), forward and reverse primers (900 nM final), and water, to bring volume to 25 µl/well.

Combine the three reaction mixes with the three template DNAs according to **Table 24.1**, that is, add 5 µl of DNA to each 20-µl reaction mix to give a final volume of 25 µl/well. Set up no-template controls (NTCs), using water, in place of DNA.

Cycling

95°C 10 min;
(92°C—15 s, 60°C—1 min) × 40.

Analyze using the anneal step to generate real-time data. Use the real-time data in assay development and endpoint data once the assay has been optimized.

24.3. Troubleshooting a Genotyping Assay

24.3.1. Problem: No Signal or Poor Signal

A poor signal is characterized by a noisy, jagged, amplification plot. A poor signal on the ABI PRISM® 7700 (or "7700") would be typified in the

Table 24.1. Expected amplification plot results for each mix/template combination with an "ideal" genotyping assay. No further optimization would be required for this assay. ✓ represents a positive amplification plot signal, × represents no amplification plot signal.

Template DNA	MIX 1-A FAM-specific *(FAM-detection channel)*	MIX 2-B VIC-specific *(VIC-detection channel)*	MIX 3 FAM A and VIC B	
AA	✓	×	✓	×
AA	✓	×	✓	×
AB	✓	✓	✓	✓
AB	✓	✓	✓	✓
BB	×	✓	×	✓
BB	×	✓	×	✓
NTC	×	×	×	×
NTC	×	×	×	×

"raw spectra" view, as having poor fluorescent growth of less than approximately 1000 units, although machine scales and calibrations do vary, so the jagged amplification plot is a more reliable measure. Before proceeding further, check that there is sufficient amplicon, post-PCR, to be able to see the product on a 3% agarose gel. The gel will display multiple bands, in addition to the amplicon of interest, because of the high magnesium concentration (5.5–7 mM), which is required for TaqMan. If the correct amplicon is not observed, then PCR optimization and/or primer redesign is necessary. Classically, PCR optimization would include titration of Mg^{2+}, optimization of annealing temperature, and addition of glycerol to the PCR mix, prior to redesigning the PCR primers. There are numerous excellent resources available which cover this topic. If you are using Universal Master Mix, then only optimization of the annealing temperature or redesigning the primers are feasible options.

Assays containing Uracil-*N*-glycosylase (UNG) should be kept on ice and run on an agarose gel immediately, because residual enzyme activity will quickly destroy any PCR product. The UNG decontamination system relies on replacement of dTTP in the master mix with dUTP. PCR products are thus made susceptible to degradation by UNG. Incubation with UNG before PCR destroys any carryover dUTP containing PCR products from any previous reactions.

If a strong amplicon band is observed on a gel, then the problem is likely to be intra-strand secondary structure, in the amplicon, preventing probe annealing. The MFold program (see **Section 24.6.1.** *MFold*) is particularly useful in identifying areas of secondary structure, so that probes can be redesigned to avoid these sections. This may not always be possible, specifically, with a genotyping assay where the probe position is relatively fixed.

24.3.2. Problem: Probe Cross-Hybridization

Table 24.2 shows typical amplification plot data obtained with an assay where the A (FAM) probe cross-hybridizes to the B amplicon and signals off it.

Table 24.2. Probe cross-hybridization. ✓ represents a positive amplification plot signal, ✕ represents no amplification plot signal.

Template DNA	MIX 1-A FAM-specific (FAM-detection channel)	MIX 2-B VIC-specific (VIC-detection channel)	MIX 3 FAM A and VIC B	
AA	✓	✕	✓	✕
AA	✓	✕	✓	✕
AB	✓	✓	✓	✓
AB	✓	✓	✓	✓
BB	✓	✓	✓	✓
BB	✓	✓	✓	✓
NTC	✕	✕	✕	✕
NTC	✕	✕	✕	✕

What can be done about probe cross-hybridization? In order of preference:

- Reduce the concentration of the A probe. To optimize, titrate the A-probe concentration from 200 nM to 150 nM, 100 nM, and 50 nM. Choose the concentration, which reduces the erroneous signal, but leaves enough of the specific signal to be robust in mix three.

- Optimize the annealing temperature, by performing a temperature "titration." In other words, keep all other parameters the same but cycle at the following annealing temperatures: 54°C, 56°C, 58°C,

62°C, 64°C, and 66°C. The optimal annealing temperature is that which gives the lowest A probe on B template—cross-hybridization—signal without losing the correct A probe on A template signal.

- Increase the concentration of the B (VIC) probe. The rationale behind this approach is that if the cross-hybridization cannot be eliminated, then at least its impact can be minimized—by outcompeting the nonspecific FAM probe with greater concentrations of VIC probe. In the above experiment, titrate the VIC probe, upwards, from 200 nM to 250 nM, 300 nM, 350 nM, and 400 nM. The optimal concentration is that which gives the smallest FAM, nonspecific, signal relative to a large, specific, VIC signal and allows for facile genotype clustering in Mix 3. The downside of this approach is that it consumes a disproportionate amount of VIC probe and spectral crosstalk from VIC into FAM is possible.

- Redesign the A probe to maximize the probe specificity. This may mean moving the SNP from the central third of the probe, to the last 5 bases of the 3' end, to capitalize on the specificity offered by the binding of the MGB. Reducing the probe length, by increasing the percentage of GC content, may also increase specificity. HyTher 1.0 (see **Section 24.6.2.** *HyTher™ 1.0* below) is a very useful program, which allows calculation of the probe's matched and mismatched T_ms. If you can maximize the difference between matched and mismatched T_ms, then the probe will be more specific at a particular temperature.

24.3.3. Problem: Spectral Crosstalk

In theory, this problem should only be seen with TAMRA probes, not MGB probes. **Table 24.3** shows the typical results obtained with an assay where the A probe FAM signal spectrally "spills over" into the VIC detection "channel" giving rise to an erroneous signal. The highlighted wells give a positive amplification plot, not only in the FAM-detection channel, but also in the VIC-detection channel. It should be noted that although FAM into VIC spectral crosstalk is most common, crosstalk can also occur in the opposite direction—VIC into FAM, if the VIC signal is strong enough.

Table 24.3. Spectral crosstalk. ✓ represents a positive amplification plot signal, × represents no amplification plot signal. Highlighted wells are examined in the VIC-detection channel as well as the FAM-detection channel.

Template DNA	MIX 1-A FAM-specific (FAM detection channel)	MIX 2-B VIC-specific (VIC detection channel)	MIX 3 FAM A and VIC B	
AA	✓	×	✓	✓
AA	✓	×	✓	✓
AB	✓	✓	✓	✓
AB	✓	✓	✓	✓
BB	×	✓	×	✓
BB	×	✓	×	✓
NTC	×	×	×	×
NTC	×	×	×	×

What can be done about spectral crosstalk? In order of preference:

- Reduce the concentration of the probe, which is spilling into the other detection channel. In this example, keep all other parameters the same, but titrate the FAM probe concentration from 200 nM to 150 nM, 100 nM, and 50 nM. The optimum concentration is that which reduces spectral crosstalk but still leaves sufficient FAM signal to produce a robust assay with Mix 3.

- Switch on the spectral compensation option (ABI only). This option is a "black-box" algorithm provided by ABI which can sometimes rescue assays, which are known to spectrally crosstalk.

- Perform a temperature titration, to optimize the annealing temperature, in order to reduce the spectral crosstalk from FAM into VIC. In other words, keep all other parameters the same but use the following annealing temperatures: 54°C, 56°C, 58°C, 62°C, 64°C, and 66°C. The optimum temperature is that which gives a robust FAM and VIC signal in Mix 3, but where FAM into VIC spectral crosstalk is minimized.

- Increase the concentration of the VIC probe. The rationale behind this approach is that if the spectral crosstalk cannot be eliminated, then at least its impact can be minimized by making the nonspecific signal small, relative to the large, specific, VIC signal. In the above experiment, titrate the VIC probe from 200 nM to 250 nM, 300 nM, 350 nM, and 400 nM. The optimal concentration is that which gives the smallest FAM, nonspecific, signal, without spectrally swamping from VIC into FAM.

- Redesign both probes, keeping the sequences the same but reversing the fluorophores. In other words, the A probe as the VIC fluorophore and the B probe as a FAM fluorophore. In this way the innate asymmetry of all fluorophore spectra is utilized to reduce spectral crosstalk.

- Redesign the FAM probe to try to reduce the background fluorescence. The amount of background fluorescence observed, with a particular probe, would be secondary-structure dependent, which is, in turn, sequence-dependent. By deliberately designing the FAM probe to include some secondary structure, then the FAM will be in closer proximity to the quencher and background fluorescence will be reduced. The downside of this "fix" is that this new probe design is less likely to anneal to the template; so FAM signal may be reduced.

Having performed these optimization experiments, you should be well-placed to decide which combination of cycle number, annealing temperature, A-probe concentration, B-probe concentration, and spectral compensation should be used to give the most specific genotyping, single-tube assay. It almost goes without saying that resigning probes is the last, most expensive option.

24.4. The Transition from Real-Time to Endpoint Genotyping Assay

Once optimized, a single-tube genotyping assay does not need to be performed in real time. Instead, the assay can be run under optimized cycling conditions and read at endpoint. Suitable machines for endpoint reading would include any real-time instrument such as the ABI PRISM® 7700 and 7900. A simple fluorimeter, for example, the Fluoroskan or Cytofluor may also be used, but assay reliability may be compromised. Volumes can also be reduced to around 5 µl, but it is always worth assessing the robustness of assays at this lower volume. If an assay is not very robust at lower volumes, the number of PCR cycles may be increased. One key point is to optimize cycling *every time* when there is a switch to a different PCR machine. The ABI PRISM® 7700 ramps at approximately 1°C/second and this ramping time is crucial, especially in two-step cycling—in replicating the exact cycling conditions from one machine to the next. When switching PCR machines, extra cycles may be required, a slightly different annealing temperature, a different denaturation temperature, or even an extension step.

24.5. General Practical Points and Hints

24.5.1. Plasticware and its Compatibility with Hardware

The plasticware, which is available from ABI is appropriate for most real-time and endpoint genotyping applications. It has been specifically designed for use with ABI hardware, such as the ABI PRISM® 7700 and 7900, and gives excellent results. The combination of ABI reagents, plasticware, hardware, and software is optimal for "hassle-free" genotyping. There will always be occasions, however, where there is a necessity to source alternative suppliers of plasticware and hardware. Smaller-scale genotypers may wish to consider that Abgene produce a range of plasticware, which is suited to ABI machines (for a comprehensive plasticware-compatibility table see http://www.abgene.com/qpcrComp.asp).

The ABI PRISM® 7700 can accommodate 96-well semi-skirted plates from Abgene (*Cat. No. AB-0900*). These are best used with pre-cut, "clear seal strong" sealant (*Cat. No. AB-0685*) applied with a manual sealer (*Cat. No. AB-0384/110* or *AB-0384/240*). Sealant has, anecdotally, been reported to accumulate on the heated lid of the ABI PRISM® 7700. I have never experienced any problems but would recommend the use of ABI's optical cover compression pads (*Cat. No. 4312639*) in conjunction with Abgene's plate and sealant, just to be on the safe side. This plate / sealant / optical mat combination also works in the ABI 9600.

For high-throughput operations, Abgene's thermofast 384-well plates (*Cat. No. TF-0384 natural*) are compatible with TETRADS and the ABI PRISM® 7900. These plates should be used with clear seal strong on a roll (*Cat. No. AB-3686*) and the ALPS (Automated Laboratory Plate Sealer) 300 sealer. A manual sealer will also work with 384-well plates but it is often difficult to get even sealing across the plate; so be prepared for the odd failed well. The beauty of this combination (TF-0384 and clear seal strong on a roll) is that it completely watertight and can be used in the high-throughput water bath PCR cycler, the Duncan, from Kbiosystems (contact http://www.kbiosystems.com, Kbiosystems Ltd, Units 5 to 8 Paycocke Close, Basildon, Essex SS14 3HS, United Kingdom). This machine cycles 108×384-well plates simultaneously in 2.5 hours. This equates to a throughput of 124,416 endpoint genotyping reactions in 7.5 h! A mini-Duncan (or H_2Obit—"Hobbit") is available which cycles 24×384-well plates in 2.5 hours, for those with slightly lower throughputs of 27,648 per 7.5 hours. The TF-0384 plates can be custom barcoded on either/both edges which makes them compatible with barcoders on the ABI PRISM® 7900, the "Assist" plate handler, and robotic pipetting stations such as the Biomek FX from Beckman Coulter (http://www.beckman.com/ products/instrument/automatedsolutions/biomek/biomekfx_inst_dcr.asp). TheTecan Genesis and CyBi-Well from Cybio (http://www.cybio-ag.com/ english/cybi_well2000.html) are alternative robotic pipetting stations, which you may like to consider.

For those genotyping on a budget, another advantage of TF-0384 plates is that they can be used with the Fluoroskan fluorimeter (*Cat. No. 5210470*, Thermolabsystems, http://www.thermo.com). This Fluorimeter reads fluorescence from above the plate but can be set up to read from underneath. It can also be purchased with an Assist Plate Handler, for high-throughput reading. It is quite possible to set up a 384-well genotyping reaction, to seal with a foil sealant (*Cat. No.AB-0559*) or peelable sealant (*Cat. No. AB-3739*) using a manual sealer, to cycle in a TETRAD, then to read FAM and VIC fluorescences from underneath, or above, using the Fluoroskan. The optimal filter sets to use are: excitation 485 nm/emission 530 nm for FAM and 530 nm excitation/555 nm emission for VIC.

24.5.2. ROX Including Baseline Drift

ROX is a rhodamine derivative fluorescent dye, commonly added to real-time reaction buffers at approximately 60 nM, which acts as an internal standard. It can be excited at 488 nm and will emit at around 610 nm, but its excitation is not optimal at 488 nm. For this reason some manufacturers have created a "FRET species" which uses another fluorophore to harvest light optimally at 488 nm, and transmit it by resonant energy transfer to the rhodamine moiety for emission at 610 nm. The two fluorophores are linked by a short oligonucleotide sequence. Conjugation of the two dyes to an oligonucleotide improves their solvation by polar solvents, such as water. The inclusion of ROX, in reaction mixes has a one main advantage but some significant disadvantages, when considering the development or evaluation of a new assay.

The main advantage of ROX is that it can compensate for a number of well-to-well variables, which would include:

- Temperature variability affecting fluorescent response;
- Volume differences caused by pipetting inaccuracy;
- Differences in the optics of the instrument.

The main disadvantage of including ROX in real-time reaction buffers is that it makes assessment of FAM signal rather difficult. When a real-time FAM amplification plot is generated, the signals from three fluorophores are used: FAM, TAMRA (unless a dark quencher is used), and ROX. The FAM signal is divided by the TAMRA signal, and this ratio is divided by the ROX signal. To the novice, a signal of "2.0" in one assay may appear very much like a signal of "2.0" in another assay, but it must be remembered that this is a three-way ratio. I always recommend switching ROX off, and examining the resultant FAM:TAMRA ratio, before making signal comparisons between assays. The raw spectral and multicomponent views can also be used to determine, exactly, what is happening to the three fluorophores over the course of a real-time run.

The second disadvantage of ROX is that it can be swamped by adjacent fluorophores in the spectrum. This is particularly likely to happen in a multiplex assay, where two probes are present, adding to the starting background fluorescence. **Fig. 24.2** shows the raw spectral view from the typical FAM / TET multiplex and the ROX signal, which is being detected. The ROX signal is tiny, compared to the spectrally competing TAMRA signal.

At some point the multicomponenting algorithm is no longer able to deconvolute the ROX signal from the background signal. This gives rise to a strange amplification plot, which starts out as expected and then leaps up to infinity, as the ROX signal tends towards zero, see **Fig. 24.3**. There are three solutions to this spectral swamping problem:

- Add more ROX;
- Reduce the amount of probe(s);
- Switch off ROX and reanalyze the assay.

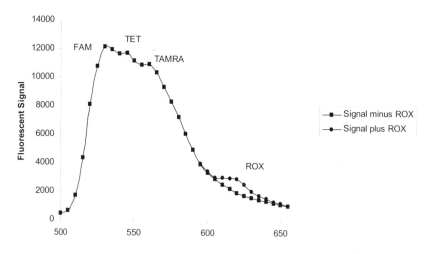

Figure 24.2. Swamping of ROX signal.

The third disadvantage of ROX is that it can lead to amplicon-plot baseline drift. Early buffer formulations were notoriously prone to ROX precipitating out of solution in the "fridge," only to re-solvate over the course of a real-time run. This would cause an increase in the ROX signal over time and a reduction in the FAM:TAMRA/ROX three-way ratio. Buffers have moved on and the inclusion of adjuncts, to improve ROX-solvation, has largely solved this problem. In addition, the use of "FRET-oligo" rhodamine, rather than the raw fluorophore alone, has improved solvation and has the added advantage of accounting for some non-specific probe degradation. Baseline drift may still be observed where the FAM:TAMRA signal is relatively small, in comparison to the change in ROX solvation over time. There is only one solution to this particular cause of baseline drift; increase the FAM:TAMRA signal.

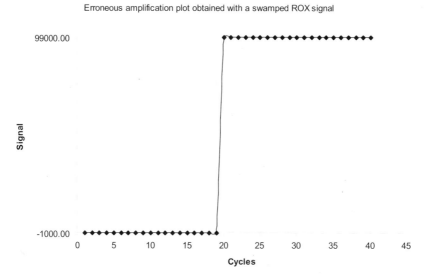

Figure 24.3. Erroneous amplification signal.

Another cause of baseline drift may be seen in reactions where the initial *Taq* activation step is omitted in favor of gradual activation during the course of the real-time run. The reason? In any synthesis of ROX, there is a subpopulation of ROX molecules, which are more likely to degrade, due to heat lability, than normal. The degradation of these heat-labile molecules would normally occur in the 10-minute *Taq* activation step at 95°C, unmeasured. In a gradual activation over the course of a real-time run, ROX degradation can cause a significant baseline drift. The solution? Revert to the 10-minute activation step, or if this is not possible, a minute or so at 95°C should allow sufficient heat-labile molecules to degrade, so as to be undetected during the run.

The fourth disadvantage of ROX is in the cost and formulation of buffers. If you are serious about cutting costs, then the idea of a "homebrew" buffer may well be appealing. I would not advise formulating a homebrew buffer containing an off-the-shelf rhodamine dye, unless you are prepared to spend some time optimizing to prevent rhodamine precipitation and heat instability problems. You may consider a FAM-oligo-ROX conjugate, available from most oligonucleotide manufacturers, which would be slightly more expensive but would be less likely to generate baseline drift problems. Or, you may consider dispensing with ROX, altogether, in your homebrew buffer, especially if your signals are large, noise is relatively small, and the threshold cycle values are stable because of excellent reaction efficiencies. Endpoint genotyping assays are another ideal candidate for eliminating ROX altogether. The genotyping result is already a "self-referencing" ratio of FAM/VIC, so unless the FAM or VIC signals are particularly small (or volumes are small), then ROX is unnecessary.

24.6. Software

24.6.1. MFold

http://www.bioinfo.rpi.edu/applications/mfold/old/dna/

This program is particularly useful for determining the secondary structure of a given amplicon, which is helpful when deciding where to position a hydrolysis probe or Molecular Beacon probe or when designing Scorpions™ primers. Parameters, which need to be altered, are the Na^+ and Mg^{2+} concentrations as well as the relevant annealing temperature. Typical values for a probe analysis would be $Na^+ = 50$ mM and $Mg^{2+} = 5.5$ mM, folding temperature = 60°C. You also need to submit an e-mail address. All other parameters are as per the default values. Look at the JPG file output. The ΔG value shows how likely the structure is to form. For instance, $\Delta G = -10$ is very likely to form, $\Delta G = -2$ is somewhat likely to form, and $\Delta G = 1.0$ is not likely to form. Avoid hairpin loops and duplexes when positioning primers and probes. See **Plate 24.1** for a typical example output.

24.6.2. HyTher™ Server 1.0

http://ozone2.chem.wayne.edu/Hyther/hytherm1main.html

This program is helpful for maximization of the T_m difference between a matched and a mismatched genotyping probe. The larger the T_m window between the two duplexes, the less likely cross-hybridization is to occur. Choose "DNA/DNA" and enter the probe sequence as the top strand. Use the complement button to enter the probe complement. Enter "user defined" values for Na^+ and Mg^{2+}. The "Monovalent Cation" value is 0.05 mol/l, and the Mg^{2+} is 0.0055 mol/l. The "Hybridization Temperature" is 60°C. The concentration of the "Top Strand" (the probe) is 2×10^{-7} mol/l and the "Bottom Strand" (the amplicon) is 2×10^{-9} mol/l. Enter your e-mail address and HyTher will calculate the matched T_m, under your conditions. Alter the "Bottom Strand" to include the SNP mismatch and obtain the mismatched T_m Take the mismatched T_m from the matched T_m to obtain the ΔT_m. Try various probe combinations to maximize the ΔT_m. HyTher is not set up to deal with MGB probes, but it would give you a feel for the likelihood of cross-hybridization and allow you to avoid it, where it is possible.

24.6.3. Primer Express® Software

This program comes with the ABI PRISM® 7700 and 7900. Version 1.5 is equipped to design MGB probes. It works efficiently to design primer and probe sets but is rather hard to use for a novice. Nevertheless, it is worth the learning curve, if you are new to TaqMan probe design. It does not take account of all amplicon secondary structures, does not calculate ΔT_ms, and annoyingly lists only the top of 200 probe/primer combinations. It is available for both Macs and PCs. Version 2.0 is now available.

24.6.4. Oligo Primer Analysis Software

A personal favorite for designing probe and primer sets. It would not deal with MGB probes but does allow you to check for duplexes and hairpin loops. It has all the usual features of a primer-design program, with a well thought out graphical user interface. The primers Gibbs free energies, extinction coefficients, and GC content are calculated for you. What are most useful, are the plots of melting temperature and stability (Gibbs free energy), which enable you "at a glance" to place primers and probes in the most appropriate position in the whole sequence. Other useful features include calculation of hybridization times and the ability to vary concentrations of primers, magnesium and sodium ions and observe the effects. See http://www.lifescience-software.com/ for details.

24.6.5. Beacon Designer 2.1

Premier Biosoft International offers, among other software, Beacon Designer 2.1. This novel software is especially suited to the design of Molecular Beacons and TaqMan/dual labeled probes for real-time reactions. Future upgrades are anticipated to be able to deal with MGB TaqMan probes. An advantage of this software is that the secondary structure of the amplicon is taken into account when positioning probes. The only disadvantage is that a sequence "map" displaying the position of the forward and reverse primers and probe(s) is not available. See http://www.premierbiosoft.com/molecular_beacons/taqman_molecular_beacons.html for more information and a demonstration.

24.6.6. Microsoft Excel

This spreadsheet software is particularly useful when analyzing endpoint genotyping data from a simple fluorimeter, when you do not have access to ABI software. Using Visual Basic macros, it is a relatively straightforward task to assign genotypes using the FAM:VIC ratio sorted into ascending order. The resultant "staircase plot" allows you to easily distinguish between the three genotype groups.

24.6.7. JMP Version 5.1

This statistics package is useful for performing cluster analysis, on FAM and VIC endpoint signals, to assign the three genotype groups. Again, it is good for situations where endpoint readings are being taken with a simple fluorimeter, without the benefit of the ABI clustering software, which comes with the ABI PRISM® 7700 or 7900. It has to be said, however, that the results of the clustering analysis often are not the same as would be generated by ABI's own cluster analysis software. See http://www.jmpdiscovery.com for further details.

24.7. Reagents and Buffers

It has to be said, that the optimum genotyping setup is available from ABI. Their TaqMan reagents are well manufactured, well quality-controlled, and promptly delivered to the end user. The chemistries are already optimized to generate the best possible genotyping results, using FAM and VIC MGB probes and dark quenchers. Their Universal Master Mix is optimized to function as designed, and results do not seem to deteriorate much, even when assays are left, for a day or two, in the 'fridge' before running. There may, however, be occasions when you may need to use non-ABI reagents. There are two options, which you may like to consider:

24.7.1. Alternative Suppliers of Reagents

Three manufacturers, among many, which produce reagents suitable for 5'-hydrolysis probe reactions include **Eurogentech**, **Qiagen**, and **ABgene**. Each one has their own formulations, which are suitable for slightly different applications. They all contain a heat-activated enzyme, similar to AmpliTaq Gold®. AmpliTaq Gold is based on a covalent chemical anhydride modification to selected lysine residues within the *Taq* molecule. This modification is reversed by the drop in pH, which occurs as *Tris* buffer is heated. Some companies supply reagents containing a proprietary rhodamine-based internal standard, which is a "ROX" equivalent. Some include dUTP to prevent contamination by UNG treatment, although the UNG may have to be purchased independently.

- **Qiagen** have a slightly different proprietary hot-start enzyme "HotStarTaq DNA polymerase" in their "Quantitect" range, which is formulated with dUTP and ROX. HotStarTaq uses an aldehyde modification to the *Taq* molecule, which is reversible by an increase in temperature (not pH). Their "ROX" is a proprietary rhodamine dye and UNG must be purchased separately.

- **Eurogentech** have a proprietary hot-start enzyme called "HotGoldStar," which is based on a covalent modification to *Taq*. Their formulations "qPCR Master Mix" and "qPCR Core Kit" contain dUTP but it is possible to request that dUTP be excluded and dTTP included instead. UNG is included in the qPCR Master Mix and available separately in the qPCR Core Kit. "ROX" is included as a proprietary dye conjugate.

- **ABgene** (http://www.abgene.com/productDetails.asp?prodID=7) has a proprietary hot-start enzyme system called "Thermo-Start®." 2× formulations are available—with and without ROX and dUTP.

The ROX is a proprietary rhodamine dye, which is provided in a separate vial within the kit, for customized addition. UNG must be purchased separately, elsewhere. Their "ABsolute" range will cover most applications, but customized mixes are available on request.

I have found that these reagents work well for most TaqMan reactions. However, it must be stressed that the formulations are different from those of ABI and there will inevitably be some reactions that will not transfer successfully from ABI to an alternative supplier's reagents. In a survey of over 50 genotyping assays, only one could not be transferred to an alternative reagent system. Quantitative assays may be expected to be slightly less robust than genotyping assays, so the transfer rate would be expected to be lower. The Mg^{2+} concentration of these reagents is designed for application to 5'-nuclease assays and, consequently, will be too high for most Molecular Beacons and Scorpions™ Primers reactions.

24.7.2. Formulate Your Own Reagents

To make your own reaction mix, use the general "recipe" given in **Table 24.4**.

Table 24.4. General real-time/endpoint assay reaction mix.

dNTPs	200–500 µM
Buffer (*ABI Cat. No. N808-0190*)	1× final
MgCl$_2$	5.5 mM final concentration for TaqMan, 3.5 mM for Molecular Beacons and Scorpions™ primers
ATG or other heat-activated enzyme ABI *Cat. No. N808-0247*	1 unit/25 µl reaction final

Rhodamine may be added at an "empirically" determined concentration, around 60 nM, aiming for a fluorescent signal equivalent to that, which you are measuring, but beware of it precipitating out of solution (see **Section 24.5.2**). It is not strictly necessary for reactions, which give a strong fluorescent signal or large volume, self-referencing genotyping reactions. Glycerol can also be included at approximately 10% v/v to reduce secondary structure problems, but if using glycerol, you should "bump up" the Magnesium level, for example, to around 7–7.5 mM to improve probe hybridization.

24.8. Melting Curves

24.8.1. Types of Melting Curves

Melting curves are the main way to elucidate the fluorescence signal/temperature profile of a real-time or endpoint assay. They can be loosely categorized into **pre-PCR** melting curves and **post-PCR** melting curves. Pre-PCR melting curves use an artificial template to determine the temperature-dependent hybridization characteristics of TaqMan probes, Molecular Beacons, and Scorpions™ primers. This will allow you to select the optimum annealing temperature to maximize probe/template interaction during a real-time run. Unfortunately, Pre-PCR melting curves do not tell you anything about the efficiency of amplicon generation in the real-time run, which, of course, is primer dependent. Another disadvantage with a pre-PCR melting curve is that there may be a difference in melting profile between an artificial template and a longer amplicon, which is more prone to develop secondary structures. Disadvantages aside, if a pre-PCR melting curve has been successfully performed then you will be able to:

1. Determine the optimum annealing temperature at a particular probe/amplicon concentration to maximize probe/amplicon hybridization.

2. Determine the "quantum yield" of fluorescence at a given template concentration.

3. Use this information, in conjunction with the post-PCR reaction, run on a 3% agarose gel to give you a feel for the amount of amplicon being generated during the PCR and how this impacts on signal generation.

   Note: Reactions containing UNG will need to be kept on ice and run out on an agarose gel immediately post-PCR to prevent amplicon degradation by residual enzyme activity.

4. Use all this information, in conjunction with a post-PCR melting curve, to determine whether intra-strand amplicon secondary structure is likely to be preventing probe annealing.

24.8.2. Performing a Pre-PCR Melting Curve

Order an artificial template containing the complement to your melting curve, plus 6 or 7 bases either side of the probe. Care must be taken not to contaminate future reactions with this artificial template. If possible, use a separate room (or even building) when setting-up and sealing these melting curve tubes. Three tubes should be set up in duplicate:

Tube 1

- Real-time buffer (e.g., Universal master mix/core reagent), 1× final concentration;
- Probe, 200 nM final concentration;
- Artificial template at 20 nM (representing a typical amplicon concentration);
- Water to make up volume to 25 µl.

Tube 2

- Real-time buffer (e.g., Universal master mix/core reagent), 1× final concentration;
- Probe, 200 nM final concentration;
- Artificial template at 1 µM representing 5× molar excess;
- Water to make up volume to 25 µl.

Tube 3

- Real-time buffer (e.g., Universal master mix/core reagent), 1× final concentration;
- Probe, 200 nM final concentration;
- No artificial template, representing a no-template PCR control;
- Water to make up volume to 25 µl.

Cycling

Step 1: Set the ABI PRISM® 7700 to heat for 1 minute, 95°C. This initial heating step controls for differences in profiles, which may be observed, due to hysteresis ("a retardation of an effect when the forces acting upon a body are changed"—in its broadest sense, the *history* dependence of physical systems).

Step 2: Cool to 20°C, for 15 seconds, repeat 74 times. Use the auto-increment function to increase the temperature at each cycle by 1°C.

Melting Curve Analysis

Post-run and analyze without ROX, selecting **step 2** in the cycling profile for analysis.

Baseline. Apply the baseline from cycles "1" to "1," in other words, deselect the baselining function (an alternative way of deselecting the baseline function is to use the R_n-option, instead of the ΔR_n-option). Export the relevant wells data, in the "clipped" data file format to Excel.

Plot fluorescent signal versus temperature. Then take the gradient of this curve and plot it against temperature. This second plot is known as the "derivative" or, more precisely, the "1st derivative" plot. Typical melting curve results for a FAM–TAMRA TaqMan probe, Molecular Beacon, and Scorpions™ primer are shown in **Figs. 24.4, 24.5**, and **24.6**, respectively. 1st derivatives are shown in **Figs. 24.7, 24.8**, and **24.9**.

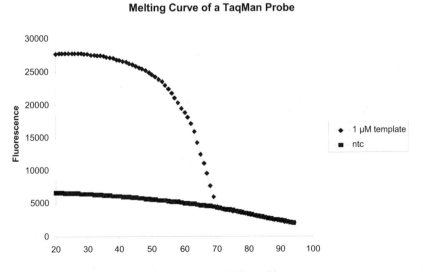

Figure 24.4. TaqMan pre-PCR melting curve.

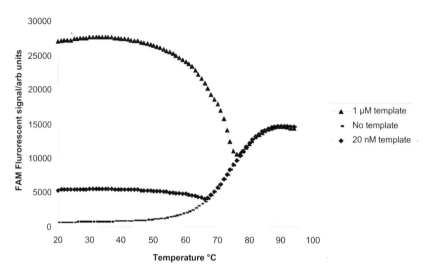

Figure 24.5. Molecular Beacon pre-PCR melting curve.

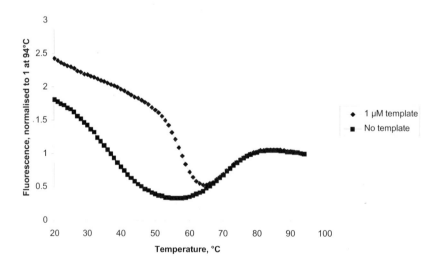

Figure 24.6. Scorpions primer pre-PCR melting curve.

TaqMan Probe 1ˢᵗ Derivative Plot

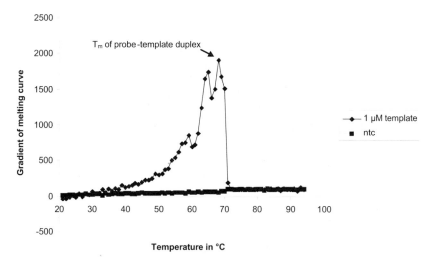

Figure 24.7. TaqMan pre-PCR 1ˢᵗ derivative plot.

Gradient (or 1ˢᵗ Derivative) Plots of Typical Molecular Beacon Melting Curve

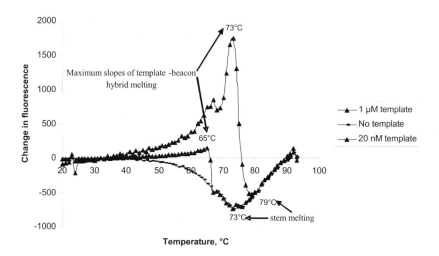

Figure 24.8. Molecular Beacon pre-PCR 1ˢᵗ derivative plot.

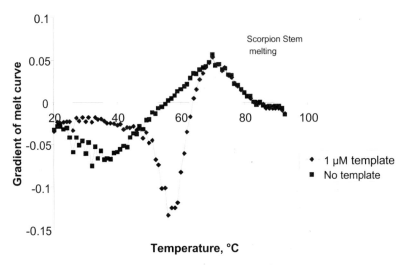

Figure 24.9. Scorpions primer pre-PCR 1st derivative plot.

24.8.3. Post-PCR Melting Curves

Post-PCR melting curves are easier to set up, compared with the pre-PCR melting curves because they do not require an artificial template. They rely, instead, on the melting profile of the post-PCR reactions but are more difficult to interpret. In essence, they will tell you about the temperature dependence of the fluorescent signal, after cycling.

Post-PCR, run the melting curve, as described above in **Section 24.8.2.** *Performing a Pre-PCR Melting Curve*, paragraph *Cycling*, and compare the profiles of a positive control with a no-template control.

Typically, the fluorescence response in each well will be a dependent on:

- The hybridization signal from probe–amplicon interaction;
- Signal due to cleavage of the probe;
- Amount of amplicon produced (dependent on primer efficiency);
- Background signal from residual probe;
- The temperature dependence of fluorescence (fluorescence tends to reduce as temperature increases);
- Any nonspecific signal due to primer dimers and/or mispriming.

This long list of factors makes interpretation of post-PCR melting curves rather difficult. However, if you have performed a pre-PCR melt, a post-PCR melt, and a real-time analysis and have run the post-PCR reactions on a 3% agarose gel, then you will be better placed to understand how to "fix" a nonfunctioning assay.

I find that post-PCR melting curves, in conjunction with all the other data described, can be most useful in:

- Identifying reactions prone to primer-dimer signal (SYBR Green I and Scorpions™ primers reactions);
- Determining the temperature profile of the fluorescent signal produced, for selection of an appropriate annealing temperature;
- Assessing the amount of signal and, by inference, the amount of amplicon produced;
- Evaluating the role of amplicon secondary structure, in reducing the affinity of the probe for the amplicon (looking for melting domains).

You will, no doubt, be able to extract additional information from a post-PCR melting curve, which is relevant to your particular assay. I have included a typical post-PCR melting curve for a TaqMan (FAM–TAMRA) reaction, which shows the temperature dependence of the TaqMan signal (**Fig. 24.10**).

TaqMan Post-PCR Melting Curve

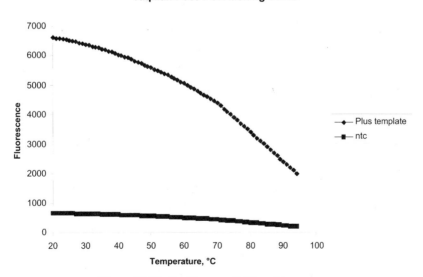

Figure 24.10. TaqMan post-PCR melting curve.

In addition, a SYBR Green melting curve and first derivative plots are shown, demonstrating the presence of primer dimers (see **Figs. 24.11** and **24.12**).

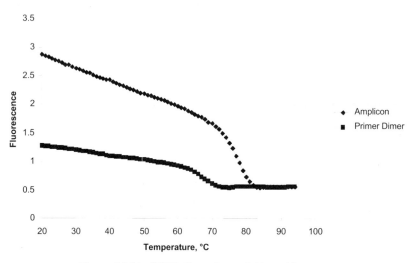

Figure 24.11. SYBR Green I post-PCR melting curve.

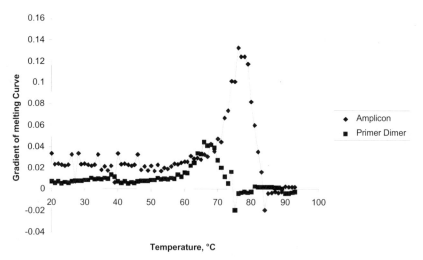

Figure 24.12. SYBR Green I post-PCR 1st derivative plot.

24.9. A Useful Protocol to Quantify Total Human DNA Based on Detection of the APO B Gene

One very useful application of TaqMan assays is in the determination of DNA concentration. Other methods, which have been applied, include PicoGreen quantification and absorbance at 260 nm. Both these methods have advantages and disadvantages. The main advantage of a TaqMan-based approach is that it tells you something about the "amplifiability" of the DNA with which you are working. Most downstream analytical techniques rely on PCR, so it makes sense to quantify DNA, in a way, which takes account of the factors, which influence amplification efficiency.

24.9.1. Primer and Probe Sequences

Forward   5' ACAGTACGAAAAACCACTTACAGCTAGAGG 3'
Reverse   5' ATGGACCTGAACAAGAGCTGACATT 3'
Probe   5' FAM CCACCCTGGAACTCTCTCCATGGCA TAMRA 3'

24.9.1.1. Standard Curve Preparation

Prepare the standard curve freshly each time you run the assay. Create a 2× serial dilution of Roche standard DNA 200 ng/µl (Human Genomic DNA, *Cat. No. 1 691 112*, from Roche Applied Science) in water. When serially diluting, mix and spin down each tube after adding DNA. Use a fresh tip for each dilution. The standard curve should include the following dilutions:

- neat (200 ng/µl);
- 100 ng/µl;
- 50 ng/µl;
- 25 ng/µl;
- 12.5 ng/µl;
- 6.25 ng/µl;
- 3.125 ng/µl.

Note: Any unknown lower than 3.125 ng/µl requires further standard curve dilutions to be prepared.

Dispense 5 µl of each of the standard dilutions, in duplicate, into an ABI PRISM® 7700 plate. Add 5 µl of water to a further two wells, to act as no-template controls.

24.9.1.2. Reaction Mix

For each 25 µl of reaction mix, add:

Universal master mix (2×)	12.5 µl	1× final;
Reverse primer (50 µM)	0.25 µl	final 500 nM;
Forward primer (50 µM)	0.25 µl	final 500 nM;
APO B Probe (15 µM)	0.5 µl	final 300 nM;
Space for DNA	5 µl	Concentration ~ 3.125 –200 ng/µl;
Water	6.5 µl;	
Total	**25 µl.**	

Add 20 µl of the reaction mix to 5 µl of DNA (standard curve/ unknowns). Cap the plate and spin down.

24.9.1.3. Cycling

95°C—10 min;

(95°C—15 s, 60°C—1 min) ×40.

Set the ABI PRISM® 7700 to read FAM, TAMRA, and ROX. Enter the standard concentration values in ng/µl. Post-PCR, check the baseline and analyze data to determine the concentrations of the unknowns (as per the ABI manual). Concentrations are expressed in ng/µl. Average the duplicate values, checking the CVs (coefficients of variation) of every duplicate pair.

Acknowledgements

Many thanks must go to Neil Gibson of AstraZeneca Pharmaceuticals for his support in the writing of this chapter.

25

Scorpions Primers for Real-Time Genotyping and Quantitative Genotyping on Pooled DNA

David M. Whitcombe, Paul Ravetto, Antony Halsall, and Nicola Thelwell

Abstract

Scorpions are novel signaling systems that provide both primer and probe on the same molecule. This configuration has many benefits in real-time PCR applications due its unique, unimolecular mode of action. We describe the main features of the technology and its use. We then focus on a particular application in which Scorpions are coupled with allele-specific PCR, allowing highly specific genotyping in real time and endpoint formats.

25

Scorpions Primers for Real-Time Genotyping and Quantitative Genotyping on Pooled DNA

David M. Whitcombe, Paul Ravetto, Antony Halsall, and Nicola Thelwell

DxS Limited, Manchester, United Kingdom

25.1. Introduction

The ability to monitor PCR reactions[1] in closed tubes throughout the process has massively improved the power of the PCR in a number of ways:

- Closed-tube detection of PCR products is quicker and simpler than any methods that require post-PCR manipulation (such as gels).

- Fluorescence monitoring is at least as sensitive as most post-PCR analysis methods, allowing detection of small amounts of product.

- Continuous monitoring of PCR through the process allows accurate quantitation of the initial number of templates introduced.

- Closed tube fluorescence reporting systems allow analysis to be performed without opening the reaction vessel, thus minimizing the potential for product contamination.

- Probe-based reporter systems such as TaqMan,[2] Molecular Beacons,[3] and the one described in this chapter (Scorpions)[4,5] offer enhanced levels of specificity because the product of the PCR is identified by an amplicon-specific probe, a level specificity comparable to screening of product by dot blot or Southern blotting.

25.2. Genotyping

In addition to quantifying template numbers in starting material, genotyping can be achieved through real-time PCR, in at least two ways. The first is by allele-specific probing and the second is by allele-specific priming also known as amplification refractory mutation system (ARMS).[6] Allele-specific priming uses primers that extend specifically (or at least with differential efficiency) depending upon the match or mismatch at the 3' end of the primer and its complementary target. Additional mismatches can be introduced close to the 3' end of the primer to further destabilize the complex and enhance the differential amplification. The allele-specific PCR can be very discriminatory, with specificity routinely reaching 10,000:1 or greater (i.e., more than 10,000 mismatched templates would be required to produce amplification comparable to a single matched target).

The differential amplification can then be detected by a number of methods. Initially, gel-based methods were used but the allele-specific PCR can be susceptible to "breakthrough" in which the mismatch product eventually appears. After 35 cycles of PCR it is possible that both products will be present although one product appeared much earlier than the other. For that reason, the ability to monitor the whole of the PCR allows the differential amplification to be accurately monitored.

Products can be detected by a number of signaling methods:

1. *Intercalation:* an intercalating dye is incorporated into the reaction mix and the accumulation of double-stranded product is observed due to the enhanced fluorescence of the dye. Only one allele-specific reaction per tube can be used.

2. *Amplicon-specific methods (TaqMan and Molecular Beacons):* an amplicon-specific probe is included in the reaction and used to monitor specifically the accumulation of amplification product. Again only one allele per tube can be monitored since the presence of signal indicates presence of appropriate amplicon.

3. *Scorpions (see Section 25.3 below):* each allele-specific primer can be tailed with identical probe sequences but labeled with different fluorophores. In this way, each allele-specific product is linked to a particular color and both reactions can be included in the same tube.

25.3. Scorpions

25.3.1. Structure and Mechanism

(See **Fig. 25.1.**)

Scorpions are bifunctional molecules that carry both probe and priming functions on the same oligonucleotide construct. The probe element is attached as a tail to the primer element through a PCR blocker that ensures the probe element does not get incorporated into the double-stranded product.

The Scorpions construct is arranged such that the probe element is complementary to the anticipated extension product of the primer element, i.e., it binds to the opposite strand than the primer element. The probe element also carries a reporter fluorophore that (in the initial conformation) is quenched with a "dark quencher" (usually DABCYL or Methyl Red) through a collisional mechanism. The quencher is held in close proximity to the fluorophore by base pairing and this can be achieved by the introduction of a stem-loop in the probe (**Fig. 25.1A**), or through a second molecule, substantially complementary to the probe element (**Fig. 25.1B**).

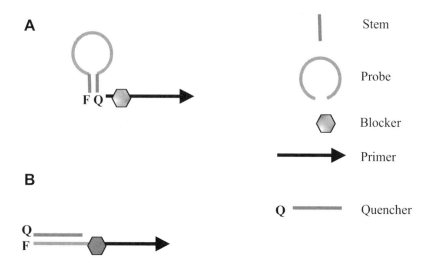

Figure 25.1. Two alternative formats for Scorpions primers. (**A**) The "Closed" format in which quenching is achieved through a stem loop. (**B**) The "Open" format in which the quencher is brought adjacent to the fluorophore through a complementary quencher molecule.

After the primer element has been extended, the probe element has become attached to its complementary target. Upon subsequent rounds of heating and cooling, the extension product becomes single stranded and the probe can bind to its complement in a rapid intramolecular rearrangement and the fluorophore becomes unquenched leading to an increase in specific fluorescence. When complementary strand is synthesized, the probe becomes displaced and resumes its quenched conformation (either stem-loop or double-stranded). The blocker group prevents DNA synthesis from "copying through" the probe rendering the probe element double stranded and producing a nonspecific "always on" configuration. If that were to happen, nonspecific PCR products and primer dimers would all lead to apparently positive signals.

25.3.2. Benefits of the Scorpions Mechanism

1. ***Speed:*** Because of the unimolecular rearrangement mechanism, the kinetics of probe binding are extremely rapid. This ensures that signal generation is not the rate-limiting step in a given PCR application.

2. *Reliability of probing:* With most probing systems, the thermodynamic design of the probe can be easily calculated, but kinetically the probe/target hybridization reaction is in competition with a number of other reactions such as:

   • The amplicon folding to assume a conformation in which the probe site is hidden;

   • Synthesis of the complementary strand by PCR;

   • Reannealing of the two complementary strands in the mixture;

   • Folding up of the probe itself, making it unavailable for hybridization to its target.

3. *High signal-to-noise ratio:* Reannealing as a quenched probe system, background signals are low, and the efficiency of probing ensures that signals are high. This allows relatively small amounts of labeled material to be used and is important for multiplexing where optical crosstalk is a limiting factor.

4. *Stoichiometry:* One amplicon gives one fluorescent signal. This is important in quantitative reactions.

5. *Concentration independence:* Probing occurs irrespective of the concentration of the reagents since the reaction is zero order. This means that all probing is equally efficient and enhances the overall sensitivity of the detection.

25.4. Methods

DxS has worked with DNA Software Inc. of Ann Arbor, Mich., to develop software that designs both Scorpions and ARMS primers in either *Open* or *Closed* format. This contains detailed thermodynamic parameters for all possible base pairs, mismatches, overhangs, etc.

Alternatively, standard primer design software (Primer 3, Oligo, etc.) can be used for initial primer design as well as the Tetra-Primer ARMS design software discussed below in **Section 25.4.1** for allele-specific primer design. Folding of extension products and stem-loop Scorpions can be modeled using the MFold program detailed in **Subsection 25.4.2.1**.

25.4.1. Design of ARMS Allele-Specific Primers

Allele-specific primers are designed to match or mismatch each variant at their 3' ends. There are therefore two possible orientations for any given assay. We advise the following steps in the design of allele-specific primers:

- Select the direction of the assay;

- Design primers that terminate with the variant base (aim for a T_m around 10°C higher than the intended assay temperature;

- Design a common primer, compatible with both allele-specific variants. Where gene families and pseudogenes are known, it is important to ensure that the common primer is specific for the gene of interest (there is less flexibility in the location of the allele specific primers);

- Introduce additional mismatches close to the 3' end of the allele-specific variants. We usually introduce a –3 mismatch on one primer and a –2 mismatch on the other (the terminal base being designated –1). This prevents any possibility of the two primers "cross-priming" since they differ at the 3 terminal bases. We also attempt to keep the GC content of the last 3 or 4 bases equal between the two variants;

- Check that the new terminal sequences have not introduced the possibility of mispriming by "slippage" (particularly on a mismatched target). That is, having modified the terminus of the primer, have we now created a 3-base sequence that could efficiently prime on the mismatch target by looping forward a few (up to 5) bases?

We have found it useful to use the website:

http://cedar.genetics.soton.ac.uk/public_html/primer1.html[7]

to design both bidirectional ARMS reactions but also as a start point for the design of reactions that run in the same direction. This program automatically inserts an additional mismatch at the –3 position of the ARMS primers. A small amount of manual manipulation is required to convert the output of this program to a pair of appropriate primers.

25.4.2. Design and Synthesis of Scorpions

Scorpions primers contain a blocker group in the middle and the fluorophore of choice at the 5' end. The preferred blocking group is HEG (hexaethyleneglycol), which is available as a phosphoramadite. Order the second molecule with the quencher at the 3' end. Both Methyl Red and DABCYL are suitable as quenchers and both are readily available. The Scorpion and the quencher probe should be purified by HPLC.

25.4.2.1. Open Format

Open format Scorpions primers contain a blocker group in the middle and the fluorophore of choice at the 5' end. The preferred blocking group is HEG (hexaethyleneglycol), which is available as a phosphoramadite. The second molecule is substantially complementary to the probe region, and carries a quencher at the 3' end. Both Methyl Red and DABCYL are suitable as quenchers and both are readily available. The Scorpions and the quencher probe should be purified by HPLC.

The major benefits of this format are that the molecules are easy to synthesize and purify, backgrounds tend to be even lower than the hairpin-loop version, and signals are still higher.

To create an Open format:

1. Select target region (includes region of interest, polymorphism, etc.).

2. Design primer pairs using standard methods; the primer design programs Primer 3 and Oligo 5 work well and give accurate T_ms.

3. Select a probe region:
   a. 0–50 bases from the end of the primer to which it will be attached—ideally 5–15 bases. Remember the probe and the primer to which it is attached will bind to different strands of the target.
   b. T_m similar to the primer or slightly below.
   c. No sequence homology to either primer (as with all probe systems).
   d. No significant self-homology within the probe.

4. Design a quencher oligonucleotide that is complementary to the probe element.

5. In order to ensure that the probing of the target is the most favored reaction, we often make the quencher oligonucleotide 2 bases shorter than the probe element.

6. Check out design using the MFold folding program of Michael Zuker that can be found at: http://www.bioinfo.rpi.edu/applications/mfold/old/dna/. Create the Scorpion molecule as a single oligo

sequence (5'–3': probe element, blocker, primer element); paste on the remainder of the amplicon (extended primer product). Cut and paste the entire sequence into the folding program, select conditions of salt, Mg, and temperature and run the program. In general, anything with a ΔG of –4 kcal/mol or less (more negative) is a favored form. It should be more favored than any other possible structure by at least 2 kcal/mol. Check out the unextended version (without the amplicon attached). Any secondary structure should be less stable than the extended version.

25.4.2.2. Closed Format

Closed format Scorpions contain from (5'–3'): a fluorophore, stem 1, probe region, stem 2, Quencher, Blocker (HEG as above), and primer region. HPLC is essential for these molecules.

The major benefits of this format are that the molecules very simple in their design, elegant in their mechanism, and extremely rapid in their performance.

To create a Closed format:

1. Select target region (includes region of interest, polymorphism, etc.).

2. Design primer pairs using standard methods; the primer design programs Primer 3 and Oligo 5 work well and give accurate T_ms.

3. Select a probe region:

   a. 0–50 bases from the end of the primer to which it will be attached—ideally 5–15 bases. Remember the probe and the primer to which it is attached will bind to different strands of the target.

   b. T_m similar to the primer or slightly below.

   c. No sequence homology to either primer (as with all probe systems).

   d. No significant self-homology within the probe except for the intentional hairpin.

4. Add in a stem sequence (not found elsewhere in the primers or probe).

5. Check out the design using the Michael Zuker's MFold folding program, which can be found at: http://www.bioinfo.rpi.edu/applications/mfold/old/dna/. Create the Scorpion molecule as a single oligo sequence (5'–3': probe element, blocker, primer element);

paste on the remainder of the amplicon (extended primer product). Cut and paste the entire sequence into the folding program, select conditions of salt, Mg, and temperature and run program. Also analyze the structure of the Scorpion in the closed, unextended form. The ΔGs should be at least -2 kcal/mol for the closed form, at least -4 kcal/mol (preferably around -6 kcal/mol) for the "true" hybridized form, and any suboptimal folding of the extended amplicon should be no more stable than the unextended form.

For allele discrimination, optimize the "off" form to be more stable than extended mismatch form but less stable than the fully matched form.

25.5. Examples

25.5.1. Genotyping with Allele Specific Primers and Intercalation

Primers were purchased from Oswel DNA Services (Southampton, United Kingdom).

Control DNA was purchased from European Collection of Animal Cell

Wild Type Primer	2C19 × 2 RG	GCAAGGTTTTTAAGTAATTTGTTATGGGTTCTC
Mutant Primer	2C19 × 2 RA	GCAAGGTTTTTAAGTAATTTGTTATGGGTTTCT
Common Primer	2C19 × 2 FOR	GTTTTAAATTACAACCAGAGCTTGGCAT

Cultures (ECACC, Wiltshire, United Kingdom) and working dilutions (2 ng/µl) were prepared.

PCR reactions were carried out in 25-µl volumes and contained 1 unit of HotGoldStar DNA polymerase, supplied by Eurogentec (Seraing, Belgium), with 1× manufacturer's buffer, 200 µM dNTP, 2.5 mM MgCl$_2$, and 0.25 µM primers. YO-PRO-1 (Molecular Probes, Oregon United States) was added at 1 µM final concentration. 5–20 ng of DNA was added to each reaction and cycled on an Mx4000 real-time PCR

Instrument (Stratagene): 95°C 10 min, followed by 45 cycles of 95°C 30 s and 64°C 1 min. Fluorescence reads were taken each cycle at 64°C.

Examples of the amplification plots for wild type, heterozygous and mutant samples are shown in **Plate 25.1**.

25.5.2. Single-Tube Genotyping

We labeled allele-specific Scorpions primers with FAM or ROX and used these together in a single tube to genotype 192 DNA samples for a polymorphism in the *Il1α* gene.[8]

Scorpions and primers are shown in the European Collection of Animal Cell Cultures table below. Bold indicates the stem and underlining indicates the additional mismatch to enhance specificity.

IL "G"	FAM- **CCCG**TCAGGAAGCTAAA**CGGG**– *MR-HEG*	TTTTAGAAATCATCAAGCCTAGGT TAG
IL unlabeled "G"		TTTTAGAAATCATCAAGCCTAGGT TAG
IL "T"	ROX- **CCCG**TCAGGAAGCTAAA**CGGG**– *MR-HEG*	TTTTAGAAATCATCAAGCCTAGGTC GT
IL common		CATTGGCTCGAATTATACTTTGATTGA

Typical reactions (25 µl) comprised 1× ARMS Buffer (10 mM *Tris*-HCl, pH 8.3, 50 mM KCl, 2.5 mM MgCl$_2$, 0.01% [w/v] gelatin), containing 500 nM primer or Scorpions primer, 1 unit of AmpliTaq Gold (PE-Biosystems, Warrington, United Kingdom) per 25 µl reaction mix. For the *Il1α* test, it was necessary to balance the fluorescence outputs, so the FAM-bearing Scorpions primer was included at half the levels of the ROX labeled variant.

After 10-minute incubation at 95°C and 40 cycles of PCR (95°C 15 s, 60°C 60 s), the fluorescence for both FAM and ROX was read (wavelengths: 485 nm excitation, 530 nm emission for FAM (F) and 560 nm excitation, 620 nm emission for ROX (R)).

The difference between the two readings was used as a measure of the relative efficiency of the competing amplification reactions and the sum of the two readings was used to normalize the data for overall amplification efficiency in the tube. In short: (F–R)/(F+R) was calculated for each reaction. Genotyping results are shown in **Fig. 25.2**.

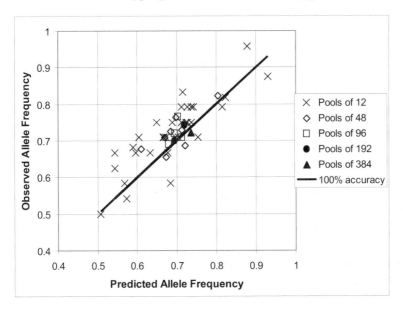

Figure 25.2. Fluorescence value as a predictor of allele frequency in pools. The *Ill*α assay was performed on the same 384 samples in pools of various sizes. A standard line generated from admixtures of known allelic ratios was used to convert fluorescence values to a predicted allele frequency and this was plotted against the actual allele frequency as determined from the individual genotypes within the pool. Pool sizes were 12 (×), 48(◇), 96 (□), 192 (●) and 384 (▲). For comparison, an ideal line in which the predicted exactly matches the observed is also shown.

25.5.3. Quantitative Genotyping of Pooled Samples

The same DNA samples plus another 192 DNAs were pooled in groups of 12, 48, 96, 192, and 384 and analyzed with each test mix. After PCR, the fluorescence output of the two dyes was measured and the data was processed as described.

To calibrate the quantitative approach we prepared standard admixtures in the following way. We generated PCR fragments from homozygous samples, using flanking primers and quantified the products, using real-time PCR and an intercalating dye. These were mixed in various ratios to produce a standard line, which was used to predict an allele frequency from the fluorescence data. For each pool, the allele frequency predicted by the fluorescence ratio was plotted against the "true" allele frequency as calculated from the individual genotypes for the samples within the pools. **Fig. 25.2** shows the relationship between predicted and observed frequencies for the $III\alpha$ polymorphism.

In each case, we found that the larger the pool, the closer the approximation to the true allele frequency as determined on individual samples.

25.6. Conclusions

ARMS allele-specific PCR combined with intercalation and real-time monitoring provides a simple and cost-effective way to genotype using real-time PCR. Reagent costs are low and the assay is easily optimized. However, each allele tested requires a separate tube and instrument; time quickly becomes limiting when large genotyping projects are undertaken. By converting the ARMS primers to Scorpions that have different labels associated with different alleles, both variants can be examined in a single tube. Furthermore, the Scorpions signal can be read at endpoint, allowing PCRs to be performed on any PCR block and fluorescence reads to be taken after the PCR, without opening the tube.

A further advance is to use the ratio between the two fluorophores to allow quantitative genotyping on pooled samples. It is worth noting that these samples were not normalized in any way and likely the DNA concentration varied significantly between samples. By pooling in large numbers the skewing effect of any individual sample is quickly diluted. The combination of ARMS and Scorpions allowed highly accurate estimation of allele frequencies in pooled samples offering a highly cost effective way to genotype large populations for alleles of interest.

References

1. Higuchi R, Fockler M, Dollinger G, Watson R: **Kinetic PCR analysis: Real-time monitoring of DNA amplification reactions.** *Biotechnology* 1993, **1**:1026–1030.

2. Holland PM, Abramson RD, Watson R, Gelfand DH: **Detection of specific polymerase chain reaction product utilizing the 5'---3' exonuclease activity of** *Thermus aquaticus* **DNA polymerase.** *Proc Natl Acad Sci USA* 1991, **88**:7276–7280.

3. Tyagi S, Kramer FR: Molecular Beacons: **Probes that fluoresce upon hybridisation.** *Nat Biotechnology* 1996, **14**:303–308.

4. Whitcombe D, Theaker J, Guy SP, Brown T, Little S: **Detection of PCR products using self-probing amplicons and fluorescence.** *Nat Biotechnology* 1999, **17**:804–807.

5. Thelwell J, Millington S, Solinas A, Booth J, Brown T: **Mode of action and application of Scorpion primers to mutation detection.** *Nucleic Acids Res* 2000, **28**:3752–3761.

6. Newton CR et al.: **Analysis of any point mutation in DNA. The amplification refractory mutation system (ARMS).** *Nucleic Acids Res* 1989, **17**:2503–2516.

7. Ye S, Dhillon S, Ke X, Collins AR, Day INM: **An efficient procedure for genotyping single nucleotide polymorphisms.** *Nucleic Acids Res* 2001, **29**:E88:1–8.

8. van der Velden PA, Reitsma PH: **Amino-acid dimorphism in** *IIIα* **is detectable by PCR amplification.** *Human Molecular Genetics* 1993, **2**:1753.

26

Simultaneous Detection and Sub-Typing of Human Papillomavirus in the Cervix Using Real-Time Quantitative PCR

Rashmi Seth, Tania Nolan, Triona Davey, John Rippin, Li Guo, and David Jenkins

Abstract

More than forty types of Human Papillomaviruses (HPV) infect the human genital tract. High-risk HPV types are found in almost all cases of high-grade cervical cancer. Molecular technique such as DNA hybridization and nucleic acid sequencing are both costly and labor intensive and so far no method can differentiate between individual genotypes without additional laboratory procedures.

In this study, a real-time quantitative polymerase chain reaction (qPCR) using the existing GP5+/GP6+ primers and SYBR Green I dye was adapted and developed for simultaneous detection and genotyping of HPV in cervical DNA. Samples from women identified as having borderline or mildly dyskaryotic cervical smears were analyzed using this assay. This provided a rapid, efficient amplification and genotyping of genital HPVs based on the dissociation profile of the PCR products.

The preliminary validation of this assay suggests that it is a sensitive, robust and user-friendly technique that has considerable potential for diagnostic and prognostic studies and other clinical or molecular epidemiological applications.

26

Simultaneous Detection and Sub-Typing of Human Papillomavirus in the Cervix Using Real-Time Quantitative PCR

Rashmi Seth,[*] **Tania Nolan,**[†] **Triona Davey,**[*] **John Rippin,**[*] **Li Guo,**[*] **and David Jenkins**[*]

[*]*Department of Pathology, Queens Medical Centre, University Hospital, Nottingham, United Kingdom*
[†]*Stratagene Europe, Amsterdam, The Netherlands*

26.1. Introduction

The second most frequent cause of death from cancer in women worldwide is cervical cancer.[1] It has been established recently that a subset of Human Papillomaviruses (HPV) known as high-risk HPV is associated with cervical Intraepithelial Neoplasia (CIN) and cervical carcinoma, and that HPV DNA is present in over 99% of these cancers.[2]

Papillomaviruses are a heterogeneous group of double-stranded DNA viruses with 8 kb closed circular genomes. There are currently 84 types of HPV, approximately 30 of which infect the genital tract.[3] The infecting HPV type, the viral load, and the integration state of the HPV genome are all believed to have profound implications for patient prognosis.[4-7] The high-risk group embraces 17 HPV types, including HPV16 and HPV18. HPV16 is the most prevalent type worldwide but there are also reports that HPV18 infection can lead to development of more clinically aggressive disease.[8]

National Cervical Screening programs have reduced the incidence of cervical cancer.[9] However, since 50% of invasive cervical cancers arise in women despite screening with existing cytological methodologies,[10] HPV detection, and typing techniques have been proposed as an adjunct to or a replacement for, the current cytological screening regime.[11-14] The success of such strategies will depend on the development of rapid, sensitive, and specific HPV detection methods, which are suitable for application in the clinical setting.

There are many approaches to the detection and typing of HPV. Serological testing aims to assess whether an immune response has been mounted to a viral antigenic protein but these techniques result in high false-positive assessment rates. Additionally neither of the serological approaches can distinguish between separate multiple infections caused by more than one HPV genotype nor do they adequately distinguish even between high-risk and low-risk HPV types.

A method known as Hybrid Capture was developed by Digene (Gaithersburg, Md.). This test detects specific HPV nucleic acid sequences by forming DNA-RNA hybrids.[15,16] Although this test is sensitive and can discriminate between high- and low-risk HPVs, it does not currently distinguish between individual genotypes.

Various PCR-based tests have been developed to detect HPV DNA using primers that amplify a region of the major viral capsid L1 gene that is highly conserved between HPV viral subtypes. Different groups have designed alternative consensus primer pairs including MY09/MY11,[17] the GP5+/GP6+,[18] and PGMY09/11.[19] All of these assays require considerable post-PCR processing using ELISA to identify positive samples and to define individual genotypes of infection. As an alternative, more efficient approach, to obtain genotyping information from clinical specimens, a pool of HPV type-specific primers were combined in a single PCR.[20-22] A PCR product was indicative of infection by one of the types tested for, and the individual HPV genotypes could then be identified by Southern blotting or reverse line blot techniques.

With the availability of quantitative real-time PCR instruments using different detection chemistries, new assays were reported. Swan et al. used TaqMan probes to detect and quantitative HPV genotypes.[5] Other methods include VESPA (Viral Evaluation using Self Probing Amplicons/Scorpions) method,[23,24] and Molecular Beacon labeled probes have also been developed and applied[25] in conjunction with reverse line blot to detect and genotype HPV. The main disadvantages to all of these approaches are the cost of synthesis of dual dye labeled oligonucleotides.

There is a need for a cost-effective and rapid test that can distinguish between the different genotypes of HPV. One such method has been reported by Cubie et al. using real-time PCR on a commercial LightCycler (Idaho Technology Inc., Salt Lake City, Utah) and incorporating a non-specific fluorogenic SYBR Green I dye (Molecular Probes, Inc., Eugene, Oreg.).[26] This approach combined PCR amplification with post-PCR amplicon melting curve analysis. There were a number of limitations with this pioneering attempt. The PCR reaction was performed in very small reaction volumes (5–7 μl) that could not be retrieved for further analysis. Secondly, there were problems with the apparatus overheating and as a result, melting curve analysis could not be carried out on all the samples analyzed. The system also used fragile glass capillaries that smashed easily in inexperienced hands. This approach was not suitable for performing high-throughput clinical work required in cervical screening or in a molecular epidemiology laboratory.

In order to address these shortcomings we developed a sensitive, robust, and high-throughput PCR-based test using non-specific SYBR Green I dye. In this example it is performed on the Mx4000 real-time PCR instrument (Stratagene, La Jolla, Calif.) but the technique is designed to be adaptable to any real-time PCR platform. Specificity and sensitivity were achieved by using an optimized in-house reaction mix to detect low copy numbers of HPV infection and also to allow simultaneous analysis of individual HPV genotypes. The assay was applied to detect HPV DNA extracted from fresh cervical swab samples. The HPV genotype was interrogated by a post real-time PCR melting curve analysis. The HPV16 positive status of the samples were confirmed using HPV16 type specific assay and the genotypes were confirmed using DNA sequencing, as the "gold" standard for conclusive, but labor-intensive, genotype information.

26.2. Materials and Methods

Cloned DNA of HPV types (6, 11, 16, 18, 31, 33, 35, 39, 45, 51, 52, 56, 58, 66, and 68) were available in the laboratory as part of collaboration established by David Jenkins, as plasmid containing *E.coli* colonies. Plasmid DNA was isolated from bacterial cell cultures and purified using miniprep spin columns (Qiagen, Crawley, United Kingdom). The extracted DNA was quantified using GeneQuant II spectrophotometric analysis (Pharmacia, Sweden) and used in the real-time PCR as the positive controls as well as reference controls for the genotype analysis.

Real-time PCR reactions were performed in 25 µl volume containing SureTaq Brilliant PCR amplification buffer (Stratagene, La Jolla, Calif.), 7 mM magnesium chloride, 0.4 mM dNTP, 100 nM oligonucleotide primers GP5+/6+, which targets the HPV L1 gene GP5+ 5' –TTT GTT ACT GTG GTA GAT ACT AC 3' and bioGP6+ (biotinylated at 5' for EIA assay) 5' –GAA AAA TAA ACT GTA AAT CAT ATT C–3', 1/30,000 final dilution of SYBR Green I dye (Molecular Probes, Inc., Eugene, Oreg.), 6 0 nM ROX reference dye (Stratagene Brilliant Core Reagent Kit), 5% glycerol, 2.0 µl of dimethyl sulphoxide 37%, 0.5 units of SureTaq polymerase (Stratagene, La Jolla, Calif.), 2.5 µl of template DNA. The master mix was made up in bulk and stored at –20°C in aliquots. A standard curve was constructed using HPV16 viral DNA control purchased from Advanced Biotechnologies (USA) with a known concentration of 50 ng/µl and diluted in a 10-fold dilution series to cover the range from 10 ng to 0.1 pg/tube. Standards were included in duplicate in all the assays to obtain viral load measurements. Also included in each assay were negative, no-template controls from the DNA extraction (internal negative controls) as well as water controls (blanks) for the real-time PCR assay. A standard PCR profile was followed by a stringent melting curve analysis. The details of this thermal profile are shown on **Table 26.1**.

Table 26.1. Thermal profile for the GP5+/6+ amplification using SYBR Green qPCR reaction mix.

95°C for 15 minutes × 1—Hot-start enzyme activation

Followed by 40 cycles of PCR amplification:

94°C for 1.00 min
45°C for 2.00 min (fluorescent data collection)
72°C for 1.30 min

Followed by high stringency dissociation of 125 cycles of:

The final qPCR products were melted by a heating to 95°C for 1 min, cooled to 65°C, and then subjected to temperature increments of 0.2°C. The reaction was incubated at each temperature for 1 min 30 s and fluorescent data collected at each of these stages.

Clinical samples ($n = 222$) were examined during this pilot study. These were cervical swab specimens collected from women identified as having borderline or mildly dyskaryotic smears during routine cervical screening and being studied in the MRC clinical trial called "TOMBO-LA" trial (Trial of Management of Borderline and Other Low-Grade Abnormalities). Cells from cervical swabs were centrifuged and resuspended in lysis buffer according to the manufacturer's instructions (Qiagen DNA mini kit). Purified DNA was eluted (100 µl) in AE buffer. Negative, cell-free, internal controls were included in each batch of extractions and were treated in exactly the same manner as the samples.

The assay was developed and optimized in terms of sensitivity, specificity, and inter-and intra-assay variations. A selection of PCR positive samples was sequenced to verify the predicted HPV genotype.

26.3. Results

Four factors were considered when assessing which PCR mix was optimal and should be adopted for the clinical study: the efficiency and sensitivity of the reaction; preventing potential primer dimer product formation; and maximum discrimination between viral subtype sequences.

Efficiency and sensitivity was determined by analysis of the standard curve (**Plate 26.1**). Using the PCR reaction composition as stated in **Section 26.2.** *Materials and Methods*, the gradient of the HPV16 standard curve was obtained as –3.330, which translates to an equivalent of a PCR reaction of 99.7% efficiency (**Fig. 26.1**). The assay was sensitive to 0.1 pg HPV16 DNA, which equates to less than 0.2 viral copies/tube. The inter-assay variation over ten consecutive tests was found to be less than 10% and the intra-assay variation using 15 replicates to be less than 5%.

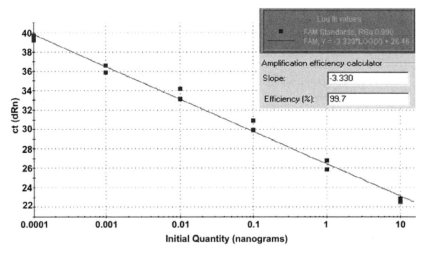

Figure 26.1. Analysis of the standard calibration graph. The standard curve was analysed to determine the sensitivity and efficiency of the PCR reaction. The gradient of the HPV16 standard curve was obtained as –3.330, which translates to an equivalent of a PCR reaction of 99.7% efficiency. The assay was sensitive to 0.1 pg HPV16 DNA, which equates to less than 0.2 viral copies/tube.

Since SYBR Green I detects all double-stranded DNA, it was critical to determine that there were no primer dimer products or nonspecific products formed in the reaction. Primer dimers usually form with an inverse proportionality to the amount of starting template. In the absence of template (NTC) any tendency for primers to self-hybridize is usually exacerbated. Primer dimers can be identified using a SYBR Green I dissociation curve and are identified as products showing a lower melting temperature than the specific product formed in the presence of template. As can be seen in **Plate 26.2A**, there is no product evident in the NTC sample and it is clear that these primers do not interact significantly. In **Plate 26.2B** it can be seen that the products formed from the template of the standard curve were homologous indicating that the primers produce a single product. The intensity of the peaks of the rate of change of fluorescence with respect to temperature ($-R_n'(T)$) measurement decreased in correlation with the amount of endpoint PCR product as determined by the endpoint fluorescence level (ΔR_n) of the amplification plot.

Finally, the reaction conditions were required to be applied to distinguish between the differences in amplicon sequence of other HPV subtypes by comparing melting profiles. The cloned HPV L1 genes were used as templates for this comparison. In order to obtain the greatest differentiation between melting profiles, a selection of dissociation curve parameters were compared. These were empirically determined comparisons of temperature increments (from 1°C to 0.1°C per cycle) and the period of time for each hold (60 seconds or 90 seconds). Greatest differentiation was achieved after a melting profile of 0.2°C increments held for 90 seconds. **Plate 26.3** shows the melting profile of each of the PCR amplicons from the cloned HPV sequences. From this figure it is clear that some profiles are more readily distinguished than others and so the melting profiles of the four most prevalent HPV subtypes—16, 18, 31, and 33—were compared in isolation from other HPV subtype profiles (**Plate 26.4**). Critically, these profiles are clearly distinct from each other, with a 4°C difference between HPV33 and HPV18.

After optimization of reaction components and conditions, clinical specimens were analyzed using the same master mix and 2.5 µl of the purified DNA. For each experiment the HPV16 standard curve, negative controls from samples extraction, blank template controls, as well as cloned HPV DNA plasmids of types 6, 11, 16, 18, 31, 33, 35, 39, 45, 51, 52, 56, 58, 66, and 68 were included with the samples. It was found to be essential to make direct comparisons of the melting profile of the amplified products from clinical samples to each cloned sequence in turn (**Plate 26.5**). Using this technique was found to be important since there is similarity between some of the HPV melting profiles and there were also subtle variations in melting profile from experiment to experiment. In **Plate 26.5** it is clearly evident that the samples illustrated contain infection with either HPV16 or HPV18, as indicated. Another feature of this technique was the identification of clinical samples infected with two viral subtypes. These were identified by the presence of two distinct products, which could be differentiated by comparison of the melting temperature to plasmid positive controls (**Plate 26.6**). The different HPV types in 222 samples are shown in **Fig. 26.2**. HPV16 is the most prevalent genotype, and was present in over 37% of the series. From the sequencing data of 19 cases there was 100% agreement with the predicted genotype. There was also agreement with type-specific HPV16 Scorpion-based assay for cases identified by the novel SYBR Green I method as being HPV16 positive.

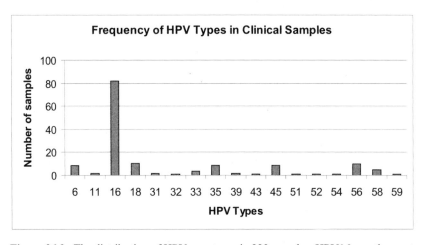

Figure 26.2. The distribution of HPV genotypes in 222 samples. HPV16 was the most prevalent high-risk genotype identified and was present in over 37% of the cervical samples infected with HPV.

26.4. Conclusion

The aim of this study was to develop a technique for the rapid, simultaneous identification of HPV infection and genotype from clinical samples. This method does not require the use of multiple type-specific internal oligonucleotide probes or primers. The complete process starting with DNA extraction through to genotyping can be performed within a working day. The instrument can run automatically overnight and has a capacity to handle 70 specimens simultaneously in addition to essential control samples. Therefore, this method is suitable for large-scale use in studies of cervical screening and HPV epidemiology.

The most prevalent high-risk infections were HPV16 and HPV18 so identification and distinction of these two subtypes was considered to be an essential requirement of the technique. The melting profile of the plasmid positive controls of HPV16 and HPV18 were shown along with clinical samples identified and confirmed (by PCR-EIA and DNA sequencing) as being of these subtypes. The profiles are clearly separate and distinct from each other indicating that these infections could be identified and distinguished from each other using this technique.

Another unique feature of this technique was identification of clinical samples infected with two viral subtypes. These were identified by the presence of two distinct products, which could be differentiated by comparison of the melting temperature. The initial validation of this assay suggests that it is a robust, user-friendly technique that has considerable potential for diagnostic and prognostic studies and other clinical or molecular epidemiological applications. Further clinical epidemiological studies on both fresh and archived smears are in progress.

Acknowledgements

The authors would like to thank the staff of TOMBOLA trial teams in Aberdeen, Dundee, and Nottingham (United Kingdom) for the collection of cervical swabs and access to the specimens used. We are also grateful to Miss Anne Kane for assistance with artwork.

References

1. Parkin DM, Laara E, Muir CS: **Estimates of the worldwide frequency of sixteen major cancers in 1980.** *Intl J Cancer* 1988, **41**:184–197.

2. Walboomers J, Jacobs M, Manos M: **Human papillomavirus is necessary cause of invasive cervical cancer world-wide.** *J Pathol* 1999, **189**:12–19.

3. Pfister H: **The role of human papillomavirus in anogenital cancer.** *Obstetrics & Gynecology Clinics North America* 1996, **23**:579–595.

4. Jenkins D, Sherlaw-Johnson C, Gallivan S: **Can papillomavirus testing be used to improve cervical cancer screening?** *Intl J Cancer* 1996, **65**(6):768–773.

5. Swan D, Tucker RA, Tortolero-Luna G, Mitchell MF, Wideroff L, Unger ER, Nisenbaum RA, Reeves WC, Incenogle JP: **Human papillomavirus (HPV) DNA copy number is dependent on grade of cervical disease and HPV types.** *J Clin Microbiol* 1999, **37**:1030–1034.

6. Josefsson AM, Magnusson, PK, Ylitalo P, Sorensen P, Qwarforth-Tubbin PK, Andersen M, Melbye M, Adami HO, Gyllensten UB: **Viral load of human papillomavirus 16 as a determinant for development of cervical carcinoma *in situ*: A nested case-control study.** *Lancet* 2000, **355**:2189–2193.

7. Ylitalo N, Sorensen P, Josefsson AM, Magnusson PK, Andersen PK, Ponten J, Adami HO, Gyllensten UB, Melbye M: **Consistent high viral load of human papillomavirus 16 and risk of cervical carcinoma *in situ*: A nested case-control study.** *Lancet* 2000, **355**:2194–2198.

8. Zerbini M, Venturoli S, Cricca M, Gallinella G, De Simone P, Costa S, Santini D, Musiani M: **Distribution and viral load of type specific HPVs in different cervical lesions as detected by PCR-ELISA.** *J Clin Path* 2001, **54**:377–380.

9. Sasieni P, Cuzick J, Farmery E: **Accelerated decline in cervical cancer mortality in England and Wales.** *Lancet* 1995, **346**:1566–1567.

10. Cuzick J, Meijers CJLM, Walboomers JMM: **Screening for cervical cancer.** *Lancet* 1998, **351**:1439–1440.

11. Costa SM, Sideri K, Syrjanen P, Terzano M, De Nuzzo P, De Simone P, Cristiani P, Finarelli AC, Bovicelli A, Zamparelli A, Bovicelli L: **Combined Pap smear, cervicography and HPV DNA testing in the detection of cervical intraepithelial neoplasia and cancer.** *Acta Cytol* 2000, **44**:310–318.

12. Cuzick J, Sasieni P, Davies P, Adams J, Normand C, Frater A, van Ballegooijen M, van den Akker-van Marle E: **A systematic review of the role of human papilloma virus (HPV) testing within a cervical screening programme: Summary and conclusions.** *Brit J Cancer* 2000, **83**(5):561–565.

13. Meijer CJ, Rozendaal L, Voorhorst FJ, Verheijen R, Helmerhorst TJ, Walboomers JM: **Human papillomavirus and screening for cervical cancer: State of art and prospects.** *Nederlands Tijdschrift Voor Geneeskunde* 2000, **144**(35):1675–1679.

14. Wise J: **UK pilot scheme for HPV testing announced.** *BMJ (Clinical Research Ed.)* 2000, **320**(7235):600.

15. Schiffman, MH, Kiviat NB, Burk RD, Shah KV, Daniel RW, Lewis R, Kuypers J, Manos MM, Scott DR, Sherman ME, Kurman RJ, Stoler MH, Glass AG, Rush BB, Mielzynska I, Lorincz AT: **Accuracy and interlaboratory reliability of human papillomavirus DNA testing by hybrid capture.** *J Clin Microbiol* 1995, **33**:545–550.

16. Schiffman MH, Herrero R, Hildesheim A, Sherman ME, Bratti M, Wacholder S, Alfaro M, Hutchinson M, Morales J, Greenberg MD Lorincz AT: **HPV DNA test-**

ing in cervical cancer screening: Results from women in a high-risk province of Costa Rica. *JAMA* 2000, **283**:87–93.

17. Manos MM, Ting Y, Wright DK, Lewis AJ, Broker TR, Wolinsky SM: **Use of polymerase chain reaction amplification for the detection of genital human papillomaviruses.** *Cancer Cells* 1989, **7**:209–214.

18. Jacobs MV, de Roda Husman AM, Van den Brule AJC, Sniders PJF, Meijers CJLM, Walboomers JMM: **Group-specific differentiation between high-and low-risk human papillomavirus genotypes by general primer-mediated PCR and two cocktails of oligonucleotide probes.** *J Clin Microbiol* 1995, **33**:901–905.

19. Gravitt PE, Peyton CL, Alessi Q, Wheeler CM, Coutlee F, Hildesheim A, Schiffman MH, Scott DR, Apple RJ: **Improved amplification of genital human papilloma- viruses.** *J Clin Microbiol* 2000, **38**:357–361.

20. Evander M, Boden E, Bjersing L, Rylander E, Wadell G: **Oligonucleotide primers for DNA amplification of the early regions 1, 6 and 7 from human papillomavirus types 6, 11, 16, 18, 31 and 33.** *Arch.Virol* 1991, **116**: 221–233.

21. Kleter B, Van Droon L, ter Schegget J, Schrauwen L, van Krimpen K, Burger M, ter Harmsel B, Quint W: **Novel short-fragment PCR assay for highly sensitive broad-spectrum detection of anogenital human papillomaviruses.** *Am J Pathol* 1998, **153**:1731–1739.

22. Gravitt PE, Peyton CL, Apple RJ, Wheeler CM: **Genotyping of 27 human papillomavirus types by using L1 consensus PCR products by a single hybridisation, reverse line blot detection method.** *J Clin Microbiol* 1998, **36**:3020–3027.

23. Hart KW, Martin WO, Thelwell N, Fiander AN, Brown T, Borysiewicz LK, Gelder CM: **Novel method for detection, typing, and quantification of human papillomaviruses in clinical samples.** *J Clin Microbiol* 2001, **39**(9): 3204–3212.

24. Whitcombe D, Theaker J, Guy SP, Brown T, Little S: **Detection of PCR products using self-probing amplicons and fluorescence.** *Nature (Biotech)* 1999, **17**:804–807.

25. Zoe J, Jordens SL, Pickett MA, Amarasekara S, Abeywickerema I, Watt PJ: **Amplification with molecular beacon primers and reverse line blotting for the detection and typing of human papillomaviruses.** *J Virol Meths* 2000, **89**:29–37.

26. Cubie HA, Seagar AL, McGoogan E, Whitehead J, Brass A, Arends MJ, Whitley MW: **Rapid real-time PCR to distinguish between high-risk human papillomavirus types 16 and 18.** *J Clin Pathol (Mol Pathol)* 2001, **54**:24–29.

✦

APPENDICES

✦

- **Appendix** 1   Useful Information

- **Appendix** 2   Glossary

Appendix A1:

Useful Information

Appendix 1:

Useful Information

A1.1. Sizes and Molecular Weights of Eukaryotic Genomic DNA and rRNAs

A detailed database of genome sizes can be consulted at
http://www.genomesize.com

Genome Sizes

Organism	Chromosomes/haploid genome	Base pairs/haploid genome
SV40	n/a.	5,243
ΦX174	n/a	5,386
Adenovirus 2	n/a	35,937
Lambda	n/a	48,502
Escherichia coli	1	4.7×10^6
Saccharomyces cerevisiae	16	1.5×10^7
Aspergillus fumigatus	8	2.9×10^7
Neurospora crassa	7	4.0×10^7
Candida albicans	8	1.6×10^7
Theileria parva	4	9×10^6
Trypanosoma brucei	11	3.5×10^7
Chlamydomonas reinhardtii	17	1.0×10^8
Plasmodium falciparum	14	3.0×10^7
Dictyostelium discoideum	6	3.4×10^7
Arabidopsis thaliana	5	1.2×10^8
Zea mays	10	3.3×10^9
Caenorhabditis elegans	6	8.0×10^7
Drosophila melanogaster	4	1.4×10^8
Xenopus laevis	17	3.1×10^9
Takifugu niphobles	44	4.0×10^8
Gallus domesticus	39	1.2×10^8
Mus musculus	20	2.7×10^9
Rattus norvegicus	21	3.0×10^9
Felis domesticus	36	1.6×10^9
Pan troglodytes	24	3.4×10^9
Homo sapiens	23	3.3×10^9

A1.2. Nucleic Acids in Typical Human Cell

DNA content	6 pg
Coding sequences/genomic DNA	3–10%
Total number of genes	$3–6 \times 10^4$
Active genes	$1–2 \times 10^4$
Total RNA content	2–50 pg
of which: rRNA (28S, 18S, 5S)	80–85%
tRNA, snRNA, miRNA	15–20%
mRNA	1–3%
mRNA molecules	$2 \times 10^5 – 1 \times 10^6$
of which: low abundance (< 20 copies)	$1–1.5 \times 10^4$
medium abundance (> 20 < 1,000 copies)	5×10^2
high abundance (> 1,000 copies)	10–30
Typical mRNA size	1.5–2.0 kb

A1.3. Nucleotide Molecular Weights

Nucleotide	M.W.
ATP	507.2
CTP	483.2
GTP	523.2
UTP	484.2
AMP	347.2
CMP	323.2
GMP	363.2
UMP	324.2
dATP	491.2
dCTP	467.2
dGTP	507.2
TTP	482.2
dAMP	331.2
dCMP	307.2
dGMP	347.2
TMP	322.2

A1.4. Molecular Weights of Common Modifications

Modification	Molecular Weight
5'-Biotin	405.45
5'-(6 FAM)	537.46
5'-HEX	744.13
5'-TET	675.24
5'-Cy5	533.63
5'-Cy3	507.59
5'-Dabcyl	430.18
3'-TAMRA	623.60
3'-Dabcyl	498.49
3'-Fluorescein-dT	815.71
3'-(6 FAM)	569.46

A1.5. Nucleic Acid Molecular Weight Conversions

http://elvis.rowan.edu/~yao/sampleJavaScript2.html#microgrampico-mole: A useful website that performs the following calculations from a single page:

- Micrograms of dsDNA to picomoles;
- Picomoles of dsDNA to micrograms and nanograms;
- Micrograms per milliliter of oligonucleotides (ssDNA) to picomoles per microliter;
- Picomoles per microliter of oligonucleotides (ssDNA) to micrograms per milliliter;
- Micrograms of linear DNA to picomoles of ends;
- Molar ratio of insert to vector;
- Temperature conversions;
- Oligonucleotide melting temperature calculations;

A1.5.1. Exact M.W. of ssRNA

1. (Ambion)
   M.W. $= (A_n \times 328.2) + (C_n \times 304.2) + (G_n \times 344.2) + (U_n \times 305.2)$.

A1.5.2. Exact M.W. of ssDNA (e.g., Oligonucleotides)

1. (Ambion) $= (A_n \times 331.2) + (C_n \times 288.2) + (G_n \times 328.2) + (T_n \times 287.2)$, if phosphorylated add 79.

2. (Qiagen) $= (A_n \times 335.2) + (C_n \times 311.2) + (G_n \times 351.2) + (T_n \times 326.2)$, if phosphorylated add 40, if dephosphorylated subtract 84.

3. (Genamics $= (A_n \times 313.21) + (C_n \times 289.19) + (G_n \times 329.21) + (T_n \times 288.2) + 18.02$
   Expression)   (http://genamics.com/expression/calculator.htm).

4. (Roche) $= (A_n \times 312.2) + (C_n \times 288.2) + (G_n \times 328.2) + (T_n \times 303.2)$, if phosphorylated $+17$, if dephosphorylated -61.

5. (Trilink $= (A_n \times 249.24) + (C_n \times 225.23) + (G_n \times 265.2) + (T_n \times 240.23) +$ (number of
   Biotechnologies)   phosphodiester linkages in sequence $\times 63.97$)
                      (http://www.trilinkbiotech.com/new site/Technical_Info/molecular_weight.asp).

A1.5.3. Approximate M.Ws. of Nucleic Acids (in g/mol)

1. (Ambion):   M.W. of ssRNA = (# nucleotides $\times 320.5$) + 159.0;

                   M.W. of ssDNA = (# nucleotides $\times 303.7$) + 79.0;

                   M.W. of dsDNA = (# nucleotides $\times 662$) + 157.9.

2. (Qiagen):   M.W. of ssRNA = (# nucleotides $\times 343$);

                   M.W. of ssDNA = (# nucleotides $\times 331$);

                   M.W. of dsDNA = (# nucleotides $\times 607.4$).

3. (Fermentas)   M.W. of ssRNA = (# nucleotides $\times 333$);

                   M.W. of ssDNA = (# nucleotides $\times 340$).

4. (Roche)   M.W. of ssRNA = (# nucleotides $\times 340$);

                   M.W. of ssDNA = (# nucleotides $\times 330$).

5. (ABI)   M.W. of ssDNA = (# nucleotides $\times 350$).

A1.5.4. ssRNA Size and Mass Conversions

Size (nt)	Daltons or g/mol	1 µg equivalent	
		pmol	molecules
20	6,569	152.23	9.17×10^{13}
100	32,209	31.05	1.87×10^{13}
300	96,309	10.38	6.25×10^{12}
500	160,409	6.23	3.75×10^{12}
1000	320,659	3.12	1.88×10^{12}
1800	577,059	1.73	1.04×10^{12}

A1.5.5. ssDNA Size and Mass Conversions

Size (nt)	Daltons or g/mol	1 µg equivalent	
		pmol	molecules
20	6,153	162.52	9.79×10^{13}
100	30,449	32.84	1.98×10^{13}
300	91,189	10.97	6.6×10^{12}
500	151,929	6.58	3.96×10^{12}
1000	303,779	3.29	1.98×10^{12}
1800	546,739	1.83	1.1×10^{12}

A1.5.6. dsDNA Size and Mass Conversions

Size (nt)	Daltons or g/mol	1 µg equivalent	
		pmol	molecules
20	12,306	81.26	4.89×10^{13}
100	60,898	16.42	9.89×10^{12}
300	182,378	5.48	3.3×10^{12}
500	303,858	3.29	1.98×10^{12}
1000	607,558	1.65	9.91×10^{11}
1800	1,093,478	0.91	5.51×10^{11}

A1.6. Nucleotide Absorbance Maxima and Molar Extinction Coefficients

Nucleotide	Absorbance Maximum at pH 7.0 (nm)	Molar Extinction Coefficient at pH 7.0
ATP	259	15,400
CTP	271	9,000
GTP	253	13,700
UTP	262	10,000
dATP	259	15,200
dCTP	271	9,300
dGTP	253	13,700
TTP	267	9,600

$$C = A / e \times 10^3 ,$$

where C is mM concentration of compounds, A is observed absorbance at A_{max}, and e is extinction coefficient

A1.7. Conversions

Typically, oligonucleotides are supplied by the manufacturer ready to use in water or 20% (v/v) acetonitrile/water at a given concentration of x OD units/ml. Alternatively, they may be supplied as lyophilised pellets requiring the addition of water to obtain a concentration of x OD units/ml. How to convert that to units commonly used with PCR?

The terms "Mol," "molar," and "molar equivalence" are all designed to confuse the average molecular biologist.

A1.7.1. Mole

Describes the absolute amount of a substance: 1 mol of anything is 6.022×10^{23} molecules (Avogadro's number).

A1.7.2. Molarity

Describes the concentration of a substance in a liquid, e.g., 1 M. This actually means 1 mol per liter, i.e., a 1-M solution = a solution with a molarity of one = 6.022×10^{23} molecules per liter.

A1.7.3. Molar Equivalence

What is the concentration of a primer at 0.1 pmol in a reaction volume of 25 μl?

   0.1 pmol in 25 μl = 0.4 pmol in 100 μl = 4 pmol in 1 ml = 4 nM

A1.7.3. Molecular Weight

The molecular weight of a compound is the weight of 1 mol of molecules of that compound. To find the molecular weight of a compound, look up the atomic weights of the atoms in the molecule and add them up. The molecular weight is used to convert from grams to moles and vice versa. To convert from a weight of a substance to the number of atoms (or moles) just divide the weight by the molecular weight. To convert from moles to grams, multiply the number of moles by the molecular weight.

A1.7.4. Converting between Weight and Molarity for ssDNA

To convert	Calculate*
μg to pmol	$\mu g \times 10^{6}/325 \times N = pmol$ Example: 0.1 μg of a 20 -mer $(0.1 \times 1{,}000{,}000)/(20 \times 325) = 15.4$ pmol primer
pmol to μg	$pmol \times N \times 325/10^{6} = \mu g$ Example: 10 pmol of a 25-mer $(10 \times 25 \times 325)/1{,}000{,}000 = 0.081$ μg primer

*N = number of nucleotides in DNA; Average M.W. of dNMP is 325.

A1.7.5. Converting between Weight and Molarity for dsDNA

To convert	Calculate*
µg to pmol	$\mu g \times 10^6 / 660 \times N = pmol$
pmol to µg	$pmol \times N \times 325 / 10^6 = \mu g$

* N = number of base pairs in DNA; 660 is average molecular weight of a base pair.

A1.7.6. Sample Calculations

Example: Cox-2 reverse primer: 5'-TTTCTGTACTGCGGGTGGAAC-3', a 21 nucleotide primer comprising 3A, 4C, 7G, 7T supplied as 2.8 OD/ml at A_{260}.

A1.7.6.1 What is the concentration of the oligonucleotide in µg/ml?

Multiply the OD/ml by the concentration of ssDNA that produces an OD of 1 at A_{260} in a 1-cm cuvette:

$$2.8 \times 37 = 103.6 \; \mu g/ml$$

Therefore, the concentration of the oligonucleotide is 104 µg/ml.

A1.7.6.2. What is its molecular weight?

$$M.W. = (A_n \times 331.2) + (C_n \times 288.2) + (G_n \times 328.2) + (T_n \times 287.2)$$
$$= 993.6 + 1152.8 + 2297.4 + 2010.4 = 6454.2$$

A1.7.6.3. What is its molarity?

Divide the concentration by the molecular weight:

$$0.104/6454.2 = 1.6 \; 10^{-5} \; M = 16 \; \mu M$$

A1.7.6.4. How much oligonucleotide to add to PCR assay?

Lyophilized oligonucleotide primer is supplied at 30 nmol. The PCR assay is carried out at 0.5 µM final concentration in a 25-ml reaction volume. How much primer must be added to the reaction?

1. Decide on a stock concentration and standardize units.

Note: The quantity of oligonucleotide must be expressed in micromoles (μmoles) to calculate the volume for a micromolar solution. Therefore total micromoles of oligonucleotide = 30/1000 = 0.03 μmol

2. Make a 100× stock solution (100 × 0.5 μM = 50 μM).

Note: Calculation of volume (V) required to resuspend 0.03 μmol of oligonucleotide to give a stock concentration of 50 μM: 50 μmol/1000 ml = 0.03 μmol/V ml; solve for V; V = (0.03 μmol × 1000 ml)/50 μmol = 0.6 ml = 600 μl. This 100× stock must be aliquoted and kept frozen at –70°C.

3. Use serial dilutions to make a 10× stock (10 × 0.5 μM = 5 μM).

Tip: For pipetting accuracy, avoid using small volumes (less than 2 μl) of stock solutions in your reactions. It may be necessary to serially dilute the stock oligonucleotide solution. Make a 10× stock by diluting the 100× stock as follows:

1:10 dilution of 100× stock: 10 μl of 50 μM (100×) stock + 90 μl TE gives 100 μl of 5 μM (10×) stock.

4. This is the 10× working solution that is used to give the final concentration of 0.5 μM in the reaction. Store at +4°C and use within two–four weeks.

5. Final reaction volume is 25 μl: *Volume of 10× stock (x μl) × stock concentration (5 μM) = Final reaction volume (25 μl) × Final oligonucleotide concentration (0.5 μM)*

$$x = (25 \ \mu l \times 0.5 \ \mu M)/5 \ \mu M$$

$$x = 2.5 \ \mu l$$

Therefore, 2.5 μl of the 10× stock solution must be added

A1.7.7. Calculation of Copy Numbers

A1.7.7.1. RNA

Example: 1αOHase amplicon: α

GCUAUUGGCGGGAGUGGACACGGUGUCCAACACGCUCUCUUGGGCUC
UGUAUGAGCUCUCCCGGC

is a 65 nucleotide sequence comprising 9A, 19C, 21G, 16U (62% G/C).

1. First calculate its molecular weight:

M.W. $= (A_n \times 328.2) + (C_n \times 304.2) + (G_n \times 344.2) + (U_n \times 305.2)$

$= (2953.8 + 5779.8 + 7228.2 + 4883.2) = 20845$ g mol^{-1}

2. Next use Avogadro's number ($N_0 = 6.023 \times 10^{23}$ molecules/mol) to calculate the number of molecules/ng (N) using the equation:

$$N = (g/M.W.) \times N_0$$

$= (1 \times 10^{-9}$ g$/20845$ g mol$^{-1}) \times 6.023 \times 10^{23}$ molecules mol^{-1}

$= 2.9 \times 10^{10}$ molecules/ng

Therefore, if the concentration of the amplicon is 3 ng/μl, there are 8.7×10^{10} molecules/μl.

A1.7.7.2. DNA

Calculate the number of target molecules per nanogram of a 250-bp PCR product:

1. First calculate its M.W.:

$$250 \text{ bp} \times 660 \text{ g/mol per bp} = 1.7 \times 10^5 \text{ g/mol}$$

2. Then calculate the number of molecules (n) per ng:

For 1 ng of PCR product:

n/ng $= [(1 \times 10^{-9}$ g$)/(1.7 \times 10^5$/mol$)] \times (6.02 \times 10^{23}$ molecules/mol$)$

$= 3.5 \times 10^9$ molecules/ng

A1.7.8. Conversions between Molecular Weight and Molarity for Various DNAs

Type	Size (bp)	Molecular weight	pmol/μg	Molecules/μg	μg/pmol
ssDNA	20	6600	152	9.1×10^{13}	6.6×10^{-3}
dsDNA	1×10^3	6.6×10^5	1.52	9.1×10^{11}	0.66
E. coli genome	4.7×10^6	3.1×10^9	3.2×10^{-4}	1.9×10^8	3.1×10^3
S. cerevisiae	1.5×10^7	9.9×10^9	1.0×10^{-4}	6.0×10^7	9.9×10^3
M. musculus	2.7×10^9	1.8×10^{12}	5.6×10^{-7}	3.4×10^5	1.8×10^6
H. sapiens	3.3×10^9	2.2×10^{12}	4.6×10^{-7}	2.8×10^5	2.2×10^6
Z. mays	3.9×10^9	2.6×10^{12}	3.9×10^{-7}	2.3×10^5	2.6×10^6

S. cerevisiae, M. musculus, H.sapiens, Z.mays: haploid genome.

A1.8. DNA Conformations:

Helix type	Direction of rotation	Residues per turn	Rotation per residue	Helix rise per residue	Helix pitch
A	Right	11	33°	2.55 Å	28 Å
B	Right	10	36°	3.4 Å	34 Å
Z	Left	12	30°	3.7 Å	45 Å

A1.9. Efficiency of PCR Reactions

The slope of the standard curve can be used to determine the exponential amplification and efficiency of the PCR reaction by the following equations:

$$Exponential\ Amplification = 10^{(-1/\text{slope})}$$

$$Efficiency = [10^{(-1/\text{slope})}] - 1$$

The following table shows the amplification and efficiency for various values of the slope:

Slope	Amplification rate	Efficiency
−4.00	1.78	78%
−3.95	1.79	79%
−3.90	1.80	80%
−3.85	1.82	82%
−3.80	1.83	83%
−3.75	1.85	85%
−3.70	1.86	86%
−3.65	1.88	88%
−3.60	1.90	90%
−3.55	1.91	91%
−3.50	1.93	93%
−3.45	1.95	95%
−3.40	1.97	97%
−3.35	1.99	99%
−3.30	2.01	101%
−3.25	2.03	103%
−3.20	2.05	105%
−3.15	2.08	108%
−3.10	2.10	110%
−3.05	2.13	113%
−3.00	2.15	115%

A1.10. Centrifugation

Calculate and convert between rpm and *g* force:
                    http://www.labcentrifuge.com/gforce5.html

A1.11. Splice Junctions

It often can be difficult to design optimal primer/probe combinations that span splice junctions. This is probably related to the sequence context around the splice junction.

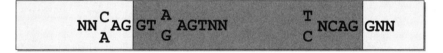

Appendix A2:

Glossary

A2

Appendix 2:

Glossary

3'-5' exonuclease activity:

Enzymatic activity to remove a mispaired nucleotide from the 3' end of the growing strand. The reaction is a hydrolysis of a phosphoester bond. The presence of a 3'–5' exonuclease, or **proofreading**, **activity** improves the **fidelity** of the polymerization (same as **proofreading** activity).

5'-3' exonuclease activity:

Enzymatic activity to remove a nucleotide from the 5' end of a polynucleotide strand. This activity is actually that of a single-strand dependent endonuclease, and is needed to remove RNA **primers** of Okazaki fragments, the RNA strand in the intermediate DNA/RNA heteroduplex during reverse transcription and during DNA repair.

5'-3' polymerase activity:

Enzymatic activity to catalyze the linkage of a 5' α-phosphate of a mononucleotide-triphosphate to the 3' oxygen of a polynucleotide chain.

Absolute quantification:

Number of copies of a specific RNA per cell or unit volume or mass of tissue. A **standard** curve (two-, five-, or ten-fold serial dilutions) of known **standards** is used to quantify the "unknowns" of interest. Absolute quantification relies on a set of knowns and since there is no way to know exactly how much or how many copies of a known template truly exists in a given well of a known sample, this method is not really absolute.

Absorbance:

Absorbance A is the logarithm to the base 10 of the ratio of the spectral radiant power of light transmitted through a reference sample (I_0) to that of the light transmitted through a control solution (I), both observed in identical cells.

$$A = \lg(I_0/I)$$

This definition supposes that the entire incident light is either transmitted or absorbed, reflection or scattering being negligible.

Amplicon:

A short segment of DNA generated by the PCR process whose sequence is defined by forward and reverse **primers**. Sometimes referred to as amplimer.

Amplification plot:

The plot of fluorescence signal versus cycle number.

Annealing:

Hybridizing or binding of complementary nucleic acids, usually at an optimal temperature.

Baseline:

During PCR, fluorescence is influenced by changing reaction conditions and environment. In general, the level of fluorescence in any one well corresponds to the amount of target present. Fluorescence levels may fluctuate due to changes in the reaction medium creating a background signal. This background signal is most evident during the initial cycles of PCR prior to significant accumulation of the target **amplicon**. During these early PCR cycles, the background signal in all wells is used to determine the "baseline fluorescence" across the entire reaction plate. The goal of data analysis is to determine when target amplification is sufficiently above the background signal, enabling an accurate calculation of the **threshold cycle**.

Bulge loop:

Bulge loop is formed if there are extra bases (specifically those that do not have any possible pairing partners and cause "kinks" in the helix) within a stem.

Calibrator:

Real-time PCR is performed on both the experimental samples and reference **standards**. Relative values for target abundance in each experimental sample are extrapolated from the **standard** curve generated from the reference **standard**. One sample is typically designated as the "calibrator" (or 1× sample), and the relative expression levels of all other samples are then expressed relative to the calibrator sample.

Capping:

Any free 5'-OH groups that do not undergo coupling must be capped to prevent further elongation during the next cycle.

Chi-square:

A goodness-of-fit-test statistic used to test the assumption that the distribution of a set of data is similar to the expected distribution, such as a normal distribution.

Competitive PCR:

An internal control, usually similar in size and sequence to the target nucleic acid, competes with the latter for reagents (such as common **primers**) in the same reaction tube.

Confidence interval (limit):

The confidence intervals for specific statistics (e.g., the mean or regression lines) provide a range of values around the statistic where the "true" (population) statistic can be expected to be located (with a given level of certainty). If a sample mean is 5×10^6 copies of mRNA/µg total RNA, and the lower and upper limits of the $p = 0.05$ confidence interval are 2×10^6 and 8×10^6 respectively, then is a 95% probability that the population mean is greater than 2×10^6 and lower than 8×10^6. If the p-level is set to a smaller value, then the confidence interval would become wider thereby increasing the "certainty" of the estimate and vice versa. Note that the width of the confidence interval depends on the sample size and on the variation of data values. The calculation of confidence intervals is based on the assumption that the variable is normally distributed in the population. This estimate may not be valid if this assumption is not met, unless the sample size is large (greater than $n = 100$).

Correlation:

Correlation is a measure of the relation between two or more variables. Correlation coefficients can range from -1 to $+1$. The value of -1 represents a perfect negative correlation while a value of $+1$ represents a perfect positive correlation. A value of 0 represents a lack of correlation. The most widely used type of correlation coefficient is the Pearson. It determines the extent to which values of two variables are "proportional" to each other. Proportional means linearly related; that is, the correlation is high if it can be approximated by a straight line (sloped upwards or downwards). This line is called the regression line or least-squares line, because it is determined such that the sum of the squared distances of all the data points from the line is the lowest possible. Pearson correlation assumes that the two variables are measured on at least interval scales. Spearman correlation is computed from ranks and assumes that the variables under consideration can be ranked into two ordered series.

Cost:

The cost of real-time assays is considerable, because (1) duplicate or triplicate assays have to run, (2) a **standard** curve must be included with every assay, (3) reagents, especially probes, do not always work because of faulty labeling, (4) reagents and thermal cyclers are excessively expensive. Costs can be decreased by reducing the volume of the **RT**-PCR/PCR assay, but there is no getting away from the fact that these assays cost a lot-approximately \$2.00–\$4.00 per **RT**-PCR assay.

Dangling end:

That is a portion of a sequence that is left over after the energetically most-favorable segments have been identified and paired with computer-aided folding algorithms.

Domain:

One or more in a contiguous series of linked stems and loops, which may possibly act in concert as a topological structure, or which collectively may contribute to functionality of a sequence region.

Deblocking:

As a first step during oligonucleotides synthesis, Trityl group of the support bound monomer is removed with a mild acid treatment. The resulting Trityl cation that is orange in acid solution is collected and colorimetrically quantified to determine the stepwise coupling efficiencies.

Divalent ion requirement:

RTs require a divalent ion for activity. Enzymes that use Mg^{2+} are likely to produce more accurate cDNA copies than those that use Mn^{2+}, since Mn^{2+} adversely affects the **fidelity** of DNA synthesis.

ΔR, ΔRn—*see* R, Rn

Elongation rate:

The elongation (turnover) rate is the maximum number of nucleotides polymerized per minute per molecule of DNA polymerase. It should not be confused with **processivity**; the turnover rate does not consider whether a polymerase is processive.

Emission spectrum:

The emission spectrum of a fluorescent dye is a plot of the intensity of emitted light (fluorescence) as a function of the wavelength of the emitted light.

Energy transfer:

This describes the process in which an excited state of one molecular entity (the donor) is deactivated to a lower-lying state by transferring energy to a second molecular entity (the acceptor), which is thereby raised to a higher energy state.

Excitation spectrum:

The excitation spectrum of a fluorescent dye is a plot of the intensity of emitted light as a function of the wavelength of the exciting light.

FAM:

6-carboxyfluorescein.

Fidelity:

Fidelity is the enzyme's ability to faithfully replicate a DNA molecule, i.e., the frequency of incorporating a mismatched nucleotide in the growing strand during the replication of the **template** strand. Error rates are commonly expressed as the mutation rate per base pair duplicated, and accuracy is the average number of nucleotides the polymerase incorporates before making an error. Usually, for cells with a complex genome, a high fidelity is required, but some viruses like HIV can take advantage from a low fidelity and a high mutation rate. Fidelity is a measure of the accuracy of replication. Because of the dramatic levels of amplification provided by PCR, one needs to consider the faithfulness of the replication. Differences in the fidelity of the amplification can lead to dramatic differences in the fraction of PCR products with a sequence identical to the original target. Fidelity is the result of a complex process that must take into consideration many elements. The enzyme is only one of these elements. Other elements include: buffer conditions, thermal cycling parameters, number of cycles, efficiency of amplification, and the sequence of the DNA being copied. For example, individual bases or regions of a DNA sequence may be copied with different fidelity. There are a number of ways to calculate fidelity. Two useful parameters are the misincorporation rate and the cumulative error frequency. The misincorporation rate is expressed as the errors per nucleotide polymerized. For example, if one mutation is made for every 20,000 bases polymerized, the misincorporation rate is 5×10^{-5}. Cumulative error frequency takes into consideration both the misincorporation rate and the number of doublings; it is therefore directly applicable to PCR.

Fluorescein and derivatives:

The amine-reactive fluorescein derivatives are been the most common fluorescent derivatization reagents for covalently nucleic acid probes. In addition to its relatively high absorptivity, excellent fluorescence **quantum yield**, and good water solubility, fluorescein has an excitation maximum (494 nm) that closely matches the 488 nm spectral line of the argon-ion laser. In addition, fluorescein's protein conjugates are not inordinately susceptible to precipitation. Their drawbacks include:

- A relatively high rate of **photobleaching** limits the **sensitivity** that can be obtained;
- pH-sensitive fluorescence;
- A relatively broad fluorescence **emission spectrum**, limiting their utility in **multiplex** reactions;
- A tendency toward **quenching** of their fluorescence on conjugation to nucleic acid.

Fluorescence lifetime:

The fluorescence lifetime (τ) of a fluorophore is the mean time spent in the excited state, i.e., the probability of the molecule existing in the excited state. There are a number of ways of expressing fluorescence lifetime, for example, using the fluorescent rate constant k_f:

$$\tau = 1 \, / \, k_f \, .$$

Fluorescence Resonance Energy Transfer (FRET):

A distance-dependent interaction between the electronic excited states of two dye molecules in which excitation is transferred from a donor to an acceptor molecule without emission of a photon. FRET depends on the inverse sixth power of the intermolecular separation, making it useful over distances comparable with the dimensions of biological macromolecules (e.g., a separation of reporter and acceptor by up to 30 bases).

FRET—*see* Fluorescence Resonance Energy Transfer

Hairpin:

Antiparallel duplex structure that forms by pairing of **inverted repeat** sequences within a single-stranded nucleic acid. The helical section is called the stem and the unpaired base segment at the end the structure is called the loop.

HEX:

hexachloro-6-carboxyfluorescein. With excitation and emission maxima of 535 and 556 nm, respectively, the succinimidyl ester of 6-carboxy-2',4,4',5',7,7'-hexachlorofluorescein has the longest wavelengths of these chlorinated **fluorescein derivatives**.

Hot-start PCR:

"Hot-start" PCR is a method that generally produces cleaner PCR products. This technique is commonly used to improve the **sensitivity** and **specificity** of PCR amplifications. The major obstacle to obtaining highly sensitive and specific amplifications appears to be competing side reactions such as the amplification of nontarget sequences in background DNA (mispriming) and **primer** oligomerization. In an otherwise optimized PCR amplification, most nonspecific products can be attributed to pre-PCR mispriming. Pre-PCR mispriming can occur at anytime all components necessary for amplification are present at permissive (or below optimal **annealing**) temperatures such as during reaction set up. A "hot start" is performed by withholding from the reaction mix a key component necessary for amplification until the reaction reaches a temperature above the optimal annealing temperature of the **primers**. The component withheld from the reaction mix can be **primers**, AmpliTaq DNA Polymerase, $MgCl_2$, or dNTPs. The reaction mix, minus this component, is heated to a temperature slightly above the annealing temperature (60–72°C). Once the reaction mix reaches this temperature, the missing component is added and the PCR amplification is allowed to proceed. Because a key component is withheld from the reaction at permissive temperatures, competing side reactions are minimized and a specific amplification is occurred.

Interior loop:

Formed if there are bases within a **hairpin** stem whose pairing partners are not complementary and causes a distortion of the helix.

Inverted repeat:

Tandem, identical sequences within a single linear segment of nucleic acid), where the second segment is the reverse-complement of the first. (e.g., '5-AAATTGCNNNNGCAATTT-3'). Can hybridize and form **primer** dimers or **hairpin** structures.

LNA-Locked Nucleic Acid

Also known as bridged nucleic acid. Conformationally restricted oligonucleotide analogues that form extremely strong duplexes with their cognate targets.

Melting curves:

Melting curves are the measurements of the melting temperature values T_ms of double stranded nucleic acids. If the duplex incorporates an intercalating dye such as SYBR Green, fluorescence is brightest when the strands are annealed. As the temperature is raised towards to T_m of the duplex, fluorescence will decrease at a constant rate (slope). At the T_m there is a significant reduction in fluorescence with a noticeable change in slope. The rate of this change is determined by plotting the negative first derivative ($-dF/dT$) versus temperature. The greatest rate change yields visible peaks, representing the T_m of the dsDNA complexes.

Minor groove binder (MGB) probes:

These have a fluorescent reporter dye on the 5' end and a nonfluorescent **quencher** at the 3' end. Because the **quencher** does not fluoresce, the Sequence Detection System instruments can measure the reporter dye contributions more precisely. A minor groove binder is also located on the 3' end. The minor groove binder increases the melting temperature (T_m) of probes, thus allowing the use of shorter probes. The shorter probe contributes to greater **specificity** when performing Allelic Discrimination or an SNP assay.

Molarity:

The molarity of a solute is the number of moles of that solute divided by the volume of the solvent in liters. It is the handiest measure for most aqueous solutions, since one is usually interested in the number of moles of the solute but works with volumes. To figure out the molarity of a solution, simply work out the number of moles of the solute (probably from the molecular weight) and divide by the volume of the solvent. To convert a volume and a molarity of a solution to moles of solute, simply solve the above equation for moles of solute:

$$moles\ solute = molarity \times liters\ of\ solution.$$

Multiplex:

Simultaneous amplification of multiple gene products within the same reaction.

Nested PCR:

A second PCR is performed on the product of an earlier PCR using **primers**, which are internal to the originals. Famous for contaminating laboratories.

NTC-No-Template Control:

The no-template control is one of the basic controls that must always be included in real-time PCR assays. There is some debate as to whether there can be some amplification in the NTC. For example, if all unknown samples generate C_ts of 20–25, and the NTC is 36, it is probably correct to use those data, since any contamination is not going to interfere with the target quantification.

Nonparametrics:

Nonparametric methods were developed to be used when the researcher does not know the parameters of the distribution of the variable of interest in the population. Nonparametric methods do not rely on the estimation of parameters (such as the mean or the standard deviation) describing the distribution of the variable of interest in the population.

Normalization:

Adjusting a set of raw measurements, e.g., a variable storing mRNA levels represented in copy numbers, according to some transformation function in order to make them comparable between different samples. For example, adjusting copy numbers for total RNA concentration will produce measurements normalized against ng, μg, mg, etc., of total RNA, hence they are expressed in specific meaningful/compatible units. Without relevant normalization, the raw measurements do not carry interpretable information.

Palindrome:

Inverted repeat where the sequence can be read the same in either the positive or the negative strand (e.g., AAGCTT). If intrastrand pairing does occur, a cruciform structure results from the apposed **hairpins**, at the junction of the four duplex regions.

Passive reference:

The passive reference is a fluorescent molecule (usually ROX) that provides an internal reference to which the reporter signal can be normalized during data analysis. Each reporter signal is divided by the fluorescent signal of ROX. This is one way of normalizing for fluorescent fluctuations due to slight differences in reagent concentration or volume, caused usually by pipetting errors.

Peltier effect:

The Peltier effect transfers heat from one side of a semiconductor to another, creating an efficient heating and cooling system without refrigerants or compressors.

Phosphodiester bond:

A bond between a two sugar groups and a phosphate group; such bonds form the sugar-phosphate-sugar backbone of DNA and RNA.

Photobleaching:

Photobleaching is the irreversible destruction of a fluorophore in the excited state. Different fluorophores have different rates of photobleaching, for example, **fluorescein** photobleaches very easily. Often the rate of decomposition is proportional to the intensity of illumination. So a simple practical way to overcome this is to reduce the incident radiation.

PNA-Peptide Nucleic Acid:

An analogue of DNA in which the backbone contains neutral amide backbone linkages composed of aminoethyl glycine units instead of the usual phosphodiester linkage of deoxyribose groups.

Primase:

DNA polymerases need RNA oligonucleotides as **primers** to initialize the synthesis of new DNA strands. Primases are RNA polymerases, which synthesize the **primers** needed for DNA replication *in vivo*.

Primer:

Nucleic acid polymerases link a mononucleotide to a chain of nucleic acids, which is called the primer. RNA polymerases are able to use a single nucleotide as primer, but DNA polymerases always need an oligonucleotide.

Processivity:

The ability of an enzyme to add nucleotides to the growing strand without dissociating from its substrate. The more processive an enzyme is, the longer it will act on DNA before falling off. This number varies between some tens for polymerase I and polymerase II and several thousands for polymerase III. It provides some indication how well the enzyme can be read through secondary structures. Processivity refers to the number of nucleotides added by a DNA polymerase before it dissociates from its **template** and the processivity of some polymerases depends on accessory factors. Since saturating concentrations of enzyme are used in qPCR assays, and **amplicons** are very short, processivity is probably not a crucial consideration.

Proofreading activity:

Enzymatic activity to remove a mispaired nucleotide from the 3' end of the growing strand. The reaction is a hydrolysis of a phosphoester bond. The presence of a 3'–5' exonuclease, or proofreading, activity improves the **fidelity** of the polymerization. (see **3'-5' exonuclease activity**).

Pseudoknot:

A triple-stranded RNA structure formed when the loop at the top of a **hairpin** has sequences complementary to an unpaired segment near (or at) the base of the stem. Stringent topological rules determine the probability of pseudoknots formation.

Quantum yield:

The quantum yield of a dye is the number of photon emission (fluorescence) events divided by the number of photon absorption events (effectively the number of photons transferred to the excited state). The quantum yield of fluorophores attached to a nucleic acid is dependent on a number of environmental factors. One of these factors is the base that is adjacent to the dye molecule. Fluorescent **quenching** by an adjacent guanine has been demonstrated and can be significant, up to 40% depending on the attached fluorophore. The mechanism of fluorophore **quenching** may be explained by the electron sharing/donor properties of the adjacent base. **Quenching** of 2-aminopurine fluorescence in DNA is dominated by distance-dependent electron transfer from 2-aminopurine to guanosine, and photoinduced electron transfer plays an important role for this **quenching**. The order of **quenching** efficiency is G < A < C < T if the nucleobase is reduced. However, if the nucleobase is oxidized, the sequence is reversed. **Quenching** is also dependent on the location of the dye within the oligonucleotide.

Quencher:

A molecular entity that deactivates (quenches) an excited state of another molecular entity either by **energy transfer**, electron transfer or by a chemical mechanism.

Quenching:

Quenching refers to any process that causes a reduction in the **quantum yield** of a given fluorescence process. Quenching can be either collisional or static. Multiple labeling of a molecule with a bright fluor does not always lead to an increase in fluorescent intensity due the phenomenon of "self-quenching." Different dyes quench variably under certain conditions and many dyes exhibit self-quenching where the presence of large concentrations of dyes will significantly impact on the **quantum yield**.

R, Rn, ΔR, ΔRn:

Amplification plots can be based on four different types of fluorescence: R (raw fluorescence), ΔR (baseline-corrected raw fluorescence), Rn (normalized fluorescence), and ΔRn (baseline-corrected normalized fluorescence). Rn: reporter signal normalized to the **passive reference** for a given reaction. Normalization is accomplished by dividing the emission intensity of the reporter dye by the emission intensity of the **passive reference** to obtain a ratio defined as the Rn (normalized reporter) for a given reaction tube. Rn^+ is the Rn value of a reaction containing all components including the **template**. Rn^- is the Rn value of an unreacted sample. This value may be obtained from the early cycles of a **real-time** run; those cycles are prior to a detectable increase in fluorescence. This value may also be obtained from a reaction not containing **template**. ΔRn is the difference between the Rn^+ value and the Rn^- value. It reliably indicates the magnitude of the signal generated by the given set of PCR conditions. The following equation expresses the relationship of these terms:

$$\Delta Rn = (Rn^+) - (Rn^-),$$

where

Rn^+ = *Emission Intensity of Reporter / Emission Intensity of Passive Reference in the PCR + template reaction* and

> Rn^- = *Emission Intensity of Reporter* / *Emission Intensity of Passive Reference on the PCR* minus *template or early cycles of a Real-Time reaction.*

Reverse transcriptase (RT):

The reverse transcriptase is a RNA-dependent DNA polymerase, which is found with retroviruses. Retroviruses like the human immuno-deficiency virus (HIV) are carrying a RNA genome but after entering a host cell the RNA is transcripted into DNA by the viral reverse transcriptase.

RNase H activity:

This degrades RNA in an RNA:cDNA hybrid and can be a problem if the RNA hydrolysis competes with cDNA synthesis.

Sensitivity:

RTs have differing ability to copy small amounts of **template**. Sensitivity is the inverse of the number of false negatives and represents the ratio of number of true-positive results to the number of positive samples (true positives + false positives).

Specificity:

RTs differ in their ability to transcribe RNA secondary structures accurately. Specificity is the inverse of the number of false-positives results and represents the ratio of true-negative results to number of negative samples (true negatives + false negatives).

Standard:

A sample of known concentration used to construct a standard curve. By running standards of varying concentrations, you create a standard curve from which you can extrapolate the quantity of an unknown sample.

Statistical significance (p-level):

The statistical significance of a result is an estimated measure of the degree to which it is representative of the population. The value of the *p*-level represents a decreasing index of the reliability of a result. The higher the *p*-level, the less likely is that the observed relation between variables in the sample is a reliable indicator of the relation between the respective variables in the population. A *p*-level of 0.05 is usually treated as a "borderline acceptable" error level but still involves a pretty high probability of error (5%).

Stokes shift:

Photons from molecules in an excited state are emitted by fluorescence at longer wavelengths and consequently are less energetic than the photons responsible for the excitation. This difference between the excitation and emission maxima is termed the Stokes shift. It represents the energy lost whilst the molecule was in the excited state and allows the emitted fluorescent photons to be easily distinguished from the excitation photons, leading to the possibility of very low backgrounds in fluorescent studies.

TAMRA:

TAMRA is carboxytetramethylrhodamine. It has spectral overlap with **FAM**, **HEX**, **TET**, JOE, VIC, and is the first **FRET quencher** used with commercial real-time PCR assays. Now being superseded by dark **quenchers** because (1) it being a fluorophore and (2) its broad **emission spectrum** makes its use in **multiplex** reactions problematic.

Template:

Most nucleic acid polymerases need a single-stranded nucleic acid as a cofactor for synthesizing another strand. The first strand acts as a template and determines the sequence of the new strand, which is complementary in sequence to the template strand. The template strand and the new strand form a double helix with Watson-Crick base pairs between the complementary bases.

TET:

Like JOE, the succinimidyl ester of 6-carboxy-2',4,7,7'-tetrachloro-fluorescein has a chlorinated xanthene ring, but also additional chlorination of the "bottom" ring. As a result, TET has red-shifted absorption and emission maxima of 521 and 536 nm, respectively. TET and **FAM** are often used simultaneously as **FRET** donors to **TAMRA** for **RT**-PCR and SSP-PCR applications.

Thermal stability:

Carrying out the **RT** step at as high a temperature as is possible without denaturing the RNA has several advantages: (1) RNA secondary structure is less of a problem, as the intra- and intermolecular base pairing is reduced; (2) false priming is abolished, resulting in improved **specificity**. On the other hand, oligo-dT or random hexamers will not hybridize and initiate priming from the RNA.

Threshold cycle:

The threshold cycle, or C_t value, is the cycle at which a statistically significant increase in ΔRn is first detected. Threshold is defined as the average standard deviation of Rn for the early cycles multiplied by an adjustable factor.

Touchdown PCR:

Touchdown PCR is a technique used to improve PCR **specificity** by decreasing the annealing temperature during initial cycles by 1°C every second cycle starting with 65°C, for example, to a "touchdown" annealing temperature, such as 55°C, which is then used for 10 or so cycles. The reaction is then cycled at this temperature for 15–20 more cycles. It was originally intended to bypass more complicated optimization processes for determining optimal annealing temperatures. The idea is that any differences in T_m between correct and incorrect **annealing** gives a 2-fold difference in product amount per cycle (or 4-fold per 1°C), resulting in an enrichment for the correct product over any incorrect products.

Two-temperature PCR:

Two-temperature PCR is a PCR cycling method in which the **annealing** and the extension steps are combined into a single step. This method works optimally when **primers** used in PCR have T_ms greater than 60°C. This is true because *Taq* has substantial activity at these temperatures and **annealing** and DNA synthesis will occur efficiently.

Uracil-*N*-glycosylase (UNG):

The inclusion of UNG helps eliminate carryover of PCR product by modifying the PCR products; so that they can be digested prior to the next PCR assay. During amplification, dUTP is substituted for dTTP. It results in dUTP-containing amplification products. UNG is active on single and double stranded dUTP-containing DNA. Uracil ribonucleotide residues in RNA, novel DNA containing dTTP, or cDNA containing dTTP are not suitable substrates for UNG.

PCR Glossary

http://www.genomicglossaries.com/content/gene_amplification_pcr_gloss.asp

Acknowledgement

We are grateful to Mary Chitty for helpful discussions.

Index

Greek